ADEA | AMERICAN DENTAL EDUCATION ASSOCIATION | The Voice of Dental Education

OFFICIAL GUIDE TO Dental Schools

2013

For Students Entering Fall 2014

American Dental Education Association

1400 K Street, NW, Suite 1100
Washington, DC 20005

Phone: 202-289-7201
Fax: 202-289-7204

publications@adea.org
www.adea.org

ADEA | AMERICAN DENTAL EDUCATION ASSOCIATION | The Voice of Dental Education

ISBN 978-0-9887106-0-3
Printed in the United States of America.

Disclaimer
ADEA has made every effort to ensure that the information in this publication is correct, but makes no warranty, either express or implied, of its accuracy or completeness. ADEA intends the reader to use this publication as a guide only and does not intend that the reader rely on the information herein as a basis for advice for personal or financial decisions. The school-specific information was supplied to ADEA by each dental school in the fall of 2012; however, ADEA reminds the reader that authoritative, up-to-date information about a school's admissions policies and practices is issued directly by the school itself.

Editor: Nancy Lang
Director of Publishing: Susan Kimner
Contributors: Anne Wells, Ed.D.
Paul Garrard
Designer: Judy Myers
Cover Designer: Gustavo A. Mendoza

Photo Credits:
Page 8. First-Year Dental Student Olga Ruby Salinas. Used with permission.
Page 10. Third-Year Dental Student Brandi Lewis. Used with permission.
Page 17. Second-Year Dental Student Timothy A. Downing, CDR USN (Ret). Used with permission.
Page 21. Second-Year Dental Student Michele Graham. Used with permission.
Page 29. First-Year Dental Student Kasey Oxendine. Used with permission.
Page 53. Fourth-Year Dental Student Hao Chen. Used with permission.

Welcome, readers of the *ADEA Official Guide to Dental Schools*:

As the American Dental Education Association (ADEA) marks the release of this 51st edition of the *Official Guide to Dental Schools*, the Association continues to provide leadership for the future of dental education. This comprehensive, authoritative guide helps countless men and women explore dental careers and serves as a valuable resource to their advisers.

For those interested in pursuing careers in dentistry, reading this guide is an initial step to learning about all the profession can offer. I can personally share with you that the practice of dentistry has stimulated my scientific and intellectual inquisitiveness and desire to give back to others. I can also affirm that dental students' intelligence, quest for knowledge, and discipline lead them to exceed their academic expectations and to develop new research interests and projects that help improve their communities' oral health. And finally, I can tell you that, after graduation, new dentists find that their degrees offer them many options in the dental profession and also give them the ability to enter dentistry with confidence. As you evaluate a possible future in dentistry or embark upon the application process, I wish you the best!

As a former dental faculty member, I can identify with those of you advising students interested in the health professions. You and I know that dental school can be a transformative experience and that this guide will be a useful tool. It will help you provide information on careers in dentistry and stimulate your advisees' curiosity about the field. A dynamic profession, dentistry is open to people from all backgrounds, cultures, races, and ethnicities who have the desire and intellect to pursue the education. Thank you for making dentistry an option for the wide variety of those who value your guidance.

More than six years ago, ADEA opened its membership to students at U.S. and Canadian dental schools at no charge. The increase in membership has bolstered the community, enhancing both member networking opportunities and resources available to members. I invite entering dental students to consider joining and using ADEA's resources. ADEA is committed to upholding and improving the already high quality of dental education and looks forward to assisting each entering class.

Best Wishes,

Richard W. Valachovic, D.M.D., M.P.H.
Executive Director
American Dental Education Association

ORDERS

Orders for this book should be addressed to:

Publications Department
American Dental Education Association
1400 K Street, NW, Suite 1100
Washington, DC 20005
www.adea.org
202-289-7201

CONTENTS

LIST OF TABLES

INTRODUCTION

Welcome to the *ADEA Official Guide to Dental Schools*! Whether you're seeking specific information about becoming a dentist or just beginning to wonder if dental school might be a career path for you, this book will be of value. And if you're in a position to advise and mentor students considering and preparing for the dental profession, this book will help you give them the information they need.

The *ADEA Official Guide to Dental Schools* is the only authoritative guide to dental education on the market. This comprehensive, annually updated resource has been edited and published for more than five decades by the American Dental Education Association (ADEA). Indeed, since 1923, ADEA has worked to promote the value and improve the quality of dental education, as well as to expand the role of dentistry among other health professions. The Voice of Dental Education, ADEA is the only national organization dedicated to serving the needs of the dental education community. As such, ADEA is perfectly positioned to provide you with both the most up-to-date information about dental schools in the United States and Canada and the most useful insights into how to prepare, apply to, and finance your dental education.

The *ADEA Official Guide to Dental Schools* has two parts:

Part I, BECOMING A DENTIST, contains five chapters that will familiarize you with the dental profession and guide you through all the steps toward becoming a dental student.

Chapter 1, Exploring a World of Opportunities, explains the wide range of careers in dentistry.

Chapter 2, Applying to Dental School, describes the academic preparation generally necessary for admission to dental school and prepares you for the application process.

Chapter 3, Deciding Where to Apply, defines important factors to help you decide which schools are the best match for your educational, professional, and personal goals.

Chapter 4, Financing a Dental Education, is an in-depth look at financing options for dental school.

Chapter 5, Getting More Information, lists additional resources about topics covered in the previous chapters.

Part I also contains tables of information about dental schools and dental students across a wide range of categories. These data were collected from ADEA, the American Dental Association (ADA), and the dental schools.

Part II, LEARNING ABOUT DENTAL SCHOOLS, introduces each of the U.S. and Canadian dental schools. The information on each school is designed to help you decide which will best suit your academic and personal needs.

The entry for each school includes the following:

- General information
- Admissions requirements
- Application and selection factors
- Timetable for submitting application materials
- Degrees granted and characteristics of the dental program
- Estimated costs
- Information about financial aid
- Special programs and services
- Websites, addresses, and telephone numbers for further information

The *ADEA Official Guide to Dental Schools* gives you everything you need to increase the likelihood of success in planning for and entering dental school and the dental profession.

We wish you well!

PART I

BECOMING A DENTIST

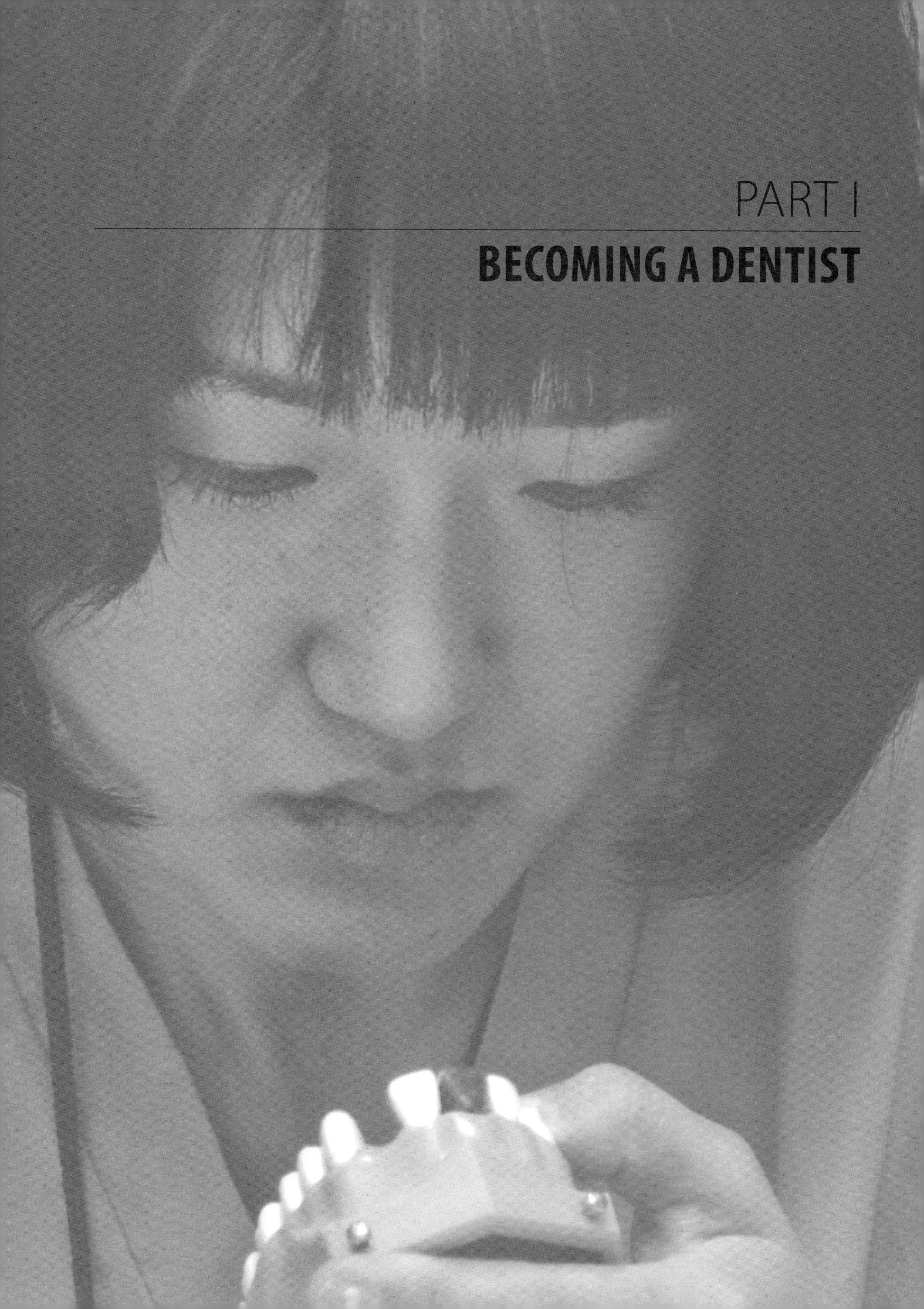

CHAPTER 1
EXPLORING A WORLD OF OPPORTUNITIES

Choosing a dental career will open up a world of opportunities that can lead to success and satisfaction for the rest of your life. Consider these facts about dentists and dentistry:

- **Dentistry is a dynamic health profession.**
- **Dentists are financially successful health professionals and highly respected members of their communities.**
- **The demand for dental care will continue to be strong in the future, ensuring the stability and security of the profession.**

The opportunities that exist for dentists now and in the future make oral health one of the most exciting, challenging, and rewarding professions. Individuals who choose to pursue dental careers are motivated, scientifically curious, intelligent, ambitious, and socially conscious health professionals. They are men and women from diverse backgrounds and cultures, and they all want to do work that makes a difference.

This chapter provides an overview of the field of dentistry and its many facets. If you are exploring career alternatives and want to know more about dentistry, this information will be useful for you. And if you have already decided to become a dentist, this information will help you summarize the range of specialties and practice options. The first section, An Introduction to Dentistry, briefly explains what dentistry is and what dentists do; Opportunities in Dentistry shows that there is a growing demand for dentists; Rewards of Practicing Dentistry describes the professional and personal satisfactions of being a dentist; and, finally, Career Options surveys the various fields and practice options in dentistry.

AN INTRODUCTION TO DENTISTRY

Dentistry is the branch of the healing arts and sciences devoted to maintaining the health of the teeth, gums, and other hard and soft tissues of the oral cavity and adjacent structures. A dentist is a scientist and clinician dedicated to the highest standards of health through prevention, diagnosis, and treatment of oral diseases and conditions.

The notion of dentists as those who merely "fill teeth" is out-of-date. Today, dentists are highly sophisticated health professionals who provide a wide range of care that contributes enormously to the quality of their patients' day-to-day lives by preventing tooth decay, periodontal disease, malocclusion, and oral-facial anomalies. These and other oral disorders can cause significant pain, improper chewing or digestion, dry mouth, abnormal speech, and altered facial appearance. Dentists are also instrumental in early detection of oral cancer and systemic conditions of the body that manifest themselves in the mouth. Dentists are also at the forefront of a range of new developments in cosmetic and aesthetic practices.

The dental profession includes not only those who provide direct patient care but also those who teach, conduct research, and work in public and international health. All of these individuals are vital links in the health care delivery system, which is necessary to promote social and economic change and individual well-being. Dentists understand the importance of and have made contributions to serving both disadvantaged populations and populations with limited access to dental care. The dental profession is very involved in influencing current health care reform efforts to ensure that the importance of oral health is understood and that oral health care is available to everyone.

Opportunities for all individuals interested in becoming dentists are growing because of the intense national need to improve access to general and oral health care and because of the continuously increasing demand for dental services.

Dental school faculty play an especially critical role because they influence an entire field of study and contribute to shaping the profession in the United States and around the world. They are responsible for bringing new discoveries into the classroom, stimulating students' intellect, and helping determine the future of oral health care through dental medicine.

OPPORTUNITIES IN DENTISTRY

Based on results from the 2007-09 *Distribution of Dentists* (DOD), the American Dental Association (ADA) reports that, as of 2009, there were 186,084 professionally active dentists in the United States. On average, that is one dentist for every 1,648 people. Current dental workforce projections indicate a decreasing number of dentists. With continuing population growth and the upcoming retirement of a large group of dentists educated during the 1960s and 70s, the need for new dentists is likely to escalate over the next decades.

Dentists tend to be unevenly distributed across the nation. Rural and inner-city communities are often underserved. Consequently, practicing dentist-to-population ratios are significantly different from state to state, including the District of Columbia, and range from roughly one dentist for every 900 people to one for every 2,500. These numbers clearly demonstrate the importance in the years ahead of maintaining an adequate supply of dentists, accompanied by more efficient practice methods, better use of allied personnel, and improved prevention programs that will enable future dentists to extend professional care to more patients.

Opportunities for all individuals interested in becoming dentists are growing because of the intense national need to improve access to general health and oral care and the continuously increasing demand for dental services. Although at this point, women and minorities remain underrepresented in dentistry, the profession is strongly committed to increasing its diversity. Consequently, in response to the clear need for dentists to serve all citizens, dental schools are strengthening their efforts to recruit and retain all highly qualified students, including intensively recruiting women and underrepresented minorities.

REWARDS OF PRACTICING DENTISTRY

The rewards of being a dentist are many, starting with the personal satisfaction dentists obtain from their daily professional accomplishments. Highly regarded by the community for their contributions to the well-being of citizens, dentists are often called upon to provide community consultation and services.

In addition, dentists are well-compensated. Though incomes vary across the country and depend on the type of practice, the ADA reports in its most recent survey—the 2010 *Survey of Dental Practice*—that in 2009 the average net income for an independent private general practitioner who owned all or part of his or her practice was $192,680; it was $305,820 for dental specialists.

The public's need and respect for dentists continues to grow with the increasing popular recognition of the importance of health in general and oral health in particular. The national health care reform legislation signed into law on March 23, 2010, is expected to increase the demand for dental practitioners. Increases in preventive dental care, geriatric dental care, and cosmetic treatments also have contributed to growth in the demand for dental care.

CAREER OPTIONS

A career in dentistry has two key components: what the dentist does and how he or she does it. The "what" refers to the specific field of dentistry in which he or she practices; the "how" refers to the type of practice itself. These components offer many options for fulfilling professional and personal goals. If you choose to become a dentist, making decisions about these components will allow you to develop a career that suits your professional interests and fits your lifestyle. This section's overviews of both clinical fields and professional and research opportunities should help your decision process.

Dentistry has many clinical fields. While most dentists in active private practice are general practitioners (80%), others choose to specialize in one particular field. The overviews below provide a brief description of the procedures dentists perform in each field. The descriptions indicate whether education beyond dental school (advanced dental or specialty education) is required, along with information about the current number of advanced dental programs available, their duration, and the number of residents enrolled therein. Table 1-1 provides a summary of the available advanced dental programs.

As a potential dental student, you are not ready at this time to apply for a position in an advanced dental education program. However, you should know that the ADEA Postdoctoral Application Support Service (ADEA PASS) simplifies the process of applying to many advanced dental programs, such as general practice residencies, oral and maxillofacial surgery, and pediatric dentistry. You will learn more about PASS once you are in dental school and begin to consider dental career options that require additional education and training.

Clinical Fields

General Dentistry

General dentists use their oral diagnostic, preventive, surgical, and rehabilitative skills to restore damaged or missing tooth structures and to treat diseases of the bone and soft tissue in the mouth and in adjacent structures. General dentists also provide patients with programs of preventive oral health care. Currently, the United States has 65 dental schools, including one in Puerto Rico. These schools enroll approximately 5,000 students in their first-year classes. Advanced dental education is not required to practice as a general dentist. However, General Practice Residencies (GPR) and Advanced Education in General Dentistry (AEGD) residencies are available and can expand the general dentist's career options and scope of practice. The length of these general dentistry advanced dental programs varies, but most are 12 months long. In the United States, there are currently 188 GPR programs with 1,002 first-year residents, and 84 AEGD programs with 609 first-year residents.

Why consider a dental career?

Not only are dentists part of a dynamic, stimulating field that offers a variety of professional opportunities, but

- Dentistry is not generally subject to the effects of managed care and reductions in federal funding that have affected other health care professions.
- Employment of general dentists and specialists is projected to grow 21% through 2020, according to the U.S. Bureau of Labor Statistics.
- Dentists are generally able to enter practice directly upon completion of their four years of dental school.
- The lifestyle of a private practice dentist is typically predictable and self-determined.
- Dentists enjoy unusual loyalty among their patients.
- The entire dental profession is at the forefront of important new research substantiating the relationship between oral health and systemic health.
- While most graduates of dental schools eventually choose to set up private practices, the profession offers a wide range of clinical, research, and academic opportunities to both new graduates and dentists at any stage of their career.

Dental Public Health

Individuals who enter the dental public health field are involved in developing policies and programs, such as health care reform, that affect the community at large. Advanced dental education is required. The types of programs available vary widely from certificate

STUDENT PROFILE

OLGA RUBY SALINAS

FIRST-YEAR DENTAL STUDENT
THE UNIVERSITY OF TEXAS
SCHOOL OF DENTISTRY AT HOUSTON
SAN JUAN, TEXAS

Why did you choose dentistry as your career path?

My family could not always afford dentistry, and even after saving money, we had to travel out of the country to afford dental treatment. After my orthodontic treatment, I felt like a brand new person and carried myself with more confidence. My personal experience sparked a fire within me to pursue a career in dentistry. As a first-generation college student I always knew education would be the key to breaking the cycle within my family. I hope to have set high standards and to be an inspiration and driving force to many others like me, especially my sisters.

What classes, externships, clinical, or other experiences are you involved in now?

I am a first-year dental student at The University of Texas School of Dentistry at Houston (UTSD) and am taking courses such as dental anatomy, clinical applications, biomedical sciences, and pre-clinical simulation lab. I am also serving as the ADEA Representative for my class and am a member of the Hispanic Student Dental Association (HSDA).

What are your short- and long-term goals?

As of now, my goal is to learn as much as possible to build a strong foundation in basic skills. I have no specializing plans as of yet, but I am sure I will know when and if it's right for me. Upon graduation, I plan to return to the Rio Grande Valley and have my own private practice after gaining mentorship and knowledge in a dental office. I would love to be actively involved in my community, organizing health fairs offering free access to care on a regular basis. With my background in education, I know I would also enjoy becoming part of the educational component of dentistry. It's all about giving back and making a difference in the life of others.

As an applicant, how did you prepare for dental school? For example, did you participate in summer programs, shadowing, research, or other activities?

I participated in a great six-week summer academic enrichment program, Summer Medical and Dental Education Program (SMDEP) at The University of Texas at Houston. I also did extensive shadowing in a family-owned practice as well as at community-organized health fairs, where essential medical and oral care was provided for low-income families.

What advice would you like to share with applicants or those considering dental school?

Apply early! Applicants need to not only do their best in their undergraduate courses, but also become involved in their communities. Most schools want to see the person behind the numbers, and at times, this could be a huge factor in your application. For undergraduate students, it is important to network with faculty and to remain informed about program opportunities from your advisors.

Did you move to a new city to attend dental school? If so, what factors helped you make the transition?

I moved from the Rio Grande Valley, where the population is predominantly Hispanic, to one of the most culturally diverse cities in America—Houston. To say I'm in culture shock is an understatement, but it's great to get out of one's comfort zone and experience the world. Having a strong support system back home and such a strong sense of "family" from faculty and classmates in UTSD has been imperative in helping make my transition a smooth one. Get involved in social and networking activities as it is important to keep a balance between academics and personal life to release the amount of stress that accompanies the profession.

Before applying to dental school, what activities did you undertake to improve your manual dexterity?

I enjoy doing arts and crafts, especially hand sewing, and believe these activities have helped improve my dexterity. Once in dental school, you will find plenty of room to grow and perfect the dexterity to become a successful dentist.

Did you participate in any shadowing opportunities before applying to dental schools? What value did you gain from the experience(s)? Would you recommend shadowing to others?

I had the privilege of shadowing a family owned and operated dental practice in Brownsville, Texas, during my junior year. Dr. J. Patrick Pirtle and his wife, Dr. Claudia E. Rodriguez, encompassed all the characteristics of successful dentists. I was able to experience various doctor-patient scenarios, and even a hospital-sedation procedure. I learned the importance of communicating with patients, providing preventive education, and working with employees to create a comfortable environment. There is no set number of hours I would recommend to shadow, but I strongly encourage anyone to do so in order to get a true feel of what dentistry is all about.

Have you taken advantage of scholarship, loans, or loan repayment programs? What advice would you give applicants about financial aid and dental education financing?

My dental school is completely financed by student loans, and although scary, it is essential to keep in mind that it is an investment in my future. Don't take out more loans than you need and keep a budget. My advice is to stay humble: Live like a dental student while in dental school if you don't want to live like a dental student when you're a dentist. To help alleviate the burden of my student loans, I personally plan on applying to loan repayment programs that are available to students interested in working in medically underserved areas.

Are you married, partnered, or single? Do you have any children?

My fiancé is a dentist in Mexico. Long-distance relationships are what one decides to make of them. In the end it will all be worth it, and when the time is right, we will be together.

programs to master's (M.P.H.) and doctoral (D.P.H.) programs. The length of programs also varies, but the average program is 14 months long. There are currently 10 programs and 14 first-year residents in the United States.

Endodontics

Endodontists diagnose and treat diseases and injuries that are specific to the dental nerves, pulp (the matter inside the tooth), and tissues that affect the vitality of the teeth. Advanced dental education is required. The length of programs varies, but the average program is 26 months long. There are currently 54 programs and 211 first-year residents in the United States.

Oral and Maxillofacial Pathology

Oral pathologists are dental scientists who study and research the causes, processes, and effects of diseases with oral manifestations. These diseases may be confined to the mouth

CHAPTER 2
APPLYING TO DENTAL SCHOOL

As you prepare to apply to dental school, you will find it helpful to become acquainted with the usual educational curriculum, typical admissions requirements, and the application process. This chapter offers essential information about these topics, organized into four sections: THE DENTAL SCHOOL PROGRAM provides an overview of the basic educational curriculum at most schools, recognizing that each dental school has its own mission and distinguishing features; QUALIFYING FOR DENTAL SCHOOL reviews the typical numbers of students involved in applying to and attending dental schools and summarizes general admission requirements; THE APPLICATION PROCESS describes the steps of applying to dental school; and SPECIAL ADMISSIONS TOPICS addresses the special topics of advanced standing and transferring, combined degree programs, and admissions for international students.

THE DENTAL SCHOOL PROGRAM

A common goal of all dental school programs is to produce graduates who are:

- Competently educated in the basic biological and clinical sciences
- Capable of providing quality dental care to all segments of the population
- Committed to high moral and professional standards in their service to the public

The traditional dental school program requires four academic years of study, often organized as described below. Since each curriculum varies in its focus and organization, dental school profiles in Part II show academic specifics that aren't covered here.

Years One and Two

Students generally spend the major part of their first two years studying the biological sciences to learn about the structure and function of the human body and its diseases. Students receive instruction about basic sciences, such as human anatomy, physiology, biochemistry, microbiology, pharmacology, and dentally oriented biological sciences, such as oral anatomy, oral pathology, and oral histology. In many dental schools, first- and second-year students learn about providing health care to diverse populations. They also learn the basic principles of oral diagnosis and treatment and begin mastery of dental treatment procedures through practice on models of the mouth and teeth. While completing courses in the basic and clinical sciences, students at many schools begin interacting with patients and providing basic oral health care.

Years Three and Four

The focus of the final two years of dental school generally concentrates on clinical study. Clinical training, which is broad in scope, is designed to provide competence in the prevention, diagnosis, and treatment of oral diseases and disorders. Students apply basic principles and techniques involved in oral diagnosis, treatment planning, restorative dentistry, periodontics, oral surgery, orthodontics, pediatric dentistry, prosthodontics, endodontics, and other types of treatment through direct patient care. They learn to attend to chronically ill, disabled, special care, and geriatric patients and children. In addition, dental schools provide instruction in practice management and in working effectively with allied dental personnel to provide dental care.

During these two years, students may rotate through various clinics of the dental school to treat patients under the supervision of clinical instructors. They often have an opportunity to acquire additional clinical experience in hospitals and other off-campus, community settings. These experiences give students an appreciation for the team approach to health care delivery through their association with other health professionals and health professions students.

Because curricula are designed to help future dentists meet the anticipated oral health needs of the public, every dental school continually modifies its curriculum to better correlate the basic and clinical sciences. In clinical training, there is increased emphasis on providing comprehensive patient care—a method of training that permits a student to meet all the patient's needs within the student's existing levels of competence. Many schools also offer opportunities for participation in community service and in research activities.

The D.M.D. and the D.D.S. are equivalent degrees that are awarded to dental students upon completion of the same types of programs.

QUALIFYING FOR DENTAL SCHOOL

At least 64 U.S. and 10 Canadian dental schools will be accepting applications to the first year of their Doctor of Dental Medicine (D.M.D.) or Doctor of Dental Surgery (D.D.S.) programs in 2014–15. The D.M.D. and the D.D.S. are equivalent degrees that are awarded to dental students upon completion of the same types of programs.

Numbers of Applicants and Enrollees

A total of 5,311 first-time, first-year students were enrolled in D.M.D. and D.D.S. programs in the United States in 2011-12. Of the 12,039 individuals who applied for admission, 44.1% were enrolled. Women comprised 46.0% of the applicants and 45.1% of the enrollees in 2011. Black or African Americans, Hispanic/Latinos, American Indian or Alaska Natives, and Native Hawaiian or Pacific Islanders comprised 13.4% of the applicants and 12.9% of the enrollees in 2011. These underrepresented minority figures are expected to increase in the future. See **Table 2-1** for a comparison of the number of dental school applicants to the number enrolled for the 2011-12 academic year.

General Admission Requirements

Dental schools consider many factors when deciding which applicants to accept into their programs. Using "whole" application review, admissions committees assess biographical and academic information provided by the applicant and by the undergraduate and graduate schools the applicant attended. These committees generally also assess the applicant's results from the Dental Admission Test (DAT), grade point average (GPA), additional information provided in the application, letters of evaluation, and interviews.

All U.S. dental schools require students to take the DAT (all Canadian dental schools require students to take the Canadian Dental Aptitude Test), but other admission requirements vary from school to school. For example, differences may exist in the areas of undergraduate courses required, interview policies, and state residency requirements. Part II of this guide specifies each school's requirements.

Although most schools state that they require a minimum of at least two years (60 semester hours) or three years (90 semester hours) of undergraduate education (also called "predental education"),

TABLE 2-1. TOTAL U.S. DENTAL SCHOOL APPLICANTS AND FIRST-YEAR ENROLLEES, FOR CLASS ENTERING FALL 2011

	Total*	Men/Women	Asian	Black or African American	Hispanic or Latino	Native Hawaiian or Other Pacific Islander	White	American Indian or Alaska Native	Two or More Races	Do Not Wish to Report/ Unknown
Applicant	12,039	6,448/5,551	2,918	692	880	14	6,143	39	317	340
Enrollee	5,311	2,686/2,260	1,176	258	403	3	2,930	17	150	146

*The sum of applicants and enrollees by gender does not equal the total number of applicants and enrollees because a small number did not provide this information.

Source: American Dental Education Association, U.S. Dental School Applicants and Enrollees, 2011 Entering Class

the majority of students admitted to dental school will have earned a bachelor's degree prior to the start of dental school. Of all U.S. students entering dental schools, 90.2% have completed four or more years of college and about 6.3% have graduate training.

Individuals pursuing dental careers should take certain science courses. However, you do not have to be a science major to gain admission to a dental school and successfully complete the program. As shown in **Table 2-2**, most dental students are science majors as undergraduates, but many major in fields not related to science.

ADEA Admissions Guidelines

As the primary dental education association in North America, the American Dental Education Association (ADEA) has developed guidelines addressing dental school admission. Although adhering to the guidelines is voluntary, member institutions (which include all U.S. and Canadian dental schools) are encouraged to follow these guidelines as they consider and accept applicants to their schools. The guidelines are as follows:

- ADEA encourages dental schools to accept students from all walks of life who, on the basis of past and predicted performance, appear qualified to become competent dental professionals.
- ADEA further encourages dental schools to use, whenever possible as part of the admissions process, a consistently applied assessment of an applicant's nonacademic attributes.
- ADEA urges dental schools to grant final acceptance only to students who have completed at least two years of postsecondary education and have taken the DAT.
- ADEA further suggests that dental schools encourage applicants to earn their baccalaureate degrees before entering dental school.

The recommendation for at least two years of postsecondary education may be waived for students accepted at a dental school under an early selection program. Under these programs, a dental school and an undergraduate institution have a formal, published agreement that gives a student, at some time before the completion of the predental curriculum, guaranteed admission to the dental school. Admission depends upon successful completion of the dental school's entrance requirements and normal application procedures.

TABLE 2-2. UNDERGRADUATE MAJORS OF DENTAL SCHOOL APPLICANTS AND ENROLLEES, 2011–12

Predental Major	Percent of Applicants	Percent of First-Time Enrollees	Percent Rate of Enrollment
Biological and Biomedical Science	59.6	61.2	45.4
Physical Sciences	6.6	6.4	42.5
Engineering and Engineering-Related Fields	1.8	1.9	47.8
Health Professions and Related Programs	7.5	5.7	33.8
Dental Support Services and Allied Professions	*2.9%*	*2.3%*	*35.3%*
Dental, Medical, or Health Preparatory Programs	*2.7%*	*1.7%*	*28.8%*
Health Professions and Related Programs, Others	*1.9%*	*1.7%*	*38.3%*
Social Sciences	3.1	3.0	41.8
Business, Management, Marketing, and Related Support Services	3.8	3.8	44.1
Psychology	4.0	4.0	44.5
Parks, Recreation, Leisure, and Fitness Studies	2.0	2.3	51.6
Family and Consumer Sciences or Human Sciences	1.8	2.0	50.0
No Major	1.8	1.5	44.6

Source: American Dental Education Association, U.S. Dental School Applicants and Enrollees, 2011 Entering Class

- ADEA recommends that dental schools notify applicants, either orally or in writing, of provisional or final acceptance on or after December 1 of the academic year prior to the academic year of matriculation.
- ADEA further recommends that:
  - –Applicants accepted on or after December 1 be given at least 30 days to reply to the offer
  - – Applicants accepted on or after February 1 be given a response period of 15 days
  - – Applicants accepted on or after May 15 may have the response period lifted

- ADEA suggests that, because response periods are subject to change, applicants be sure to consult schools' websites for any updates.
- Finally, ADEA recommends that dental schools encourage a close working relationship between their admissions and financial aid staff in order to counsel dental students early and effectively on their financial obligations.

THE APPLICATION PROCESS

The dental school application process involves a number of procedures but is easily followed once you learn what is needed. This section explains how the application process works in general, recognizing that specific details may vary somewhat from school to school. Once you have a basic framework, you will find it easier to adapt to these variations.

The application process has three main steps:

- Taking the DAT, or for Canadian schools, taking the Canadian Dental Aptitude Test
- For U.S. schools, submitting an online application through the ADEA Associated American Dental Schools Application Service (ADEA AADSAS^{SM})
- Acquiring and submitting institution-specific materials.

Following is a brief description of each step and and the name of a person you can contact for more information. This section concludes with advice on how to effectively manage the timing of the application process. The application process for an individual school may vary from this general information; Part II of this guide contains specific application requirements by school.

Not sure what to write about in your essay? Consider these ideas.

The ADEA AADSAS application requires a personal essay on your reasons for pursuing a dental education. Where do you start? Put yourself in the shoes of the admissions committees that read application essays. They are looking for individuals who are motivated, academically prepared, articulate, socially conscious, and knowledgeable about the profession. What can you tell admissions committees about yourself that will make you stand out?

Here are some possible topics for your essay:

- How did you become interested in studying dentistry? Be honest. If you knew you wanted to be a dentist from the age of six, that's fine, but if you didn't, that's all right, too. Explain how you discovered dentistry as a career possibility and what you have done to research the career. Admissions committees are looking for how well thought-out your career plans are.
- What have you done to demonstrate your interest in dentistry? Have you observed or worked in dental offices? Have you talked to practicing dentists? How good is your understanding of general dental practice? How do you envision yourself using your dental degree?
- What have you done to demonstrate your commitment to helping others?
- Do you have any special talents or leadership skills that could be transferable to the practice of dentistry?
- Have you benefited from any special experiences such as participating in research or internships?
- Did you have to work to pay for your education? How has that made you a stronger applicant?
- Have you had to overcome hardships or obstacles to get where you are today? How has this influenced your motivation for advanced education?

Taking the DAT

All U.S. dental schools require applicants to take the DAT, which is designed to measure general academic ability, comprehension of scientific information, and perceptual ability. This half-day, multiple-choice exam is conducted by the American Dental Association (ADA). A computer-based test, the exam is given at Prometric Testing Centers at various sites around the country on almost any day of the year.

Candidates for the DAT should have completed prerequisite courses in biology, general chemistry, and organic chemistry. Advanced-level biology and physics are not required. Most applicants complete two or more years of college before taking the exam. ADEA strongly encourages applicants to prepare for the DAT by reviewing the content of the examination and basic principles of biology and chemistry and by taking practice tests. The DAT Candidate's Guide, the online tutorial, and the application and preparation materials are available at www.ada.org/dat.aspx/ in the DAT section of the ADA website.

The ADA suggests that applicants take the DAT well in advance of their intended dental school enrollment and at least one year prior to the date they hope to enter dental school.

STUDENT PROFILE

TIMOTHY A. DOWNING, CDR USN (RET)

SECOND-YEAR DENTAL STUDENT
INDIANA UNIVERSITY SCHOOL OF DENTISTRY
HOMETOWN: WEST LAFAYETTE, INDIANA

Why did you choose dentistry as your career path?

While serving in the U.S. Navy, I witnessed the improvement in oral health of many sailors—in particular, those coming from regions where regular dental care is scarce. The transformation in the sailors' personal appearance and self-confidence amazed me, and I realized that by choosing the dental profession, I could make a strong, positive impact on people's lives.

What classes, externships, clinical, or other experiences are you involved in now?

I am currently the Vice Chairman of the Student Professional Conduct Committee at the Indiana University School of Dentistry.

What are your short- and long-term goals?

My wife's and my goal is to purchase a general dentistry practice in the Midwest after my graduation from dental school.

As an applicant, how did you prepare for dental school? For example, did you participate in summer programs, shadowing, research, or other activities?

I served as an officer in the U.S. Navy for 20 years, flying F-14 and then F/A-18 fighter aircraft. I also earned a master's degree in aerospace science and graduated from U.S. Naval Test Pilot School.

While I know it seems like a stretch, my career prepared me for dental school by teaching me essential skills: to work with diverse populations, learn new things, and maintain peak performance, even in the most demanding situations. I feel that applying these skills daily during my first career—as a naval officer—helped prepare me for my second career—as a dentist.

To prime my basic sciences learning skills, I enrolled in a few courses the last two years I was in the navy while working as an Associate Professor at Purdue University's Naval Reserve Officer Training Corps (NROTC).

What advice would you like to share with applicants or those considering dental school?

Make sure you invest the time to shadow a dentist prior to spending the time and money for dental school. The last thing you want is to find out during your first year that this career is not the right fit for you.

Did you move to a new city to attend dental school? If so, what factors helped you make the transition?

Because Indiana University School of Dentistry is close to our home in West Lafayette, we did not have to move as a family, allowing our children to stay in the same schools. We were able to locate a place for me to live in Indianapolis during the week, so that I could come home once a week and on the weekends. The time spent away from my family is minimal compared to my six deployments of six months or more.

Before applying to dental school, what activities did you undertake to improve your manual dexterity?

My career in the navy required manual dexterity to fly the F/A-18 Super Hornet and operate the weapons systems with Hands on Throttle and Stick (HOTAS) switches.

Did you participate in any shadowing opportunities before applying to dental schools? What value did you gain from the experience(s)? Would you recommend shadowing to others?

Before I applied to dental school, I was able to shadow our local dentist in West Lafayette, Indiana. Shadowing allowed me to see the everyday activities of general dentistry and make an informed decision about my career choice.

Have you taken advantage of scholarship, loan, or loan repayment programs? What advice would you give applicants about financial aid and dental education financing?

I am attending dental school using the Post 9/11 G.I. Bill, which pays for tuition, books and a housing stipend for three years.

Are you married, partnered, or single? Do you have any children?

Brenda and I have been married 21 years and have two children, Elizabeth (13) and William (11).

See **Table 3-3** in this guide for an overview of individual schools' requirements regarding the DAT, including the average scores of enrollees and timelines that will help you schedule the DAT. The DAT can be taken a maximum of three times. Applicants who wish to take the DAT more than three times must apply for special permission to take the test again. For details, see the DAT section of the ADA website.

The DAT, which consists of multiple-choice test items presented in the English language, requires four hours and 15 minutes for administration. The four separate parts of the exam cover:

- Natural sciences (biology, general chemistry, and organic chemistry)
- Perceptual ability (two- and three-dimensional problem solving)
- Reading comprehension (dental and basic sciences)
- Quantitative reasoning (mathematical problems in algebra, numerical calculations, conversions, etc.)

Most dental schools view the DAT as one of many factors in evaluating candidates for admission. As a result, the emphasis that schools place on different parts of the test varies.

Candidates applying to take the DAT must submit application information to the DAT testing program from the DAT section of the ADA website. The fee is $360. After the application and fee payment are processed, the ADA notifies Prometric that the candidate is eligible for DAT testing. At the same time, the candidate receives notification from the

ADA including instructions on how to register with the Prometric Candidate Contact Center to arrange the day, time, and place to take the DAT at a Prometric Testing Center. A current listing of testing centers is at https://www.prometric.com/en-us/clients/ADA/Pages/landing.aspx. The candidate is eligible to take the test, upon approval, once per 12-month period. If the candidate does not call, register, and take the exam during this period, he or she will have to submit another application and fee in order to take the exam later. Candidates must submit a new application and fee for each re-examination, and the re-examination must be taken at least 90 days after the previous exam. Individuals with disabilities or special needs may request special arrangements for taking the DAT. For details, visit the Special Accommodations section of the Prometric website at https://www.prometric.com/en-us/for-test-takers/Prepare-for-Test-Day/Pages/arrange-testing-accommodations.aspx.

Since many schools have a rolling admissions process and begin to admit highly qualified applicants as early as December 1, applicants are encouraged to submit their applications early.

The Canadian Dental Association (CDA) and the Association of Canadian Faculties of Dentistry (ACFD) have developed the Dental Aptitude Test for applicants to Canadian dental schools. All Canadian dental schools require the test.

For more information, contact the Dental Aptitude Test Program of the Canadian Dental Association (L'Association Dentaire Canadienne), 1815 Alta Vista Drive, Ottawa, Ontario, Canada, K1G 3Y6; dat@cda-adc.ca; www.cda-adc.ca.

■ Submitting an ADEA AADSAS Application

ADEA's AADSAS (pronounced "add-sass," the acronym for the Associated American Dental Schools Application Service) is a centralized application service sponsored and administered by ADEA.

The Application

The ADEA AADSAS application is available online at www.adea.org. The online AADSAS application requires you to submit the following information:

- Biographical information
- Your DENTPIN®—you may have obtained this unique identification number when you registered for the DAT. If not, you will be prompted to register for one when you create your ADEA AADSAS application.
- Colleges/universities attended
- Coursework completed and planned prior to enrollment in dental school
- DAT scores (reported electronically to the dental schools you select on the DAT application)
- Personal statement (essay)—a one-page essay in which you present yourself and your reasons for wanting to attend dental school
- Background information—information about your personal background, including experiences related to the dental profession; extracurricular, volunteer, and community-service experiences; honors, awards, and scholarships; and work and research experiences
- Release for criminal background check for individuals who have received admissions offers from participating dental schools. They will be contacted by Certiphi® Screening Inc. for a background check. Nonparticipating dental schools may have a separate background check process.
- Dental school designations—the section where you select the dental schools that you want to receive your application
- Official transcripts—submission of an official transcript from each college or university you have attended to the AADSAS Verification Department

Submitting your ADEA AADSAS Application: Words of Advice

Before you begin the application process:

- Meet with your health professions advisor to discuss the application process, including the timing of application submission and the DAT; services that may be provided by your advisor such as a Pre-Dental Committee Report or other application assistance; and potential dental schools to which you plan to apply.
- Consider the timing of the Dental Admissions Test (DAT). You may submit an ADEA AADSAS application before taking the DAT, but you should know that many schools consider you for admission only after they have received your DAT scores. However, you should also be aware that delaying the submission of an ADEA AADSAS application prior to taking the DAT can result in a late application and can reduce your chances of being accepted for admission.
- Collect copies of all transcripts and have them available for reference.
- Begin early to line up individuals who will be providing letters of evaluation. Plan around school vacations when faculty advisors may not be available.
- ADEA AADSAS staff strongly recommend that you submit your application well in advance of the deadlines of the schools to which you apply.
- Your application will ask you to indicate the names of individuals who will be providing letters of evaluation on your behalf. While ADEA AADSAS accepts letters in print format, it strongly recommends that letters be electronically submitted. Refer to the instructions for details about submitting letters of evaluation.
- The ADEA AADSAS application becomes available on or around June 1. Watch the ADEA website (www.adea.org) for the start date of the application cycle.

While completing the application:

- When you set up your ADEA AADSAS account, identify a user name and password. Keep these in a safe yet accessible place.
- Read all application instructions before you start to fill out the application.
- Any time after you set up your account, you can go back (using your user name and password) to add or change information in your application up until the time you submit it for processing.
- Print the Transcript Matching Form from your application. Request that an official transcript—including transferred coursework posted to later transcripts—from each college and university you have attended be sent to ADEA AADSAS. The Transcript Matching Form must be attached by each college's registrar to the official transcript and mailed by the registrar to ADEA AADSAS. Applications are not processed until all official transcripts are received.
- Remember that ADEA AADSAS accepts only official transcripts sent directly from the registrar. ADEA AADSAS does not accept student-issued transcripts.

After submitting the application:

- Check with the schools to which you are applying (and their individual entries in this guide) to find out what supplemental materials or fees are required. These must be submitted directly to the school, not to ADEA AADSAS.
- Log on to your ADEA AADSAS account to monitor the status of your application while it is being processed and after it has been sent to the dental schools.
- Update any changes of address or other contact information in your application at any time in the application process, even after your application has been sent to your designated schools.
- ADEA AADSAS does not retain application information from year to year. Individuals reapplying for admission to dental school must complete a new application each year, including providing new transcripts and letters of evaluation. For further information, visit the ADEA website at www.adea.org, and select the ADEA AADSAS link. Processing the application, including transcript verification, generally takes about one month. Remember that your ADEA AADSAS application is not considered complete until ADEA AADSAS receives your online application, fee payment, and official transcripts from every college and university attended.

- Letters of evaluation—also called "letters of recommendation." AADSAS also accepts and distributes letters of evaluation with your AADSAS application

Submission Deadlines

ADEA AADSAS applications become available online on or around June 1, and applicants may complete and submit the application any time after the application is available. Each school has a specific application deadline date, which is noted in the online AADSAS application and in the individual school entries in Part II of this guide. These dates are subject to change; consult each dental school's website for the most up-to-date information on deadline dates. Your completed application, transcripts, payment, and other required documents must be received by AADSAS no later than the stated deadline of the schools to which you are applying. Since many schools have a rolling admissions process and begin to admit highly qualified applicants as early as December 1, applicants are encouraged to submit their applications early.

TABLE 2-3. DENTAL SCHOOLS PARTICIPATING IN ADEA AADSAS (AS OF JANUARY 1, 2013)

Alabama	University of Alabama at Birmingham School of Dentistry
Arizona	Arizona School of Dentistry & Oral Health Midwestern University College of Dental Medicine-Arizona
California	Loma Linda University School of Dentistry University of California, Los Angeles, School of Dentistry University of California, San Francisco, School of Dentistry University of the Pacific Arthur A. Dugoni School of Dentistry University of Southern California Ostrow School of Dentistry Western University of Health Sciences College of Dental Medicine
Colorado	The University of Colorado School of Dental Medicine
Connecticut	University of Connecticut School of Dental Medicine
District of Columbia	Howard University College of Dentistry
Florida	Lake Erie College of Osteopathic Medicine School of Dental Medicine Nova Southeastern University College of Dental Medicine University of Florida College of Dentistry
Georgia	Georgia Regents University College of Dental Medicine
Illinois	Midwestern University College of Dental Medicine-Illinois Southern Illinois University School of Dental Medicine University of Illinois at Chicago College of Dentistry
Indiana	Indiana University School of Dentistry
Iowa	University of Iowa College of Dentistry
Kentucky	University of Kentucky College of Dentistry University of Louisville School of Dentistry
Louisiana	Louisiana State University School of Dentistry
Maine	University of New England College of Dental Medicine
Maryland	University of Maryland School of Dentistry
Massachusetts	Boston University Henry M. Goldman School of Dental Medicine Harvard School of Dental Medicine Tufts University School of Dental Medicine
Michigan	University of Detroit Mercy School of Dentistry University of Michigan School of Dentistry
Minnesota	University of Minnesota School of Dentistry
Missouri	Missouri School of Dentistry & Oral Health University of Missouri - Kansas City School of Dentistry
Nebraska	Creighton University School of Dentistry University of Nebraska Medical Center College of Dentistry
Nevada	University of Nevada, Las Vegas, School of Dental Medicine
New Jersey	University of Medicine and Dentistry of New Jersey, New Jersey Dental School
New York	Columbia University College of Dental Medicine New York University College of Dentistry Stony Brook University School of Dental Medicine University at Buffalo School of Dental Medicine
North Carolina	East Carolina University School of Dental Medicine University of North Carolina at Chapel Hill School of Dentistry
Ohio	Case Western Reserve University School of Dental Medicine The Ohio State University College of Dentistry
Oklahoma	University of Oklahoma College of Dentistry
Oregon	Oregon Health & Science University School of Dentistry
Pennsylvania	University of Pennsylvania School of Dental Medicine University of Pittsburgh School of Dental Medicine The Maurice H. Kornberg School of Dentistry, Temple University
Puerto Rico	University of Puerto Rico School of Dental Medicine
South Carolina	Medical University of South Carolina James B. Edwards College of Dental Medicine
Tennessee	Meharry Medical College School of Dentistry University of Tennessee Health Science Center College of Dentistry
Texas	The Texas A&M University Baylor College of Dentistry University of Texas Health Science Center at San Antonio Dental School The University of Texas School of Dentistry at Houston
Utah	Roseman University of Health Sciences College of Dental Medicine University of Utah School of Dentistry
Virginia	Virginia Commonwealth University School of Dentistry
Washington	University of Washington School of Dentistry
West Virginia	West Virginia University School of Dentistry
Wisconsin	Marquette University School of Dentistry
Nova Scotia	Dalhousie University Faculty of Dentistry

Visit https://portal.aadsasweb.org for an up-to-date list of ADEA AADSAS participating dental schools.

Application Fees

Check the AADSAS website for complete information about application fees. Payment may be made by check, money order, or credit card (Visa, MasterCard, Discover, or American Express). All fees must be paid in U.S. currency drawn on a U.S. bank or the U.S. Postal Service. AADSAS offers a Fee Assistance Program (FAP) for applicants with demonstrated financial hardship. Details may be obtained on the AADSAS website.

ADEA AADSAS Schools

The schools that use AADSAS are listed by state in **Table 2-3**. If you are applying only to the schools that do not participate in AADSAS, you should apply directly to those schools. Texas residents applying to Texas dental schools must use the Texas Medical & Dental Application Schools Application Service (TMDSAS), www.utsystem.edu/tmdsas. Graduates of non-ADA accredited dental schools (i.e., international dental school graduates) may be eligible for admission into advanced placement programs offered by many

STUDENT PROFILE

MICHELE GRAHAM

SECOND-YEAR DENTAL STUDENT
VIRGINIA COMMONWEALTH UNIVERSITY
SCHOOL OF DENTISTRY
CHESAPEAKE VA

Why did you choose dentistry as your career path?

I always knew I wanted to be a health care provider and dedicate my career to helping others. As I began to observe in different health care settings, I became very confident that dentistry was the specialty for me. I was attracted to dentistry, in part, because it gives you the ability to diagnose problems and also the ability to fix them. I was exposed to how fulfilling dentistry is as a profession by watching my father, a dentist in Virginia, who enjoys going to work every day and being able to help others through his profession.

While exploring dentistry further, I was struck by how much dentists love their profession. It is not uncommon to hear about dentists working well past retirement because they love so much what they do. Last month at our Virginia Commonwealth University (VCU) dental reunion, I talked to a member of the 1962 class who had been practicing for almost 50 years and had no intention of retiring. Hearing these stories—which seem to be very common in dentistry—is one of the reasons I was so attracted to the profession. I feel honored that I will become a part of such a fulfilling profession.

What classes, externships, clinical, or other experiences are you involved in now?

I was invited to be on the Dean's Student Alumni Ambassador Program, which helps with various activities throughout the year dealing with alumni and fund-raising. I am a member of the committee that organizes and runs the dental alumni golf tournament every spring. We raise money for various dental charities, as well as for scholarship programs. I am also a member of the dental service fraternity Psi Omega, which serves homeless shelters by providing free oral health screenings, and I participate in numerous other social and fund-raising events. I have volunteered for the dental school's annual "Miles for Smiles" 5K race, which raises money for dental service missions in Virginia. I plan on volunteering for the Missions of Mercy weekend-long outreach programs providing free dental care to individuals in need in underserved areas. I also recently became a student member of the Virginia Dental Association's Dental Practice Committee.

What are your short- and long-term goals?

After school, I have plans to practice in Virginia with my father, and I am also considering a general practice residency program following my four years at VCU. I would like to be involved in organized dentistry and look forward to continuing education throughout my career. On a personal level, I would like to have a family, and I firmly believe that women can have fulfilling careers and children. One of my long-term goals is to continue competing in amateur golf tournaments, specifically the U.S. Women's Amateur Championship. Short term, I will to continue both to be involved with my dental school class through volunteering and to do well academically in order to develop the skills it takes to be a great clinician.

As an applicant, how did you prepare for dental school? For example, did you participate in summer programs, shadowing, research, or other activities?

Here are a few things I did during and after my undergraduate and graduate education that I believe helped me prepare for dental school:

- Captain of University of Virginia Women's Golf Team
- Medical Services Volunteer at the University of Virginia Hospital
- Kappa Delta Sorority
- Physical Therapist Aide
- Volunteer with the Housing Improvement Program
- Student Athlete Mentors Program
- Volunteer at a Cardiac Rehabilitation Center
- Master's of Kinesiology Thesis
- Founder of Advanced Golf Performance Company
- Ambulance Observation

What advice would you like to share with applicants or those considering dental school?

I would advise students to have a positive attitude and open mind when going through the application process. I would suggest applying to many programs and considering new towns and different parts of the country. Programs can be very diverse and you don't want to limit yourself to just one geographic area.

I would highly recommend applying to any program you have interest in and then going to the interview if invited. Doing the interview will ensure you have a personal experience with the school and have the chance to talk to students and faculty about the program, as well as see the area where the school is located. It is a great way to formulate an opinion about a school, and I would advise having an open mind at each interview.

Another suggestion would be to have a positive attitude if you are not successful in gaining admission to a program the first year you apply. The application process is very competitive, and you might be a good fit for a school but just need to do things slightly differently to receive an interview at a program. If you don't get invited for an interview your first application year, contact the admissions office. Ask the department if you can talk to someone about your application and try to get information about why you were not selected. Talking with someone in the admissions office is a great way to know what you can improve upon so as to increase your chances for the following year.

Most programs want you to get your application in early, so I would also recommend getting your application in as early as possible. Try and take your Dental Admission Test (DAT) early and ask for recommendation letters well in advance so nothing is holding up your application. I would suggest that prior to starting school, you participate in activities that involve working with people less fortunate than you. Such an experience will give you both a wonderful perspective on how much need there is in the health care profession and a hands-on experience in the field that you are entering.

Did you move to a new city to attend dental school? If so, what factors helped you make the transition?

Yes, I moved to Richmond, a city that was new to me at the time. Making an effort as soon as I started school to go to events and activities with my new classmates made my transition easier. I also asked many students at my interview where they lived and what different areas of interest the city had to offer. Students are a perfect resource, and I found their advice extremely helpful.

Before applying to dental school, what activities did you undertake to improve your manual dexterity?

I enjoy hobbies enabling me to create things with my hands and express myself artistically. I feel that woodworking has helped me improve my manual dexterity. I also enjoy music, and I played the clarinet for six years as a student in the school symphonic band. Playing golf in college also helped me to improve my manual dexterity. Additionally, I enjoy playing pool. I believe any activity that requires fine movements and eye-hand coordination can help develop the manual dexterity it takes to be a great clinical dentist.

Did you participate in any shadowing opportunities before applying to dental schools? What value did you gain from the experience(s)? Would you recommend shadowing to others?

Yes, I shadowed both general dentists and specialists, and doing so provided extremely valuable experiences. Shadowing allowed me to see exactly what a dentist does throughout the workday, both relating to patients and running a business. The experience also allowed me to talk to and get to know many dentists and learn what they loved about the profession and what it takes to be a great dentist. It was one of the best things I did to prepare for my dental school experience, and I would strongly recommend shadowing to any predental student.

Have you taken advantage of scholarship, loans, or loan repayment programs? What advice would you give applicants about financial aid and dental education financing?

I have not taken advantage of a loan program; however, I would give this advice to applicants about all financial programs: Take the time not only to research what is available to you but also to fully understand all loan programs. Dental school is a major financial commitment and the choices you make during dental school will affect your financial well-being for many years after school. Try to get as much information as you can so that you can make well-informed choices when it is time to apply for loans.

Are you married, partnered, or single? Do you have any children?

I am single and have no children.

dental schools. International dental graduates may want to refer to the ADEA Centralized Application for Advanced Placement for International Dentists (ADEA CAAPID), located on the ADEA website (www.adea.org) for information about these programs and the application process.

AADSAS serves as an information clearinghouse only. It does not influence any school's evaluation or selection of applicants, nor does ADEA recommend applicants to dental schools or vice versa.

Acquiring and Submitting Institution-Specific Materials

Each school has its own policy regarding the payment of a separate application fee and the submission of additional application materials. These materials may include an institution-specific supplemental (or secondary) application form, documentation of dentistry shadowing experience, and official academic transcripts. Part II of this guide briefly reviews each dental school's application requirements. In addition, the ADEA AADSAS application website (https://portal.aadsasweb.org) includes a chart that identifies the supplemental requirements for the participating schools. This information is subject to change; consult dental schools' websites for the most up-to-date requirements.

After you have submitted all of your materials, the dental schools that wish to consider you for a place in the entering class will contact you for a visit to the campus. This visit will likely include an interview with the admissions committee, a tour of the campus and facilities, meetings with faculty and students, and other meetings and activities. When you visit a dental school, the admissions committee is evaluating you as a prospective student; at the same time, you will have the opportunity to evaluate the dental school program and environment to determine if you think it would be a good fit for you and your goals.

Manage the Timing of the Application Process

The trick to managing the timing of the application process is summed up in two words: Don't procrastinate! Most dental schools will fill a large percentage of their 2014 entering classes by December 2013. Therefore, even though schools have deadlines ranging from October 2013 to February 2014 for completing all the application requirements, it is not wise to wait until the last minute to take the DAT, submit the AADSAS application, or complete any supplemental materials requested by the schools to which you are applying.

The individual dental school information in Part II of this guide includes an admissions timetable for each school's entering class. It is essential that you become familiar with the timetables for the schools to which you are applying and that you plan to complete the admission application requirements on time.

SPECIAL ADMISSIONS TOPICS

For those of you interested in advanced standing and transferring, combined degree programs, and admission for international students, this section briefly addresses those areas. Part II of this guide provides some additional information on these topics for each dental school, but you should contact the dental schools you are considering for more details.

Advanced Standing and Transferring

Advanced standing means that a student is exempted from certain courses or is accepted as a second- or third-year student. Advanced standing is offered at the time of admission to students who have mastered some aspects of the dental school curriculum due to previous training. An individual who has a Ph.D. in one of the basic sciences, such as physiology, for example, may be exempted from taking the physiology course in dental school. Some schools may also grant advanced standing to students who have transferred from other U.S. or Canadian dental schools or who have graduated from international dental schools. In these cases, applicants may be allowed to enter as second- or third- year students.

Each dental school has its own policy on advanced standing and transferring students; see the individual school entries in Part II of this guide. Most students do not obtain advanced standing, and very few students transfer from one school to another.

Combined Degree Programs

Many dental schools in the United States and Canada offer combined degree programs that give students the opportunity to obtain other degrees along with their D.D.S. or D.M.D., such as the following:

- A baccalaureate degree (B.A. or B.S.)
- A master's degree (M.A., M.S., M.B.A., or M.P.H.)
- A doctoral degree (Ph.D., M.D., or D.O.)

Numerous dental schools have formal combined baccalaureate and dental degree programs. Combined degree programs expand career options, especially for those interested in careers in dental education, administration, and research. Specific agreements that have been made between a dental school and its parent institution may also shorten the length of training. The undergraduate and dental school portions of some combined degree programs take place at the same university, while other combined programs are the result of arrangements made between a dental school and other undergraduate institutions. Sometimes colleges independently grant baccalaureate degrees to students who attended as undergraduates and did not finish their undergraduate education but did successfully complete some portion of their dental training.

Many dental schools also sponsor combined graduate and dental degree programs. These programs, which usually take six to seven years to complete, are offered at the master's or doctoral level in subjects that include the basic sciences (biology, physiology, chemistry), public policy, medicine, and other areas. See **Table 3-6** in Chapter 3 of this guide for a list of dental schools with combined degree programs. For more information about combined degree programs, contact the schools directly.

Preparing for Dental School : A Guide for High School and College Students

Maybe you already know that you have a strong interest in dentistry but don't know where to start. It's never too early to begin preparing. Below are a few guidelines to help you plan your course work and get in touch with mentors and other professionals who can help you along the way.

This guide offers a general timeline for preparation. Many successful dental students have been nonscience majors or pursued other careers before deciding dentistry was right for them. In fact, the guide can be used at any point in your academic or professional career. If you are not completely sure that dentistry is where you want to focus your energy, the guide can help you decide if attending dental school is a commitment you want to make.

FOR HIGH SCHOOL STUDENTS

- Take science and math classes, including chemistry, biology, and algebra. If available, take Advanced Placement (AP)courses.
- Talk to people in the field. Call local dentists or contact the dental society in your city or town to find people who can help answer your questions. You can locate your local dental society through the American Dental Association (ADA) website at: http://www.ada.org/statelocalorg.aspx
  Information on the ADA's mentoring program can also be found at: www.ada.org/2196.aspx.
- Check out ExploreHealthCareers.org (EHC) and go to http://explorehealthcareers.org/en/Career/1/Dentist to visit the "Dentist" page.

FOR FIRST-YEAR COLLEGE STUDENTS

Fall semester

- Meet with your prehealth advisor and plan coursework.
- If your school doesn't have a prehealth advisor, look into obtaining the latest edition of the *ADEA Official Guide to Dental Schools* to review the admission requirements. Although most schools require a minimum of one year of biology, general and inorganic chemistry, organic chemistry, and physics, specific requirements vary from school to school.
- Complete required predental coursework.

Spring semester

- Think about summer volunteer or employment opportunities in dentistry, such as shadowing a dentist or volunteering in a community health clinic.
- Complete required coursework and register for the fall semester.
- Research prehealth enrichment programs at: www.explore-healthcareers.org. Also, look into the Association of American Medical Colleges/ADEA Summer Medical and Dental Education Program (AAMC/ADEA SMDEP) for college freshmen and sophomores at www.smdep.org. Prehealth enrichment programs can help you decide if a career in dentistry is a good fit and help you prepare for the application process.

Summer

- Complete an internship or volunteer program.
- Attend summer school if necessary.

FOR SECOND-YEAR COLLEGE STUDENTS

Fall semester

- Schedule a time to meet with your prehealth advisor.
- Attend prehealth activities.
- Join your school's predental society if one is available.
- Complete required coursework.
- Explore community service opportunities through your school (they don't necessarily need to be health-related). If possible, continue activities throughout your undergraduate career.

Spring semester

- Look into paid or volunteer dental-related research opportunities.
- Complete second semester course work and register for the fall.

Summer

- Complete a summer research or volunteer dental-related program.
- Attend summer school if necessary.
- Prepare for the Dental Admission Test (DAT).

FOR THIRD-YEAR COLLEGE STUDENTS

Fall semester

- Meet with your prehealth advisor to make sure coursework completion is on schedule.
- Discuss dental schools.
- Complete coursework and register for spring semester.
- Visit ADEA's website at www.adea.org to learn about applying to dental schools.
- Place your order for the *ADEA Official Guide to Dental Schools.*
- Research schools.

Spring semester

- Review each dental school's required documents early in the semester.
- Identify individuals to write letters of recommendation.
- Take the DAT during late spring or early summer.
- Prepare to submit the ADEA Associated American Dental Schools Application Service (ADEA AADSAS) application. Applications become available on or around June 1.
- Complete coursework and register for the fall semester.
- Schedule a volunteer or paid dental-related activity.

Summer

- Take the DAT if you have not done so already.
- Prepare for school interviews in the fall.
- Budget time and finances appropriately to attend interviews.
- Participate in a volunteer or paid opportunity.
- Attend summer school if necessary.

FOR FOURTH-YEAR COLLEGE STUDENTS

Fall semester

- Meet with your prehealth advisor and complete coursework.
- Attend interviews with schools.
- Notification of acceptances begins December 1.

Spring semester

- Apply for federal financial aid.

Summer

- Relax and get ready for the first semester of dental school!
- Attend school's open houses and/or other events.
- Prepare to relocate if necessary.

Admission for International Students

The term "international student" refers to a native of a foreign country who plans to study in the United States or Canada on a student visa. Students who have permanent residency status in the United States are not considered international students; they have the same rights, responsibilities, and options as U.S. citizens applying for admission to dental school.

Applicants who have completed coursework outside the United States or Canada (except through study abroad) should supply a copy of their transcripts, translated into English, plus a course-by-course evaluation of all transcripts. Application details for international applicants are contained in the ADEA AADSAS application.

International applicants who are not graduates of international dental schools are considered for admission to most U.S. and Canadian dental schools. Each dental school has its own policies on admission requirements for international students. However, most dental schools require international students to complete all the application materials mandated for U.S. citizens and permanent residents. In addition, international students may be asked to take the Test of English as a Foreign Language (TOEFL) or demonstrate English language proficiency. International students should expect to finance the entire cost of their dental education.

International Dental Graduates

Graduates of international (non-ADA accredited) dental schools may be eligible for admission into an advanced placement program. These programs provide an opportunity for dentists educated outside the United States and Canada to obtain an accredited degree that is recognized by state and provincial licensing officials. The ADEA CAAPID provides an online portal for applicants to submit materials, which are directed to multiple institutions. Information about these programs, their admission requirements, and the application process can be found at www.adea.org.

CHAPTER 3
DECIDING WHERE TO APPLY

Selecting the dental schools to which you want to apply is a very personal decision. Every applicant is looking for different characteristics in an educational experience. Your individual decision depends on many factors, such as career goals, personal interests, geographical preference, and family circumstances. For this reason, dental school rankings tend to be misleading. The education provided by U.S. and Canadian dental schools is of a high quality overall. This chapter offers a framework from which you can tailor a list of potential dental schools to match your interests and needs. The chapter covers fundamental issues that will both help you decide the kind of educational experience you are looking for and begin to identify the schools most likely to offer it.

The general information in Chapter 2 provides a broad introduction to the dental school program. However, dental school variations can make your decision about where to apply. If you have a commitment to providing community-based care, for example, you may prefer to attend a dental school that offers a public health focus and varied opportunities for gaining experience in community clinics. Similarly, if you are interested in ultimately focusing on oral health research, you may want to look for a dental school with a strong research focus and student research opportunities. Academic dental institutions also offer a range of curriculum options. Some schools offer innovative problem-based curricula, and some organize their curricula along more integrative rather than discipline-based lines, while others follow a more traditional discipline-based, classroom-instruction-followed-by-clinical-training structure. You should therefore consider what type of educational environment makes you feel most comfortable and best prepares you for the kind of career you may choose to follow.

The same approach holds true as you consider dental schools in different areas of the country. You may want to determine whether you are more comfortable in a particular geographical or physical location—a rural versus a big city setting, for example—or if you prefer to attend a school near where you grew up or one in a new area where you may want to remain after graduation. The composition of the student body also varies. Some schools have student bodies made up of individuals from all over the country (and some, even, from around the world); some (primarily those affiliated with state universities) give preference to students from their home states; and some have partnership agreements with states that do not have dental schools, allowing students from those states to attend for the in-state tuition fee.

The key is to define your needs and preferences and then identify dental schools that correspond to your selections. To help you do that, here are some questions that can help you think through what you are looking for in a dental school:

What is the focus of the dental school's training, and does it match my interests and needs?

You might say, for example:

- I want to become a general practitioner, either in my own practice or in a group practice environment.
- I have a strong interest in scientific research regarding oral health.
- I am undecided about the type of dentistry I would like to practice, so I want to be in a school where I have a range of options from which to choose.
- My dream is to become a professor, so I'd like opportunities to prepare for an academic career while I'm in dental school. I want to prepare myself for eventual specialty training. I hope to obtain a combined degree.

What is the structure of the curriculum in terms of what is taught and when?

You might say, for example:

- I would like to start getting hands-on clinical experience as soon as possible.
- I would like the opportunity to participate in research while in dental school.
- I am very interested in externships, especially the opportunity to participate in short-term service programs in other countries.
- I am devoted to helping the underserved. I want to make sure there are plenty of opportunities for community service.
- I plan to return to my home community as a general practitioner, so I want to focus on the training I need for that.
- I learn best in active learning situations. I want to find a curriculum that focuses on that style of education.

What academic resources are available?

You might say, for example:

- I want to gain experience working with the most state-of-the-art technologies in dentistry.
- I am very interested in having easy access to modern clinical facilities and a large number of patients.
- I would like to get as much experience as possible working in a community setting.
- I would like to get as much experience as possible in a hospital setting.
- I want to have the opportunity to earn a Ph.D. as well as a dental degree.

What services are available to students?

You might say, for example:

- I need to feel comfortable about seeking academic help if I need it.
- I would like to be active in student government.
- I want to attend a school that provides a supportive atmosphere for women and minorities.
- I want to attend a school in which the faculty and administration are sensitive to the stresses dental students experience.
- I want to be able to live on campus or to obtain inexpensive housing near campus.

Where is the school located?

You might say, for example:

- My family situation requires me to attend dental school close to home.
- I prefer attending dental school in an urban setting.
- I need to attend a school where I can benefit from in-state tuition.
- I would like to attend a dental school in an area where hiking and outdoor recreation are easily available.

Dental School Rankings

Dental school applicants should be aware that there are proprietary publications available that purport to rank dental schools according to the quality of their programs.

The American Dental Education Association (ADEA) and the American Dental Association (ADA) advise applicants to view these rankings with caution. The bases for these rankings are questionable, and even those individuals most knowledgeable about dental education would admit to the difficulty of establishing criteria for, and achieving consensus on, such rankings. The accrediting organization for all U.S. dental schools is the ADA's Commission on Dental Accreditation (CODA). Applicants interested in the current accreditation status of any U.S. dental school should contact CODA at 800-621-8099. All schools have their relative strengths. A dental school ideally suited for one applicant might not be appropriate for another. ADEA and the ADA recommend that applicants investigate on their own the relative merits of the dental schools they wish to attend.

STUDENT PROFILE

KASEY OXENDINE

FIRST-YEAR DENTAL STUDENT
EAST CAROLINA UNIVERSITY
SCHOOL OF DENTAL MEDICINE
LUMBERTON, NORTH CAROLINA

Why did you choose dentistry as your career path?

I have always been interested in health care, and I have always enjoyed math and science. In high school, I began thinking more about dentistry and completed a career portfolio on the profession. I was impressed with the combination of medicine and manual dexterity in dentistry. Later, as an undergraduate, I learned of the need for dentists in Robeson County, my home county, where the dentist-to-patient ratio is 1 to 5,637. Furthermore, the number of minority dentists in this ratio is even lower. As a child, I was affected by the lack of access to dental care. The memory of this experience and the need for dentists sparked a passion in me to serve my community as a dentist.

What classes, externships, clinical, or other experiences are you involved in now?

As a first year dental student, I am currently engaged in basic science classes and will begin simulation laboratories in the upcoming months. I have attended interest meetings for the East Carolina University School of Dental Medicine chapter of the Student National Dental Association (SNDA) and for Scrubs & Stilettos, an organization for women dentists. I plan to join and become involved with these organizations and their missions.

What are your short- and long-term goals?

My short-term goals include learning as much as possible in dental school in order to provide my patients with the best standard of care. I hope to seize opportunities to network and build relationships with my future colleagues while in school. I also want to help others who are interested in dentistry by sharing how I prepared for and applied to dental school. Long term, I plan to return to Robeson County and provide dental care and oral health education to the community there. As a Native American dentist, I will contribute to the diversity of the dental profession and show the importance of dental care in rural communities. I would also love to mentor predental students and offer them insight and guidance into the profession. Getting married and starting a family are also two of my long-term goals.

As an applicant, how did you prepare for dental school? For example, did you participate in summer programs, shadowing, research, or other activities?

To prepare for dental school I participated in two summer programs, Summer Medical and Dental Education Program (SMDEP) and Medical Education Development (MED) Program. These programs were created for prehealth students from disadvantaged backgrounds. These programs helped me—as a psychology major—to strengthen my science background and learn better study strategies for dental school. I completed the SMDEP program at Howard University in Washington, DC. During this program, I was able to volunteer in the free dental clinic, which further exposed me to the need for dental care. MED, a nine-week a program hosted by the University of North Carolina at Chapel Hill, simulated the first year of dental school. During MED, I was exposed to manual dexterity more when I performed a restoration on a synthetic tooth. Furthermore, upon completion of my undergraduate studies, I had the opportunity to work as a dental assistant at Dr. Dalton P. Brooks Family and Cosmetic Dentistry in Lumberton, North Carolina. I had previously shadowed Dr. Brooks at the Robeson County Health Department during the summer of 2008. Working in a private practice kept me motivated in my pursuit of a dental career and gave me invaluable experience to take with me to dental school.

What advice would you like to share with applicants or those considering dental school?

I would suggest not giving up if you are not admitted the first time. I was not admitted when I first applied; however, becoming a dentist is my passion and I did not give up. I improved myself as an applicant and applied again. Once you have perfected your application, the interview is the next key. I would suggest doing a mock interview with someone who is not a family member, such as a dentist or counselor. Review your ADEA Associated American Dental Schools Application Service (AADSAS) application—as well as your supplemental application—and be prepared to elaborate on the experiences you have discussed in your application.

Did you move to a new city to attend dental school? If so, what factors helped you make the transition?

I moved from Lumberton to Greenville, both in North Carolina, to attend dental school. To help with the transition to a new city, I visited Greenville multiple times before moving. I also moved three weeks before school started to give myself time to learn my way around the area and settle into my apartment.

Before applying to dental school, what activities did you undertake to improve your manual dexterity?

Before applying to dental school, I began teaching myself how to sew and attended pottery workshops in college to improve my manual dexterity. I also took advantage of the opportunity to use a high-speed hand piece to excavate tooth structure from extracted crowns and prepared teeth on a dental model for restorations while working at Dr. Brooks' Family and Cosmetic Dentistry practice.

Did you participate in any shadowing opportunities before applying to dental schools? What value did you gain from the experience(s)? Would you recommend shadowing to others?

I shadowed at the local health department and in a general practice before applying to dental school. In addition, I shadowed dental students during the SMDEP and MED summer programs. With the exception of working in a dental office, shadowing is the best way to learn what dentistry is all about; therefore, I would recommend anyone interested in applying to dental school to shadow as much as possible.

Have you taken advantage of scholarship, loans, or loan repayment programs? What advice would you give applicants about financial aid and dental education financing?

I am a recipient of the East Carolina University School of Dental Medicine Creating Opportunities for Dental Education (CODE) Scholarship. I would advise applicants to research scholarship opportunities and loan repayment programs in addition to submitting the Federal Application for Student Aid (FAFSA). When utilizing loans, only borrow what you will need. Financing your dental education is possible, and while the cost of a dental education is important, it should not be the determining factor in your decision to attend dental school.

Are you married, partnered, or single? Do you have any children?

I am currently in a relationship with my boyfriend, Matthew Epps. Matt and I have been dating for six years. Matt is a graduate of North Carolina State University and is the Planning Engineer at Lumbee River Electric Membership Corporation in Red Springs, North Carolina. He has been the single most supportive person in my life, with the exception of my parents.

Your answers to all these questions—and others that you may think of as well—should help you conduct an initial analysis of the information you can find on individual schools in Part II of this book. You can then expand your research by asking for more information directly from each school that you consider a prospect.

To get you started, the tables in this chapter provide an at-a-glance, cumulative comparison of a number of aspects of the individual dental schools.

Table 3-1 presents the number of applicants and enrollees at each school, broken down by gender, race, and ethnicity.

Table 3-2 shows the number of applicants (including the number interviewed and the number accepted) and enrollees at each school, broken down by in-state/in-province and out-of-state/out-of-province categories.

Table 3-3 summarizes specific admissions requirements for each school.

Table 3-4 provides characteristics of the entering class of each school.

Table 3-5 shows the geographic break down of each school's entering class.

Table 3-6 provides information on the combined degree programs at each school.

Table 3-7 offers a national perspective on admissions trends.

The tables present the information alphabetically by state, territory, and province. Although ADEA has made every effort to ensure that the information in the tables is correct, the Association makes no warranty, either express or implied, of its accuracy or completeness. The school-specific information is supplied annually to ADEA by each dental school.

For more information and detailed admissions requirements for each school, consult the individual school profiles in Part II of this book. **As you determine where you plan to send applications, you should contact those dental schools directly for the most complete information about admission requirements. The telephone numbers, addresses, and websites of each school are included in the profiles.**

TABLE 3-1. DENTAL SCHOOLS' APPLICANTS AND ENROLLEES BY GENDER, RACE, AND ETHNICITY—CLASS ENTERING FALL 2012

		APPLICANTS										ENROLLEES									
STATE, TERRITORY, OR PROVINCE	DENTAL SCHOOL	TOTAL	M	W	HISP LATINO	AMER IND AK NAT	ASIAN	BLACK AF AMER	NAT HI PAC ISL	WHITE	TWO OR MORE	TOTAL	M	W	HISP LATINO	AMER IND AK NAT	ASIAN	BLACK AF AMER	NAT HI PAC ISL	WHITE	TWO OR MORE
ALABAMA	University of Alabama at Birmingham	650	368	306	51	3	125	51		407	13	60	34	26	0	1	4	4		51	0
ARIZONA	Arizona School of Dentistry & Oral Health	3,601	1,779	1,266	223	44	1,085	109	7	1,575	0	76	43	33	3	1	17	4	2	46	3
ARIZONA	Midwestern University-Arizona	2,658	1,544	1,114	68	5	354	52	3	1,388	709	112	65	47	4	0	9	0	0	88	10
CALIFORNIA	Loma Linda University	2,029	NR	NR	61	4	827	73	4	817	162	95	NR	NR	6	0	38	3	0	32	8
CALIFORNIA	University of California, Los Angeles	1,891	985	886	70	3	862	52	1	665	156	88	42	46	4	0	56	0	0	24	2
CALIFORNIA	University of California, San Francisco	1,803	935	848	132	9	815	45	7	632	141	88	37	51	15	1	46	5	0	20	9
CALIFORNIA	University of the Pacific Arthur A. Dugoni School of Dentistry	3,155	1,692	1,423	81	5	1,237	51	3	1,134	221	138	69	69	10	1	57	0	1	56	4
CALIFORNIA	University of Southern California Ostrow School of Dentistry	3,463	1,913	1,550	87	1	1,590	106	3	1,260	416	145	86	59	8	0	63	6	1	67	NA
CALIFORNIA	Western University of Health Sciences	2,678	1,481	1,190	178	4	1,026	49	0	1,009	165	67	36	31	6	0	22	1	0	22	8
COLORADO	The University of Colorado	1,490	871	598	48	3	245	23	0	994	130	80	51	29	8	2	12	2	0	56	5
CONNECTICUT	University of Connecticut	1,235	615	605	73	0	331	53	1	603	29	40	25	15	2	0	7	2	0	25	0
DISTRICT OF COLUMBIA	Howard University	2,384	1,123	1,227	85	4	900	477	2	578	239	78	31	47	6	0	15	45	1	4	7
FLORIDA	Lake Erie College of Osteopathic Medicine	2,584	1,329	1,255	199	8	676	122	3	1,050	69	100	43	57	5	1	8	1	1	76	6
FLORIDA	Nova Southeastern University	2,933	NR	NR	NR	NR	NR	NR	NR	NR	NR	123	60	63	21	0	33	4	0	62	0
FLORIDA	University of Florida	1,531	750	782	224	9	370	82	5	759	28	83	36	47	13	0	14	8	0	44	2
GEORGIA	Georgia Regents University	336	178	158	25	0	64	36	0	188	6	80	45	35	5	0	8	12	0	52	2
ILLINOIS	Midwestern University-Illinois	2,420	1,308	1,087	84	1	712	44	9	1,100	47	130	74	56	6	0	28	1	0	93	1
ILLINOIS	Southern Illinois University	562	275	287	9	1	159	34	0	301	41	51	31	20	2	0	6	0	0	42	0
ILLINOIS	University of Illinois at Chicago	1,640	783	842	39	3	504	85	0	838	106	68	36	32	6	0	24	4	0	34	6
INDIANA	Indiana University	1,662	895	748	17	0	489	58	0	942	98	104	44	60	2	0	11	8	0	74	0
IOWA	University of Iowa	939	537	402	41	0	165	35	0	651	22	80	46	34	3	0	8	1	0	68	0
KENTUCKY	University of Kentucky	1,673	929	730	78	20	392	75	3	1,172	412	57	37	20	3	2	5	2	0	50	3
KENTUCKY	University of Louisville	3,032	1,747	1,256	39	3	532	126	0	1,819	185	120	72	48	0	0	10	7	0	93	9
LOUISIANA	Louisiana State University	727	373	340	13	1	146	54	1	420	73	65	21	37	1	0	9	4	1	43	

(continued)

TABLE 3-1. DENTAL SCHOOLS' APPLICANTS AND ENROLLEES BY GENDER, RACE, AND ETHNICITY—CLASS ENTERING FALL 2012 (CONTINUED)

		APPLICANTS										ENROLLEES									
STATE, TERRITORY, OR PROVINCE	DENTAL SCHOOL	TOTAL	M	W	HISP LATINO	AMER IND AK NAT	ASIAN	BLACK AF AMER	NAT HI PAC ISL	WHITE	TWO OR MORE	TOTAL	M	W	HISP LATINO	AMER IND AK NAT	ASIAN	BLACK AF AMER	NAT HI PAC ISL	WHITE	TWO OR MORE
MARYLAND	University of Maryland	2,850	1,488	1,362	46	19	1,013	156	1	1,332	189	130	67	63	11	2	28	12	0	70	7
MASSACHUSETTS	Boston University	4,590	2,347	2,187	285	26	1,537	113	2	1,794	114	115	60	55	7	0	28	1	0	42	4
MASSACHUSETTS	Harvard School of Dental Medicine	1,062	559	503	63	1	334	32	1	406	30	35	16	19	3	0	13	0	0	16	1
MASSACHUSETTS	Tufts University	4,635	2,400	2,179	297	6	1,598	135	4	1,966	126	190	89	101	14	0	65	9	0	91	11
MICHIGAN	University of Detroit Mercy	1,640	857	758	68	1	611	95	2	755	39	144*	87	57	9	1	38	6	0	84	3
MICHIGAN	University of Michigan	2,168	1,148	1,020	98	1	694	70	1	1,025	51	108	63	45	2	0	24	0	0	78	2
MINNESOTA	University of Minnesota	1,166	590	576	15	4	298	28	3	750	52	98	44	54	1	0	18	0	0	76	3
MISSISSIPPI	University of Mississippi	117	61	56	2	0	6	22	0	79	1	35	21	14	0	0	1	3	0	31	0
MISSOURI	University of Missouri - Kansas City	761	403	358	15	2	156	22	1	476	62	109	60	49	2	1	12	3	0	81	8
NEBRASKA	Creighton University	2,727	1,632	1,095	163	8	656	72	2	1,509	83	85	57	28	4	1	8	5	0	62	5
NEBRASKA	University of Nebraska Medical Center	835	445	382	21	10	158	25	1	556	36	48	25	23	2	0	0	0	1	44	4
NEVADA	University of Nevada, Las Vegas	2,182	1,302	880	60	3	820	46	1	996	175	81	53	28	6	0	25	1	0	49	0
NEW JERSEY	University of Medicine and Dentistry of New Jersey	1,865	851	995	59	0	701	109	1	784	137	89	45	44	6	0	19	8	0	42	9
NEW YORK	Columbia University	2,454	1,202	1,252	140	0	829	105	1	874	60	80	43	37	8	0	24	4	0	36	3
NEW YORK	New York University	5,127	2,600	2,462	354	15	2,332	201	5	1,993	40	247	120	127	20	1	102	7	0	109	2
NEW YORK	Stony Brook University	1,097	518	564	60	0	352	44	0	492	17	41	21	19	0	0	6	0	0	31	1
NEW YORK	University at Buffalo	1,807	843	721	89	2	592	57	0	775	37	90	48	42	1	0	21	2	0	66	0
NORTH CAROLINA	East Carolina University	369	208	161	17	1	64	43	0	223	13	52	28	24	1	0	8	5	0	38	0
NORTH CAROLINA	University of North Carolina at Chapel Hill	1,694	835	840	138	2	369	108	0	1,006	5	81	40	41	6	0	8	13	0	49	1
OHIO	Case Western Reserve University	2,999	1,663	1,306	130	2	922	90	2	1,391	70	74	29	45	4	0	28	4	0	33	5
OHIO	The Ohio State University	884	492	381	6	1	192	25	1	575	44	110	60	50	2	0	13	3	0	83	6
OKLAHOMA	University of Oklahoma	691	390	296	47	8	152	12	0	391	57	56	36	20	0	2	8	1	0	44	1
OREGON	Oregon Health & Science University	1,184	703	471	64	4	295	13	1	667	54	75	45	30	3	0	18	0	0	46	5
PENNSYLVANIA	The Maurice H. Kornberg School of Dentistry, Temple University	4,051	2,197	1,854	246	3	1,393	168	1	1,687	114	136	73	55	14	0	28	5	0	73	2
PENNSYLVANIA	University of Pennsylvania	2,216	1,209	1,176	121	1	832	81	0	968	64	119	53	66	9	0	47	3	0	39	3
PENNSYLVANIA	University of Pittsburgh	2,289	1,436	1,233	105	15	899	72	0	1,198	NR	79	44	35	4	1	35	2	0	37	0
PUERTO RICO	University of Puerto Rico	474	249	225	NR	NR	NR	NR		NR	NR	42	17	25	41	NR	0	0		1	NR
SOUTH CAROLINA	Medical University of South Carolina	922	465	457	0	2	126	40	1	658	41	72	31	41	0	0	7	3	0	59	2
TENNESSEE	Meharry Medical College	1,969	932	1,037	67	9	619	475	3	587	167	60	23	37	2	0	4	51	0	2	0

TENNESSEE	University of Tennessee Health Science Center	1,224	690	524	60	3	235	68	1	771	42	89	62	27	3	0	10	4	0	71	1
TEXAS	Texas A&M University Baylor College of Dentistry	1,640	825	815	183	13	515	93	0	761	25	104	54	50	23	0	17	15	0	45	1
TEXAS	University of Texas Health Science Center at San Antonio	1,446	696	742	180	3	432	61	2	635	37	100	55	45	19	0	26	3	0	47	3
TEXAS	The University of Texas School of Dentistry at Houston	1,452	758	688	185	8	429	88	0	602	90	99	47	52	20	2	23	6	0	46	1
UTAH	Roseman University of Health Sciences	1,419	904	499	91	1	436	23	1	673	39	80	59	21	0	0	19	0	0	59	0
VIRGINIA	Virginia Commonwealth University	2,534	1,418	1,116	124	4	886	137	7	1,376	0	94	42	52	4	0	24	7	0	59	0
WASHINGTON	University of Washington	1,085	599	476	77	2	347	19	1	525	44	62	42	20	4	0	17	0	0	37	3
WEST VIRGINIA	West Virginia University	1,216	666	534	60	0	307	27	0	703	31	60	33	27	0	0	10	0	0	48	1
WISCONSIN	Marquette University	2,582	1,440	1,142	55	5	645	70	2	1,553	177	80	45	35	3	1	7	4	0	61	4
ALBERTA	University of Alberta	399	185	214	NR	NR	NR	NR	NR	NR	NR	32	20	12	NR	NR	NR	NR	NR	NR	NR
BRITISH COLUMBIA	University of British Columbia	361	NR	NR	NR	NR	NR	NR	NR	NR	NR	48	NR	NR	NR	NR	NR	NR	NR	NR	NR
MANITOBA	University of Manitoba	285	146	139	NR	NR	NR	NR	NR	NR	NR	30	23	7	NR	NR	NR	NR	NR	NR	NR
NOVA SCOTIA	Dalhousie University	410	NR	NR	NR	NR	NR	NR	NR	NR	NR	38	16	22	NR	NR	NR	NR	NR	NR	NR
ONTARIO	University of Toronto	479	215	264	NR	NR	NR	NR	NR	NR	NR	65	30	35	NR	NR	NR	NR	NR	NR	NR
ONTARIO	University of Western Ontario	508	244	264	NR	NR	NR	NR	NR	NR	NR	56	28	28	NR	NR	NR	NR	NR	NR	NR
QUEBEC	Université Laval	575	231	344	NR	NR	NR	NR	NR	NR	NR	48	15	33	NR	NR	NR	NR	NR	NR	NR
QUEBEC	McGill University	361	NR	NR	NR	NR	NR	NR	NR	NR	NR	26	NR	NR	NR	NR	NR	NR	NR	NR	NR
QUEBEC	Université de Montréal	743	310	433	NA	NA	NA	NA	NA	NA	NA	90	39	51	NA	NA	NA	NA	NA	NA	NA
SASKATCHEWAN	University of Saskatchewan	403	183	220	NR	NR	NR	NR	NR	NR	NR	28	16	12	NR	NR	NR	NR	NR	NR	NR

Sources: ADEA and dental schools

Note: The numbers presented above may not match those listed by the individual schools in Part II because of different reporting procedures. Neither set of numbers is intended to be an exact statistic but is presented to give a sense of the applicant and enrollee profiles of each school.

NR = Not Reported
HISP LATINO = Hispanic/Latino of any race
AMER IND AK NAT = American Indian or Alaska Native
BLACK AF AMER = Black or African American
NAT HI PAC ISL = Native Hawaiian or Other Pacific Islander

TABLE 3-2. DENTAL SCHOOLS' APPLICANTS AND ENROLLEES, IN STATE VERSUS OUT OF STATE—CLASS ENTERING FALL 2012

		APPLICANTS						ENROLLEES			
		IN STATE OR PROVINCE			OUT OF STATE OR PROVINCE			IN STATE OR PROVINCE		OUT OF STATE OR PROVINCE	
STATE, TERRITORY, OR PROVINCE	DENTAL SCHOOL	TOTAL	NUMBER INTERVIEWED	NUMBER ACCEPTED	TOTAL	NUMBER INTERVIEWED	NUMBER ACCEPTED	TOTAL	% OF TOTAL ENROLLEES	TOTAL	% OF TOTAL ENROLLEES
ALABAMA	University of Alabama at Birmingham	108	63	46	566	71	40	43	72%	17	28%
ARIZONA	Arizona School of Dentistry & Oral Health	210	55	43	2,971	328	68	26	34%	50	65%
ARIZONA	Midwestern University-Arizona	166	54	29	2,493	428	83	29	26%	83	74%
CALIFORNIA	Loma Linda University	NR	NR	NR	NR	NR	NR	NR	NR	NR	NR
CALIFORNIA	University of California, Los Angeles	1,022	142	111	869	16	13	82	93%	6	7%
CALIFORNIA	University of California, San Francisco	930	191	71	770	109	49	73	83%	15	17%
CALIFORNIA	University of the Pacific Arthur A. Dugoni School of Dentistry	1,213	188	104	1,942	73	34	104	75%	34	25%
CALIFORNIA	University of Southern California Ostrow School of Dentistry	1,216	212	102	2,246	231	42	96	67%	48	33%
CALIFORNIA	Western University of Health Sciences	1,121	270	127	1,557	243	88	41	61%	26	39%
COLORADO	University of Colorado	148	109	46	1,342	142	34	46	61%	34	39%
CONNECTICUT	University of Connecticut	91	41	34	1,144	125	60	25	62%	15	38%
DISTRICT OF COLUMBIA	Howard University	6	2	1	2,378	154	78	2	1%	76	99%
FLORIDA	Lake Erie College of Osteopathic Medicine	1,442	290	145	1,142	293	138	48	48%	52	52%
FLORIDA	Nova Southeastern University	NR	NR	NR	NR	NR	NR	75	61%	48	39%
FLORIDA	University of Florida	622	343	78	904	53	5	78	94%	5	6%
GEORGIA	Georgia Regents University	336	180	80	37	12	4	76	95%	4	5%
ILLINOIS	Midwestern University-Illinois	381	111	93	2,039	295	222	47	36%	83	64%
ILLINOIS	Southern Illinois University	327	103	84	235	5	3	51	100%	0	0%
ILLINOIS	University of Illinois at Chicago	459	173	87	1,181	31	15	62	91%	6	9%
INDIANA	Indiana University	233	164	77	1,429	202	27	77	74%	27	26%
IOWA	University of Iowa	125	89	62	814	144	72	57	71%	23	29%
KENTUCKY	University of Kentucky	166	80	56	1,507	65	37	39	70%	18	30%
KENTUCKY	University of Louisville	169	117	54	2,862	341	205	44	40%	76	60%
LOUISIANA	Louisiana State University	185	80	56	542	37	9	56	86%	9	14%
MARYLAND	University of Maryland	211	127	NR	2,639	329	NR	67	52%	63	48%
MASSACHUSETTS	Boston University	168	82	58	4,422	302	242	30	26%	85	74%
MASSACHUSETTS	Harvard School of Dental Medicine	60	6	2	1,015	95	44	2	6%	33	94%
MASSACHUSETTS	Tufts University	172	65	50	4,463	476	353	34	18%	156	82%
MICHIGAN	University of Detroit Mercy	369	159	128	1,271	188	134	90	62%	54	38%
MICHIGAN	University of Michigan	325	113	73	1,843	183	116	65	60%	43	40%
MINNESOTA	University of Minnesota	225	80	65	941	138	32	66	67%	32	33%
MISSISSIPPI	University of Mississippi	117	64	35	7	0	0	35	100%	0	0%
MISSOURI	University of Missouri - Kansas City	163	96	79	598	80	56	77	71%	32	29%
NEBRASKA	Creighton University	71	NR	9	2,656	NR	76	9	11%	76	89%
NEBRASKA	University of Nebraska Medical Center	78	49	29	757	74	19	29	60%	19	40%
NEVADA	University of Nevada, Las Vegas	73	59	44	2,109	318	37	44	54%	37	46%
NEW JERSEY	University of Medicine and Dentistry of New Jersey	349	154	63	1,516	153	26	63	71%	26	29%%
NEW YORK	Columbia University	412	86	46	2,042	240	118	27	34%	53	66%

TABLE 3-2. DENTAL SCHOOLS' APPLICANTS AND ENROLLEES, IN STATE VERSUS OUT OF STATE—CLASS ENTERING FALL 2012 (CONTINUED)

		APPLICANTS						ENROLLEES			
		IN STATE OR PROVINCE			OUT OF STATE OR PROVINCE			IN STATE OR PROVINCE		OUT OF STATE OR PROVINCE	
STATE, TERRITORY, OR PROVINCE	DENTAL SCHOOL	TOTAL	NUMBER INTERVIEWED	NUMBER ACCEPTED	TOTAL	NUMBER INTERVIEWED	NUMBER ACCEPTED	TOTAL	% OF TOTAL ENROLLEES	TOTAL	% OF TOTAL ENROLLEES
NEW YORK	New York University	5,127	NR	NR	NR	NR	NR	83	33%	164	66%
NEW YORK	Stony Brook University	451	111	NR	646	46	NR	37	90%	4	10%
NEW YORK	University at Buffalo	450	152	98	1,357	104	77	69	77%	21	23%
NORTH CAROLINA	East Carolina University	369	224	85	0	0	0	52	100%	0	0
NORTH CAROLINA	University of North Carolina at Chapel Hill	313	174	80	1,014	83	19	68	84%	13	16%
OHIO	Case Western Reserve University	200	61	42	2,799	326	179	24	32%	50	68%
OHIO	The Ohio State University	235	109	102	649	71	64	88	80%	22	20%
OKLAHOMA	University of Oklahoma	146	107	46	545	84	34	45	80%	11	20%
OREGON	Oregon Health & Science University	105	49	40	1,079	74	70	38	51%	37	49%
PENNSYLVANIA	The Maurice H. Kornberg School of Dentistry, Temple University	329	136	93	3,722	345	254	58	45%	70	55%
PENNSYLVANIA	University of Pennsylvania	169	33	NR	2,247	291	NR	15	13%	104	87%
PENNSYLVANIA	University of Pittsburgh	250	60	28	2,015	238	53	28	35%	51	65%
PUERTO RICO	University of Puerto Rico	111	77	38	363	24	4	38	90%	4	10%
SOUTH CAROLINA	Medical University of South Carolina	173	105	55	749	69	26	53	74%	19	26%
TENNESSEE	Meharry Medical College	85	21	9	1,884	199	114	7	12%	53	88%
TENNESSEE	University of Tennessee Health Science Center	167	71	56	1,057	105	63	47	52%	43	48%
TEXAS	Texas A&M University Baylor College of Dentistry	961	217	98	679	21	6	98	94%	6	6%
TEXAS	University of Texas Health Science Center at San Antonio	949	280	150	497	22	11	94	94%	6	6%
TEXAS	The University of Texas School of Dentistry at Houston	980	275	163	472	6	0	99	100%	0	0%
UTAH	Roseman University of Health Sciences	142	56	49	1,277	172	126	29	36%	51	64%
VIRGINIA	Virginia Commonwealth University	299	122	75	2,235	153	112	62	66%	32	34%
WASHINGTON	University of Washington	219	107	63	866	47	17	54	90%	8	10%
WEST VIRGINIA	West Virginia University	78	78	43	1,138	62	34	41	68%	19	32%
WISCONSIN	Marquette University	189	96	42	2,393	192	78	40	50%	40	50%
ALBERTA	University of Alberta	239	NR	33	160	NR	0	32	100%	0	0%
BRITISH COLUMBIA	University of British Columbia	232	101	43	129	20	5	43	90%	5	10%
MANITOBA	University of Manitoba	285	61	27	186	12	3	27	90%	3	10%
NOVA SCOTIA	Dalhousie University	410	90	29	200	30	9	29	76%	9	24%
ONTARIO	University of Toronto	379	139	73	100	23	10	59	91%	6	9%
ONTARIO	University of Western Ontario	392	208	49	115	47	6	50	89%	6	11%
QUEBEC	Université Laval	532	154	73	43	NR	NR	48	100%	0	0%
QUEBEC	McGill University	110	36	19	251	30	7	19	73%	7	27%
QUEBEC	Université de Montréal	743	0	178	NA	0		86	95%	4	5%
SASKATCHEWAN	University of Saskatchewan	115	53	21	288	26	7	21	75%	7	25%

Sources: ADEA and dental schools

Note: The numbers presented above may not match those listed by the individual schools in Part II because of different reporting procedures. Neither set of numbers is intended to be an exact statistic but is presented to give a sense of the applicant and enrollee profiles of each school.

Percentages may not equal 100% because of rounding.

NR = Not Reported

TABLE 3-3. ADMISSIONS REQUIREMENTS BY DENTAL SCHOOL

						RESIDENCY REQUIREMENT		
STATE, TERRITORY, OR PROVINCE	DENTAL SCHOOL	NUMBER YRS. REQUIRED PREDENTAL EDUCATION	DAT	GPA	INTERVIEW MANDATORY	DISTINGUISH IN STATE OR PROV./ OUT OF STATE OR PROV.	PREFERENCE GIVEN TO	ACCEPT INTER-NATIONAL
ALABAMA	University of Alabama at Birmingham	Formal minimum 3 yrs.	Mandatory	3.3 or above recommended	Yes	Yes	Alabama	Yes
ARIZONA	Arizona School of Dentistry and Oral Health	Minimum 3 yrs.	Mandatory	Minimum of 2.5, 3.0 or above recommended	Yes	No	NR	Yes
ARIZONA	Midwestern University-Arizona	Minimum 3 yrs., bachelor's degree recommended	Mandatory	3.0 or above recommended	Yes	No	None	Yes
CALIFORNIA	Loma Linda University	Preference given to those with a B.S./B.A.	Mandatory	Minimum of 2.7; above 3.0 recommended	Yes	No	None	Yes
CALIFORNIA	University of California, Los Angeles	Minimum 3 yrs.	Mandatory	NA	Yes	Yes	Alaska, Arizona, California, Hawaii, Montana, New Mexico, North Dakota, Wyoming	Yes
CALIFORNIA	University of California, San Francisco	Minimum 3 yrs.	Mandatory	2.70 in Science and Total GPA (CA Residents); 3.0 in Science and Total GPA (all others)	Yes	Only by minimum GPA as indicated previously	None	Yes
CALIFORNIA	University of the Pacific Arthur A. Dugoni School of Dentistry	Minimum 3 yrs.	Mandatory	Assessed	Yes	No	None	Yes
CALIFORNIA	University of Southern California Ostrow School of Dentistry	Minimum 2 yrs.	15 required	NA	Yes	No	NR	Yes
CALIFORNIA	Western University of Health Sciences	Minimum 90 semester hours	Mandatory	Assessed	Yes	No	None	Yes
COLORADO	The University of Colorado	Minimum 3 yrs. plus	Mandatory	No specific requirements	Yes	Yes	Colorado	No
CONNECTICUT	University of Connecticut	Minimum 3 yrs.; usual 4 yrs.	Mandatory	3.0 or above	Yes	Yes	Connecticut	Yes
DISTRICT OF COLUMBIA	Howard University	Minimum 4 yrs.	18 required	2.85	Yes	No	None	Yes
FLORIDA	Lake Erie College of Osteopathic Medicine	90 semester hours	17	2.7	Yes	No	No	No
FLORIDA	Nova Southeastern University	Minimum 90 semester hours	Mandatory	Cumulative GPA of 3.25 or higher, science GPA of 3.25 or higher, grade of 2.0 or better in prerequisite courses	Yes	No	None	Yes
FLORIDA	University of Florida	Bachelor's degree strongly recommended	Mandatory, minimum 15	3.2 or above recommended	Yes	Yes	Florida	No
GEORGIA	Georgia Regents University	Minimum 90 semester hours	Academic, at least 14 required; perceptual, at least 14 required	Total GPA minimum 2.8; SGPA minimum 2.8	Yes	Yes	Georgia	No
ILLINOIS	Midwestern University-Illinois	Bachelor's degree required	Mandatory	Minimum 2.75	Yes	No	None	Yes
ILLINOIS	Southern Illinois University	Formal minimum 3 yrs.; usual bachelor's degree.	Mandatory	3.0 or above recommended	Yes	Yes	Illinois	No

ILLINOIS	University of Illinois at Chicago	A bachelor's degree is required	Mandatory	3.5 or above is recommended	Yes	Yes	Illinois	No
INDIANA	Indiana University	Minimum 3 yrs.	Minimum of 17 in Academic Average and Total Science; 16 in all other areas	Sci GPA: 3.3; Cum. GPA: 3.3	Yes	Yes		Yes
IOWA	University of Iowa	Minimum 3 yrs.; 4 yrs. recommended	Prefer minimum national average on each section	Prefer a 3.0 or above in sciences	Yes	Yes	Iowa	Yes
KENTUCKY	University of Kentucky	Minimum 4 yrs.	Mandatory	No minimum	Yes	Yes	Kentucky	Yes
KENTUCKY	University of Louisville	Minimum 90 credit hours, including 32 science hours	Mandatory	No minimum but 3.0 or above in sciences recommended	Yes	Yes	Arkansas, Kentucky	Yes
LOUISIANA	Louisiana State University	Minimum 3 yrs.	Mandatory	NA	Yes	Yes	Arkansas, Louisiana	No
MARYLAND	University of Maryland	Bachelor's degree strongly recommended	Mandatory	NA	Yes	Yes	Maryland	Yes
MASSACHUSETTS	Boston University	Bachelor's degree required	Mandatory	3.3 or above recommended	Yes	No	None	Yes
MASSACHUSETTS	Harvard School of Dental Medicine	Formal minimum 3 yrs.; usual minimum 4 yrs.	Mandatory	3.0 or above	Yes	No	None	Yes
MASSACHUSETTS	Tufts University	Bachelor's degree required	16 AA, 17 PAT, 17 Reading Comprehension, 16 Total Science	Preference given to those above 3.3	Yes	No	None	No
MICHIGAN	University of Detroit Mercy	Formal minimum 2 yrs.; generally accepted 3+ yrs.	Mandatory (recommended 20 or higher in science sections)	No cutoff, but 3.2 or above recommended; 3.2 or above in science recommended	Yes	No	None	Yes
MICHIGAN	University of Michigan	Formal minimum of 2 yrs.; rarely acceptable minimum of 2 yrs.; usual and recommended 4 yrs.	Mandatory	No minimum	Yes	Yes	Michigan	Yes
MINNESOTA	University of Minnesota	Formal minimum 3 yrs.; preferred minimum 4 yrs.	Mandatory	NR	Yes	Yes	Minnesota	Yes
MISSISSIPPI	University of Mississippi	Minimum 4 yrs.	Yes	NA	Yes	Yes	Mississippi	No
MISSOURI	Missouri School of Dentistry & Oral Health	Minimum 3 yrs.	Mandatory	Minimum of 2.5; 3.0 or above recommended	Yes	No	NR	No
MISSOURI	University of Missouri - Kansas City	Bachelor's degree strongly preferred	17 preferred	3.4 science preferred	Yes	Yes	Arkansas, Hawaii, Kansas, Missouri, New Mexico (Candidates from other states welcome to apply)	No
NEBRASKA	Creighton University	Formal minimum 2 yrs.; generally accepted minimum 4 yrs.	Mandatory	Above 3.0 recommended	No	No	Idaho, North Dakota, New Mexico, Wyoming	Yes
NEBRASKA	University of Nebraska Medical Center	Minimum 4 years, degree preferred	Yes	NA	Yes	Yes	Nebraska	Yes
NEVADA	University of Nevada, Las Vegas	Formal minimum 3 yrs.; bachelor's degree preferred	Mandatory	NR	Yes	Yes	Nevada	Yes
NEW JERSEY	University of Medicine and Dentistry of New Jersey	Minimum 3 yrs.; preferred 4 yrs.	Mandatory	3.3 science preferred	Yes	Yes	None	Yes
NEW YORK	Columbia University	Preferred minimum 4 yrs.; formal minimum 90 credits	No minimum	No minimum	Yes	No	None	Yes
NEW YORK	New York University	B.A./B.S. from United States/ Canada required	Mandatory	Above 3.2 recommended	Yes	No	None	Yes

(continued)

TABLE 3-3. ADMISSIONS REQUIREMENTS BY DENTAL SCHOOL (CONTINUED)

						RESIDENCY REQUIREMENT		
STATE, TERRITORY, OR PROVINCE	DENTAL SCHOOL	NUMBER YRS. REQUIRED PREDENTAL EDUCATION	DAT	GPA	INTERVIEW MANDATORY	DISTINGUISH IN STATE OR PROV./ OUT OF STATE OR PROV.	PREFERENCE GIVEN TO	ACCEPT INTER-NATIONAL
NEW YORK	Stony Brook University	Minimum 3 yrs.; bachelor's degree preferred	Yes, must be taken within 3 yrs. of application	3.0 or above recommended	Yes	Yes	New York State	Yes
NEW YORK	University at Buffalo	Minimum 90 credit hours of undergraduate study prior to enrollment in the D.D.S. program, with a minimum of 60 credit hours--two full years--at an accredited U.S. or Canadian college or university completed prior to application	Mandatory	3.0 or above recommended	Yes	Yes	New York	Yes
NORTH CAROLINA	East Carolina University	B.A./B.S.	Mandatory	NR	Yes	Yes	North Carolina	No
NORTH CAROLINA	University of North Carolina at Chapel Hill	Minimum 3 yrs.	Mandatory	3.2 or above recommended	Yes	Yes	North Carolina	Yes
OHIO	Case Western Reserve University	Minimum 2 yrs.; 4 yrs. suggested	Mandatory	3.2 or above recommended	Yes	No	None	Yes
OHIO	The Ohio State University	Formal minimum 3 yrs.; usual acceptable minimum 4 yrs.	Mandatory, 13 minimum PAT	3.5 or above recommended	Yes	Yes	Ohio	Yes
OKLAHOMA	University of Oklahoma	Minimum 90 semester hours	17 minimum	2.5 minimum; 3.0 to be competitive	Yes	Yes	Oklahoma	Yes
OREGON	Oregon Health & Science University	Formal minimum 3 yrs.; usual 4 yrs.; bachelor's degree strongly preferred	Mandatory, 15 required in all scored categories	3.0 or above recommended in both overall and BCP	Yes	Yes	Oregon	Yes
PENNSYLVANIA	The Maurice H. Kornberg School of Dentistry, Temple University	Minimum 3 yrs.	19 required	Recommended 3.4 or above	Yes	Yes	Delaware, Pennsylvania	Yes
PENNSYLVANIA	University of Pennsylvania	Formal minimum 3 yrs.; usual minimum 4 yrs.	Mandatory	3.2 or above recommended	Yes	No	None	Yes
PENNSYLVANIA	University of Pittsburgh	Prefer 4 yrs.	Minimum of 16 on each section	Minimum of 3.0	Yes	No	None	Yes
PUERTO RICO	University of Puerto Rico	Minimum 90 semester credits	Mandatory	Minimum general and science GPA of 2.5	Yes	Yes	Puerto Rico	Yes
SOUTH CAROLINA	Medical University of South Carolina	Minimum 4 yrs.; but strongly recommend applicant earn bachelor's degree	Mandatory	No specific requirement	Yes	Yes	South Carolina	Yes
TENNESSEE	Meharry Medical College	Minimum 3 yrs.	Mandatory	Minimum 3.0	Yes	No	None	Yes
TENNESSEE	University of Tennessee Health Science Center	Minimum 4 yrs.	17 on all sections required	Minimum 3.0	Yes	Yes	Tennessee	No
TEXAS	Texas A&M University Baylor College of Dentistry	Formal minimum 3 yrs.; usual minimum 4 yrs.	Mandatory	3.0 or above recommended	Yes	Yes	Arkansas, Louisiana, New Mexico, Oklahoma, Texas, Utah	Yes
TEXAS	University of Texas Health Science Center at San Antonio	Minimum 3 yrs.	Mandatory	Competitive	Yes	Yes	Texas	Yes
TEXAS	The University of Texas School of Dentistry at Houston	Formal minimum 3 yrs.; usual minimum 4 yrs.	Mandatory	3.2 or above strongly recommended	Yes	Yes	Texas	Yes
UTAH	Roseman University of Health Sciences	Minimum 60 semester hours or 90 quarter hours	Yes	2.8 Science	Yes	No	None	Yes

UTAH	University of Utah School of Dentistry		Mandatory	Minimum 3.3	Yes	Yes	Utah Residents	No
VIRGINIA	Virginia Commonwealth University	Formal minimum 3 yrs.; generally acceptable minimum 4 yrs.	Mandatory; should be taken no later than December of the year prior to desired matriculation	No specific requirements	Yes	Yes	Virginia	Yes
WASHINGTON	University of Washington	Minimum 3 yrs.; most entering students have 4 yrs.	Mandatory; must be taken no later than Oct. 31 of year prior to admission	GPA needs to be competitive within applicant pool	Yes	Yes	Washington	No
WEST VIRGINIA	West Virginia University	Minimum 3 yrs.; 90 semester credit hours completed at time of application	Mandatory	3.5 or above strongly recommended	Yes	Yes	West Virginia	Yes
WISCONSIN	Marquette University	Formal minimum 3 yrs.; usual minimum 4 yrs.	Mandatory; Canadian DAT accepted	No specific requirements; 3.3+ recommended	Yes	Yes	None	Yes
ALBERTA	University of Alberta	Minimum 2 yrs. (10 full course requirements)	Canadian DAT mandatory; minimum score is 15/30 for Reading Comprehension, PAT, MAN	Minimum 3.0 out of 4.0	Yes	Yes	Alberta	Yes
BRITISH COLUMBIA	University of British Columbia	Minimum 3 yrs.	Mandatory; USA or Canadian DAT	Minimum 70%	Yes	Yes	90% of class for in-province applicants	No
MANITOBA	University of Manitoba	Minimum 2 yrs.	Mandatory	Minimum 2.5 in core science courses	Yes	Yes	Manitoba	No, Canadians only
NOVA SCOTIA	Dalhousie University	Minimum 2 yrs.	Mandatory	Minimum 3.5 to be competitive	Yes	Yes	Atlantic Canada	Yes
ONTARIO	University of Toronto	Minimum 3 yrs.	Mandatory	Minimum 3.0	Yes	Yes	Ontario	Yes
ONTARIO	University of Western Ontario	Four-year bachelor's degree required	Mandatory	Minimum 80% in 2 yrs. Equivalent of 3.7	Yes	No	NR	Yes
QUEBEC	Université Laval	Minimum 2 yrs.	Yes	NR	Yes	Yes	New Brunswick, Ontario, Quebec	No
QUEBEC	McGill University	Minimum 4 yrs.	Not required	3.5 minimum	Yes	Yes	Quebec	Yes
QUEBEC	Université de Montréal	4 yrs. preferred; formalminimum 1 yr.	Yes	NA	NA	Yes	Quebec	No
SASKATCHEWAN	University of Saskatchewan	Minimum 2 yrs. predentistry courses	Mandatory 15% overall weight on CDA DAT scores on Reading Comprehension (25%), Perceptual Ability (25%), Carving (25%), Academic Avg. (25%) *Note:* Minimum score of 3 is required on the Carving	65% weight on 2 best yrs. Minimum acceptable overall 2-year average is 75%.	Yes	Yes	Saskatchewan	Yes (accept non-Canadian)

Sources: ADEA and dental schools
DAT = Dental Admission Test
GPA = Grade Point Average
NA = Not Available
NR = Not Reported

TABLE 3-4. CHARACTERISTICS OF THE CLASS ENTERING FALL 2012 BY DENTAL SCHOOL

STATE, TERRITORY,		AGE			PREDENTAL EDUCATION							MEAN DAT		MEAN GPA	
OR PROVINCE	DENTAL SCHOOL	MEAN	RANGE	# OVER 30	2 YRS.	3 YRS.	4 YRS.	BACC.	M.S.	PH.D.	M.D.	AA	PAT	TOTAL	SCI
ALABAMA	University of Alabama at Birmingham	23	20-31	1	0	0	0	60	2	0		20.0	20.0	3.70	3.60
ARIZONA	Arizona School of Dentistry & Oral Health	26	21-37	13	0	0	2	65	9	0		18.5	19.2	3.34	3.22
ARIZONA	Midwestern University-Arizona	26	21-44	14	0	0	3	93	14	2		19.6	20.4	3.56	3.50
CALIFORNIA	Loma Linda University	26	NR	NR	NR	NR	NR	NR	NR	NR		20.2	21.1	3.61	3.33
CALIFORNIA	University of California, Los Angeles	23	20-32	6	0	0	0	83	4	1		22.0	22.0	3.69	3.66
CALIFORNIA	University of California, San Francisco	24	20-27	4	0	0	2	81	5	0		21.0	20.0	3.47	3.40
CALIFORNIA	University of the Pacific Arthur A. Dugoni School of Dentistry	25	20 - 44	12	4	0	1	132	2	0		21.0	21.0	3.50	3.40
CALIFORNIA	University of Southern California Ostrow School of Dentistry	26	22-45	18	0	0	0	131	12	1		20.0	20.0	3.53	3.45
CALIFORNIA	Western University of Health Sciences	25	21-45	4	1	2	0	57	7	0		19.4	20.3	3.32	3.24
COLORADO	The University of Colorado	25	21-45	7	0	0	1	77	2	0		19.0	20.0	3.68	3.61
CONNECTICUT	University of Connecticut	24	22-40	1	0	0	0	39	1	0		21.0	21.0	3.54	3.50
DISTRICT OF COLUMBIA	Howard University	24	20-35	4	0	0	0	68	13	0		17.8	17.9	3.47	3.04
FLORIDA	Lake Erie College of Osteopathic Medicine	24	21-26	0	0	0	100		17	0		18.5	18.3	3.41	3.28
FLORIDA	Nova Southeastern University	24	19-35	5	0	0	0	100	23	0		20.3	19.6	3.69	3.65
FLORIDA	University of Florida	24	21-36	6	0	0	0	70	13	0		20.0	20.0	3.60	3.50
GEORGIA	Georgia Regents University	25	20-37	12	0	0	0	69	10	1		19.0	20.0	3.52	3.50
ILLINOIS	Midwestern University-Illinois	24	20-37	5	0	0	0	105	25	0		19.0	20.0	3.44	3.30
ILLINOIS	Southern Illinois University	23	20-37	1	0	6	3	41	1	0		19.4	19.7	3.64	3.52
ILLINOIS	University of Illinois at Chicago	23	20-35	4	0	0	0	68	5	0		20.0	20.0	3.60	3.50
INDIANA	Indiana University	25	21-34	6	NA	1	1	80	22	0		19.0	19.0	3.50	3.42
IOWA	University of Iowa	23	20-35	2	0	1	0	76	2	1		20.0	20.0	3.75	3.68
KENTUCKY	University of Kentucky	23	21-34	2	0	0	0	57	7	0		18.0	19.0	3.46	3.34
KENTUCKY	University of Louisville	24	21-40	7	0	0	0	109	10	0	1	19.0	20.0	3.56	3.44
LOUISIANA	Louisiana State University	24	21-33	1	0	0	2	63				19.6	19.6	3.67	3.60
MARYLAND	University of Maryland	24	21-37	7	0	0	0	114	16	0		20.5	20.3	3.60	3.50
MASSACHUSETTS	Boston University	24	21-34	2	0	1	0	113	32	3		20.0	20.0	3.45	3.40
MASSACHUSETTS	Harvard School of Dental Medicine	23	21-28	0	0	0	0	35	0	0		23.2	22.2	3.86	3.85
MASSACHUSETTS	Tufts University	24	20-40	9	0	0	0	170	20	0		20.0	21.0	3.41	3.31
MICHIGAN	University of Detroit Mercy	23	20-40	4	1	14[1]	0	76	4	1		20.0	20.0	3.57	3.50
MICHIGAN	University of Michigan	23	21-38	1	0	2	2	92	11	1		20.0	21.0	3.57	3.49
MINNESOTA	University of Minnesota	24	21-46	6			1	95	1	1		19.9	20.9	3.60	3.52
MISSISSIPPI	University of Mississippi	23	22-37	2	0	0	0	35	13	0		18.0	19.0	3.50	3.40
MISSOURI	University of Missouri - Kansas City	24	21-44	11	0	0	0	105	4	0		19.0	18.9	3.63	3.62
NEBRASKA	Creighton University	24	21-35	4	0	5	80	84	8	0		19.4	20.5	3.58	3.45
NEBRASKA	University of Nebraska Medical Center	24	21-34	2	0	0	1	47	0	0		20.0	21.0	3.80	3.73
NEVADA	University of Nevada, Las Vegas	26	22-40	12	0	3	0	74	5	0		19.7	20.0	3.43	3.31
NEW JERSEY	University of Medicine and Dentistry of New Jersey	23	20-33	2	0	0	0	81	8	0		20.1	20.9	3.59	3.53
NEW YORK	Columbia University	23	20-37	2	0	0	80	80	2	1		23.0	21.5	3.60	3.60

TABLE 3-4. CHARACTERISTICS OF THE CLASS ENTERING FALL 2012 BY DENTAL SCHOOL (CONTINUED)

STATE, TERRITORY,		AGE			PREDENTAL EDUCATION							MEAN DAT		MEAN GPA	
OR PROVINCE	DENTAL SCHOOL	MEAN	RANGE	# OVER 30	2 YRS.	3 YRS.	4 YRS.	BACC.	M.S.	PH.D.	M.D.	AA	PAT	TOTAL	SCI
NEW YORK	New York University	24	20-40	15	0	20	0	227	37	0		21.0	20.0	3.53	3.44
NEW YORK	Stony Brook University	23	21-31	2				38	1	1	1	21.0	21.0	3.67	3.60
NEW YORK	University at Buffalo	24	20-37	2	0	5	0	72	13	0		19.9	20.7	3.28	3.11
NORTH CAROLINA	East Carolina University	25	23–34	5	0	0	0	46	6	0		19.2	19.0	3.39	3.28
NORTH CAROLINA	University of North Carolina at Chapel Hill	24	21-40	7	0	0	4	72	5	0		20.0	20.0	3.57	3.52
OHIO	Case Western Reserve University	24	19-37	8	3	3	0	56	11	1		19.7	19.7	3.53	3.46
OHIO	The Ohio State University	24	21-37	9	0	0	90	0	19	1		20.1	20.6	3.65	3.40
OKLAHOMA	University of Oklahoma	25	20-41	7	0	0	2	46	6	2		20.2	20.1	3.61	3.58
OREGON	Oregon Health & Science University	24	21-30	2	0	0	0	75	0	0		19.1	20.1	3.65	3.59
PENNSYLVANIA	The Maurice H. Kornberg School of Dentistry, Temple University	24	21-30	0	0	6	0	109	12	1		19.7	20.0	3.51	3.41
PENNSYLVANIA	University of Pennsylvania	23	21-39	5	0	1	0	107	8	2	1	21.0	21.0	3.62	3.57
PENNSYLVANIA	University of Pittsburgh	26	21-34	1	0	0	0	75	4	0		20.8	21.3	3.61	3.51
PUERTO RICO	University of Puerto Rico	24	21-35	3	0	2	2	38	3	0		17.0	18.0	3.50	3.41
SOUTH CAROLINA	Medical University of South Carolina	24	21-39	5	NR	NR	NR	67	4	0		19.0	20.0	3.67	3.62
TENNESSEE	Meharry Medical College	25	21-40	4	0	0	0	52	8	0		18.0	18.0	3.20	3.06
TENNESSEE	University of Tennessee Health Science Center	24	20-45	5	0	1	0	89	5	0		19.0	20.0	3.57	3.49
TEXAS	Texas A&M University Baylor College of Dentistry	24	21-34	3	0	0	0	102	2	0		20.0	20.0	3.52	3.47
TEXAS	University of Texas Health Science Center at San Antonio	23	20-43	7	0	16	22	61	1	0		20.0	19.0	3.59	3.52
TEXAS	The University of Texas School of Dentistry at Houston	24	20-39	11	0	0	1	92	2	1		19.7	19.8	3.69	3.63
UTAH	Roseman University of Health Sciences	26	21-42	8			18	56	6	0		20.0	22.0	3.31	3.20
VIRGINIA	Virginia Commonwealth University	25	19-40	10			3	77	9			20.0	20.0	3.57	3.50
WASHINGTON	University of Washington	25	21-38	7	0	0	1	61	1	0		20.4	21.3	3.58	3.51
WEST VIRGINIA	West Virginia University	23	21-34	4	0	0	11	47	2	0		18.0	19.0	3.62	3.47
WISCONSIN	Marquette University	23	20-41	1	0	16	0	64	0	0		19.5	19.6	3.63	3.58
ALBERTA	University of Alberta	23	20-32	1	8	6	18	17	1	0		NA	21.3	3.86	NA
BRITISH COLUMBIA	University of British Columbia	NR	NR	NR	0	0	NR	46	2	0		21.4	22.1	80.55%	NR
MANITOBA	University of Manitoba	NR	NR	NR	6	12	0	11	1	0		19.5	22.1	4.02	3.86
NOVA SCOTIA	Dalhousie University	24	21-31	4	0	2	8	28	0	0		19.0	21.0	3.90	4.00
ONTARIO	University of Toronto	NR	NR	NR	0	9	0	29	26	0		21.0	22.0	3.85	NR
ONTARIO	University of Western Ontario	23	21-39	5	NA	NA	NA	52	4	0		21.0	21.0	3.9	NA
QUEBEC	Université Laval	21	19-30	0	20	0	0	27	0	0		NR	19.0	NR	NR
QUEBEC	McGill University	NR	NR	NR	0	0	0	16	9	1		NR	NR	3.71	NR
QUEBEC	Université de Montréal	NR	NR	NR	52	0	0	38	0	0		NR	NR	NR	NR
SASKATCHEWAN	University of Saskatchewan	22	19-28	0	2	10	6	10	0	0		18.7	19.7	89.66%	NA

Sources: ADEA and dental schools

Note: The numbers presented above may not match those listed by the individual schools in Part II because of different reporting procedures. Neither set of numbers is intended to be an exact statistic but is presented to give a sense of the applicant and enrollee profiles of each school. Canadian DAT scores are listed in individual Canadian school profiles.

NR = Not Reported

DAT = Dental Admission Test

GPA = Grade Point Average

[1]This figure includes 9 from University of Detroit Mercy 7-year B.S./D.D.S. program who will receive baccalaureate degree in May 2014.

TABLE 3-5. THE CLASS ENTERING FALL 2012 AT DENTAL SCHOOLS BY STATE OF RESIDENCE

STATE, TERRITORY, OR PROVINCE	DENTAL SCHOOL	TOTAL ENROLLEES	IN STATE OR PROV.	OUT OF STATE OR PROV.	ORIGIN OF OUT-OF-STATE OR PROVINCE ENROLLEES
ALABAMA	University of Alabama at Birmingham	60	43	17	FL-6, GA-5, LA-2, SC-1, TN-2, Taiwan-1
ARIZONA	Arizona School of Dentistry & Oral Health	76	26	50	AL-1, CA-11, CO-1, FL-2, GA-1,Guam-1, HI-2, IL-2, MI-1, MN-3, MT-1, NC-1, NH-1, NJ-2, NM-1, NV-3, NY-1,OH-1, OR-1, SD-1, TX-4, UT-5, WA-2, WI-1
ARIZONA	Midwestern University-Arizona	112	29	83	AR-1, AZ-1, CA-20, CO-2, FL-4, GA-1, HI-2, ID-2, IL-3, IN-1, LA-1, MA-1, MI-1, MO-1, MT-1, NC-1, ND-3, NE-1, NY-1, OH-2, OR-3, PA-1, TX-3, UT-10, VA-2, WA-7, WI-3, WY-1, Canada-3
CALIFORNIA	Loma Linda University	97	NR	NR	NR
CALIFORNIA	University of California, Los Angeles	88	82	6	AZ-1, ID-1, OR-1, UT-1, Indonesia-1, Korea-1
CALIFORNIA	University of California, San Francisco	88	73	15	AZ-1, FL-2, GA-1, HI-1, IL-3, NY-1, OH-2, PA-1, UT-1, WA-1, South Korea-1
CALIFORNIA	University of the Pacific Arthur A. Dugoni School of Dentistry	138	104	34	AZ-5, CT-1, FL-3, HI-4, ID-1, MD-1, NJ-1, NM-2, NV-3, OR-2, TX-1, UT-3, WA-1, WI-1, Canada-1, South Korea-3
CALIFORNIA	University of Southern California Ostrow School of Dentistry	144	102	42	AK, AZ, CO, FL, GA, HI, IL, IN, MD, MN, NJ, NM, NY, PA, TX, UT, VA, Canada, South Korea
CALIFORNIA	Western University of Health Sciences	67	41	26	AK-1, AZ-1, CO-1, FL-2, GA-3, IL-1, MD-1, MI-1, NC-2, NY-2, OK-1, OR-1, TX-3, VA-1, WA-3, WI-1, South Korea - 1
COLORADO	The University of Colorado	80	47	33	AR-1, AZ-12, CA-1, FL-2, HI-2, ID-1, IL-1, MT-3, NC-1, ND-1, NM-6, WY-2
CONNECTICUT	University of Connecticut	40	25	15	ME-1, MA-5, MI-1, NH-1, NJ-3, NY-2, RI-1, WA-1
DISTRICT OF COLUMBIA	Howard University	78	2	76	AZ-2, CA-2, FL-8, GA-4, IL-1, IN-1, LA-4, MA-2, MD-8, MI-1, MN-1, MO-2, NC-1, NJ-3, NY-3, PA-3, TX-4, VA-7, Antigua-1, Bahamas-2, Gabon-1, Haiti-1, India-1, Iran-1, Jamaica-2, Nigeria-1, South Korea-3, St. Lucia-1, Trinidad and Tobago-2, Venezuela-1
FLORIDA	Lake Erie College of Osteopathic Medicine	100	48	52	AL, AR, AZ, CA, CT, GA, IL, IN, KS, LA, MI, NC, ND, NJ, NY, OH, OK, PA, SC, TX, VA, WA
FLORIDA	Nova Southeastern University	123	75	48	CA-6, CO-1, GA-3, ID-1, IL-2, MD-1, MI-2, MO- 1, ND- 1, NJ- 2, NV-1, NY-2, OK-1, PA-1, SC- 1, TN- 1, TX-2, UT-4, VA-2, Canada-9, China-1, France-1, South Korea-2
FLORIDA	University of Florida	83	78	5	GA-3, MD-1, OK-1
GEORGIA	Georgia Regents University	80	76	4	SC, TX, UT, VA
ILLINOIS	Midwestern University-Illinois	130	47	83	AR-1, AZ-4, CA-10, CO-1, FL-2, GA-3, IA-2, ID-2, IN-7, KS-2, LA-1, MA-2, ME-1, MI-5, MN-3, MO-1, NC-1, NE-1, NJ-2, NY-2, OH-4, OK-1, PA-3, SC-1, SD-1, TX-8, VA-2, WA-2, WI-8
ILLINOIS	Southern Illinois University	51	51	0	
ILLINOIS	University of Illinois at Chicago	68	62	6	CA-1, FL-1, IN-1, MI-1, MO-1, WI-1
INDIANA	Indiana University	104	77	27	AZ-1, CA-1, FL-3, GA-2, IL-8, MI-2, MN-1, NY-1, OH-1, TN-1, TX-1, Canada-5,
IOWA	University of Iowa	80	57	23	CO-1, HI - 1, ID-1, IL-7, MN-3, OK-1, PA-1, UT-2, VA-1, WA-1, WI-3, Canada-1
KENTUCKY	University of Kentucky	57	39	18	CA-1, CT-1, FL-3, GA-1, ID-1, IN-1, OH-4, PA-1, MO-1, MD-1, TN-2, WV-1, South Korea- 1
KENTUCKY	University of Louisville	120	44	76	AL-2, AR-2, FL-9, GA-5, ID-3, IL-3, IN-15, MI-3, NC-4, NJ-1, OH-1, PA-1, SC-3, TN-7, TX-1, UT-7, VA- 3, WI-4, Canada-1, Active-duty military with no state-1
LOUISIANA	Louisiana State University	65	56	9	AR-4, FL-1, MS-1, NC-1, TX-1, UT-1
MARYLAND	University of Maryland	130	67	63	AL-1, CA-3, CT-3, DC-1, FL-10, GA-1, IL-1, IN- 1, MA-1, MI-4, NC- 2, NH-2, NJ-4, NY-5, OH-1, PA-13, VA-9, WA-1
MASSACHUSETTS	Boston University	115	30	85	CA-5, CT-5, FL-8, GA-3, ME-2, MD-1, MI-2, MN-1, NJ-2, NY-6, PA-1, RI-4, TX-5, VT-2, VA-3, WI-2, Canada-24, South Korea-8, Kuwait-1
MASSACHUSETTS	Harvard School of Dental Medicine	35	4	31	CA- 7, CT-1, DE-1 ,FL-5 ,HI-1, KY-1, NJ-3, NY-5, OR-1, PA-3, TX-1, WA-1, WI-1
MASSACHUSETTS	Tufts University	190	34	156	CA- 18, CO-1, CT-5, FL-17, GA-4, ID-1, IL-4, IN-1, KS-1, KY-1, LA-1, ME-10, MI-7, MN-1, MO-1, NC-4, NE-1, NH-8, NJ-12, NM-1, NV-2 NY-15, OH-1, OR-3, PA-9, RI-5, TN-1, TX-9, VA-4, VT-3, WA-2, WI-3
MICHIGAN	University of Detroit Mercy	144	90	54	CA-9, FL-4, GA-2, IL-4, IN-2, MN-1, MS-2,OH-2, TN-3, TX-2, UT-1, VA-1, Canada-20 (AB-3, BC-4, ON-13), Korea-1
MICHIGAN	University of Michigan	108	65	43	AK-1, AL-1, CA-16, FL-3, GA-2, IL-6, IN-1, MN-1, NJ-1, NM-1, NV-1, NY-1, PA-1, UT-1, WA-3, WI-1, Canada-1,China-1

TABLE 3-5. THE CLASS ENTERING FALL 2012 AT DENTAL SCHOOLS BY STATE OF RESIDENCE (CONTINUED)

STATE, TERRITORY, OR PROVINCE	DENTAL SCHOOL	TOTAL ENROLLEES	IN STATE OR PROV.	OUT OF STATE OR PROV.	ORIGIN OF OUT-OF-STATE OR PROVINCE ENROLLEES
MINNESOTA	University of Minnesota	98	66	32	CO, GA, IL, MD, MI, ND, NJ, OR, SD, VA, WA, WI, Canada, South Korea
MISSISSIPPI	University of Mississippi	35	35	0	
MISSOURI	University of Missouri - Kansas City	109	77	32	HI-3, IA-1, KS-21, MD-1, NM-5, OK-1
NEBRASKA	Creighton University	85	9	76	CA-3, CO-3, FL-2, GA-2, HI-2, IA-4, ID-8, IL-3, KS-6, MN-6, MO-5, ND-4, NM-5, OK-1, TN-1, TX-2, UT-10, WA-4, WY-4, Vietnam-1
NEBRASKA	University of Nebraska Medical Center	48	29	19	AZ-1, CO-1, KS-4, MN-1, MO-1, SD-5, UT-1, WY-4, WA-1
NEVADA	University of Nevada, Las Vegas	81	44	37	AK-1, AZ-3, CA -15, FL-1, GA-1, NC-1, ND-1, NJ-1, UT-10, VA-1, WA-1, Canada- 1
NEW JERSEY	University of Medicine and Dentistry of New Jersey	89	63	26	FL-6, IL-1, NY-16, PA-2, South Korea-1
NEW YORK	Columbia University	80	27	53	CA-9, CT-2, FL-9, GA-1, IL-3, MA-5, MD-1,MN-1, NC-3, NJ-7, PA-4,TX-4, UT-1, VA-2
NEW YORK	New York University	247	83	164	AL-2, AZ-1, CA-27, CO-2, CT-1, FL-17, IL-2, KY-1, LA-1, MA-3, MI-2, MD-2, ME-2, MN-2, MO-2, MS-1, NC-5, NJ-36, OH-3, PA-3, SC-1, TX-3, UT-1, VA-1, WA-2, WI-2, Afghanistan-1, Belarus-1, Canada-16, China-2, Columbia-1, India-2, Iran-5, Israel-1, Jordan-1, Libya-1, Mexico-1, Poland-1, South Korea-22, Spain-1, Taiwan-1, Thailand-1, Venezuela-1
NEW YORK	Stony Brook University	41	37	4	CO-1, NJ-2, UT-1
NEW YORK	University at Buffalo	90	69	21	AZ-2, CA-1, CT-1, GA-1, IL-1, NJ-3, PA-3, RI-1, UT-1, WA-2, Canada-3, Haiti-1, Tanzania-1
NORTH CAROLINA	East Carolina University	52	52	0	N/A
NORTH CAROLINA	University of North Carolina at Chapel Hill	81	68	13	AL-1, FL-1, GA-2, IL-1, IN-1, KS-1, MI-1, NY-1, PA-1, OH-1, TX-1, Jamaica-1
OHIO	Case Western Reserve University	74	24	50	AZ-1, CA-6, CT-1, FL-2, GA-1, IL-1, IN-3, MA-3, MD-1, NJ-2, NY-2, OR-1, PA-5, PR-1, TX-2, VA-1 Canada-10, China-1, Kenya-1, Nigeria-1, South Korea-3, United Kingdom-1
OHIO	The Ohio State University	110	88	22	CA-2, GA-1, IA-2, IN-1, MI-3, MN-1, MO-2, NY-1, OK-1, PA-3, SC-1, TN-1, China-1, Hong Kong-1, Korea-1
OKLAHOMA	University of Oklahoma	56	45	11	AR-1, GA-1, MN- 1, TX- 2, UT-4, WA-1, VA-1
OREGON	Oregon Health & Science University	75	38	37	AZ-4, CA-4, HI-2, ID-3, IN-1, LA-1, MT-4, ND-1, PA-1, UT-5, VA-1, WA-6, WY-1, Canada (BC)-2, Sweden-1
PENNSYLVANIA	The Maurice H. Kornberg School of Dentistry, Temple University	128	58	70	AL-1, AZ-2, CA-4, DE-3, FL-8, GA-2, HI-1, IL-1, MD-3, NC-1, NJ-13, NY-11, OH-1, SD-1, TX-3, UT-3, VA-6, WI-3, Canada-1, South Korea-1, Colombia-1
PENNSYLVANIA	University of Pennsylvania	119	15	104	AL-1, AZ-2, CA-19, CT-5, DC-1, FL-10, GA-2, IL-5, KY-1, MA-6, MD-4, MI-3, NC-1, NH-1, NJ-9, NY-8, SC-2, TX-3, VA-7, WA-1, WI-1, Canada-4, Kenya-1, People's Republic of China-1, South Korea-5 , Zambia-1
PENNSYLVANIA	University of Pittsburgh	79	28	53	CA-5, FL-4, GA-3, IL-1, IN-1, MA-2, MD-1, MI-1, MN-1, NC-5, NH-1, NJ-3, NY-5, OH-2, OR-1, TX-4, VA-1, WA-3, Canada-2, China-2, Hong Kong-1, South Korea-7, Zimbabwe- 1
PUERTO RICO	University of Puerto Rico	42	38	4	ID-1, FL-2, TX-1
SOUTH CAROLINA	Medical University of South Carolina	72	53	19	CA-2, FL-2, GA-3, ID-1, MD-1, MN-1, NC-2, NJ-1, NM-1, NY-1, OH-1, TN-1, UT-1, VA-1
TENNESSEE	Meharry Medical College	60	10	45	AL-3, AR-1, CA-4, FL-4, GA-7, IL-3, IN-1, KS-1, LA-7, MI-1, MS-2, NC-5, NJ-2, NY-3, OH-1, OK-1, SC-1, TN-7, TX-3, VA-2, Jamaica-1
TENNESSEE	University of Tennessee Health Science Center	90	48	43	AL-1, AR- 35, FL-1, GA-2, KS-1, LA-1, MS-1, TX-1, India-1
TEXAS	Texas A&M University Baylor College of Dentistry	104	98	6	AR-1, LA-1, MI-1, NM-1, SC-1, UT-1
TEXAS	University of Texas Health Science Center at San Antonio	100	94	6	CA-1, CO-1, KS-1, NM-1, OK-1, UT-1
TEXAS	The University of Texas School of Dentistry at Houston	99	99	0	NA
UTAH	Roseman University of Health Sciences	80	29	51	AZ-3, CA-16, FL-1, GA-1, IA-1, ID-4, IL-2, MD-3, MO-2, NH-1, NY-1, OR-4, SD-1, TX-4, VA-1, WA-3, WY-1, ON-1, Korea-1

(continued)

TABLE 3-5. THE CLASS ENTERING FALL 2012 AT DENTAL SCHOOLS BY STATE OF RESIDENCE (CONTINUED)

STATE, TERRITORY, OR PROVINCE	DENTAL SCHOOL	TOTAL ENROLLEES	IN STATE OR PROV.	OUT OF STATE OR PROV.	ORIGIN OF OUT-OF-STATE OR PROVINCE ENROLLEES
VIRGINIA	Virginia Commonwealth University	94	62	32	AZ-1, CA-2, FL-2, GA-1, ID-1, IL-1, MD-2, ME-1 NC-1, NJ-1, NY-2, OH-1, PA-4, TN-1, TX-1, UT-6, VT-1, Kuwait-3
WASHINGTON	University of Washington	62	54	8	AK-1, AZ-2, HI-1, ID-1, MT-3
WEST VIRGINIA	West Virginia University	60	41	19	AR-1, FL-1, IL- 1, MD-1, NC-2, NM-1, OH-2, PA-2, TN-1, UT-1, VA-4, Kuwait-2
WISCONSIN	Marquette University	80	40	40	AK-1, CA-3, CO-1, CT-1, FL-2, IL-10, IN-3, IA-2, MI-1, MN-4, MO-2, NE-1, NV-1, OH-3, OR-1, UT-1, WA-1, Bahamas-1, South Korea-1
ALBERTA	University of Alberta	32	32	0	NR
BRITISH COLUMBIA	University of British Columbia	48	43	5	Ontario-3, Alberta-1, Saskatchewan-1
MANITOBA	University of Manitoba	30	27	3	
NOVA SCOTIA	Dalhousie University	38	29	9	Alberta-1, Kuwait-2, United States-6
ONTARIO	University of Toronto	65	59	6	NR
ONTARIO	University of Western Ontario	56	50	6	Canada: AL-2, BC-1, PE-1; United States: CA-1, NY-1
QUEBEC	Université Laval	48	48	0	
QUEBEC	McGill University	26	19	7	NR
QUEBEC	Université de Montréal	90	86	4	From other Canadian provinces: Ontario-2, New Brunswick-2
SASKATCHEWAN	University of Saskatchewan	28	21	7	Ontario-4, Alberta -1, (2 - NR)

Sources: ADEA and dental schools

Note: The numbers presented above may not match those listed by the individual schools in Part II because of different reporting procedures. Neither set of numbers is intended to be an exact statistic but is presented to give a sense of the applicant and enrollee profiles of each school.

NR = Not Reported

TABLE 3-6. COMBINED AND OTHER DEGREE PROGRAMS BY DENTAL SCHOOL

STATE, TERRITORY, OR PROVINCE	DENTAL SCHOOL	DOCTORAL DENTAL DEGREE	Ph.D.	M.S.	M.P.H.	M.D.	B.A./B.S.	Other	Additional Information
ALABAMA	University of Alabama at Birmingham	D.M.D.	Yes	No	No	No	No	No	
ARIZONA	Arizona School of Dentistry & Oral Health	D.M.D.	No	No	Yes	No	No	No	
ARIZONA	Midwestern University-Arizona	D.M.D.	No	No	No	No	No	No	
CALIFORNIA	Loma Linda University	D.D.S.	Yes	Yes	Yes	Yes	Yes	No	
CALIFORNIA	University of California, Los Angeles	D.D.S.	Yes	Yes	Yes	No	No	Yes	M.B.A.
CALIFORNIA	University of California, San Francisco	D.D.S.	Yes	Yes	No	No	No	Yes	M.B.A.
CALIFORNIA	University of the Pacific Arthur A. Dugoni School of Dentistry	D.D.S.	No	No	No	No	No	No	
CALIFORNIA	University of Southern California Ostrow School of Dentistry	D.D.S.	No	No	No	No	No	No	
CALIFORNIA	Western University of Health Sciences	D.M.D.	No	No	No	No	No	No	
COLORADO	The University of Colorado	D.D.S.	No	No	No	No	Yes	No	
CONNECTICUT	University of Connecticut	D.M.D.	Yes	Yes	Yes	No	Yes	No	M.S. in Clinical and Translational Research
DISTRICT OF COLUMBIA	Howard University	D.D.S.	No	No	No	No	Yes	Yes	B.S./D.D.S. offered to Howard undergraduates only, D.D.S./M.B.A.
FLORIDA	Lake Erie College of Osteopathic Medicine	D.M.D.	No	No	No	No	No		
FLORIDA	Nova Southeastern University	D.M.D.	No	Yes	Yes	No	No	Yes	D.O./D.M.D..
FLORIDA	University of Florida	D.M.D.	No	No	No	No	No	Yes	Honors combined B.S./D.M.D. program and combined D.M.D./ Ph.D. program
GEORGIA	Georgia Regents University	D.M.D.	Yes	Yes	No	No	No	No	
ILLINOIS	Midwestern University-Illinois	D.M.D	No	Yes	No	No	No	Yes	D.M.D./Master's in Biomedical Science
ILLINOIS	Southern Illinois University	D.M.D.	No	No	No	No	No	No	
ILLINOIS	University of Illinois at Chicago	D.M.D.	Yes	Yes	No	No	No	No	
INDIANA	Indiana University	D.D.S.	Yes	Yes	Yes	No	No	Yes	We offer M.S.D. programs in most areas
IOWA	University of Iowa	D.D.S.	No	Yes	Yes	No	No	Yes	D.D.S./M.S. in Dental Public Health
KENTUCKY	University of Kentucky	D.M.D.	Yes	Yes	No	No	No	No	
KENTUCKY	University of Louisville	D.M.D.	Yes	Yes	No	No	No	No	M.S. in Oral Biology
LOUISIANA	Louisiana State University	D.D.S.	Yes	No	No	No	No	No	
MARYLAND	University of Maryland	D.D.S.	Yes	Yes	Yes	No	No	Yes	M.S. in Clinical Research
MASSACHUSETTS	Boston University	D.M.D.	No	No	No	No	Yes	Yes	B.A./D.M.D. 7-year program offered to Boston University undergraduates. Advanced dental education programs offered in Advanced Education in General Dentistry, Dental Public Health, Endodontics, Operative Dentistry, Oral Biology, Oral and Maxillofacial Pathology, Oral and Maxillofacial Surgery, Orthodontics, Pediatric Dentistry, Periodontics, and Prosthodontics; CAGS, M.S., M.S.D., D.Sc., D.Sc.D., Internship, Ph.D. degrees.
MASSACHUSETTS	Harvard School of Dental Medicine	D.M.D.	Yes	Yes	Yes	No	No	Yes	M.B.A.
MASSACHUSETTS	Tufts University	D.M.D.	No	Yes	Yes	No	Yes	No	
MICHIGAN	University of Detroit Mercy	D.D.S.	No	No	No	No	No	Yes	B.S./D.D.S. offered to UDM undergraduates enrolled in and successfully completing 7-Year B.S./D.D.S. Program; B.S. granted after completing second year of D.D.S. curriculum.
MICHIGAN	University of Michigan	D.D.S.	Yes	Yes	Yes	No	No	No	
MINNESOTA	University of Minnesota	D.D.S.	Yes	Yes	Yes	No	Yes	No	
MISSISSIPPI	University of Mississippi	D.M.D.	No	No	No	No	No	No	
MISSOURI	Missouri School of Dentistry & Oral Health	D.M.D.	No	No	Yes	No	No	No	
MISSOURI	University of Missouri - Kansas City	D.D.S.	Yes	Yes	No	No	No	No	M.S. Oral Biology
NEBRASKA	Creighton University	D.D.S.	No	No	No	No	No	No	
NEBRASKA	University of Nebraska Medical Center	D.D.S.	Yes	Yes	No	No	No	No	

TABLE 3-6. COMBINED AND OTHER DEGREE PROGRAMS BY DENTAL SCHOOL (CONTINUED)

STATE, TERRITORY, OR PROVINCE	DENTAL SCHOOL	DOCTORAL DENTAL DEGREE	Ph.D.	M.S.	M.P.H.	M.D.	B.A./B.S.	Other	Additional Information
NEVADA	University of Nevada, Las Vegas	D.M.D.	No	No	No	No	No	Yes	M.B.A.
NEW JERSEY	University of Medicine and Dentistry of New Jersey	D.M.D.	Yes	Yes	Yes	No	No	No	
NEW YORK	Columbia University	D.D.S.	No	Yes	Yes	No	No	Yes	M.B.A., M.A. in Education, M.A. in Dental Informatics
NEW YORK	New York University	D.D.S.	No	No	Yes	No	Yes	Yes	B.A./D.D.S.
NEW YORK	Stony Brook University	D.D.S.	Yes	Yes	Yes	No	No	Yes	M.B.A.
NEW YORK	University at Buffalo	D.D.S.	Yes	Yes	No	No	Yes	Yes	M.B.A.
NORTH CAROLINA	East Carolina University	D.M.D.	No	No	No	No	No	No	Plans are under way for a combined D.M.D./M.P.H. in the future.
NORTH CAROLINA	University of North Carolina at Chapel Hill	D.D.S.	Yes	Yes	Yes	No	No	No	
OHIO	Case Western Reserve University	D.M.D.	No	No	Yes	No	Yes	Yes	M.C.R.T
OHIO	The Ohio State University	D.D.S.	Yes	No	No	No	No	Yes	D.D.S./Ph.D.
OKLAHOMA	University of Oklahoma	D.D.S.	No	No	No	No	No	No	
OREGON	Oregon Health & Science University	D.M.D.	No	No	No	No	No	No	
PENNSYLVANIA	The Maurice H. Kornberg School of Dentistry, Temple University	D.M.D.	No	Yes	Yes	No	Yes	Yes	D.M.D./M.B.A., M.S. Oral Biology
PENNSYLVANIA	University of Pennsylvania	D.M.D.	Yes	Yes	Yes	No	Yes	Yes	M.S. in Education, M.S. in Bioethics, M.S.E. in Bioengineering, M.B.A. (Business Administration))
PENNSYLVANIA	University of Pittsburgh	D.M.D.	Yes	Yes	Yes	No	No	No	
PUERTO RICO	University of Puerto Rico	D.M.D.	Yes	No	No	No	No	No	
SOUTH CAROLINA	Medical University of South Carolina	D.M.D.	No	No	No	No	No	Yes	D.M.D./Ph.D.
TENNESSEE	Meharry Medical College	D.D.S.	No	No	No	No	No	No	
TENNESSEE	University of Tennessee Health Science Center	D.D.S.	Yes	No	No	No	No	No	
TEXAS	Texas A&M University Baylor College of Dentistry	D.D.S.	Yes	Yes	No	No	No	Yes	D.D.S./O.M.S.
TEXAS	University of Texas Health Science Center at San Antonio	D.D.S.	Yes	Yes	Yes	No	No	No	
TEXAS	The University of Texas School of Dentistry at Houston	D.D.S.	No	No	No	No	No	No	
UTAH	Roseman University of Health Sciences	D.M.D.	No	No	No	No	No	No	
UTAH	University of Utah School of Dentistry	D.D.S.	No	No	No	No	No	No	
VIRGINIA	Virginia Commonwealth University	D.D.S.	Yes	Yes	Yes	No	No	No	
WASHINGTON	University of Washington	D.D.S.	Yes	No	Yes	No	No	No	Regional Initiatives in Dental Education (RIDE) program for Washington residents
WEST VIRGINIA	West Virginia University	D.D.S.	No	No	Yes	No	No	Yes	A dual degree in business administration is also available.
WISCONSIN	Marquette University	D.D.S.	Yes	Yes	No	No	Yes	No	
ALBERTA	University of Alberta	D.D.S.	No	No	No	No	No	No	
BRITISH COLUMBIA	University of British Columbia	D.M.D.	No	No	No	No	No	No	
MANITOBA	University of Manitoba	D.M.D.	No	No	No	No	Yes	No	
NOVA SCOTIA	Dalhousie University	D.D.S.	No	Yes	No	Yes	No	No	
ONTARIO	University of Toronto	D.D.S.	Yes	No	No	No	No	Yes	Other degree offered is M.Sc.
ONTARIO	University of Western Ontario	D.D.S.	No	Yes	No	Yes	No	Yes	M.Sc./M.D.
QUEBEC	Université Laval	D.M.D.	No	Yes	No	No	No	No	
QUEBEC	McGill University	D.M.D.	Yes	Yes	No	No	No	No	
QUEBEC	Université de Montréal	D.M.D.	No	No	No	No	No	Yes	M.Sc. in Dentistry, M.Sc. in dental sciences, one-year multidisciplinary residency program
SASKATCHEWAN	University of Saskatchewan	D.M.D.	No	No	No	No	No	No	

Sources: ADEA and dental schools
NR = Not Reported

TABLE 3-7. NATIONAL DENTAL ADMISSIONS INFORMATION 2012

APPLICANTS AND ENROLLEES

TOTAL APPLICANTS	MEN	WOMEN	AMERICAN INDIAN OR ALASKA NATIVE	ASIAN	BLACK OR AFRICAN AMERICAN	WHITE	HISPANIC/ LATINO[1]	NATIVE HAWAIIAN OR PACIFIC ISLANDER	TWO OR MORE RACES	DO NOT WISH TO REPORT/UNKNOWN
12,075	50.9%	47.9%	0.2%	28.0%	6.0%	51.6%	7.9%	0.1%	3.0%	3.3%

TOTAL ENROLLEES	MEN	WOMEN	AMERICAN INDIAN OR ALASKA NATIVE	ASIAN	BLACK OR AFRICAN AMERICAN	WHITE	HISPANIC/ LATINO[1]	NATIVE HAWAIIAN OR PACIFIC ISLANDER	TWO OR MORE RACES	DO NOT WISH TO REPORT/UNKNOWN
5,456	52.1%	47.3%	0.1%	23.7%	5.2%	56.3%	7.7%	0.1%	3.0%	3.5%

DAT/GPA

	Academic Average		Perceptual		Total Science	
	Range	Mean	Range	Mean	Range	Mean
Applicant DAT	11–28	18.7	9–30	19.3	10–30	18.5
Enrollee DAT	13–28	19.9	10–30	20.1	12–30	19.8

	Science GPA		Total GPA	
	Range	Mean	Range	Mean
Applicant GPA	1.33–4.33	3.24	1.77–4.29	3.36
Enrollee GPA	2.13–4.33	3.47	2.11–4.29	3.55

Source: Based on preliminary data from the ADEA Survey of U. S. Dental School Applicants and Enrollees, 2012 Entering Class (ADEA AADSAS Application Cycle 2011-12)
Consider data final only when the report is published by ADEA.
[1]Hispanic/Latino of any race

CHAPTER 4
FINANCING A DENTAL EDUCATION

ADEA partnered with a longtime expert in the field of higher education financing and educational debt management to present up-to-date and relevant information to those considering a dental education. Our expert has more than 30 years of experience—on university campuses, at higher education associations, and in the lending industry—helping applicants, students, alumni, and their institutions to promote not only responsible borrowing, but also responsible repayment.

The same considerable amount of time you have spent thinking about applying to dental school should be spent thinking about how to pay for your dental education. As you learn about financing options in this chapter and consider the ways to finance your dental education, there are four key messages to keep in mind.

- **While expensive, a dental education is an affordable and worthwhile investment.**
- **Many options and types of financial aid are available to help you finance your dental education.**
- **You can help minimize any adverse long-term implications of financing through smart budgeting and responsible borrowing.**
- **You are ultimately responsible for securing financial assistance for dental school, but there is plenty of help available along the way.**

This chapter is broken into a series of questions you may have about financing your dental education. Some quality time spent studying the responses should help give you confidence that you can both make and effectively manage the financial commitment a dental education entails.

ADEA makes every effort to ensure that the most current information is presented. However, financial aid terms, conditions, and programs are subject to change. You should keep in close contact with your dental school's financial aid office (FAO) for any changes that may impact the financial aid available to you.

QUESTION 1

HOW MUCH DOES A DENTAL EDUCATION COST, AND HOW MUCH MONEY WILL I NEED?

Dentistry is a financially rewarding career and should provide a great return on your investment. Dentists are among the top wage earners in the nation. Average incomes for independent dentists were $225,950 for full-time practitioners and $167,940 for part-timers according to the 2010 Survey of Dental Practice by the American Dental Association (ADA), and specialists earn even more. With some thoughtful planning, smart budgeting, and responsible borrowing, the costs can be quite manageable.

In considering the cost of dental education, look at two different types of costs:

1. Out-of-Pocket Costs
2. Financing Costs

■ Out-of-Pocket Costs

This is the category you may be most familiar with. It includes the items you pay for directly, including tuition and fees, books, supplies, equipment, and living expenses. Your dental school's FAO can provide an estimate of these costs, sometimes referred to as cost of attendance (COA) or financial aid budget. ***A breakdown of these numbers for each dental school is in Part II of this book.*** Be sure you know your COA each year because this figure represents the maximum amount of financial aid you can receive each year from any combination of sources.

Budgeting: Control What You Can

Your room, board, and living expenses are, for the most part, the only out-of-pocket costs you can control. You can reduce the amount of money you borrow and will have to repay by making a realistic student budget and sticking to it. Financial aid that does not have to be repaid, such as grants and scholarships, usually goes to cover tuition, fees, and institutional charges, with loans being used for any remaining charges and for living expenses. See Question 4 for more information on unsubsidized loans, including the Unsubsidized Stafford Loan and the Graduate PLUS Loan (Grad PLUS).

Sample First-Year Cost of Attendance

Tuition and Fees	$31,246
Books and Lab Fees	$4,518
Instruments	$5,095
Living Expenses	$33,107
Total	$73,966

Note that credit card payments and other consumer obligations cannot be included in your COA. Make every attempt to pay off consumer debts in full before starting dental school, as any financial distraction could adversely impact your academic work.

How Much Do You Really Need?

Determine how much you will need for each year of dental school by asking yourself three simple questions:

- *How much does it cost this year?* This is the COA or financial aid budget previously discussed. Use smart budgeting to reduce this number. While it's important to look at your cost over the entire duration of your program, you apply for financial aid each year.
- *How much do I have to contribute to this year's costs?* Once you have been admitted, your FAO will review your completed financial aid application (an important reminder not to wait until you have been accepted to apply for financial aid). A combination of income, savings, and other related information as reported on your Free Application for Federal Student Aid (FAFSA)—www.fafsa.ed.gov—will be used to determine how much you have to put toward your COA. If the amount you are expected to contribute does not match what you think you have available, you can contact your FAO to discuss the discrepancy and to see if your financial aid can be adjusted accordingly to better reflect your specific financial circumstances. Be prepared to document why you need additional help.
- *How much more do I need this year to cover the cost?* The difference between your total COA and how much you can contribute will be used by your FAO to determine the type and amount of financial aid you may receive.

One way to reduce how much you pay back on your student loans is to ask family members or others to pay the interest on one of your unsubsidized loans for a short period of time.

■ Financing Costs

The costs associated with borrowing money for dental school include the principal of a loan (the amount borrowed) and any financing costs. Financing costs can greatly increase your total repayment amount, but understanding how they work may make these costs more manageable. Several variables affect financing costs and how much you must pay back: interest rates, capitalization, use of postponement options such as deferment and forbearance, and the length of repayment. These financing costs explain how two dental students can borrow the same amount but pay back vastly different amounts. *See the Glossary at the end of this chapter for full definitions of these and other financial aid terms.*

See Question 4 for more information on student loans and their financing costs and repayment plans.

QUESTION 2

I NEED FINANCIAL AID. ARE THERE OPTIONS OTHER THAN STUDENT LOANS?

While the majority of dental students take out student loans to help pay for school, other financing options may be available as part of a financial aid package.

Some of these options are awarded through the FAO. However, some types of financial aid may be awarded by organizations outside your school, including outside scholarships and service commitment scholarships through the armed forces and programs like the National Health Service Corps (NHSC).

■ Grants and Scholarships

Unlike student loans, grants and scholarships do not have to be repaid and may be referred to as "gift" aid; thus they are always preferable to loans. In general, there are three categories of grants and scholarships:

- *Institutional Grants and Scholarships* are awarded by the school as part of a financial aid award package. Check with your FAO about application forms and deadlines.
- *Outside Scholarships* are awarded by organizations other than the school. You must apply for these independently. They can be found through search engines or organizations, such as www.fastweb.com or ADEA. Use caution with any scholarship searches that require payment for their services. Outside scholarships should be reported to the FAO, as they may impact other aid you are receiving. Outside scholarships are often disbursed directly to your institution.
- *Service Commitment Scholarships* are sometimes referred to as "up-front" service commitment scholarships. They provide financial support while you are in school in exchange for your promise of service after graduation. Programs are offered by the armed forces, NHSC, and the Indian Health Service (IHS):

  —www.goarmy.com/amedd/education/hpsp
  —www.navy.com/careers/healthcare/dentist
  —http://airforce.com/benefits/commissioned-officer-education
  —www.nhsc.hrsa.gov/scholarships
  —www.ihs.gov/JobsCareerDevelop/DHPS/Scholarships

These programs also offer loan repayment programs (help repaying your student loans in exchange for a service commitment you make after school.) *See Question 3 for details on these loan repayment programs.*

> Your financial aid office (FAO) should always be your first point of contact for financial aid. However, consider all kinds of financial aid and assistance when figuring out how to pay for your dental education, including:
>
> - Grants and scholarships with or without a service commitment
> - Loans and loan repayment programs
> - Work-study programs
> - Research fellowships and traineeships
> - Education tax breaks

■ Education Tax Breaks

A number of tax credits and deductions—including some during the repayment period—may help defray the cost of your dental education. To find detailed information on tax credits and deductions, review Internal Revenue Service Publication 970: Tax Benefits for Education, available on the Web at www.IRS.gov/publications/p970. You may want to consult a professional tax advisor or other qualified financial advisor for assistance, especially as these are subject to change.

The *Lifetime Learning Credit* provides a credit on your tax return for qualified tuition and related expenses for any level of postsecondary education including graduate school.

The *Student Loan Interest Deduction* allows eligible borrowers to deduct interest paid on qualified student loans.

The *American Opportunity Tax Credit* is a refundable tax credit of up to $2,500 for undergraduate education.

> The federal government offers Scholarships for Disadvantaged Students (SDS). These awards are available to students from disadvantaged backgrounds as defined by the U.S. Department of Health and Human Services (HHS). *See the Glossary for a full definition.* Contact your FAO for availability of funds and application process and deadlines.

■ Research Fellowship or Traineeship

Your dental school may offer a scholarship or stipend that involves conducting scientific research. Contact your FAO to see if these funds are available at your school.

■ Work Study

Work-study programs provide an opportunity to receive income by working part time. Due to the demands of the dental school curriculum, you may find it difficult to take advantage of this kind of financial aid. Nonetheless, you may want to ask your FAO about work-study programs if you are thinking about working while in school.

QUESTION 3

IS ANY FINANCIAL AID AVAILABLE FOR INTERNATIONAL STUDENTS?

International students coming to the United States to attend dental school should check with their institution's FAO regarding financial aid opportunities. While you must be a U.S. citizen or permanent resident to qualify for federal financial aid, other options may be available. Check out www.edupass.org/finaid for information on financial aid for international students, including scholarships, loans, helpful organizations, and the process for applying for aid.

Loans for International Students

If you do not qualify for a federal student loan, you may be eligible for a private loan for dental school. You can expect a lender to require a creditworthy cosigner who is a U.S. citizen or permanent resident. While some lenders offer private loans with fixed rates, the majority of private loans still have variable interest rates, often with no interest rate cap. Private loans are unsubsidized, and if the interest is not paid as it accrues, it will eventually be added back to the principal through a process called capitalization. Please refer to the section on private loans in Question 4.

Scholarships for International Students

Check with your FAO to see if your school designates any scholarship funds for international students. These scholarships may be based on merit or academic interest. The cultural department or education minister's office at your embassy may also be able to offer assistance.

QUESTION 4

WHAT TYPES OF STUDENT LOANS ARE THERE?
WHAT ARE MY REPAYMENT OPTIONS?

According to results from the Annual ADEA Survey of Dental School Seniors, 88.8% of 2011 graduates left school with student loan debt. The average debt for all indebted graduates was $203,374. The average debt from public and private schools was $177,795 and $245,497 respectively. Nearly one out of every five students in the class of 2011 graduated with $250,000 or more in student loans; however, nearly the same ratio of students reported leaving dental school without any educational debt or debt under $80,000.

Before you look at individual loan programs, consider the following:

- For the best financial aid possible, contact your FAO early and apply as directed, making sure you meet all stated deadlines.
- Be extremely cautious when considering a private or consumer loan to pay for your dental education. Federal and campus-based loans almost always offer more favorable terms and conditions, including flexible repayment plans and postponement options for postdoctoral and residency programs, should you decide to pursue additional study after dental school. Private loans have extremely limited consolidation options, and they are not eligible for repayment under income-related plans such as Income-Based Repayment (IBR) plan, nor are they eligible for federal forgiveness programs.

- If you do not apply or qualify for any institutional financial aid, such as grants, scholarships, or campus-based loans, you can borrow up to your full COA with loans such as Federal Stafford and Federal Grad PLUS.

The following list describes various available loan programs. Stafford and Grad PLUS Loans make up the bulk of many dental students' loan portfolios. Campus-based loans—

STUDENT PROFILE

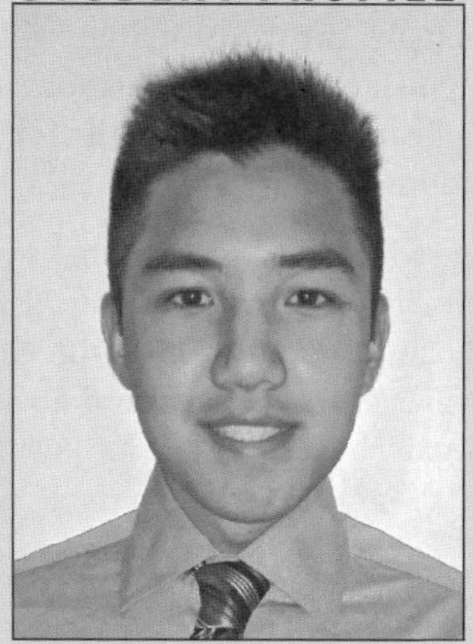

HAO CHEN

FOURTH-YEAR DENTAL STUDENT
STONY BROOK UNIVERSITY SCHOOL OF DENTAL MEDICINE
NEW YORK CITY (QUEENS), NEW YORK

Why did you choose dentistry as your career path?

I was born and raised in a rural farm village in Southeast China, and I had never seen a dentist until I came to the United States at the age of 10. In fact, I did not even consider becoming a dentist until sophomore year of college. During my undergraduate studies, my chosen major was philosophy with a concentration in ethics. I became particularly interested in health care ethics involving the application of moral principles in complex clinical scenarios. This experience pushed me toward a career in the health care field, and I began shadowing at many dental and medical offices. Ultimately, I decided on dentistry because it involves art, creativity, technical skills, and medical knowledge. Additionally, I always wanted a career with a balanced lifestyle, and dentistry is a perfect fit because it offers the flexibility to balance my professional and personal lives.

What classes, externships, clinical, or other experiences are you involved in now?

Currently, I am a fourth-year dental student enrolled in the D.D.S./M.B.A. dual-degree program with a concentration in health care management. Aside from my dental coursework and patient responsibilities, I am taking business courses nights and weekends in anticipation of completing both degrees simultaneously. I am also working on a joint research project between the dental and business schools involving quality assurance and patient satisfaction at the dental clinic, and I hope to have the project published within the next year.

Aside from academics, I am actively involved in many leadership positions at the dental school. I was selected to represent the student body on the Stony Brook Committee for Dental Accreditation in preparation for the upcoming site visit. Additionally, I am serving as the coordinator of the North Eastern Regional Board (NERB) committee.

Lastly, I just returned from an externship mission to Pine Ridge, South Dakota, where I had an eye-opening experience providing dental care for the Lakota Native American Tribe.

What are your short- and long-term goals?

My short-term goal is to make my last year of dental school as memorable as possible. I want to continue challenging myself by taking on increasingly difficult cases. I also want to complete well above the minimal requirements to graduate as a proud and confident clinician. I am also in the process of applying for orthodontic residencies, and my goal is to become enrolled in a renowned program by next year.

In addition to practicing orthodontics, my long-term goal is to become a prominent figure in organized dentistry and academia. My dream is to one day become director of an orthodontics program or the dean of a dental school.

As an applicant, how did you prepare for dental school? Summer programs, shadowing, research, other opportunities.

As a predental student, I wanted to get as much exposure to dentistry as possible. So I shadowed many dentists, including a general dentist and specialists. I also visited a few dental schools to get a glimpse into the day-to-day activities of dental students. Attending open house events is a great way to learn what dental school and dentistry is all about. Looking back, I don't think anything can fully prepare students for the many challenges they will face in dental school. So my recommendation for prospective applicants is to get as much exposure to dentistry as possible, and get a feel for what they are about to enter into.

What advice would you like to share with applicants or those considering dental school?

If there were one piece of advice I could give to applicants considering dental school, I would tell them to pursue their interests and to carve their own paths. An oral health career is possible for people from all walks of life, and a science background is not required in order to succeed. The world of dentistry involves art, science, entrepreneurship, management, technology, and so much more. No matter what your interests are, dentistry has a niche for you.

Many of my peers questioned my decision to pursue a college major in philosophy, but it turned out to be my greatest asset in dental school. Philosophy taught me to crave knowledge and to always think outside the box. In addition, my concentration in ethics taught me to look at complex patient management issues from a variety of angles. So feel free to explore your interests, and don't let anyone discourage you from pursuing this wonderful profession.

Did you move to a new city to attend dental school? If so, what factors helped you make the transition?

I grew up in New York City, and luckily for me, Stony Brook is only an hour's drive away from home. However, it was still somewhat of a transition moving from the most populous city in the country to a mostly suburban area. Going out with classmates to explore the town and meet new people really helped to facilitate the transition. Now that I've gotten to know the surrounding neighborhood and found some nice venues, it feels a lot like my second home.

Before applying to dental school, what activities did you undertake to improve your manual dexterity?

I have had years of experience playing the piano, which has greatly improved my fine motor skills. My hobby of playing video games also helped to bolster my hand-eye coordination. However, I always knew that the dexterity in my left hand was lagging far behind that of my right hand, while dentistry is a profession that requires a certain degree of ambidexterity. So once I began applying to dental schools, I decided to use my left hand for brushing my teeth, eating my meals, and even for operating my computer mouse. I am certain that these changes have resulted in major improvements in my manual dexterity.

Did you participate in any shadowing opportunities before applying to dental schools? What value did you gain from the experience(s)? Would you recommend shadowing to others?

I think shadowing is a great way to get some exposure to dentistry. Before applying to dental school, I shadowed a general dentist and many dental specialists. Not only did I get to see some of the procedures that specialists perform, but I was also exposed to the intricate relationship between specialists and their referring general dentists. Additionally, I worked as a chair-side assistant at a general dentist's office, and was able to get some first-hand experience with many dental procedures. I had a great experience with shadowing, and I would recommend that all potential applicants do the same.

Have you taken advantage of scholarship, loans, or loan repayment programs? What advice would you give applicants about financial aid and dental education financing?

You may not realize it now, but the amount of debt you graduate with will have a direct impact on the rest of your life. When you go to the bank in the future for a loan to buy that dream practice or your dream home, they will look closely at your debt-to-income ratio. If you graduated with an excessive amount of student loans, your choices will be severely limited, and the interest rates on your home or business loan will be sky-high. My advice to applicants is to explore your options because there are many scholarships and loan repayment programs offered to students in the health professions. They are available through many local, state, and national agencies, and taking advantage of these programs early on could save you a ton of money in the long run.

Are you married, partnered, or single? Do you have any children?

I am currently single, and I do not have any children.

which are awarded by the school and usually carry better terms and conditions—may not be available at all dental schools and for all students (check with your FAO). You can find a list of Federal Stafford, Grad PLUS, Federal Perkins, and Federal Consolidation Loans on the National Student Loan Data System at www.nslds.ed.gov. *See the Glossary for more information on this important site.*

Effective July 1, 2012, new Stafford loans will no longer be eligible for an interest subsidy—the government will no longer pay the interest while the borrower is enrolled or during grace or deferment periods. You will still be able to borrow up to $40,500 each year, but the entire amount will be unsubsidized.

Federal Stafford Loans

Federal Stafford Loans are often considered the foundation of a dental student's loan portfolio, and many FAOs will require you to borrow a Federal Stafford Loan before considering you for other financial aid. There are actually two types of Stafford Loans: Subsidized Stafford Loans, which are need-based and interest-free throughout school and during any grace or deferment periods; and Unsubsidized Stafford Loans, for which borrowers are responsible for all accrued and unpaid interest.

However, note that effective this past July 1, 2012, graduate and professional students (including dental students) are no longer eligible for new Subsidized Stafford Loans. Therefore, any borrowing you do in the Stafford Loan Program will be with the Unsubsidized Stafford Loan. In other words, interest will accrue on all Stafford Loans you borrow during dental school, interest you will eventually be responsible for paying and which can greatly increase your total repayment costs.

Some schools may require you to borrow Stafford loans first before considering you for campus-based loans.

- Effective July 1, 2010, the federal government became the lender for all new Stafford Loans through its William D. Ford Federal Direct Loan Program.
- You may currently borrow a combined maximum of $40,500 per year from subsidized and unsubsidized Federal Stafford Loans. As mentioned, this entire amount will be in an Unsubsidized Stafford Loan. A cumulative maximum of $224,000 can be borrowed for undergraduate and graduate education combined in the Stafford Loan program.
- A 6.8% fixed interest rate is assigned for the life of the loan.
- Stafford Loans carry a six-month grace period following graduation or a reduction to less than half-time enrollment.
- Stafford Loans are listed at www.NSLDS.ed.gov.

Federal Graduate PLUS Loans (Grad PLUS)

Grad PLUS loans may be used to supplement borrowing needs beyond those that can be met by Stafford loans. Federal Grad PLUS loans almost always offer more favorable terms than private loans. Interest does accrue from disbursement and will eventually be capitalized if not paid prior to repayment.

- Grad PLUS loans are based in part on the borrower being "credit-ready" *(see Question 5 for more information).*
- Effective July 1, 2010, the federal government is the lender for all new Grad PLUS loans through its William D. Ford Federal Direct Loan Program.
- You may borrow up to the full amount of your COA with Grad PLUS loans, minus any other aid, including Federal Stafford Loans.
- There is no annual or cumulative maximum.
- A 7.9% fixed interest rate is assigned for the life of the loan.
- Grad PLUS Loans (disbursed on or after July 1, 2008) carry a six-month post-enrollment deferment following graduation or a reduction to less than half-time enrollment.
- Grad PLUS Loans are listed at www.NSLDS.ed.gov.

■ Federal Perkins Loans

Federal Perkins Loans are federal loans administered by your school and sometimes referred to as "campus-based" loans. Your school acts as the lender on behalf of the federal government. These loans are distributed based on need. Typically you are automatically considered for them if you apply for financial aid with the FAO and meet any established deadlines.

- Perkins loans are interest-free during both school and during grace or deferment periods.
- A 5% fixed interest rate is assigned for the life of the loan.
- Perkins Loans carry a nine-month grace period following graduation—or a drop to less than half-time enrollment—and a "post-deferment six-month grace period" for borrowers who qualify for deferment after the original nine-month grace period.
- Perkins Loans are listed at www.NSLDS.ed.gov.

■ Health Professions Student Loans (HPSL)

The HPSL program, which is administered by your school, is part of the Title VII federal loan program provided through HHS. You are usually automatically considered for HPSL if you apply for financial aid with the FAO, meet any established deadlines, and provide the additional information required (such as parental financial information). These loans are based on exceptional financial need. Check with your FAO regarding availability at your dental school.

- These loans are subsidized and interest-free both during school and during grace or deferment periods.
- A 5% fixed interest rate is assigned for the life of the loan.
- HPSL loans carry a 12-month grace period.

■ Loans for Disadvantaged Students (LDS)

The LDS program has similar terms and conditions as HPSL. A borrower must be from a disadvantaged background, based on criteria established by HHS. *See the Disadvantaged Background definition in the Glossary.* Your FAO will determine your eligibility for this program.

■ Institutional Loans

Your school may offer loans with favorable terms and conditions. Check with your FAO on their availability and application requirements.

■ Private Loans

Given the availability of Grad PLUS loans with no annual or cumulative limits, private loans should not be necessary for dental school, except in rare cases (such as for international students, as referenced earlier). Private loans are based in part on the credit of the borrower or the cosigner, or both. They often have limited repayment flexibility and limited options for postponing payments, especially when compared with federal loans. They are not eligible to be repaid under income-related plans, such as IBR, nor are they eligible for federal forgiveness programs. They may only be needed for help with costs associated with residency interviews during your last year of school, and to assist with relocation expenses during any transition period between school and residency, should you choose to enter a residency program after graduation.

ADEA strongly encourages you to consult with your FAO if you're considering a private loan to help pay for dental school.

- These unsubsidized loans most often have variable interest rates that may not have a cap.
- Grace periods vary and may be anywhere from 6 months to 36 months.

REPAYMENT

Repayment Strategies and Repayment Plans

Most student loans have some type of grace period that will allow you to get settled before you are required to begin making regularly scheduled payments. However, just as smart budgeting and responsible borrowing start now as you prepare to start dental school, so too does planning your repayment strategy well in advance of the date your first payment comes due. During school, you will learn about repayment plan options, which should be covered in detail at your required Senior Loan Exit Interview prior to graduation.

Below is a brief description of options for federal loan repayment. While there are exceptions, there are two generally accepted industry standards regarding student debt and repayment to consider as you review these repayment plans:

1. Student loan payments should not exceed 8% to 12% of your gross income.
2. Total student loan debt should not exceed your starting salary in order to comfortably make payments on your student loans (although income related plans—such as the IBR plan—are designed to help when this standard is not possible).

Remember that dentistry is a financially rewarding field. This fact, combined with the numerous repayment plans available, may help explain why dental school graduates have a strong record of repaying their student loans.

A number of factors may influence your repayment strategy, but, generally, repayment strategies fall into one of the three categories below.

1. *Aggressively pay back your student loans to minimize interest cost.* Someone with no other outstanding financial obligations whose monthly cash flow allows for higher monthly payments may use this strategy. He or she pays more than the minimum required each month and may even target the additional payment amount on their most expensive loan (for example, Grad PLUS). There is never a penalty for early repayment of federal loans.
2. *Maximize your monthly cash flow to free up as much cash as possible for other financial commitments or obligations.* Someone with consumer debt, medical expenses, family commitments, or any combination of these might choose this strategy. He or she uses a repayment plan that minimizes payments, at least initially. Doing so can increase interest costs in the long term.
3. *Pursue a program that repays your loan or forgives a portion of the balance in exchange for your service commitment.* Some programs allow dental graduates to receive student loan repayment or forgiveness in exchange for their service. See the listing of programs at the end of this section.

Remember that it is important to reassess your repayment strategy at least once a year, as your dental career plans start to take shape and you experience possible changes in family and financial status during dental school, residency, postdoctoral work, and practice. You are allowed to switch repayment plans with a few exceptions.

IMPORTANT NOTE: If you have private student loans borrowed prior to dental school, be sure to check the terms and conditions of those loans, especially the repayment terms (when the loans come due and what kind of options you have regarding repayment). Be sure to check on postponement options during dental school and any postponement options that might be available during residency or advanced dental education programs you might pursue later. Checking these options is extremely important because you do not want these loans to adversely impact any career plans later on.

Standard Repayment

- Standard Repayment is based on a 10-year schedule for unconsolidated loans with the same payment each month.

- Monthly payments tend to be higher; however, this plan is the least expensive in the long term because the repayment term is relatively short.
- If you do not choose another repayment plan, you will be assigned a standard repayment plan.
- This plan may be of interest to a borrower with a steady income that is high enough to manage the monthly payments. It might be appropriate for someone moving into a practice right out of dental school as well as someone who might have other financial resources from a spouse or partner to help.
- With Federal Consolidation Loans, Standard Repayment is up to 30 years, with the same payment each month.

Graduated Repayment

- Graduated Repayment is usually based on a 10-year schedule, though some plans are extended with an interest-only option for several years.
- Payments start relatively small and increase by designated amounts at designated intervals.
- Lower initial payments result in higher overall repayment costs compared to the standard plan, as long as borrowers do not accelerate payments.
- This plan may be of interest to a borrower with other short-term financial obligations who is moving into a practice right out of dental school.

Income "Related" Repayment

- Payment amounts are calculated (at least in part) on a borrower's income and thus may grow each year as income increases.
- The repayment period may run from 10 to 25 years.
- Several variations exist, including the IBR and the new Pay-As-You-Earn plans, which cap payments at a low percentage of a borrower's discretionary income.
- Lower initial payments result in higher overall interest costs when compared to a standard plan, as long as borrowers do not accelerate payments.
- This option may interest borrowers with variable incomes or other financial obligations, as well as dental residents who have limited income but want to start repayment during their residency as part of their repayment strategy.

Extended Repayment

- This plan offers level payments up to 25 years on nonconsolidated eligible loans, depending on your outstanding balance.
- Due to an extended repayment term, this plan offers lower monthly payments but potentially higher repayment costs if the loan is held to term (payments are not accelerated).
- This type of repayment may be of interest to a borrower with a steady income who has long-term financial obligations and is moving into a practice right out of dental school, or perhaps someone financing a mortgage and needing to show their lender a lower

Federal Scholarships During and After Dental School

Did you know that additional federally funded scholarships are available for predoctoral and advanced dental education students with interests in research?

- The National Institute of Dental and Craniofacial Research (NIDCR), part of the National Institutes of Health (NIH), offers numerous programs for dental students who have an interest in dental research. www.nidcr.nih.gov/CareersandTraining
- The Fogarty International Clinical Research Scholars & Fellows Program provides the opportunity for individuals to experience mentored research training at NIH-funded research centers in developing countries. For more information, contact the NIH/Fogarty International Center at 301-496-1653.
- The NIH Graduate Partnerships Program (GPP) provides opportunities for research and funding. www.training.nih.gov/programs/gpp.

Debt-to-Income (DTI) ratio. With a few exceptions, borrowers may switch repayment plans. Campus-based loans (such as Federal Perkins, HPSL, and LDS) usually have 10 year standard repayment plans. Private loans tend to have 15-25 year repayment terms, often with little flexibility.

Loan Consolidation

Loan consolidation is a debt management tool some borrowers consider as part of their repayment strategy, but it is not appropriate for all borrowers because there are disadvantages in addition to advantages to consolidating loans. In general, consolidation allows a borrower to pay off (or refinance) multiple loans with one new loan.

You may be a candidate for consolidation if you have multiple loans with different loan servicers, and you want the convenience of having one loan provider. However, you should already only have one lender and one loan servicer for your Stafford and Grad PLUS Loans in dental school, since these loans are all made through the federal government in the Direct Loan Program. You may also be a candidate for consolidation if you have any non-Direct Loans and are interested in the Public Service Loan Forgiveness (PSLF) program, since only Direct Loans qualify, assuming borrowers meet other eligibility requirements. Consolidation allows you to convert the balance on non-Direct Loans into a Direct Loan.

You may not be a candidate for consolidation if you think at some point after school you may adopt an aggressive repayment strategy and want to preserve the ability to pay down some of your more expensive loans first (assuming you have Grad PLUS).

Talk with your FAO about consolidation and check out the primer on consolidation at www.GoDental.org.

Loan Repayment Programs Tied to Service Commitment

You may be eligible for programs that help repay your educational loan through service commitment programs. Pay special attention to the considerations below. There are a number of factors to consider with any service commitment program. Please refer to a program's website or contact the program by phone for additional information on requirements.

Armed Forces Loan Repayment Programs, in addition to service commitment scholarships, offer loan repayment assistance. See www.goarmy.com, www.navy.com, or www.airforce.com for details.

Faculty Loan Repayment Program offers up to $40,000 for repayment of student loans for individuals from disadvantaged backgrounds who serve as faculty of an accredited health professions college or university for two years. Visit www.hrsa.gov/loanscholarships/repayment/faculty or call 800-221-9393 for more information.

Student Loan Repayment Program (Federal) is offered by individual federal agencies to recruit and retain highly trained individuals for a three-year commitment. Awards offer $10,000 per year for eligible loans, not to exceed a total of $60,000 for any one employee. Visit www.opm.gov/oca/pay/studentloan for more information.

IHS Loan Repayment Program offers up to $20,000 for repayment of eligible student loans per year of service with a two-year minimum commitment. This program is designed to help meet the staffing needs of American Indian and Alaska Native health programs. Visit www.loanrepayment.ihs.gov or call 301-443-3396 for more information.

NHSC Loan Repayment Program offers a minimum of $60,000 for repayment of a student's loans in exchange for a minimum two-year service commitment in a Health Professional Shortage Area (HPSA). A total of $170,000 is available for five years of service, with additional amounts available for additional years of service. Visit www.nhsc.hrsa.gov/loanrepayment or call 800-221-9393 for more information.

NIH Loan Repayment Program awards up to $35,000 for repayment of eligible student loans per year of research with a two-year commitment minimum. Visit www.lrp.nih.gov or call 866-849-4047 for more information.

Considerations with Loan Repayment Programs

If any of the above loan repayment programs interests you, there are a few things to consider:

False assumptions—Some students may be turned off by loan repayment programs because they're afraid they will lose control over where they will live and work for a few years. While a possibility, this scenario does not always take place. You should not let assumptions about a program prevent you from participating. Do your homework and find out what each program will require of you. Ask your FAO if there are any alumni participating in these programs with whom you could talk about their experiences.

Tax implications—Any money that you receive from a loan repayment program is likely considered taxable income. Lump-sum loan repayments can be helpful because they generally lower the amount of interest you pay over the life of your loan, but they can also result in a higher tax burden. Gradual loan repayments may lessen your tax burden, but you may end up paying more in interest costs. Ask if the program will cover the cost of your taxes before you commit.

Application dates—Some programs require that you sign up before you finish school.

Service contracts—Loan repayment in the majority of these programs is contingent on a specified length of service outlined by a service contract. Breach of the contract is serious business and can result in heavy financial penalties (and loss of repayment funds). Do not have future commitments that could adversely impact your completion of the required terms of service.

Eligibility requirements—Before spending time applying, make sure you are eligible for a loan repayment program. For example, eligibility may include the requirement that you come from a disadvantaged background (as certified by your educational institution).

Future goals—Do you want to eventually buy a house or help a sibling pay for his or her education? What about opening your own practice or entering academia? Perhaps you want to be a leader in community service? The better you manage your educational debts, the easier it may be to focus on these and other goals. Loan repayment programs may be a great way to help you accomplish your goals.

PSLF Program

This program offers eligible borrowers forgiveness of a portion of their student loan portfolio assuming they meet eligibility requirements. In order to qualify, borrowers must make 120 timely payments with an eligible repayment plan (such as IBR) on eligible loans (only Direct Loans qualify) while working in a position the federal government deems to be public service (which includes nonprofit organizations). Please see www.studentaid.ed.gov/publicservice for details.

See Question 8 for resources that provide additional information on PSLF programs.

QUESTION 5

WHAT DO STUDENT LOANS HAVE TO DO WITH MY CREDIT?

The short answer is a lot. Understanding credit and how it relates to your student loans is an important part of sound educational debt management. This discussion is broken into three areas:

Even with the new consumer protections on credit cards, it remains more important than ever to eliminate any outstanding credit card debt before you start dental school.

1. The "Double Whammy"
2. Credit-Ready and Creditworthy
3. Budgeting and Credit Education

The "Double Whammy"

More than one-third of your credit score comes from your repayment history. This fact can cause challenges for a student who, in general, often has what is called a "thin" credit file: He or she is just not old enough to have established a long credit history proving financial responsibility. While in and of itself, a thin credit file may not pose a problem (everyone starts with a thin credit file), one small mistake can have an exaggerated adverse impact on your credit.

For example, if a 55-year-old man with a solid credit history is more than 30 days late with a payment, the effect on his credit score will likely be outweighed by many years of timely payments. Creditors may assume the late payment (called a delinquency) is simply an exception and not a pattern.

However, if a 23-year-old first-year dental student is more than 30 days late with a payment, his or her credit score could drop dramatically because there is not a lengthy history of timely payments. Creditors may not know if the late payment is routine behavior or an exception.

Students don't really have a chance to work on their repayment history for their student loans until after dental school, when they start paying them back. A thin credit history combined with a delay in paying back your student loans could result in a "Double Whammy" to your credit score. While you may not think the "Double Whammy" is important now, consider the adverse impact it could have on a mortgage or other financing application (such as startup funds for a new practice) after you graduate.

Credit-Ready and Creditworthy

Credit-Ready usually means that a borrower has no credit history or that there are no adverse items in the borrower's credit history (such as payments 30 and 60 days late), or both.

Creditworthy usually means the lender will dig deeper into a borrower's credit history. The lender will likely look for a minimum credit score and a DTI ratio that indicates current income is high enough to sustain loan payments.

A lender making private loans may use a combination of requirements of "credit-ready" and "creditworthy" to determine eligibility, interest rate, and origination or other fees. There are no credit checks for Stafford loans and only a credit-ready check for Grad PLUS loans.

Budgeting and Credit Education

We have mentioned the importance of smart budgeting and the fact that credit card and other consumer obligations cannot be included in your annual COA or student financial aid budget. The past few years have seen a number of banking and credit-card-industry changes that are designed to help protect you (and other consumers), but you are ultimately responsible for demonstrating your ability to use credit wisely.

Should you have questions about credit, the following resources may be helpful:

- www.myfico.com/crediteducation: has detailed information about credit, how it works, and credit scores
- www.annualcreditreport.com: is the only government-approved site where consumers can get a free credit report on an annual basis
- www.bankrate.com: provides information you may find helpful under the "debt management" header

QUESTION 6

ARE THERE ANY RECENT CHANGES IN FINANCIAL AID THAT I SHOULD KNOW ABOUT?

You will likely see some changes in financial aid during your years in dental school. The best way to keep informed about any changes that occur while you are in dental school and during your years in repayment is to stay in contact with your institution's FAO, which continues to be one of the best sources of information.

■ Elimination of Interest Subsidy on New Stafford Loans

Based on a provision in the Budget Control Act of 2011, new Stafford loans for enrollment periods on or after July 1, 2012, will no longer be interest-free to borrowers during school and the six-month grace period. The good news is that there is no reduction in the amount you can actually borrow, so you can still borrow up to $40,500 through the Stafford Loan program each year. You are not required to make the interest payments during school and the grace period, but it will accrue and if unpaid, will eventually be added to the principal amount you borrowed through capitalization, which adds to your total repayment amount—all the more reason to budget wisely and borrow responsibly.

■ Elimination of Discount for Timely Payments

Another provision in the Budget Control Act of 2011 eliminates any discount for borrowers who make their first 12 new-loan payments on time.

■ Income-"Related" Plans

There have been a number of recent changes to repayment plans that are tied to income, including lowering the percentage of a borrower's income used when determining the monthly payment amounts under IBR and the new Pay-As-You-Earn repayment plans. Work closely with your FAO to see how these changes may apply to you when you enter repayment.

■ Stafford and Grad PLUS Loans Now Originate Solely From the Federal Government

As of July 1, 2010, the federal government originates all new Stafford and Grad PLUS loans through its William D. Ford Federal Direct Loan Program. This simply means you do not choose your lender for your loans; your lender will be the U.S. Department of Education (ED) on behalf of the federal government.

■ PSLF Program

This relatively new program offers eligible borrowers a chance to have a portion of their student loans forgiven, assuming they meet certain conditions. See Question 4 for more information.

While the financial aid office (FAO) cannot process your application for financial aid until you are accepted, you should not wait until you are accepted to start the aid application process. Complete your aid application early so that the FAO can begin reviewing your file as soon as you are enrolled.

QUESTION 7

HOW DO I GET STARTED, AND IS THERE A CHECKLIST I CAN USE TO BE SURE I DON'T FORGET ANYTHING?

We suggest several important steps:

1. Contact the FAO of your institution and ask the following questions:

- Are any grants or scholarships available for me? Are they based on need, merit, or both?
- Are there any separate forms or applications I have to complete? What are the submission deadlines?
- Does the FAO require parental information be submitted for consideration of any campus-based grants, scholarships, or loans?

- What is the first-year COA/financial aid budget? What is the expected monthly living allowance?
- What kind of student loan counseling and educational debt management help will be available to me during school and as I prepare to graduate? To avoid being surprised when I graduate, how can I estimate the impact of my yearly borrowed sums on my future loan payments? Is all the counseling done online?
- Are additional types of financial aid available through the school, such as fellowships, traineeships, or work-study programs?
- Are there any summer internships or other paid research or work opportunities for incoming dental students during the summer before school starts?

2. Complete the FAFSA.

   The FAFSA is available online at www.fafsa.ed.gov. Your FAO uses the results of your FAFSA application to consider you for financial aid. Check with your FAO about any deadlines, but plan on completing the FAFSA as soon as possible after January 1 of your anticipated matriculation year. Do not wait until you have been accepted to complete the FAFSA.

3. If you have any outstanding student loans, get your financial aid records in order.

- Contact your loan servicer(s) and ensure that he/she/they have your up-to-date contact information, including mail and email addresses and phone number. Be sure the loan servicer(s) know(s) when and where you are starting dental school and your expected graduation date. Do not have your mail sent home; these are your loans, and correspondence about them should come to you, not to your parents.
- Go to www.nslds.ed.gov and get an updated record of any outstanding federal Stafford, Grad PLUS, Federal Perkins, and Federal Consolidation Loans you have from undergraduate or perhaps a post-baccalaureate program. You should be able to find your current loan servicer(s) for federal student loans at this site.
- Set up both paper and electronic files to keep all financial aid-related documents, including:

  —Copies of any financial aid award letters or notices from the FAO

  —Copies of your Master Promissory Note (MPN) for any federal loans

  —Disclosure Notices from your lender (also called Truth-in-Lending Disclosures, or "TILs")

  —Borrower Rights and Responsibilities Statements

QUESTION 8

WHERE CAN I GO IF I NEED MORE HELP?

Your best resource will be your FAO; however, additional resources are listed below, some of which have been referenced earlier.

Credit Information and Financial Planning

www.annualcreditreport.com: This is the only website authorized by the Federal Trade Commission (FTC) to provide free credit reports. You may request a report from each of the three major credit reporting agencies once a year via this organization.

www.bankrate.com: This site provides information on credit management, mortgages, credit cards, interest rates, and more.

www.FPAnet.org: Financial Planning Association (FPA), a nonprofit organization, has useful, free information regarding basic financial planning and money management.

www.nfcc.org: This site provides information on credit counseling from the National Foundation for Credit Counseling (NFCC) and its partners. The site offers calculators, budget workshops, and tips for financially responsible behavior.

■ Financial Aid

www.finaid.org: This comprehensive website includes information on all types of financial aid, a searchable database for scholarships (www.fastweb.com), and various repayment calculators.

www.ibrinfo.org: This site contains information on the IBR Plan and the PSLF Program from the nonpartisan Project on Student Debt.

www.nslds.ed.gov: This site provides a comprehensive listing of all your federal Title IV loans (Stafford, Grad PLUS, Perkins, and Federal Consolidation loans), including information about your loan servicer(s). You will need your federal PIN to access your record.

www.studentaid.ed.gov: This ED website has information about federal financial aid and tools and resources for student borrowing.

www.studentaid.ed.gov/publicservice: This is the federal government's website with specifics on the PSLF Program.

■ Tax Information

www.irs.gov/publications/p970: This site has information on tax credits and deductions available for students with federal loans, including the Lifetime Learning Credit, Student Loan Interest Deduction, and the American Opportunity Tax Credit.

GLOSSARY

STUDENT FINANCIAL AID AND LOAN TERMS EVERY RESPONSIBLE BORROWER SHOULD KNOW

Accrued Interest: Interest assessed on the unpaid balance of the loan principal that in most cases is the responsibility of the borrower to pay.

Aggregate Debt: The total amount of outstanding student loans for one borrower from all loan programs combined.

Aggregate Loan Limit: The total amount of outstanding principal borrowed in a specific student loan program.

Amortization: The process of repaying debt over an extended period of time through periodic installment payments of principal and interest. You may hear your repayment schedule referred to as your "amortization schedule" or that your student loans are "amortized" over a designated period of time.

Annual Percentage Rate (APR): An annual interest rate that reflects the total cost of a loan, including not only the stated interest rate but also any loan fees and possible repayment benefits or discounts.

Borrower Benefits: Interest rate discounts or reimbursements—also referred to as "repayment incentives"—provided to a borrower by the lender as a means of reducing the cost of the loan. Check your promissory note or disclosure statement, or contact your lender for details. Other than a discount for automatic payments, borrower benefits on new loans are unlikely.

Campus-Based Aid: Financial aid programs administered directly by a dental school or institution. These include any grants and scholarships from the school, as well as through federal programs such as the Federal Perkins Loan, HPSL, LDS, and work-study programs.

Capitalization: The process of adding accrued and unpaid interest to the principal of a loan. Capitalization increases the total repayment amount and thus the monthly payment. Capitalization usually occurs at repayment (for example, at the end of a grace period) and whenever there is a "status change" (for example, when you move from repayment into deferment or forbearance).

Cosigner Release: Process through which a lender releases a creditworthy cosigner from his or her obligation to repay a loan he or she cosigned. A borrower should contact the lender to see if such a provision exists. See Creditworthy Cosigner for more details.

Creditworthy Cosigner: An individual—deemed creditworthy by a lender—who assumes responsibility for the loan if the borrower should fail to repay it. Usually applies only to private loan programs.

Cost of Attendance (COA): See Financial Aid Budget.

Credit Score: An evaluation—represented by a three-digit number—that represents the likelihood a borrower will repay a financial obligation. Applies only to private loan programs.

Consolidation: Paying off or refinancing multiple loans with one new loan.

Default: Failure of a borrower to make payments when due or to comply with loan terms as stated in the promissory note. In general, federal student loans are considered in default after being 270 days delinquent (time frame may differ for private loans). Default may result in actions by the holder of your loan to recover the money owed, including garnishing your wages, withholding income tax refunds, and notifying national credit bureaus of the default. Defaulting on a government loan renders a borrower ineligible for future federal financial aid unless a satisfactory repayment schedule is arranged. Default adversely impacts credit and may stay on a borrower's credit record for up to seven years.

Deferment: A period of time during which a borrower may postpone payment on a loan, assuming he or she meets the requirements established by law or regulation or contained in the promissory note. Subsidized loans (such as the Subsidized Stafford and Federal Perkins Loans) are interest-free to borrowers during periods of deferment, while unsubsidized loans (such as Unsubsidized Stafford and Grad PLUS loans) continue to accrue interest. Use of the term "deferment" when describing periods when a borrower is allowed to postpone payments on a private loan may actually be a reference to forbearance (see Forbearance).

Delinquency: Failure of a borrower to make a payment by the due date. Delinquencies greater than 30 days may be reported to national credit reporting agencies. Once the delinquency exceeds a specified number of days (varies depending on the loan program), the borrower goes into default.

Disadvantaged Background (definition from the U.S. Department of Health and Human Services [HHS]): One who comes from an environment that has inhibited the individual from obtaining the knowledge, skill, and abilities required to enroll in and graduate from a health professions school or a program providing education or training in an allied health profession; or who comes from a family with an annual income below a low-income threshold according to family size published by the U.S. Census Bureau, adjusted annually for changes in the Consumer Price Index, and adjusted by the Secretary of HHS for use in health professions and nursing programs.

Disbursement Date: The date on which the lender issues the loan proceeds, either by check or by electronic funds transfer, to the dental school or institution, typically to the student's account at the school.

Disclosure Statement: Document stating the terms and conditions of a student loan. Disclosure statements include information on the interest rate, fees, and repayment terms. Along with the promissory note, disclosure statements are among the important loan documents a borrower should keep. May also be called a "Truth in Lending" disclosure statement, or "TIL."

Electronic Funds Transfer (EFT): Method whereby loan proceeds are disbursed to the school. Stafford and Grad PLUS loans are generally disbursed via EFT to the borrower's school and automatically applied to his or her student account.

Eligible Noncitizen: Someone who is not a U.S. citizen but is nonetheless eligible for federal student aid. Eligible noncitizens include U.S. permanent residents who are holders of valid green cards, U.S. nationals, those holding Form I-94 with refugee or asylum status, and certain other noncitizens. A noncitizen who holds a student visa or an exchange visitor visa is not eligible for federal student aid.

Enrollment Status: An indication of whether you are a full-time, half-time, or part-time student. In general, you must be enrolled at least half time in order to qualify for financial aid. Some financial aid programs require you to be enrolled full time.

Expected Family Contribution (EFC): The amount of money the family is expected to contribute to a student's education, as determined by the Federal Methodology (FM) formula that uses information provided on the FAFSA. The EFC is a student or spouse's contribution based on factors including family size, number of family members in school, taxable and nontaxable income, and assets. Parental financial information is required for funds authorized by the U.S. Department of Health and Human Services (HHS) and may be required by some schools for the purpose of determining eligibility for institutional funds. Some schools may use a different methodology to determine eligibility for institutional funds.

FAFSA: See Free Application for Federal Student Aid.

FAO: Financial Aid Office

Fees: Charges assessed by the lender that are usually expressed as a percentage of the principal amount borrowed and deducted from the loan proceeds at disbursement. Fees may be charged for the origination of the loan, as a guarantee against default, and—in the case of some private loans—added to the repayment costs as back-end fees. Fees should be found on a loan's disclosure statement.

Financial Aid Award Letter: A listing of the financial aid you are eligible for (your financial aid award package) as determined by your school's FAO. It may be sent electronically or by postal mail, or it may be posted on your FAO's website (with secure access by a PIN or password). It may also be referred to as a financial aid notification letter.

Financial Aid Award Package: Combination of different types of financial aid such as grants, scholarships, and loans as determined by your school's FAO.

Financial Aid Award Year: The academic period for which financial aid is requested and awarded.

Financial Aid Budget: Total costs associated with attending dental school for a given award year. The amount usually includes tuition and fees; an allowance for books, supplies, and equipment; and an allowance for living expenses including health insurance. Each institution develops its own student budget, also known as the COA .

Financial Aid Office (FAO): The office at the dental school or institution responsible for administering financial aid funds for their students.

Financial Need: The difference between the financial aid budget (also known as cost of attendance [COA]) and a student's available resources. Financial need is determined by the FAO and is based on the difference between COA and expected family contribution (EFC).

Fixed Interest Rate: An interest rate that does not change throughout the life of loan (throughout school; any grace, deferment, or forbearance periods; and repayment). In general, federal loans, such as Stafford, Grad PLUS, Perkins loans, HPSL, and LDS, have fixed interest rates.

Forbearance: A period of time during which a borrower may postpone payment on a loan. Various types of forbearance are available on federal loans, including forbearance granted at the lender's discretion. While similar to deferments as a means for postponing payments, interest accrues on all loans during forbearance. Lenders may capitalize interest more frequently during periods of forbearance, especially in the case of Grad PLUS loans. Private loan lenders may charge a fee to postpone the payment. In addition, borrowers who use forbearance may lose any borrower benefits their lender provides on the loan.

Free Application for Federal Student Aid (FAFSA): The form approved by the U.S. Department of Education (ED) and used by students to apply for all federally sponsored student financial aid programs. The form is available at www.fafsa.ed.gov, and it can be submitted electronically or by mail. Contact your FAO for filing deadlines.

Grace Period: A period of time after graduation (or after a borrower drops below half-time status) during which a borrower is not required to begin repaying his or her student loan(s). Grace periods are loan-specific, meaning their length depends on the kind of loan, and they are attached to an individual loan. For example, a borrower who has used up a grace period on an undergraduate loan does not lose the grace periods on loans taken out in dental school. Not all loans have grace periods.

IBR: Income-Based Repayment

Interest Rate Cap: Refers to the maximum interest a borrower may be charged over the life of the loan on a variable rate loan (see Variable Interest Rate). Interest rate caps apply only to variable rate loans and should be referenced in both the promissory note and disclosure statement. Not all variable rate loans have caps.

Loan Terms and Conditions: The conditions of a loan, including requirements governing receipt and repayment. Specifically, loan terms usually refer to the interest rate, fees, and other costs associated with receipt and repayment.

Minority: According to the U.S. Government, an individual whose race/ethnicity is classified as American Indian or Alaska Native, Asian, Native Hawaiian or other Pacific Islander, Black or African American, or Hispanic/Latino.

National Health Service Corps (NHSC): NHSC connects primary health care providers to areas of the United States with limited access to care.

National Student Loan Data System (NSLDS): Federal repository accessible at www.nslds.ed.gov that provides a listing of Title IV aid (Subsidized Stafford, Graduate PLUS, Federal Perkins, Federal Consolidation) for individual students and borrowers. You can find a list of your personal loans (with the exception of HPSL, LDS, and institutional and private loans) in this database.

Outside Scholarship: A scholarship that comes from a source other than the dental school or institution.

Principal: The original amount of money borrowed or the outstanding amount immediately following capitalization of any accrued and unpaid interest.

Private Loans: Educational loans provided by private lenders and not backed by the federal government. Dental school students who already have private loans and/or are considering private loan programs should strongly consider speaking with their FAOs about the potential impact these loans may have on their repayment strategy after dental school.

Promissory Note: A binding legal document that must be signed by a borrower to show that he or she agrees to repay the loan according to terms specified in the document. The promissory note, which must be signed before loan funds can be disbursed by the lender, provides evidence of the borrower's willingness to repay the debt. Along with disclosure statements, the promissory note is a document a borrower should keep. A borrower is entitled to the return of the promissory note marked "paid in full" once the obligation has been met.

Repayment Schedule or Repayment Term: The time frame over which a borrower is required to repay his or her loan (also referred to as the amortization schedule). Usually stated in terms of number of monthly payments required with payment amounts, due dates, and terms of the loan listed.

Satisfactory Academic Progress (SAP): The academic progress a student must make in order to continue to receive federal financial aid as required and defined by the school. If a student fails to maintain an academic standing consistent with the dental school's SAP policy, he or she is unlikely to meet the school's graduation requirements and may be ineligible to receive federal financial aid.

Student Aid Report (SAR): The report summarizing the information included in the FAFSA. The SAR, which also indicates the expected family contribution (EFC), is provided to your school's FAO. For information on the SAR, go to www.fafsa.ed.gov.

Subsidized Loan: A loan that remains interest-free while the borrower is enrolled at least half-time and during periods of grace and deferment. Subsidized loans are based, at least in part, on financial need. Examples include Federal Perkins Loans, HPSL, and LDS.

Title IV Loans: Loan programs administered by the U.S. Department of Education (ED). These include Stafford, Grad PLUS, Federal Perkins, and Direct Consolidation loans.

Title IV School Code: The numerical code used to indicate to which school(s) you want your FAFSA results sent.

Title VII Financial Aid: Financial aid programs administered by the U.S. Department of Health and Human Services (HHS). These include the HPSL and LDS programs.

Unmet Need: The difference between your calculated need and the amount of financial aid awarded. Your school's FAO may put together unsubsidized loans, such as Unsubsidized Stafford and Grad PLUS loans, to meet any unmet need.

Unsubsidized Loan: Loans that accrue interest from the date of disbursement, including during the school year and during grace and deferment periods for which the borrower may be eligible. Borrowers are responsible for the interest that accrues on unsubsidized loans. Examples include Unsubsidized Stafford and Grad PLUS loans, and private loans. Unsubsidized loans are not based on financial need and may be used to cover the family contribution and any unmet need.

U.S. Department of Education (ED): The government department that administers Title IV federal student financial aid programs, including the federal work-study program, Perkins, Stafford, Grad PLUS, and Federal Consolidation loans.

Variable Interest: A loan with an interest rate that changes at designated intervals, sometimes monthly or quarterly. Variable rates usually only apply to private loans.

CHAPTER 5
GETTING MORE INFORMATION

This book provides a foundation for anyone who is considering dentistry as a career and wants to know more about obtaining a dental education. Although the information included here is extensive, you probably will want additional details to answer questions that are specific to your situation. This chapter gives you lists of individuals, organizations, and references that can help answer those questions.

INDIVIDUALS WHO CAN HELP

One very effective way of getting more information is to talk to the individuals who are involved in dental education and are interested in encouraging others like you to consider dentistry as a career.

Practicing Dentists

Dentists are knowledgeable about the variety of careers in dentistry and about the education and skills needed. They can tell you what the day-to-day work is like, what kind of preparation is required, and the kinds of benefits they receive. In addition, one way to learn more about the profession and whether it feels right for you is to arrange for an internship or a "shadowing" opportunity in a dental office. To pursue such an opportunity, discuss the possibility with your own dentist or other practitioners in your area.

Prehealth Advisors

Prehealth advisors can assist in a broad range of issues about dental education and dental schools. They are especially important during the admissions process because they can inform you about the academic preparation necessary to be accepted into a dental school. In addition, these advisors are often involved in providing or coordinating letters of recommendation.

Science Professors

Science professors, especially those in the biological sciences, can be helpful in the same way as prehealth advisors in terms of academic preparation and letters of recommendation. They are particularly important to students at undergraduate schools that do not have an official prehealth advisor.

Dental School Admissions Officers

Admissions officers are especially knowledgeable about their own dental schools and the requirements to gain admission. They can supply you with catalogs and admission criteria. They can also describe the emphasis of the academic programs, provide information on support services to help students succeed, and highlight other features of their schools.

Dental School Minority Affairs Officers

These officers play an important role in collecting and sharing information about what their dental schools are doing to increase minority enrollments and to make minority students who choose their schools feel welcome. They also have information about the academic programs, support services, and other features of their schools.

Financial Aid Administrators

Financial aid administrators are very knowledgeable about how to pay the cost of attending dental school. They can help you understand the financial aid application process and eligibility requirements for governmental, institutional, and private sources of financial aid. They can also assist in securing the funds for which you are eligible.

Dental Students

Dental students are usually forthright in sharing their perceptions of the education they are receiving at their schools. They will also tell you their views of the nonacademic aspects, such as student support services and social atmosphere. Since these individuals' perspectives are all different, the information they share can be enormously helpful. You should not hesitate to approach them in order to benefit from their knowledge and points of view. There are also online discussion boards, such as ADEA's GoDental® (www.godental.org), where future and current dental students talk about issues related to dental school. Keep in mind that all types of individual discussions are based on personal experience and do not reflect the whole perspective of a student body or school. It is always a good idea to base your decisions on information collected from a variety of sources.

ORGANIZATIONS THAT CAN HELP

A number of organizations offer information about careers in dentistry, preparing for admission, and financial aid for dental students.

EDUCATION

American Dental Education Association
1400 K Street, NW
Suite 1100
Washington, DC 20005
Phone: 202-289-7201
Fax: 202-289-7204
www.adea.org

The American Dental Education Association (ADEA) provides information about the application process for admission to dental school and advanced dental programs. ADEA sponsors the ADEA Associated American Dental Schools Application Service (ADEA AADSAS), ADEA Postdoctoral Application Support Service (ADEA PASS), and ADEA Centralized Application for Advanced Placement for International Dentists (ADEA CAAPID). Visit the ADEA Division of Educational Pathways at www.adea.org to learn more about these services and GoDental®, the official web resource for up-to-date and cutting-edge information for people on the pathway to dental education and exciting oral health careers. In addition to the *ADEA Official Guide to Dental Schools,* ADEA publishes the *Journal of Dental Education (JDE),* the *Bulletin of Dental Education Online (BDE),* and the *ADEA Opportunities for Minority Students in U.S. Dental Schools.* Ordering information is available on the ADEA website.

Membership in ADEA is free for all dental students and includes networking and advocacy opportunities, free online access to the *JDE,* and monthly delivery of the *BDE.* To become a member, visit www.adea.org/join.

American Student Dental Association
211 East Chicago Avenue
Suite 700
Chicago, IL 60611
Phone: 800-621-8099, ext. 2795 (Central Office) or 2640 (Membership Services); 312-440-2795
Fax: 312-440-2820
www.asdanet.org

Nearly 90% of U.S. dental students are members of the American Student Dental Association (ASDA) which is a student-run organization that offers educational resources, discounts on professional services, and networking opportunities. The association also offers representation on issues that include education financing, dental student rights and research, and advocacy. ASDA is a national organization but also represents the interests of dental students on the local and regional levels.

ExploreHealthCareers.org
American Dental Education Association
1400 K Street, NW
Suite 1100
Washington, DC 20005
Phone: 202-289-7201 or 347-365-9253
Email: feedback@explorehealthcareers.org
www.explorehealthcareers.org

ExploreHealthCareers.org (EHC) is a multidisciplinary, free website that allows the user to explore more than 100 health careers, including all pertaining to dentistry and allied dentistry. EHC's database of 500-plus resources includes information about dental scholarships and predental enrichment programs.

GoDental®
American Dental Education Association
1400 K Street, NW
Suite 1100
Washington, DC 20005
Phone: 202-289-7201
Email: godental@adea.org
www.godental.org

Sponsored by the American Dental Education Association (ADEA), GoDental(R) is a career-building and social-networking web resource that provides up-to-date information for people on the pathway to dental education and oral health careers. Designed to be a dynamic, easy-to-use tool, GoDental® promotes collaboration, community, and connection between prehealth and current health professionals.

International Federation of Dental Educators and Associations
2155 Webster Street
San Francisco, CA 94115
www.ifdea.org

The International Federation of Dental Educators and Associations (IFDEA) is a global community of dental educators who have joined together to improve oral health worldwide by sharing knowledge and raising standards. IFDEA contributes to improving global health by improving oral health. IFDEA serves as an axis of information, best practices, exchange programs, news, and professional development for the many regional dental education associations, academic dental institutions, and individual dental educators worldwide.

SPECIALTY

Academy of General Dentistry
211 East Chicago Avenue
Suite 900
Chicago, IL 60611
Phone: 888-AGD-DENT or 888-243-3368
Fax: 312-440-0559
www.agd.org

The Academy of General Dentistry (AGD) is the only organization dedicated exclusively to serving the community of general dentists. The AGD provides resources, continuing education programs, advocacy, professional and career services, and networking opportunities. The academy also promotes the oral health of the public and offers a 24-hour, online message board for consumers to post dental-related questions and a dentist referral service.

American Academy of Oral and Maxillofacial Pathology
214 North Hale Street
Wheaton, IL 60187
Phone: 888-552-2667 or 630-510-4552
Fax: 630-510-4501
Email: aaomp@b-online.com
www.aaomp.org

Representing the specialty of dentistry and pathology that deals with the nature, identification, and management of diseases affecting the oral and maxillofacial regions, the American Academy of Oral and Maxillofacial Pathology (AAOMP) promotes the profession and provides educational and scholarly resources. In conjunction with the North American Society of Head and Neck Pathology (NASHNP), AAOMP edits the *Head and Neck Pathology Journal.*

American Academy of Oral and Maxillofacial Radiology
3085 Stevenson Drive
Suite 200
Springfield, IL 62703
Email: ED@aaomr.org
www.aaomr.org

The American Academy of Oral and Maxillofacial Radiology (AAOMR) promotes the art and science of radiology in dentistry through scholarly and educational resources, as well as advocacy. AAOMR provides resources for educators and additional information on advanced dental education programs in oral and maxillofacial radiology.

American Academy of Pediatric Dentistry
211 East Chicago Avenue
Suite 1700
Chicago, IL 60611
Phone: 312-337-2169
Fax: 312-337-6329
www.aapd.org

The American Academy of Pediatric Dentistry (AAPD) represents the specialty of pediatric dentistry. Its members serve as primary care providers for millions of children—from infancy through adolescence—and provide advanced, specialty care for patients of all ages with special health care needs. The AAPD advocates policies, guidelines, and programs that promote optimal oral health and oral health care for children. AAPD also serves and represents its membership in the areas of professional development and governmental and legislative activities.

American Academy of Periodontology
737 North Michigan Avenue
Suite 800
Chicago, IL 60611
Phone: 312-787-5518
Fax: 312-787-3670
www.perio.org

The American Academy of Periodontology (AAP) specializes in the prevention, diagnosis, and treatment of diseases affecting the gums and supporting structures of the teeth, as well as in the placement and maintenance of dental implants. AAP works both to advance the periodontal and general health of the public and to promote excellence in the practice of periodontics. The academy achieves its objectives by making a variety of services and resources available to the periodontal community and by providing information to the public.

American Association of Endodontists
211 East Chicago Avenue
Suite 1100
Chicago, IL 60611
Phone: 800-872-3636 (North America) or +1-312-266-7255 (International)
Fax: 866-451-9020 (North America) or +1-312-266-9867 (International)
Email: info@aae.org
www.aae.org

The American Association of Endodontists (AAE) is the professional association representing endodontists, the dental specialists who save teeth through root canal treatment. The AAE provides a forum for the exchange of ideas in the field of endodontics and stimulates research studies among its members through publications, professional development, and continuing education opportunities, as well as meetings and events.

American Association of Hospital Dentists
401 North Michigan Avenue
Suite 2200
Chicago, IL 60611
Phone: 312-527-6764
Fax: 312-673-6663
www.scdaonline.org

The American Association of Hospital Dentists (AAHD) operates under the auspices of the Special Care Dentistry Association (SCDA). The AAHD helps hospital dentists develop the skills, knowledge, creativity, and leadership they need to advance their practices and the profession. As part of SCDA, the association also helps shape national health policy on hospital dentistry by providing advocacy at the federal and state levels.

American Association of Oral and Maxillofacial Surgeons
9700 West Bryn Mawr Avenue
Rosemont, IL 60018
Phone: 847-678-6200 or 800-822-6637
Fax: 847-678-6286
www.aaoms.org

The American Association of Oral and Maxillofacial Surgeons (AAOMS) represents the surgeons who provide a broad range of diagnostic services and treatments for diseases, injuries, and defects of the neck, head, jaw, and associated structures that include problem wisdom teeth, facial pain, oral cancer, and facial cosmetic surgery. The mission of the AAOMS is to promote, protect, and advance oral and maxillofacial surgery to assure excellence for surgeons and their patients.

American Association of Orthodontists
401 North Lindbergh Boulevard
St. Louis, MO 63141
Phone: 314-993-1700 or 800-424-2841
Fax: 314-997-1745
www.aaortho.org

The American Association of Orthodontists (AAO) is the organization for specialists who diagnose, prevent, and treat dental and facial irregularities. The AAO provides information to the public on the need and benefits of orthodontic treatment and supports research and education leading to quality patient care.

American Association of Public Health Dentistry
3085 Stevenson Drive
Suite 200
Springfield, IL 62703
Phone: 217-529-6941
Fax: 217-529-9120
www.aaphd.org

The American Association of Public Health Dentistry (AAPHD) provides a focus for meeting the challenge to improve the oral health of the public. Its broad base of membership provides a fertile environment and numerous opportunities for the exchange of ideas and experiences.

American College of Prosthodontists
211 East Chicago Avenue
Suite 1000
Chicago, IL 60611
Phone: 312-573-1260
Fax: 312-573-1257
www.prosthodontics.org

The American College of Prosthodontists (ACP) is the professional association of dentists with advanced specialty training in creating optimal oral health, both in function and appearance, including through the use of dental implants, dentures, veneers, crowns, and teeth whitening. The ACP represents the needs and interests of prosthodontists—within organized dentistry and to the public—by providing a means for stimulating awareness and interest in the field.

Special Care Dentistry Association
401 North Michigan Avenue
Suite 2200
Chicago, IL 60611
Phone: 312-527-6764
Fax: 312-673-6663
www.scdaonline.org

The Special Care Dentistry Association (SCDA) brings together three organizations with mutual interests: the American Association of Hospital Dentists (AAHD), the Academy of Dentistry for Persons with Disabilities (ADPD), and the American Society for Geriatric Dentistry (ASGD). SCDA works with oral health professionals and other organizations to promote the oral health of individuals with special needs. SCDA provides a variety of resources and opportunities for individuals interested in advancing the oral health of special needs patients.

RESEARCH

American Association for Dental Research
1619 Duke Street
Alexandria, VA 22314
Phone: 703-548-0066
Fax: 703-548-1883
www.aadronline.org

The American Association for Dental Research (AADR) advances research and increases knowledge for the improvement of oral health. The association also sponsors student research fellowships to encourage dental students to conduct research.

International Association for Dental Research
1619 Duke Street
Alexandria, VA 22314
Phone: 703-548-0066
Fax: 703-548-1883
www.iadr.com

The International Association for Dental Research (IADR) supports dental, oral, and craniofacial research in an effort to improve oral health worldwide. The association also supports numerous student awards and fellowships in a variety of dental research areas.

National Institute of Dental and Craniofacial Research
National Institutes of Health
Bethesda, MD 20892
Phone: 301-496-4261
Fax: 301-480-4098
www.nidcr.nih.gov

The National Institute of Dental and Craniofacial Research (NIDCR) provides grants for research training for high school, college, dental, and postgraduate dental students. It is the major source of research funding to dental schools and offers both intramural and extramural research grants and training opportunities.

PROFESSIONAL

American Association of Women Dentists
216 West Jackson Boulevard
Suite 625
Chicago, IL 60606
Phone: 800-920-2293
Fax: 312-750-1203
www.aawd.org

The American Association of Women Dentists (AAWD) celebrates the rich history of women dentists. AAWD represents women dentists across the United States, internationally, and in the uniformed services. The organization provides support and education to women in the dental industry and is constantly striving toward "becoming the recognized resource for connecting and enriching the lives of women dentists."

American College of Dentists
839J Quince Orchard Boulevard
Gaithersburg, MD 20878
Phone: 301-977-3223
Fax: 301-977-3330
www.acd.org

The American College of Dentists (ACD) is the oldest national honorary organization for dentists. Its mission is to promote excellence, ethics, professionalism, and leadership in dentistry. ACD's activities include conferences, programs, and online resources. Membership is by invitation only.

American Dental Association
211 East Chicago Avenue
Chicago, IL 60611
Phone: 312-440-2500
Fax: 312-440-7494
www.ada.org

The American Dental Association (ADA) is the professional association of dentists committed to the public's oral health, as well as to ethics, science, and professional advancement. The ADA has information about dental licensure and advanced dental study. In addition, the ADA sponsors the Dental Admission Test (DAT), which every applicant to a U.S. dental school must take (see Chapter 2).

Association of Schools of Public Health
1900 M Street, NW
Suite 710
Washington, DC 20036
Phone: 202-296-1099
Fax: 202-296-1252
www.asph.org

The Association of Schools of Public Health (ASPH) represents the deans, faculty, and students of the accredited member schools of public health and other programs seeking accreditation as schools of public health. The ASPH collects information on careers in public health.

Hispanic Dental Association
3085 Stevenson Drive
Suite 200
Springfield, IL 62703
Phone: 217-529-6517
Fax: 217-529-9120
www.hdassoc.org

The Hispanic Dental Association (HDA) provides a voice for the Hispanic oral health professional, promotes the oral health of the Hispanic community, fosters research and knowledge concerning Hispanic oral health problems, and encourages the entry of Hispanics into the oral health profession. The HDA offers scholarships for predoctoral and advanced dental education students and provides a membership category for students.

National Dental Association and Student National Dental Association
3517 16th Street, NW
Washington, DC 20010
Phone: 202-588-1697
Fax: 202-588-1244
www.ndaonline.org

The National Dental Association (NDA), which is made up of African American dentists, sponsors minority student scholarships for both undergraduate and advanced dental education students, includes a student organization (SNDA), and distributes career development tools that are available for use by schools, dentists, and other groups. The NDA's mission is to represent the concerns of ethnic minorities in dentistry; to elevate the global oral health concerns of underserved communities; to enhance educational and financial opportunities, as well as public policy awareness, for its members; and to recruit underrepresented minorities into the profession through advocacy and mentorship.

Society of American Indian Dentists
27180 Newport Road
Suite 3
Menifee, CA 92584
Phone: 951-306-2092
Fax: 951-301-9119
Email: Imelda@thesaidonline.org
www.thesaidonline.org

In addition to encouraging American Indian youth to pursue careers in dentistry, the Society of American Indian Dentists (SAID) promotes dental health—as well as American Indian heritage and traditional values—in the American Indian community. SAID also promotes and supports the unique concerns of American Indian dentists. Resources are available for high school and undergraduate students, and dental students are eligible for membership.

ORAL HEALTH CARE ADVOCACY

Oral Health America
410 North Michigan Avenue
Suite 352
Chicago, IL 60611
Phone: 312-836-9900
Fax: 312-836-9986
www.oralhealthamerica.org

Oral Health America (OHA) is a fully independent nonprofit organization supported through contributions from individuals who believe that oral health should be recognized as one of the lifetime factors critical to overall health. OHA develops, implements, and facilitates educational and service programs designed to improve the oral health of all Americans.

OTHER RESOURCES

College, university, and public libraries generally have a range of publications about careers, undergraduate and graduate education, and financial aid. As a result, it is worthwhile to visit a library to gather information about careers in dentistry, dental educational programs, and sources of student assistance. Some of the publications you may find there include the following information. If you prefer to acquire copies yourself, contact the organizations as noted.

■ Dental Admission Testing Program Application and Preparation Materials

In addition to the application form that students must complete to take the Dental Admission Test (DAT), this publication contains information that will help students prepare for the test.

Available from:

ADA Department of Testing Services
211 East Chicago Avenue
Suite 600
Chicago, IL 60611
Phone: 800-232-1694
www.ada.org/dat.aspx

■ Getting Through Dental School: American Student Dental Association's (ASDA) Guide for Dental Students

This biennial reference volume includes information on scholarships and loans, grants, public health and international opportunities, as well as ASDA membership benefits and leadership opportunities.

■ Getting into Dental School: American Student Dental Association's (ASDA) Guide for Predental Students

This resource guide specifically targets the needs of predental students and those considering careers in dentistry. It is a reference volume of facts on applying to dental school, seeking financial aid, taking advantage of ASDA membership benefits, learning about debt management, and more. The handbook also includes career options in the dental field and a survival guide for passing the DAT.

ON TO PART II

The five chapters in Part I have helped you learn the basics about careers in dentistry, meeting criteria for acceptance into dental school, paying for the costs of a dental education, deciding to which dental schools to apply, and finding additional information to answer the particular questions you have. Part II, Learning about Dental Schools, will give you an opportunity to put this general information to use by introducing you to every dental school in the United States and Canada.

PART II

LEARNING ABOUT DENTAL SCHOOLS

Part II provides an individual introduction to each U.S. and Canadian dental school. ADEA has developed a format for Part II that is consistent from school to school to make it easier for readers to gather information. However, the narrative sections are provided by the dental schools themselves so that you can discern the distinctive qualities of each institution.

Every dental school in the United States and Canada is accredited or seeking accreditation. The Commission on Dental Accreditation (CODA) accredits U.S. schools, and the Commission on Dental Accreditation of Canada (CDAC) accredits Canadian schools.

HOW TO USE PART II

The school entries are presented alphabetically by *state.*

Information about each school is organized into the areas that tend to be of most interest to dental school applicants:

As you determine where you plan to send applications, you should contact those dental schools directly for the most complete information about admission requirements. Their telephone numbers, addresses, and websites are included with their entries.

■ **General Information** describes the type of institution, history of the dental school, location, size, facilities, doctoral dental degree offered, relationship of the dental school to other health profession schools in the university, and other programs conducted by the school.

■ **Preparation** presents the school's requirements with respect to:

- Predental education (number of years, required courses, limitations on community college work, and suggested additional preparation)
- Dental Admissions Test (DAT)
- Grade point average (GPA)

■ **Application and Selection** provides information on the application process and residency requirements and demographics. Demographics information is supplied by institutions, and individual school reporting procedures vary. A timetable is provided for submitting application materials and fees (if any) to be paid to the dental school and to inform applicants when they can expect to be notified. The residency section may disclose a school's participation in regional compacts, other interstate agreements, or (for private schools) in-state agreements.

■ **Curriculum** introduces the dental school's educational program. Dental schools generally use this section to discuss program length, goals, and objectives. Student research opportunities may also be listed.

■ **Special Programs and Services** describes assistance programs and other related student organizations that are available.

■ **Costs and Financial Aid** allows schools to briefly describe their financial aid policies. The section also has a chart showing estimated expenses for both residents and nonresidents of the state in which the dental school is located. The costs given are for the most recent academic year the school has reported; you should adjust your estimated costs upward for the 2013-14 academic year.

■ **Contact Information** is listed on the left-hand side of the first page of the school's profile. This list usually provides the names, addresses, and telephone numbers for the dental school's admissions office, financial aid office, minority affairs office, and housing office.

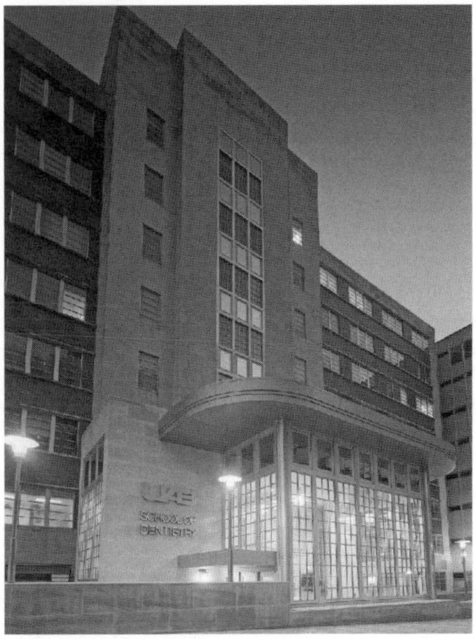

UNIVERSITY OF ALABAMA AT BIRMINGHAM
SCHOOL OF DENTISTRY

Dr. Michael S. Reddy, Dean

GENERAL INFORMATION

The University of Alabama at Birmingham School of Dentistry (UABSOD), located on the campus of the University of Alabama at Birmingham, is an integral part of the large complex of medical facilities on this urban campus at the periphery of downtown Birmingham (metropolitan population: approximately one million). The School of Dentistry was created in 1945 by an act of the state legislature, and the first class matriculated in 1948. Students at the UABSOD pursue their professional education utilizing modern equipment in recently renovated facilities.

MISSION STATEMENT:

To optimize oral health In Alabama and beyond

Type of institution: Public
Year opened: 1948
Term type: Semester
Time to degree in months: 48
Start month: July

Doctoral dental degree offered: D.M.D.
Total predoctoral enrollment: 231
Estimated entering class size: 58
Campus setting: Urban
Campus housing available: Yes

PREPARATION

Formal minimum preparation in semester/quarter hours: Semester: 90 Quarter: 120
Baccalaureate degree preferred: Yes
Number of first-year, first-time enrollees whose highest degree is:
- Baccalaureate: 58
- Master's: 2
- Ph.D. or other doctorate: 0

Of first-year, first-time enrollees without baccalaureates the number with:
- Equivalent of 60 undergraduate credit hours or less: 0
- Equivalent of 61-90 undergraduate credit hours: 0
- Equivalent of 91 or more undergraduate credit hours: 0

PREREQUISITE COURSE	REQUIRED	RECOMMENDED	LAB REQUIRED	CREDITS (SEMESTER/QUARTER)
BCP (biology-chemistry-physics) sciences				
Biology	✓		✓	12/18
Chemistry, general/inorganic	✓		✓	8/12
Chemistry, organic	✓		✓	8/12
Physics	✓		✓	8/12
Additional biological sciences				
Anatomy		✓		
Biochemistry		✓		
Cell biology		✓		
Histology		✓		
Immunology		✓		
Microbiology		✓		
Molecular biology/genetics		✓		
Physiology		✓		
Zoology		✓		

Community college coursework accepted for prerequisites: Yes
Community college coursework accepted for electives: Yes
Limits on community college credit hours: Yes

CONTACT INFORMATION

www.dental.uab.edu

Dr. Michael S. Reddy
Dean
SDB 406
1720 2nd Avenue South
Birmingham, AL 35294-0007
Phone: 205-934-4720
Fax: 205-975-6544

OFFICE OF ADMISSIONS
Dr. Steven Filler
Associate Dean of Student, Alumni, and External Affairs
SDB 125
1720 2nd Avenue South
Birmingham, AL 35294-0007
Phone: 205-934-3387
www.dental.uab.edu

FINANCIAL AID
Ann Little
HUC 317
1720 2nd Avenue South
Birmingham, AL 35294-1150
Phone: 205-934-8223

STUDENT AFFAIRS
Dr. Maureen Pezzementi
Director of Student Affairs
SDB 124
1720 2nd Avenue South
Birmingham, AL 35294-0007
Phone: 205-934-5470

MINORITY AFFAIRS/DIVERSITY
Dr. Madelyn Coar
SDB 415
1720 2nd Avenue South
Birmingham, AL 35294-0007
Phone: 205-934-1141

PREPARATION (CONTINUED)

Maximum number of community college credit hours: 60
Advanced placement (AP) credit accepted for prerequisites: Yes
Advanced placement (AP) credit accepted for electives: Yes
Comments regarding AP credit: Applicants are strongly encouraged to take prerequisite courses for which they have earned AP/International Baccalaureate (IB) or other credit at the university level.
Job shadowing: Required

DAT

Mandatory: Yes
Latest DAT for consideration of application: 12/01/2013
Oldest DAT considered: 12/01/2010
When more than one DAT score is reported: Average score is considered.
Canadian DAT accepted: Yes
Application considered before DAT scores are submitted: No

DAT: 2012 ENTERING CLASS

ENROLLEE DAT SCORES	RANGE	MEAN
Academic Average	17-25	20
Perceptual Ability	15-29	20
Total Science	17-26	20

GPA: 2012 ENTERING CLASS

ENROLLEE GPA SCORES	RANGE	MEAN
Science GPA	2.87-4.00	3.6
Total GPA	3.23-4.00	3.7

APPLICATION AND SELECTION

TIMETABLE

Earliest filing date: 06/01/2013
Latest filing date: 11/01/2013
Earliest date for acceptance offers: 12/01/2013
Maximum time in days for applicant's response to acceptance offer:
30 days if accepted on or after December 1
15 days if accepted on or after February 1
Requests for deferred entrance considered: No
Fee for application: Yes, submitted only when requested.
Amount of fee for application:
In state: $75 Out of state: $75 International: $75
Fee waiver available: No

	FIRST DEPOSIT	SECOND DEPOSIT	THIRD DEPOSIT
Required to hold place	Yes	No	No
Resident amount	$200		
Nonresident amount	$200		
Deposit due	As indicated in admission offer		
Applied to tuition	Yes		
Refundable	No		

APPLICATION PROCESS

Participates in Associated American Dental Schools Application Service (AADSAS): Yes
Accepts direct applicants: No
Secondary or supplemental application required: Yes
Secondary or supplemental application website: None
Interview is mandatory: Yes
Interview is by invitation: Yes

RESIDENCY

Admissions process distinguishes between in-state/in-province and out-of-state/out-of-province applicants: Yes
Preference given to residents of: Alabama
Reciprocity Admissions Agreement available for legal residents of: None
Applications are accepted from non-U.S. citizens/non-U.S. permanent residents: Yes

APPLICATION AND ENROLLMENT	NUMBER OF APPLICANTS	ESTIMATED NUMBER INTERVIEWED	ESTIMATED NUMBER ENROLLED
In-state or province applicants	108	63	43
Out-of-state or province applicants	566	71	17

Generally and over time, percentage of your first-year enrollment is in-state: 83%
Origin of out-of-state or -province enrollees: FL-6, GA-5, LA-2, SC-1, TN-2
Origin of international enrollees: Taiwan-1

DEMOGRAPHIC DESCRIPTIONS OF APPLICANTS: 2012 ENTERING CLASS

	APPLICANTS		ENROLLEES	
	M	W	M	W
Hispanic/Latino of any race	32	19		
American Indian or Alaska Native	1	2	1	
Asian	47	78		4
Black or African American	17	34		4
Native Hawaiian or Other Pacific Islander				
White	247	160	32	19
Two or more races	9	4		
Race and ethnicity unknown	5	9		
International	5	5		

	MINIMUM	MAXIMUM	MEAN
Previous year enrollees by age	21	38	23

Number of first-time enrollees over age 30: 2

CURRICULUM

The objective of the program at the University of Alabama at Birmingham (UAB) is to produce competent and caring oral health care providers. Our goal is to foster an academic environment that encourages the process of inquiry and the scientific method of problem solving. While much of the first two years of school is focused on basic science education, students interact with patients very early in the curriculum. The program is organized so that dental students function as assistants in their first year and hygienists in their second year; the third and fourth years are devoted to comprehensive care of patients. Specialty electives are available in the fourth year for students who progress briskly through the curriculum. The school emphasizes progressive education techniques, which include traditional lectures, small-group interactions, problem-based learning, and a systems-based basic science education.

Student research opportunities: Yes

SPECIAL PROGRAMS AND SERVICES

PREDENTAL

Summer enrichment programs

DURING DENTAL SCHOOL

Academic counseling and tutoring
Community service opportunities
Internships, externships, or extramural programs
Mentoring
Personal counseling
Professional- and career-development programming
Training for those interested in academic careers

ACTIVE STUDENT ORGANIZATIONS

American Association of Dental Research Student Research Group
American Association of Pediatric Dentistry
American Association of Women Dentists
American Dental Education Association (ADEA)
American Student Dental Association
Hispanic Dental Association
Student Government Association
Student National Dental Association

INTERNATIONAL DENTISTS

Graduates of international dental schools considered for traditional predoctoral program: No
Advanced standing program offered for graduates of international dental schools: No

COMBINED AND ALTERNATE DEGREES

Ph.D.	M.S.	M.P.H.	M.D.	B.A./B.S.	Other
✓	—	—	—	—	—

COSTS: 2012-13 SCHOOL YEAR

	FIRST YEAR	SECOND YEAR	THIRD YEAR	FOURTH YEAR
Tuition, resident	$22,484	$22,484	$23,606	$25,838
Tuition, nonresident	$54,760	$54,760	$57,684	$63,540
Tuition, other				
Fees	$2,161	$1,748	$2,245	$2,294
Instruments, books, and supplies	$11,519	$7,077	$5,150	$864
Estimated living expenses	$17,353	$17,637	$17,367	$16,147
Total, resident	$53,517	$48,946	$48,368	$45,143
Total, nonresident	$85,793	$81,222	$82,446	$82,845
Total, other				

FINANCIAL AID

Please visit http://main.uab.edu/Sites/students/32619 to learn about the UAB's financial aid award process.

A.T. STILL UNIVERSITY
ARIZONA SCHOOL OF DENTISTRY & ORAL HEALTH

Dr. Jack Dillenberg, Dean

CONTACT INFORMATION

www.atsu.edu/asdoh
5850 East Still Circle
Mesa, AZ 85206
Phone: 480-219-6000
Fax: 480-219-6180

OFFICE OF ADMISSIONS
800 West Jefferson Street
Kirksville, MO 63501
Phone: 660-626-2237
www.atsu.edu

OFFICE OF FINANCIAL AID
800 West Jefferson Street
Kirksville, MO 63501
Phone: 660-626-2529
www.atsu.edu

OFFICE OF STUDENT SERVICES
5850 East Still Circle
Mesa, AZ 85206
Phone: 480-219-6000
www.atsu.edu

GENERAL INFORMATION

The Arizona School of Dentistry & Oral Health prepares caring, technologically adept dentists to become community and educational leaders. The school offers students an experience-rich learning environment where health professionals approach patient health as part of a team. The Arizona School of Dentistry & Oral Health is part of A.T. Still University, which also includes the Kirksville College of Osteopathic Medicine, Arizona School of Health Sciences, the School of Health Management, and the School of Osteopathic Medicine in Arizona.

MISSION STATEMENT:

The mission of the Arizona School of Dentistry & Oral Health is to educate caring, technologically adept dentists who become community and educational leaders serving those in need and to be the leader in the lifelong education of community-responsive general dentists; to prepare graduates with a strong foundation of critical inquiry, evidence-based practice, research, cultural competency, an orientation to prevention, and interdisciplinary health care experiences; and to promote both the delivery of optimal patient care and the transfer of newly acquired knowledge, skills, and technology to the profession and to the community.

Type of institution: Private
Year opened: 2003
Term type: Semester
Time to degree in months: 48
Start month: July

Doctoral dental degree offered: D.M.D.
Total predoctoral enrollment: 252
Estimated entering class size: 76
Campus setting: Suburban
Campus housing available: No

PREPARATION

Formal minimum preparation in semester/quarter hours: Semester: 90 Quarter: 135
Baccalaureate degree preferred: Yes
Number of first-year, first-time enrollees whose highest degree is:
- Baccalaureate: 65
- Master's: 9
- Ph.D. or other doctorate: 0

Of first-year, first-time enrollees without baccalaureates, the number with:
- Equivalent of 60 undergraduate credit hours or less: 0
- Equivalent of 61-90 undergraduate credit hours: 0
- Equivalent of 91 or more undergraduate credit hours: 2

PREREQUISITE COURSE	REQUIRED	RECOMMENDED	LAB REQUIRED	CREDITS (SEMESTER/QUARTER)
BCP (biology-chemistry-physics) sciences				
Biology	✓		✓	8/12
Chemistry, general/inorganic	✓		✓	8/12
Chemistry, organic	✓		✓	8/12
Physics	✓		✓	8/12
Additional biological sciences				
Anatomy		✓		3/4
Biochemistry	✓			3/4
Cell biology				
Histology				
Immunology				
Microbiology		✓		3/4
Molecular biology/genetics				

(Prerequisite Courses continued)

PREPARATION (CONTINUED)

PREREQUISITE COURSE	REQUIRED	RECOMMENDED	LAB REQUIRED	CREDITS (SEMESTER/QUARTER)
Physiology	✓			3/4
Zoology				

Community college coursework accepted for prerequisites: Yes
Community college coursework accepted for electives: Yes
Limits on community college credit hours: No
Advanced placement (AP) credit accepted for prerequisites: Yes
Advanced placement (AP) credit accepted for electives: Yes
Job shadowing: Recommended
Number of hours of job shadowing required or recommended: 20
Other factors considered in admission: Community service experience is expected.

DAT

Mandatory: Yes
Latest DAT for consideration of application: 12/01/2013
Oldest DAT considered: 01/01/2010
When more than one DAT score is reported: Highest score is considered.
Canadian DAT accepted: No
Application considered before DAT scores are submitted: No

DAT: 2012 ENTERING CLASS

ENROLLEE DAT SCORES	RANGE	MEAN
Academic Average	16-22	18.5
Perceptual Ability	13-26	19.2
Total Science	15-24	18.3

GPA: 2012 ENTERING CLASS

ENROLLEE GPA SCORES	RANGE	MEAN
Science GPA	2.59-4.00	3.22
Total GPA	2.69-3.94	3.34

APPLICATION AND SELECTION

TIMETABLE

Earliest filing date: 06/01/2013
Latest filing date: 12/01/2013
Earliest date for acceptance offers: 12/01/2013
Maximum time in days for applicant's response to acceptance offer:
- 30 days if accepted on or after December 1 through January 31
- 15 days if accepted on or after February 1
- 48 hours after May 1

Requests for deferred entrance considered: In exceptional circumstances only
Fee for application: Yes, submitted only when requested
Amount of fee for application:
In state: $70 Out of state: $70 International: $70
Fee waiver available: Yes

	FIRST DEPOSIT	SECOND DEPOSIT	THIRD DEPOSIT
Required to hold place	Yes	Yes	No
Resident amount	$1,000	$1,000	
Nonresident amount	$1,000	$1,000	
Deposit due	As indicated in admission offer	05/01/2014	
Applied to tuition	Yes	Yes	
Refundable	No	No	

APPLICATION PROCESS

Participates in Associated American Dental Schools Application Service (AADSAS): Yes
Accepts direct applicants: No
Secondary or supplemental application required: Yes
Secondary or supplemental application website: Invitation will be sent by email.
Interview is mandatory: Yes
Interview is by invitation: Yes

RESIDENCY

Admissions process distinguishes between in-state/in-province and out-of-state/out-of-province applicants: No
Applications are accepted from non-U.S. citizens/non-U.S. permanent residents: Yes

APPLICATION AND ENROLLMENT	NUMBER OF APPLICANTS	ESTIMATED NUMBER INTERVIEWED	ESTIMATED NUMBER ENROLLED
In-state or province applicants	210	55	26
Out-of-state or province applicants	2,971	328	50

Generally and over time, percentage of your first-year enrollment is in-state: 34%
Origin of out-of-state enrollees (U.S.): Alabama-1, California-10, Colorado-1, Florida-2, Georgia-1, Guam-1, Hawaii-2, Illinois-2, Michigan-2, Minnesota-3, Montana-1, North Carolina-1, New Hampshire-1, New Jersey-2, New Mexico-1, Nevada-3, New York-1, Ohio-1, Oregon-1, South Dakota-1, Texas-4, Utah-5, Washington-2, Wisconsin-1
Origin of international enrollees: NA

DEMOGRAPHIC DESCRIPTIONS OF APPLICANTS: 2012 ENTERING CLASS

	APPLICANTS		ENROLLEES	
	M	W	M	W
Hispanic/Latino of any race	131	137	2	1
American Indian or Alaska Native	18	18	1	0
Asian	618	623	8	11
Black or African American	44	72	2	2
Native Hawaiian or Other Pacific Islander	3	2	1	1
White	1,133	671	30	19
Two or more races	0	0	0	0
Race and ethnicity unknown	62	50	1	0
International	0	0	0	0

	MINIMUM	MAXIMUM	MEAN
2012 entering class enrollees by age	21	37	26

Number of first-time enrollees over age 30: 13

CURRICULUM

The curriculum at the Arizona School of Dentistry & Oral Health is designed to produce graduates who are technologically adept, professionally competent, patient-centered, and compassionate. The curriculum emphasizes patient-care experiences through simulation, integration of biomedical and clinical sciences, and problem-solving scenarios to achieve clinical excellence. The curriculum includes a strong component of public health, leadership, and practice through weekly learning modules. Students have the opportunity to interact with faculty, practicing dentists, and national leaders to discuss cases in a regularly scheduled "grand rounds" format.

Student research opportunities: Yes

SPECIAL PROGRAMS AND SERVICES

DURING DENTAL SCHOOL

Academic counseling and tutoring
Community service opportunities
Internships, externships, or extramural programs
Mentoring
Personal counseling
Transfer applicants considered if space is available

ACTIVE STUDENT ORGANIZATIONS

American Association of Dental Research National Student Research Group
American Association of Women Dentists
American Dental Education Association (ADEA)
American Student Dental Association
Hispanic Dental Association
Society of American Indian Dentists, Student Chapter
Student National Dental Association

INTERNATIONAL DENTISTS

Graduates of international dental schools considered for traditional predoctoral program: Yes
Advanced standing program offered for graduates of international dental schools: No

COMBINED AND ALTERNATE DEGREES

Ph.D.	M.S.	M.P.H.	M.D.	B.A./B.S.	Other
—	—	✓	—	—	—

COSTS: 2012-13 SCHOOL YEAR

	FIRST YEAR	SECOND YEAR	THIRD YEAR	FOURTH YEAR
Tuition, resident	$54,870	$54,870	$54,870	$54,870
Tuition, nonresident	$54,870	$54,870	$54,870	$54,870
Tuition, other				
Fees	$1,050	$1,050	$1,050	$1,050
Instruments, books, and supplies	$10,544	$8,374	$7,700	$5,825
Estimated living expenses	$28,593	$30,994	$30,994	$34,402
Total, resident	$97,540	$95,288	$94,614	$96,147
Total, nonresident	$97,540	$95,288	$94,614	$96,147
Total, other				

FINANCIAL AID

A.T. Still University (ATSU) Arizona School of Dentistry & Oral Health participates in the Direct Lending Program. Student loans are available for tuition, fees, and living expenses. The Arizona School of Dentistry & Oral Health is also involved in a number of scholarship programs such as the Health Professions Scholarship Program (HPSP) – military, the National Health Service Corps (NHSC), the Indian Health Service (IHS), and the Western Interstate Commission for Higher Education (WICHE). Federal loans are the most common form of financial assistance with 95% of the student body using these loans.

MIDWESTERN UNIVERSITY
COLLEGE OF DENTAL MEDICINE-ARIZONA

Dr. Russell O. Gilpatrick, Dean

GENERAL INFORMATION

The College of Dental Medicine-Arizona is part of the campus of Midwestern University in Glendale, Arizona. Midwestern University's original campus is located in Downers Grove, Illinois, and the university was founded in 1900. The Glendale campus is situated on 146 acres 15 miles northwest of downtown Phoenix. It grew from a single building in 1996 to a full-service university with more than 34 buildings covering 1,465,032 total square feet and more than 2,925 students in 2011. Midwestern University's Glendale campus consists of more than five colleges and 17 programs offering a variety of graduate degrees, including doctoral degree programs. The four-year dental curriculum leads to a Doctor of Dental Medicine (D.M.D.) degree. The College of Dental Medicine-Arizona graduated its first class in 2012.

MISSION STATEMENT:

The mission of the Midwestern University College of Dental Medicine-Arizona is to graduate well-qualified general dentists and to improve oral health through research, scholarly activity, and service to the public.

CORE VALUES:

In pursuit of its mission, the College of Dental Medicine-Arizona is guided by this set of abiding and unchanging core values:

- Maintaining a student-friendly environment
- Encouraging encompassing diversity
- Advocating collegiality and teamwork
- Integrating multidisciplinary coursework
- Focusing on a general dentistry curriculum
- Assuring competence for general practice
- Basing decisions on scientific evidence
- Delivering ethical, patient-centered care
- Engaging the university community
- Serving the profession and the public

Type of institution: Private
Year opened: 2008
Term type: Quarter
Time to degree in months: 46
Start month: August

Doctoral dental degree offered: D.M.D.
Total predoctoral enrollment: 444
Estimated entering class size: 112
Campus setting: Suburban
Campus housing available: Yes

PREPARATION

Formal minimum preparation in semester/quarter hours: Semester: 90 Quarter: 120
Baccalaureate degree preferred: Yes
Number of first-year, first-time enrollees whose highest degree is:
Baccalaureate: 95
Master's: 12
Ph.D. or other doctorate: 0
Of first-year, first-time enrollees without baccalaureates, the number with:
Equivalent of 60 undergraduate credit hours or less: 0
Equivalent of 61-90 undergraduate credit hours: 0
Equivalent of 91 or more undergraduate credit hours: 4

PREREQUISITE COURSE	REQUIRED	RECOMMENDED	LAB REQUIRED	CREDITS (SEMESTER/QUARTER)
BCP (biology-chemistry-physics) sciences				
Biology	✓		✓	8/12
Chemistry, general/inorganic	✓		✓	8/12
Chemistry, organic	✓		✓	4/6

(Prerequisite Courses continued)

CONTACT INFORMATION

www.midwestern.edu
19555 North 59th Avenue
Glendale, AZ 85308
Phone: 623-572-3800
Fax: 623-572-3830

OFFICE OF ADMISSIONS
James Walter
Director
19555 North 59th Avenue
Glendale, AZ 85308
Phone: 623-572-3275
www.midwestern.edu

OFFICE OF STUDENT FINANCIAL SERVICES
E. Thomas Billard
Director
19555 North 59th Avenue
Glendale, AZ 85308
Phone: 623-572-3220
www.midwestern.edu

STUDENT AFFAIRS
Dr. Ross Kosinski
Dean of Students
19555 North 59th Avenue
Glendale, AZ 85308
Phone: 623-572-3329
www.midwestern.edu

HOUSING
Jose Ponce
Residence Life Coordinator
19555 North 59th Avenue
Glendale, AZ 85308
Phone: 623-572-3848

PREPARATION (CONTINUED)

PREREQUISITE COURSE	REQUIRED	RECOMMENDED	LAB REQUIRED	CREDITS (SEMESTER/QUARTER)
Physics	✓		✓	8/12
Additional biological sciences				
Anatomy	✓		✓	4/6
Biochemistry	✓			3/4.5
Cell biology				
Histology		✓		
Immunology		✓		
Microbiology	✓		✓	4/6
Molecular biology/genetics		✓		
Physiology	✓			4/6
Zoology		✓		
Other				
English composition/ technical writing	✓			6/9

Community college coursework accepted for prerequisites: Yes
Community college coursework accepted for electives: Yes
Limits on community college credit hours: No
Maximum number of community college credit hours: NA
Advanced placement (AP) credit accepted for prerequisites: Yes
Advanced placement (AP) credit accepted for electives: Yes
Comments regarding AP credit: We accept AP credit.
Job shadowing: Recommended
Number of hours of job shadowing required or recommended: 100

DAT

Mandatory: Yes
Latest DAT for consideration of application: 12/31/2013
Oldest DAT considered: 01/01/2010
When more than one DAT score is reported: Latest score is considered
Canadian DAT accepted: No
Application considered before DAT scores are submitted: No

DAT: 2012 ENTERING CLASS

ENROLLEE DAT SCORES	RANGE	MEAN
Academic Average	17-24	19.57
Perceptual Ability	14-27	20.44
Total Science	15-26	19.51

GPA: 2012 ENTERING CLASS

ENROLLEE GPA SCORES	RANGE	MEAN
Science GPA	2.63-4.00	3.50
Total GPA	2.75-4.00	3.56

APPLICATION AND SELECTION

TIMETABLE

Earliest filing date: 06/01/2013
Latest filing date: 01/01/2014
Earliest date for acceptance offers: 12/01/2013
Maximum time in days for applicant's response to acceptance offer:
30 days if accepted on or after December 1
15 days if accepted on or after January 1
Requests for deferred entrance considered: In exceptional circumstances only
Fee for application: Yes, submitted only when requested
Amount of fee for supplemental application:
In state: $50 Out of state: $50 International: $50
Fee waiver available: Yes

	FIRST DEPOSIT	SECOND DEPOSIT	THIRD DEPOSIT
Required to hold place	Yes	No	No
Resident amount	$1,000		
Nonresident amount	$1,000		
Deposit due	As indicated in admission offer		
Applied to tuition	Yes		
Refundable	Yes		

APPLICATION PROCESS

Participates in Associated American Dental Schools Application Service (AADSAS): Yes
Accepts direct applicants: No
Secondary or supplemental application required: Yes
Secondary or supplemental application website: Sent from admissions office if qualified
Interview is mandatory: Yes
Interview is by invitation: Yes

RESIDENCY

Admissions process distinguishes between in-state/in-province and out-of-state/out-of-province applicants: No
Preference given to residents of: None

Applications are accepted from non-U.S. citizens/non-U.S. permanent residents: Yes

APPLICATION AND ENROLLMENT	NUMBER OF APPLICANTS	ESTIMATED NUMBER INTERVIEWED	ESTIMATED NUMBER ENROLLED
In-state or province applicants	166	54	29
Out-of-state or province applicants	2,492	428	83

Generally and over time, percentage of your first-year enrollment is in-state: 20%-25%

Origin of out-of-state enrollees (U.S.): Alaska-1, Arkansas-1, California-20, Colorado-2, Florida-4, Georgia-1, Hawaii-2, Idaho-2, Illinois-3, Indiana-1, Louisiana-1, Massachusetts-1, Michigan-1, Missouri-1, Montana-1, Nebraska-1, New York-1, North Carolina-1, North Dakota-3, Ohio-2, Oregon-3, Pennsylvania-1, Texas-3, Utah-10, Virginia-2, Washington-7, Wisconsin-3, Wyoming-1

Origin of international enrollees: Canada-3 (Alberta-2, Ontario-1)

DEMOGRAPHIC DESCRIPTIONS OF APPLICANTS: 2012 ENTERING CLASS

	APPLICANTS		ENROLLEES	
	M	W	M	W
Hispanic/Latino of any race	37	31	2	2
American Indian or Alaska Native	1	4	0	0
Asian	207	147	3	6
Black or African American	21	31	0	0
Native Hawaiian or Other Pacific Islander	1	2	0	0
White	873	515	54	34
Two or more races	364	345	5	5
Race and ethnicity unknown	40	38	1	0
International	0	1	0	0

	MINIMUM	MAXIMUM	MEAN
2012 entering class enrollees by age	21	44	26

Number of first-time enrollees over age 30: 14

CURRICULUM

The curriculum emphasizes integrated disciplines that enhance learning and fully prepare students for the practice of general dentistry providing total patient care. The basic science curriculum is organized by body systems, rather than by biomedical discipline, and spans five academic quarters. The curriculum's systems-based approach, combined with clinical case studies, improves the learning experience for entry to patient care and prepares students for Part I of the National Dental Board Examination. The preclinical curriculum is organized by tooth segments, rather than by dental disciplines. This highly integrated course work spans six academic quarters of instruction in the simulation laboratory, emphasizing competency in a wide variety of clinical procedures. The course work stresses patient simulation, technical quality, high efficiency, and self-assessment. Students begin clinical care on a limited basis in the second year. The foundation of the clinical curriculum in the third and fourth academic years rests in the practice of general dentistry organized in practice groups led by general dentist faculty members. This eight-quarter curriculum emphasizes comprehensive patient-centered care, competency of all students in a full range of patient care services, and practice management and efficiency. It also prepares students for Part II of the National Board Dental Examination and clinical licensure examinations.

Student research opportunities: Yes

SPECIAL PROGRAMS AND SERVICES

PREDENTAL

Postbaccalaurate program in the College of Health Sciences Predental simulation courses

DURING DENTAL SCHOOL

Academic counseling and tutoring
Community service rotations in DM-2
Extramural rotations in DM-3 and DM-4 years
Mentoring
Personal counseling
Research opportunities

ACTIVE STUDENT ORGANIZATIONS

American Student Dental Association

INTERNATIONAL DENTISTS

Graduates of international dental schools considered for traditional predoctoral program: Yes

Advanced standing program offered for graduates of international dental schools: No

COMBINED AND ALTERNATE DEGREES

Ph.D.	M.S.	M.P.H.	M.D.	B.A./B.S.	Other
—	—	—	—	—	—

COSTS: 2012-13 SCHOOL YEAR

	FIRST YEAR	SECOND YEAR	THIRD YEAR	FOURTH YEAR
Tuition resident, non-resident, and other	$59,272	$59,272	$59,272	$59,272
Fees	$10,414	$10,414	$10,414	$10,414
Instruments, books, and supplies	$5,042	$1,935	$492	$150
Estimated living expenses (on-campus)	$11,916	$11,916	$15,888	$15,888
Student Services Fees	$552	$552	$552	$552
Health Disability Insurance Fees	$2,559	$1,896	$2,500	$2,500
NBDE	$260			$2,520
Total resident, non-resident, and other	$90,015	$85,985	$89,118	$91,296

FINANCIAL AID

Midwestern University (MWU) administers federal, state, and private sources of financial aid. Nearly 90% of MWU students receive some type of financial aid. All students seeking financial aid must meet general eligibility requirements regarding citizenship, financial need, and satisfactory academic progress. Our financial packages may include several sources of aid, including work-study programs, scholarships, grants, and loans. The university offers the following loan programs, among other institutional loan programs: federal Stafford Loan, federal Graduate PLUS (GradPLUS), Federal Perkins Loan Program, Primary Care Loan. Additionally, students are encouraged to pursue scholarship opportunities to minimize their reliance on student loans. Students may apply for financial aid year-round through their personal online portal at http://online.midwestern.edu, accessible once accepted to Midwestern University.

MWU's financial aid website is the central location for applicants and students to find more information on the programs available: www.midwestern.edu/Programs_and_Admission/Financial_Aid.

Applicants are encouraged to download the Financing Your Health Professions Booklet at www.midwestern.edu/Programs_and_Admission/Financial_Aid/Forms_and_Publications.html so they are fully prepared to finance their health care education.

LOMA LINDA UNIVERSITY
SCHOOL OF DENTISTRY

Dr. Charles J. Goodacre, Dean

GENERAL INFORMATION

Loma Linda University (LLU) represents distinction in quality Christian education. As a private university owned and operated by the Seventh-Day Adventist Church, the university has established a reputation for leadership in mission service, clinical excellence, research, and advancements in the health-related sciences. Located 60 miles east of Los Angeles in one of the fastest growing areas in the United States, the university is composed of eight health science schools including Schools of Dentistry, Medicine, Pharmacy, Nursing, Allied Health Professions, Public Health, Religion, and Behavioral Health and has an annual enrollment of more than 4,000 students from more than 100 countries.

MISSION STATEMENT:

Loma Linda University School of Dentistry (LLUSD) seeks to further the teaching and healing ministry of Jesus Christ, wherein students learn to provide high-quality oral health care, based on sound biologic principles. Patients receive competent care, which is preventive in purpose and comprehensive in scope, provided with compassion and respect. Faculty, students, and staff value the patient relationship, respect diversity, and share responsibility by working together toward academic, professional, spiritual, and personal growth. Scholarly activity and research provide a foundation for evidence-based learning and enhance whole-person care. The workplace environment attracts and retains a superior and diverse faculty and staff who motivate, educate, and serve. Our communities—local, global, and professional—benefit from our service, stewardship, and commitment to lifelong learning.

Type of institution: Private
Year opened: 1953
Term type: Quarter
Time to degree in months: 48
Start month: August

Doctoral dental degree offered: D.D.S.
Total predoctoral enrollment: 395
Estimated entering class size: 90
Campus setting: Suburban
Campus housing available: Yes

PREPARATION

Formal minimum preparation in semester/quarter hours: Semester: 96 Quarter: 144
Baccalaureate degree preferred: Yes
Number of first-year, first-time enrollees whose highest degree is:
- Baccalaureate: 94
- Master's: 3
- Ph.D. or other doctorate: 0

Of first-year, first-time enrollees without baccalaureates, the number with:
- Equivalent of 60 undergraduate credit hours or less: 0
- Equivalent of 61-90 undergraduate credit hours: 0
- Equivalent of 91 or more undergraduate credit hours: 1

PREREQUISITE COURSE	REQUIRED	RECOMMENDED	LAB REQUIRED	CREDITS (SEMESTER/QUARTER)
BCP (biology-chemistry-physics) sciences				
Biology	✓		✓	8/12
Chemistry, general/inorganic	✓		✓	8/12
Chemistry, organic	✓		✓	8/12
Physics	✓		✓	8/12
Additional biological sciences				
Anatomy		✓		4/4
Biochemistry	✓			4/4
Cell biology		✓		4/4
Histology		✓		4/4
Immunology		✓		4/4

(Prerequisite Courses continued)

CONTACT INFORMATION

www.dentistry.llu.edu

OFFICE OF ADMISSIONS
Esther Valenzuela
Director of Admissions
Prince Hall 5504
Loma Linda, CA 92350
Phone: 909-558-4621
www.dentistry.llu.edu

OFFICE OF FINANCIAL AID
LLU Office of Financial Aid
11139 Anderson Street
Loma Linda, CA 92350
Phone: 909-558-4509
www.llu.edu/ssweb/finaid

OFFICE OF STUDENT AFFAIRS
Dr. Graham Stacey
Associate Dean for Student Affairs
Prince Hall 5502
Loma Linda, CA 92350
Phone: 909-558-4790

OFFICE OF DIVERSITY
LLU Office of Diversity
Magan Hall, Room 103
Loma Linda, CA 92350
Phone: 909-558-4787
www.dentistry.llu.edu

HOUSING, OFFICE OF THE DEAN OF STUDENTS
Phone: 909-558-4510
www.llu.edu/central/housing

INTERNATIONAL STUDENT SERVICES
LLU International Student Services
Loma Linda, CA 92350
Phone: 909-558-4955
Email: intlstdsrv@llu.edu
www.llu.edu

PREPARATION (CONTINUED)

PREREQUISITE COURSE	REQUIRED	RECOMMENDED	LAB REQUIRED	CREDITS (SEMESTER/QUARTER)
Microbiology		✓		4/4
Molecular biology/genetics		✓		4/4
Physiology		✓		4/4
Zoology				4/4

Community college coursework accepted for prerequisites: Yes (Discouraged)
Community college coursework accepted for electives: Yes (Discouraged)
Limits on community college credit hours: Yes
Maximum number of community college credit hours: 64
Advanced placement (AP) credit accepted for prerequisites: Yes, English only
Advanced placement (AP) credit accepted for electives: Yes
Comments regarding AP credit: Must provide official Advanced Placement transcript and receive determination from LLUSD
Job shadowing: Required
Number of hours of job shadowing required or recommended: 50 hours required, more recommended

DAT

Mandatory: Yes
Latest DAT for consideration of application: 12/01/2012
Oldest DAT considered: 08/15/2011
When more than one DAT score is reported: Average score is considered
Canadian DAT accepted: Yes
Application considered before DAT scores are submitted: No

DAT: 2012 ENTERING CLASS

ENROLLEE DAT SCORES	RANGE	MEAN
Academic Average	NR	20.0
Perceptual Ability	NR	21.1
Total Science	NR	20.0

GPA: 2012 ENTERING CLASS

ENROLLEE GPA SCORES	RANGE	MEAN
Science GPA	NR	3.26
Total GPA	NR	3.38

APPLICATION AND SELECTION

TIMETABLE

Earliest filing date: 06/04/2013
Latest filing date: 12/03/2013
Earliest date for acceptance offers: 12/03/2013
Maximum time in days for applicant's response to acceptance offer:
30 days if accepted on or after December 1
15 days if accepted on or after February 1
Requests for deferred entrance considered: No
Fee for application: Yes, submitted only when requested
Amount of fee for application:
In state: $100 Out of state: $100 International: $100
Fee waiver available: Yes

	FIRST DEPOSIT	SECOND DEPOSIT	THIRD DEPOSIT
Required to hold place	Yes	Yes	No
Resident amount	$1,000	$1,000	
Nonresident amount	$1,000	$1,000	
Deposit due date	As indicated in admission offer	May 1, 2013	
Applied to tuition	Yes		
Refundable	No		

APPLICATION PROCESS

Participates in Associated American Dental Schools Application Service (AADSAS): Yes
Accepts direct applicants: No
Secondary or supplemental application required: Yes
Secondary or supplemental application website: Information is emailed to applicant
Interview is mandatory: Yes
Interview is by invitation: Yes

RESIDENCY

Admissions process distinguishes between in-state/in-province and out-of-state/out-of-province applicants: No
Applications are accepted from non-U.S. citizens/non-U.S. permanent residents: Yes

APPLICATION AND ENROLLMENT	NUMBER OF APPLICANTS	ESTIMATED NUMBER INTERVIEWED	ESTIMATED NUMBER ENROLLED
All applicants	2,029	427	96

Origin of out-of-state enrollees (U.S.): Alabama-1, Arizona-2, Florida-2, Georgia-1, Illinois-2, Maryland-1, Michigan-5, Minnesota-1, Mississippi-1, Montana-1, New Jersey-1, New Mexico-1, New York-2, Ohio-1, Oregon-1, South Carolina-1, Texas-3, Utah-2, Washington-2
Origin of international enrollees: Canada-6, South Korea-11

DEMOGRAPHIC DESCRIPTIONS OF APPLICANTS: 2013 ENTERING CLASS

	APPLICANTS		ENROLLEES	
	M	W	M	W
Hispanic/Latino of any race	22	39	2	3
American Indian or Alaska Native	1	3	0	0
Asian	385	442	17	22
Black or African American	26	47	2	1
Native Hawaiian or Other Pacific Islander	2	2	0	0
White	524	293	24	11
Two or more races	93	69	7	2
Race and ethnicity unknown	23	30	3	2
International	115	107	7	8

Note: 31 applicants and two enrollees did not report gender. Due to individual school reporting techniques, sums of applicants and enrollees do not match total by residency.

	MINIMUM	MAXIMUM	MEAN
Previous year enrollees by age	NR	NR	25

Number of first-time enrollees over age 30: NR

CURRICULUM

LLU's program is a traditional dental curriculum with emphasis in clinical training. Graduates are skilled in providing quality dental care that is comprehensive in its scope and preventive in its goals. Year 1. Basic sciences with introduction to clinical sciences. Year 2. Applied sciences and introduction to clinical practice. Year 3. Clinical sciences with extensive patient contact. Year 4. Delivery of comprehensive dental care.

Student research opportunities: Yes

SPECIAL PROGRAMS AND SERVICES

PREDENTAL

Careers in Dentistry, Minority Introduction to the Health Sciences (MITHS), Minorities in Dentistry, Gateway Summer Program
Postbaccalaureate programs
Summer enrichment programs

DURING DENTAL SCHOOL

Community service opportunities

ACTIVE STUDENT ORGANIZATIONS

American Dental Education Association (ADEA)
American Student Dental Association
Hispanic Dental Association
Junior Dental Auxiliary
Latinos in Dental Careers

INTERNATIONAL DENTISTS

Graduates of international dental schools considered for traditional predoctoral program: No
Advanced standing program offered for graduates of international dental schools: No

COMBINED AND ALTERNATE DEGREES

Ph.D.	M.S.	M.P.H.	M.D.	B.A./B.S.	Other
✓	✓	✓	✓	✓	—

COSTS: 2012-13 SCHOOL YEAR

	FIRST YEAR	SECOND YEAR	THIRD YEAR	FOURTH YEAR
Tuition, resident	$54,744	$66,316	$66,316	$66,316
Tuition, nonresident	$54,744	$66,316	$66,316	$66,316
Tuition, other				
Fees	$4,330	$5,831	$4,536	$4,297
Instruments, books, and supplies	$7,620	$8,134	$1,542	$646
Estimated living expenses	$13,680	$18,240	$18,240	$18,240
Total, resident	$86,689	$98,846	$94,334	$89,499
Total, nonresident	$80,374	$98,521	$90,634	$89,499
Total, other				

FINANCIAL AID

Various financial aid programs and a financial advisor are available. For more information visit our website at www.llu.edu/ssweb/finaid.

UNIVERSITY OF CALIFORNIA, LOS ANGELES
SCHOOL OF DENTISTRY

Dr. No-Hee Park, Dean

GENERAL INFORMATION

The University of California, Los Angeles (UCLA) School of Dentistry is one of two public dental schools in California, with a current enrollment of 88 students in the first and second years, an additional 20 advanced-standing international students in the third and fourth years, and 94 advanced dental education students in residency programs. The school has state-of-the-art facilities, close proximity to the renowned UCLA Biomedical Library, and convenient access to the recreational and cultural opportunities on the UCLA campus. The curriculum is competency-based with Pass/Not Pass evaluation, and students are well prepared for the National Board and licensure examinations, as well as for advanced dental education residency programs. In combination with a challenging curriculum in the basic and clinical dental sciences, students have dual degree programs and diverse opportunities for professional development in research, teaching, leadership, and community service.

MISSION STATEMENT:

The mission of the UCLA School of Dentistry is to improve the oral health of the people of California, the nation, and the world. To accomplish its mission, the school provides the following: education and training programs that are guided by the principles of scholarship, integrity, diversity, and mutual respect; high-quality, comprehensive, and patient-centered oral health care delivery programs; research programs that generate new knowledge, promote oral health, and investigate the cause, prevention, diagnosis, and treatment of oral disease; and service to the community and state as a health care provider, collaborative partner, continuing education center, and academic resource.

Type of institution: Public
Year opened: 1964
Term type: Quarter
Time to degree in months: 45
Start month: September

Doctoral dental degree offered: D.D.S.
Total predoctoral enrollment: 375
Estimated entering class size: 88
Campus setting: Urban
Campus housing available: Yes

PREPARATION

Formal minimum preparation in semester/quarter hours: Semester: 90 Quarter: 135
Baccalaureate degree preferred: Yes
Number of first-year, first-time enrollees whose highest degree is:
- Baccalaureate: 85
- Master's: 3
- Ph.D. or other doctorate: 0

Of first-year, first-time enrollees without baccalaureates, the number with:
- Equivalent of 60 undergraduate credit hours or less: 0
- Equivalent of 61-90 undergraduate credit hours: 0
- Equivalent of 91 or more undergraduate credit hours: 0

PREREQUISITE COURSE	REQUIRED	RECOMMENDED	LAB REQUIRED	CREDITS (SEMESTER/QUARTER)
BCP (biology-chemistry-physics) sciences				
Biology	✓		✓	8/12
Chemistry, general/inorganic	✓		✓	8/12
Chemistry, organic	✓		✓	6/8
Physics	✓		✓	8/12
Additional biological sciences				
Anatomy		✓		3/4
Biochemistry	✓			3/4
Cell biology				
Histology		✓		3/4

(Prerequisite Courses continued)

CONTACT INFORMATION

www.dentistry.ucla.edu

DEAN'S SUITE
UCLA School of Dentistry
Los Angeles, CA 90095
Phone: 310-206-6063

ADMISSIONS
Noemi Benitez
Coordinator
Office of Student Affairs, A0-111
Los Angeles, CA 90095
Phone: 310-794-7971
Email: dds_admissions@dentistry.ucla.edu
www.dentistry.ucla.edu

OFFICE OF FINANCIAL AID
Connie Steppes
Office of Student Affairs, A0-111
Los Angeles, CA 90095
Phone: 310-825-6994
Email: financial_aid@dentistry.ucla.edu
www.dentistry.ucla.edu

STUDENT AFFAIRS
Carol A. Bibb
Associate Dean for Student Affairs
Office of Student Affairs, A0-111
Los Angeles, CA 90095
Phone: 310-825-2615
www.dentistry.ucla.edu

MINORITY AFFAIRS/DIVERSITY
Edmond R. Hewlett
Associate Dean for Outreach and Diversity
Office of Student Affairs and Outreach, A0-111
Los Angeles, CA 90095
Phone: 310-825-7097
www.dentistry.ucla.edu

HOUSING
Phone: 310-825-4271
www.housing.ucla.edu

INTERNATIONAL DENTISTS
Coordinator-Professional Program
International Dentists
Office of Student Affairs
Los Angeles, CA 90095
Phone: 310-825-6218
Email: ppid_admission@dentistry.ucla.edu
www.dentistry.ucla.edu

PREPARATION (CONTINUED)

PREREQUISITE COURSE	REQUIRED	RECOMMENDED	LAB REQUIRED	CREDITS (SEMESTER/QUARTER)
Immunology				
Microbiology		✓		3/4
Molecular biology/genetics				
Physiology		✓		3/4
Zoology				

Community college coursework accepted for prerequisites: Yes
Community college coursework accepted for electives: Yes
Limits on community college credit hours: Yes
Maximum number of community college credit hours: 70
Advanced placement (AP) credit accepted for prerequisites: Yes
Advanced placement (AP) credit accepted for electives: No
Comments regarding AP credit: Maximum credit of 3 semester/4 quarter hours toward prerequisites
Job shadowing: Recommended
Number of hours of job shadowing required or recommended: NR
Other factors considered in admission: research, community service

DAT

Mandatory: Yes
Latest DAT for consideration of application: 12/31/2013
Oldest DAT considered: 01/01/2011
When more than one DAT score is reported: Most recent score only is considered
Canadian DAT accepted: No
Application considered before DAT scores are submitted: No

DAT: 2012 ENTERING CLASS

ENROLLEE DAT SCORES	RANGE	MEAN
Academic Average	17-22	22
Perceptual Ability	16-29	22
Total Science	17-30	22

GPA: 2012 ENTERING CLASS

ENROLLEE GPA SCORES	RANGE	MEAN
Science GPA	2.82-4.0	3.66
Total GPA	2.75-4.0	3.69

APPLICATION AND SELECTION

TIMETABLE

Earliest filing date: 06/01/2013
Latest filing date: 01/01/2014
Earliest date for acceptance offers: 12/01/2013
Maximum time in days for applicant's response to acceptance offer:
30 days if accepted on or after December 1
15 days if accepted on or after February 1
Requests for deferred entrance considered: No
Fee for application: Yes, submitted only when requested
Amount of fee for application:
In state: $60 Out of state: $60 International: $60
Fee waiver available: Yes, contact office for details

	FIRST DEPOSIT	SECOND DEPOSIT	THIRD DEPOSIT
Required to hold place	Yes	No	No
Resident amount	$1,000		
Nonresident amount	$1,000		
Deposit due	As indicated in admission offer		
Applied to tuition	Yes		
Refundable	No		

APPLICATION PROCESS

Participates in Associated American Dental Schools Application Service (AADSAS): Yes
Accepts direct applicants: No
Secondary or supplemental application required: Yes
Secondary or supplemental application website: www.dentistry.ucla.edu
Interview is mandatory: Yes
Interview is by invitation: Yes

RESIDENCY

Admissions process distinguishes between in-state/in-province and out-of-state/out-of-province applicants: Yes
Preference given to residents of: Alaska, Arizona, California, Hawaii, Montana, New Mexico, North Dakota, Wyoming
Reciprocity Admissions Agreement available for legal residents of: None
Applications are accepted from non-U.S. citizens/non-U.S. permanent residents: Yes

APPLICATION AND ENROLLMENT	NUMBER OF APPLICANTS	ESTIMATED NUMBER INTERVIEWED	ESTIMATED NUMBER ENROLLED
In-state or province applicants	1,022	142	82
Out-of-state or province applicants	869	16	6

Generally and over time, percentage of your first-year enrollment is in-state: 85%
Origin of out-of-state enrollees (U.S.): Arizona-1, Idaho-1, Oregon-1, Utah-1
Origin of international enrollees: Indonesia-1, South Korea-1

DEMOGRAPHIC DESCRIPTIONS OF APPLICANTS: 2012 ENTERING CLASS

	APPLICANTS		ENROLLEES	
	M	W	M	W
Hispanic/Latino of any race	30	40	3	1
American Indian or Alaska Native	1	2	0	0
Asian	435	427	22	32
Black or African American	15	37	0	0
Native Hawaiian or Other Pacific Islander	0	1	0	0
White	393	272	16	8
Two or more races	81	75	0	2
Race and ethnicity unknown	30	32	0	2
International	0	0	1	1

Notes: Number of international applicants not available

	MINIMUM	MAXIMUM	MEAN
2012 entering enrollees by age	20	32	23

Number of first-time enrollees over age 30: 6

CURRICULUM

The goals of the program are to prepare reflective practitioners who 1) possess the knowledge and skills necessary to provide patients with comprehensive dental care; 2) view their role in the profession from a humanitarian perspective; 3) are able to provide socially sensitive and responsible leadership in the community; and 4) continuously update their knowledge, techniques, and practices. The length of the D.D.S. program is 45 months. The curriculum uses lectures, small group discussion, labs, CD-ROMs, and web-based resources. Students supplement their educational experience through a variety of electives including teaching apprenticeships, mentored research projects, leadership training, and volunteer service at UCLA-sponsored outreach clinics. Early entry into the clinic is a priority. Student dentists, organized in vertical-tier teams, provide comprehensive care to an assigned patient pool, supplemented by rotations to specialty and community clinics.

Student research opportunities: Yes

SPECIAL PROGRAMS AND SERVICES

PREDENTAL

Association of American Medical Colleges/ADEA Summer Medical and Dental Education Program (AAMC/ADEA SMDEP)
Postbaccalaureate programs

DURING DENTAL SCHOOL

Academic counseling and tutoring
Community service opportunities
Externships
Mentorship programs
Personal counseling
Professional- and career-development programming
Training for those interested in academic careers

ACTIVE STUDENT ORGANIZATIONS

American Association of Dental Research Student Research Group
American Association of Pediatric Dentistry
American Association of Women Dentists
American Dental Education Association (ADEA)
American Student Dental Association
California Dental Association
Hispanic Dental Association

INTERNATIONAL DENTISTS

Graduates of international dental schools considered for traditional predoctoral program: No
Advanced standing program offered for graduates of international dental schools: Yes
Advanced standing program description: Program awarding a dental degree.

COMBINED AND ALTERNATE DEGREES

Ph.D.	M.S.	M.P.H.	M.D.	B.A./B.S.	Other
✓	✓	✓	—	—	✓

Other Degree: M.B.A.

COSTS: 2012-13 SCHOOL YEAR

	FIRST YEAR	SECOND YEAR	THIRD YEAR	FOURTH YEAR
Tuition, resident	$39,024	$42,963	$42,963	$42,963
Tuition, nonresident	$48,225	$52,164	$52,164	$52,164
Tuition, other	$0	$0	$0	0
Fees	$0	$0	$0	0
Instruments, books, and supplies	$19,652	$11,944	$3,746	$4,106
Estimated living expenses	$18,612	$24,816	$24,816	$24,816
Total, resident	$77,288	$79,723	$71,525	$71,885
Total, nonresident	$86,489	$88,924	$80,726	$81,086
Total, other	$0	$0	$0	$0

FINANCIAL AID

There were 64 resident recipients of scholarships and grants in the 2011 entering class. Residents received total scholarship/grant awards between $3,500 and $48,432, with an average award of $12,039. Nine nonresidents received scholarship/grant awards between $3,500 and $23,100, with an average award of $9,900.

There were 64 resident loan recipients in the 2011 entering class. Residents received total loan awards between $6,500 and $78,684, with an average award of $49,152. Nine nonresidents received loan awards between $42,000 and $79,784, with an average award of $59,504.

UNIVERSITY OF CALIFORNIA, SAN FRANCISCO
SCHOOL OF DENTISTRY

Dr. John D.B. Featherstone, Dean

CONTACT INFORMATION

http://dentistry.ucsf.edu
513 Parnassus Avenue, S619
San Francisco, CA 94143-0430
Phone: 415-476-2737
Fax: 415-476-4226

ADMISSIONS

James C. Betbeze, Jr., M.P.A.
Assistant Dean for Enrollment Management and Outreach
513 Parnassus Avenue, S619
San Francisco, CA 94143-0430
Phone: 415-476-2737

STUDENT FINANCIAL SERVICES

500 Parnassus Avenue
Millberry Union 200, West
San Francisco, CA 94143-0246
Phone: 415-476-4181
Fax: 415-476-6652
Email: finaid@ucsf.edu
http://finaid.ucsf.edu

STUDENT ACADEMIC AFFAIRS

http://saa.ucsf.edu

MINORITY AFFAIRS/DIVERSITY

www.aaeo.ucsf.edu/aaeod/2404-DSY.html

HOUSING

500 Parnassus Avenue
Millberry Union 102, West
San Francisco, CA 94143-0232
Phone: 415-476-2231
Fax: 415-476-6733
Email: housing@ucsf.edu
www.campuslifeservices.ucsf.edu/housing

INTERNATIONAL STUDENTS & SCHOLARS

William J. Rutter Center
1675 Owens Street, Room CC-290
San Francisco, CA 94143
Phone: 415-476-1773
Fax: 415-476-8119
http://isso.ucsf.edu

GENERAL INFORMATION

The University of California, San Francisco (UCSF), School of Dentistry provides a unique balance of clinical excellence, research opportunity, and community service as part of one of the leading health science centers in the nation. Established in 1881, the School has a service tradition that began by providing care after the 1906 earthquake, strong clinical programs that prepare dentists for the future, and research activities at the vanguard of contemporary science.

The four-year predoctoral curriculum covers the broad range of science, art, and technology that makes up contemporary dental practice. The curriculum is designed around five thematic streams: Biomedical Science, Dental Science, Scientific Methods, Preventive and Restorative Dentistry, and Patient-Centered Care. Students experience strong scientific preparation in the first years, augmented with introductory clinical activities and the fundamentals of dental therapies. During the third and fourth years, clinical experience—providing scientifically based patient-centered care—develops clinicians who graduate as competent dentists, and as women and men of science.

MISSION STATEMENT:

Advancing oral, craniofacial, and public health through excellence in education, discovery, and patient-centered care

VISION:

To lead worldwide in dental education and public health, clinical practice, and scientific discovery

VALUES:

Excellence, integrity, respect, innovation, accountability, leadership, and social responsibility

Type of institution: Public
Year opened: 1881
Term type: Quarter
Time to degree in months: 42
Start month: September

Doctoral dental degree offered: D.D.S.
Total predoctoral enrollment: 340
Estimated entering class size: 88
Campus setting: Urban
Campus housing available: Yes

PREPARATION

Formal minimum preparation in semester/quarter hours: Semester: 93 Quarter: 139
Baccalaureate degree preferred: Yes
Number of first-year, first-time enrollees whose highest degree is:
- Baccalaureate: 80
- Master's: 7
- Ph.D. or other doctorate: 0

Of first-year, first-time enrollees without baccalaureates, the number with:
- Equivalent of 60 undergraduate credit hours or less: 0
- Equivalent of 61-90 undergraduate credit hours: 0
- Equivalent of 91 or more undergraduate credit hours: 1

PREREQUISITE COURSE	REQUIRED	RECOMMENDED	LAB REQUIRED	CREDITS (SEMESTER/QUARTER)
BCP (biology-chemistry-physics) sciences				
Biology	✓		✓	8/12
Chemistry, general/inorganic	✓		✓	8/12
Chemistry, organic	✓		✓	4/8
Physics	✓		✓	8/12
Additional biological sciences				
Anatomy		✓		
Biochemistry	✓			3/4

(Prerequisite Courses continued)

PREPARATION (CONTINUED)

PREREQUISITE COURSE	REQUIRED	RECOMMENDED	LAB REQUIRED	CREDITS (SEMESTER/QUARTER)
Cell biology		✓		
Histology		✓		
Immunology		✓		
Microbiology		✓		
Molecular biology/genetics		✓		
Physiology		✓		
Zoology		✓		
Other				
English composition	✓			6/8
Introductory psychology	✓			3/4
Hum.Soc.Sci. electives	✓			11/16
Additional electives	✓			42/63

Community college coursework accepted for prerequisites: Yes
Community college coursework accepted for electives: Yes
Limits on community college credit hours: Yes
Maximum number of community college credit hours: 64
Advanced placement (AP) credit accepted for prerequisites: Yes
Advanced placement (AP) credit accepted for electives: Yes
Comments regarding AP credit: Applicants must submit official Score Report (School Code 5482). Science prerequisites can only be partially fulfilled using AP credit. See our admissions website for more detailed information.
Job shadowing: Recommended

DAT

Mandatory: Yes
Latest DAT for consideration of application: Official scores must be received by 10/15/2013
Oldest DAT considered: 06/01/2011
When more than one DAT score is reported: Most recent score only is considered
Canadian DAT accepted: No
Application considered before DAT scores are submitted: No

DAT: 2012 ENTERING CLASS

ENROLLEE DAT SCORES	RANGE	MEAN
Academic Average	17-26	21
Perceptual Ability	15-26	20
Total Science	16-30	21

GPA: 2012 ENTERING CLASS

ENROLLEE GPA SCORES	RANGE	MEAN
Science GPA	2.79-4.00	3.40
Total GPA	2.82-4.00	3.47

APPLICATION AND SELECTION

TIMETABLE

Earliest filing date: 06/03/2013
Latest filing date: 10/15/2013
Earliest date for acceptance offers: 12/02/2013
Maximum time in days for applicant's response to acceptance offer:
30 days if accepted on or after December 1
15 days if accepted on or after February 1
Requests for deferred entrance considered: No
Fee for application: Yes, submitted only when requested
Amount of fee for application:
In state: $60 Out of state: $60 International: $80
Fee waiver available: Yes; information provided with supplemental application

	FIRST DEPOSIT	SECOND DEPOSIT	THIRD DEPOSIT
Required to hold place	Yes	No	No
Resident amount	$1,000		
Nonresident amount	$1,000		
Deposit due	As indicated in admission offer		
Applied to tuition	Yes		
Refundable	No		

APPLICATION PROCESS

Participates in Associated American Dental Schools Application Service (AADSAS): Yes
Accepts direct applicants: No
Secondary or supplemental application required: Yes, accepted upon invitation only.
Secondary or supplemental application website: Provided upon invitation only
Interview is mandatory: Yes
Interview is by invitation: Yes

RESIDENCY

Admissions process distinguishes between in-state/in-province and out-of-state/out-of-province applicants: No

Applications are accepted from non-U.S. citizens/non-U.S. permanent residents: Yes

APPLICATION AND ENROLLMENT	NUMBER OF APPLICANTS	ESTIMATED NUMBER INTERVIEWED	ESTIMATED NUMBER ENROLLED
In-state or -province applicants	930	191	73
Out-of-state or -province applicants	873	109	15

Generally and over time, percentage of your first-year enrollment is in-state: about 77%

Origin of out-of-state enrollees (U.S.): Arizona-1, Florida-2, Georgia-1, Hawaii-1, Illinois-3, New York-1, Ohio-2, Pennsylvania-1, Utah-1, Washington-1

Origin of international enrollees: South Korea-1

DEMOGRAPHIC DESCRIPTIONS OF APPLICANTS: 2012 ENTERING CLASS

	APPLICANTS		ENROLLEES	
	M	W	M	W
Hispanic/Latino of any race*	65	65	6	9
American Indian or Alaska Native*	5	4	1	0
Asian	402	402	17	29
Black or African American*	13	32	2	3
Filipino*	1	6	0	0
Native Hawaiian or Other Pacific Islander	358	271	10	10
White	74	63	4	4
Did not report	31	27	0	0
International	60	41	1	0
Total	935	848	35	53
Two or More Races**	17	23	1	0
Two or More Races (URM)***	57	42	4	4

Note: Twenty applicants did not report race and ethnicity. The category "Two or More Races" is counted as additional information.

	MINIMUM	MAXIMUM	MEAN
2012 entering class enrollees by age	21	37	24

Number of first-time enrollees over age 30: 4

CURRICULUM

The curriculum is designed to organize material into five thematic streams that emphasize and reinforce the integration of basic sciences and clinical sciences in dental education. The dental curriculum prepares students to render evidence-based, high-quality, comprehensive oral care. The curriculum emphasizes thorough understanding of diagnosis, prevention, and control of disease; recognition of social needs; and knowledge of general health problems. Students are evaluated by examination and clinical competency examinations and by the quality and quantity of procedures completed. Courses are graded Passed/Not Passed/Passed With Honors.

Student research opportunities: Yes

SPECIAL PROGRAMS AND SERVICES

PREDENTAL

Postbaccalaureate programs: See school website

Special affiliation with colleges and universities: UCSF / UC Berkeley Extension – Postbaccalaureate program

DURING DENTAL SCHOOL

Academic counseling and tutoring
Community service opportunities
Internships, externships, or extramural programs
Mentoring
Personal counseling
Professional- and career-development programming
Special affiliations with colleges and universities: University of San Francisco – M.B.A. Program
Training for those interested in academic careers

ACTIVE STUDENT ORGANIZATIONS

American Association of Dental Research Student Research Group
American Dental Education Association (ADEA)
American Student Dental Association
Hispanic Dental Student Association
Student National Dental Association

For a complete list of active student organizations, visit http://dentistry.ucsf.edu/node/731

INTERNATIONAL DENTISTS

Graduates of international dental schools considered for traditional predoctoral program: No

Advanced standing program offered for graduates of international dental schools: Yes

Advanced standing program description: Program awarding a dental degree

COMBINED AND ALTERNATE DEGREES

Ph.D.	M.S.	M.P.H.	M.D.	B.A./B.S.	Other
✓	✓	—	—	—	✓

Other Degree: M.B.A., B.S. only available on a limited basis

COSTS: 2012-13 SCHOOL YEAR

	FIRST YEAR	SECOND YEAR	THIRD YEAR	FOURTH YEAR
Tuition, resident	$42,789	$42,789	$46,943	$46,943
Tuition, nonresident	$55,034	$55,034	$59,188	$59,188
Tuition, other				
Fees	$204	$204	$204	$204
Instruments, books, and supplies	$13,446	$10,794	$7,454	$6,953
Estimated living expenses	$19,455	$19,455	$25,695	$25,695
Total, resident	$75,894	$73,242	$80,296	$79,795
Total, nonresident	$88,139	$85,487	$92,541	$92,040
Total, other				

Comments: All fees and tuition are subject to University of California Regents' approval and to change without notice.

FINANCIAL AID

Approximately 94% of our students receive financial aid to cover the cost of the predoctoral program. The majority of this aid is in the form of federal student loans. Admitted students should submit the Free Application for Federal Student Aid (FAFSA), College Board Profile, and the UCSF Financial Aid application. Some need-based grant aid and scholarship funding is available. Admitted students do not have to apply for this funding separately; they will automatically be considered when they submit the above-mentioned items. More information can be found on the Student Financial Aid website: http://finaid.ucsf.edu

UNIVERSITY OF THE PACIFIC
ARTHUR A. DUGONI SCHOOL OF DENTISTRY

Dr. Patrick J. Ferillo, Jr., Dean

GENERAL INFORMATION

One of the world's most distinctive metropolitan centers, San Francisco has been the home of the Arthur A. Dugoni School of Dentistry since its incorporation in 1896 as the College of Physicians and Surgeons. The school has been recognized since its inception as a major resource for dental education in the western states and is the only dental school in which you can complete a four-academic year curriculum in just three calendar years.

- In 1962, the College of Physicians and Surgeons joined the University of the Pacific.
- In 1967, an eight-story building was completed for the teaching of clinical dentistry and for conducting dental research. Equipment and facilities are constantly updated, setting the pace for new and better methods of educating students and providing care to patients.
- In 1996, the school opened a state-of-the art preclinical simulation laboratory combining the latest in educational technology with a simulated patient experience.
- In 2004, the university renamed the dental school in honor of its long-standing Dean, Dr. Arthur A. Dugoni.
- In 2006, President DeRosa appointed Dr. Patrick J. Ferrillo, Jr., Dean of the school.
- In summer 2014, Pacific Dugoni will open its new home in San Francisco's South of Market (SoMa) neighborhood.

The Alumni Association provided a 12 operatory dental clinic, which has served as the school's major extended campus in southern Alameda County since 1973. The clinic was completely remodeled in 2002 and currently serves as one of two sites for the school's Advanced Education in General Dentistry residency program. In July 2003 a new Health Science Center was opened on the Stockton campus combining facilities for dentistry, dental hygiene, physical therapy, and speech pathology.

MISSION STATEMENT:

Vision Statement: Leading the improvement of health by advancing oral health.

Mission Statement: Our mission is to prepare oral health care providers for scientifically based practice; define new standards for education; provide patient-centered care; discover and disseminate knowledge; actualize individual potential; and develop and promote policies addressing the needs of society.

Type of institution: Private
Year opened: 1896
Term type: Quarter
Time to degree in months: 36
Start month: July

Doctoral dental degree offered: D.D.S.
Total predoctoral enrollment: 423
Estimated entering class size: 141
Campus setting: Urban
Campus housing available: No

PREPARATION

Formal minimum preparation in semester/quarter hours: Semester: 90 Quarter: 135
Baccalaureate degree preferred: Yes
Number of first-year, first-time enrollees whose highest degree is:
Baccalaureate: 132
Master's: 0
Ph.D. or other doctorate: 0
Of first-year, first-time enrollees without baccalaureates, the number with:
Equivalent of 60 undergraduate credit hours or less: 7
Equivalent of 61-90 undergraduate credit hours: 1
Equivalent of 91 or more undergraduate credit hours: 1

PREREQUISITE COURSE	REQUIRED	RECOMMENDED	LAB REQUIRED	CREDITS (SEMESTER/QUARTER)
BCP (biology-chemistry-physics) sciences				
Biology	✓		✓	4/6
Chemistry, general/inorganic	✓		✓	2/3
Chemistry, organic	✓			2/3

(Prerequisite Courses continued)

CONTACT INFORMATION

www.dental.pacific.edu
2155 Webster Street
San Francisco, CA 94115

OFFICE OF ADMISSIONS
Kathleen Candito
Associate Dean of Student Services
2155 Webster Street
San Francisco, CA 94115
Phone: 415-929-6491
www.dental.pacific.edu

OFFICE OF FINANCIAL AID
Marco Castellanos
Director of Financial Aid
2155 Webster Street
San Francisco, CA 94115
Phone: 415-929-6452
www.dental.pacific.edu

STUDENT AFFAIRS
Kathleen Candito
Associate Dean of Student Services
2155 Webster Street
San Francisco, CA 94115
Phone: 415-929-6491
www.dental.pacific.edu

MINORITY AFFAIRS/DIVERSITY
Stan Constantino
Director of Admissions
2155 Webster Street
San Francisco, CA 94115
Phone: 415-929-6491

OFFICE OF STUDENT SERVICES & HOUSING
Kathleen Candito
Associate Dean of Student Services
2155 Webster Street
San Francisco, CA 94115
Phone: 415-929-6491
www.dental.pacific.edu

INTERNATIONAL STUDENTS
Stan Constantino
Director of Admissions
2155 Webster Street
San Francisco, CA 94115
Phone: 415-929-6491
www.dental.pacific.edu

PREPARATION (CONTINUED)

PREREQUISITE COURSE	REQUIRED	RECOMMENDED	LAB REQUIRED	CREDITS (SEMESTER/QUARTER)
Physics	✓		✓	2/3
Additional biological sciences				
Anatomy		✓		
Biochemistry		✓		
Cell biology		✓		
Histology		✓		
Immunology		✓		
Microbiology		✓		
Molecular biology/genetics		✓		
Physiology		✓		
Zoology				

Community college coursework accepted for prerequisites: Yes
Community college coursework accepted for electives: Yes
Limits on community college credit hours: NA
Maximum number of community college credit hours: Courses taken at a community college will be acceptable if they are transferable as equivalent to predental courses at a four-year college.
Advanced placement (AP) credit accepted for prerequisites: Yes
Advanced placement (AP) credit accepted for electives: Yes
Comments regarding AP credit: Acceptance of advanced placement (AP) credit for prerequisites is assessed on an individual basis
Job shadowing: Required
Number of hours of job shadowing required or recommended: 40

DAT

Mandatory: Yes
Latest DAT for consideration of application: 09/15/2013
Oldest DAT considered: 09/01/2011
When more than one DAT score is reported: Most recent score only is considered
Canadian DAT accepted: Yes
Application considered before DAT scores are submitted: No

DAT: 2012 ENTERING CLASS

ENROLLEE DAT SCORES	RANGE	MEAN
Academic Average	NR	21
Perceptual Ability	NR	21
Total Science	NR	21

GPA: 2012 ENTERING CLASS

ENROLLEE GPA SCORES	RANGE	MEAN
Science GPA	NR	3.4
Total GPA	NR	3.5

APPLICATION AND SELECTION

TIMETABLE

Earliest filing date: 06/01/2013
Latest filing date: 12/01/2013
Earliest date for acceptance offers: 12/01/2013
Maximum time in days for applicant's response to acceptance offer:
30 days if accepted on or after December 1
15 days if accepted on or after February 1

Requests for deferred entrance considered: Yes
Fee for application: Yes, submitted at same time as AADSAS application
Amount of fee for application:
In state: $75 Out of state: $75 International: $75
Fee waiver available: No

	FIRST DEPOSIT	SECOND DEPOSIT	THIRD DEPOSIT
Required to hold place	Yes	Yes	No
Resident amount	$1,000	$2,000	
Nonresident amount			
Deposit due	As indicated in admission offer	As indicated in admission offer	
Applied to tuition	Yes	Yes	
Refundable	No	Yes	

APPLICATION PROCESS

Participates in AADSAS: Yes
Participates in Texas Medical and Dental Schools Application Service (for Texas applicants applying to Texas dental schools): No
Accepts direct applicants: No
Secondary or supplemental application required: No
Interview is mandatory: Yes
Interview is by invitation: Yes

RESIDENCY

Admissions process distinguishes between in-state/in-province and out-of-state/out-of-province applicants: No
Applications are accepted from non-U.S. citizens/non-U.S. permanent residents: Yes

APPLICATION AND ENROLLMENT	NUMBER OF APPLICANTS	ESTIMATED NUMBER INTERVIEWED	ESTIMATED NUMBER ENROLLED
In-state or province applicants	1,213	188	104
Out-of-state or province applicants	1,942	73	34

Generally and over time, percentage of your first-year enrollment is in-state: 75%

Origin of out-of-state enrollees (U.S.): Arizona-5, Connecticut-1, Florida-3, Hawaii-4, Idaho-1, Maryland-1, New Jersey-1, New Mexico-2, Nevada-3, Oregon-2, Texas-1, Utah-3, Washington-1, Wisconsin-1

Origin of international enrollees: Canada-1, South Korea-3

DEMOGRAPHIC DESCRIPTIONS OF APPLICANTS: 2012 ENTERING CLASS

	APPLICANTS		ENROLLEES	
	M	W	M	W
Hispanic/Latino of any race	33	48	7	3
American Indian or Alaska Native	3	2	1	0
Asian	615	622	27	30
Black or African American	11	40	0	0
Native Hawaiian or Other Pacific Islander	1	2	1	0
White	701	433	27	29
Two or more races	119	102	3	1
Race and ethnicity unknown	49	45	1	4
International	162	167	2	2

	MINIMUM	MAXIMUM	MEAN
2012 entering class enrollees by age	20	44	25

Number of first-time enrollees over age 30: 12

CURRICULUM

As suggested by the school's helix logo, biomedical, preclinical, and clinical science subjects are integrated and combined with applied behavioral sciences in a program both to prepare graduates to provide excellent-quality dental care to the public and to enter a changing world that will require them to be critical thinkers and lifelong learners. The 36-month curriculum leading to the degree of Doctor of Dental Surgery begins in July and is divided into 12 quarters, each consisting of 10 weeks of instruction, one week of examinations, and a vacation period of varying length (between one and four weeks).

Students with research interests and ability are encouraged to undertake projects under the guidance of experienced faculty members. Student progress in the program is evaluated by academic performance committees and carefully monitored by the Academic Advisory Committees that serve to identify any problems (such as undiagnosed learning disabilities) and recommend tutorial and other support. The highest standards are maintained in preparation for National Dental Examining Boards and licensure for practice. Very few students are delayed in their progress toward graduation.

Student research opportunities: Yes

SPECIAL PROGRAMS AND SERVICES

PREDENTAL

Postbaccalaureate programs
Special affiliations with colleges and universities: University of the Pacific - Accelerated Dental Program; San Francisco State/ Pacific - Postbaccalaureate Program

DURING DENTAL SCHOOL

Academic counseling and tutoring
Community service opportunities
Internships, externships, or extramural programs
Mentoring
Personal counseling
Professional- and career-development programming
Training for those interested in academic careers
Transfer applicants considered if space is available

ACTIVE STUDENT ORGANIZATIONS

American Association of Dental Research Student Research Group
American Dental Education Association (ADEA)
American Student Dental Association
Hispanic Dental Association
Student National Dental Association

INTERNATIONAL DENTISTS

Graduates of international dental schools considered for traditional predoctoral program: Yes
Advanced standing program offered for graduates of international dental schools: No

COMBINED AND ALTERNATE DEGREES

Ph.D.	M.S.	M.P.H.	M.D.	B.A./B.S.	Other
—	—	—	—	—	—

COSTS: 2012-13 SCHOOL YEAR

	FIRST YEAR	SECOND YEAR	THIRD YEAR	FOURTH YEAR
Tuition, resident	$88,986	$88,986	$88,986	NR
Tuition, nonresident	$88,986	$88,986	$88,986	NR
Tuition, other				NR
Fees	$5,509	$5,706	$6,697	NR
Instruments, books, and supplies	$16,500	$3,178	$1,100	NR
Estimated living expenses	$27,465	$27,465	$27,465	NR
Total, resident	$138,460	$125,335	$124,248	NR
Total, nonresident	$138,460	$125,335	$124,248	NR
Total, other				

FINANCIAL AID: 2012 ENTERING CLASS ESTIMATES

Federal loans continue to be the major source of funding for dental students. At the University of the Pacific Arthur A. Dugoni School of Dentistry, 92% of entering students are borrowing some type of loan with the average being $84,539 for the first year of the program.

Additional financial aid information can be found on www.dental.pacific.edu and in Chapter Four of this guide.

Ostrow School of Dentistry of USC

UNIVERSITY OF SOUTHERN CALIFORNIA
OSTROW SCHOOL OF DENTISTRY

Dr. Avishai Sadan, Dean

GENERAL INFORMATION

The Ostrow School of Dentistry of the University of Southern California (USC) is a private institution founded in 1897. Over the years, the school has become recognized for the excellence of its faculty in the clinical disciplines. This recognition is attested to by the fact that many procedures and techniques used in everyday dental practice were originated by USC faculty members. Programs of the school include those leading to a D.D.S., a B.S. in dental hygiene, certificate programs in advanced (specialty) education and continuing education for the practicing dentist, the Advanced Standing Program for International Dentists for foreign dental school graduates, and the graduate program in craniofacial biology leading to the M.S. or Ph.D. degrees. The requirements for each are given in the appropriate section of the University of Southern California Bulletin.

MISSION STATEMENT:

The USC Ostrow School of Dentistry (USCSD) is a "learning organization," dedicated to our own ongoing learning, flexibility, comfort with change, and openness to new ideas. We are committed to improving the health of all people through education and training, innovation and discovery, community health outreach, and leadership. USCSD seeks to provide outstanding undergraduate, graduate, and postgraduate academic programs of instruction for highly qualified students leading to academic degrees in the oral health professions; extend the knowledge of oral health by encouraging and assisting faculty in the pursuit of innovations and discovery scholarship; improve the oral health of all people of Southern California; stimulate and encourage in our students those qualities of scholarship, leadership, and character that mark the true oral health professional; serve California and the nation in providing lifelong learning to oral health professionals; and provide oral health leadership in the solution.

Type of institution: Private
Year opened: 1897
Term type: Trimester
Time to degree in months: 40
Start month: August

Doctoral dental degree offered: D.D.S.
Total predoctoral enrollment: 640
Estimated entering class size: 144
Campus setting: Urban
Campus housing available: Yes

PREPARATION

Formal minimum preparation in semester/quarter hours: Semester: 60 Quarter: 90
Baccalaureate degree preferred: Yes
Number of first-year, first-time enrollees whose highest degree is:
- Baccalaureate: 132
- Master's: 11
- Ph.D. or other doctorate: 1

Of first-year, first-time enrollees without baccalaureates, and the number with:
- Equivalent of 60 undergraduate credit hours or less: 0
- Equivalent of 61-90 undergraduate credit hours: 0
- Equivalent of 91 or more undergraduate credit hours: 0

PREREQUISITE COURSE	REQUIRED	RECOMMENDED	LAB REQUIRED	CREDITS (SEMESTER/QUARTER)
BCP (biology-chemistry-physics) sciences				
Biology	✓		✓	8/10
Chemistry, general/inorganic	✓		✓	8/10
Chemistry, organic	✓		✓	8/10
Physics	✓		✓	8/10
Additional biological sciences				
Anatomy		✓		
Biochemistry		✓		

(Prerequisite Courses continued)

CONTACT INFORMATION

http://dentistry.usc.edu/
925 West 34th Street
Room 201
Los Angeles, CA 90089
Phone: 213-740-2811

OFFICE OF ADMISSIONS AND STUDENT

Sandra C. Bolivar
Assistant Dean
925 West 34th Street
Room 201
Los Angeles, CA 90089
Phone: 213-740-2841
Email: uscsdadm@usc.edu

FINANCIAL AID

Sergio Estavillo
Director, Financial
925 West 34th Street
Room 201
Los Angeles, CA 90089
Phone: 213-740-2841
Email: uscsdfa@usc.edu

ADMISSIONS, MINORITY, AND STUDENT AFFAIRS

Sandra C. Bolivar
Assistant Dean
925 West 34th Street
Room 201
Los Angeles, CA 90089
Phone: 213-740-2841
Email: uscsdadm@usc.edu

MINORITY AFFAIRS/DIVERSITY

Sandra C. Bolivar
Assistant Dean
925 West 34th Street
Room 201
Los Angeles, CA 90089
Phone: 213-740-2841
Email: uscsdadm@usc.edu

TROJAN HOUSING

PSX 137
Los Angeles, CA 90089-1332
Phone: 213-740-2546

ADMISSIONS, MINORITY AND STUDENT AFFAIRS

Ryan Pineda
Admissions Coordinator
925 West 34th Street
Room 201
Los Angeles, CA 90089

PREPARATION (CONTINUED)

PREREQUISITE COURSE	REQUIRED	RECOMMENDED	LAB REQUIRED	CREDITS (SEMESTER/QUARTER)
Cell biology		✓		
Histology		✓		
Immunology		✓		
Microbiology		✓		
Molecular biology/genetics				
Physiology				
Zoology				

Community college coursework accepted for prerequisites: Yes. A very limited number may be accepted.
Community college coursework accepted for electives: Yes; maximum of 60 units
Limits on community college credit hours: Yes; 60 units
Maximum number of community college credit hours: 60
Advanced placement (AP) credit accepted for prerequisites: Yes
Advanced placement (AP) credit accepted for electives: Yes
Comments regarding AP credit: Credit must have been accepted by undergraduate college and included on transcript.
Job shadowing: Recommended
Number of hours of job shadowing required or recommended: 10-20
Other factors considered in admission: Personal background and experience, post baccalaureate experience, letters of evaluation, research experience, advanced degrees or training, and scope of academic background

DAT

Mandatory: Yes
Latest DAT for consideration of application: 02/01/2014
Oldest DAT considered: 01/01/2011
When more than one DAT score is reported: Most recent score only is considered
Canadian DAT accepted: Yes
Application considered before DAT scores are submitted: Yes

DAT: 2012 ENTERING CLASS

ENROLLEE DAT SCORES	RANGE	MEAN
Academic Average	15-30	20
Perceptual Ability	15-26	20
Total Science	15-28	20

GPA: 2012 ENTERING CLASS

ENROLLEE GPA SCORES	RANGE	MEAN
Science GPA	3.00 – 4.00	3.45
Total GPA	3.00 – 4.00	3.53

APPLICATION AND SELECTION

TIMETABLE

Earliest filing date: 06/01/2013
Latest filing date: 02/01/2014
Earliest date for acceptance offers: 12/01/2013
Maximum time in days for applicant's response to acceptance offer:
30 days if accepted on or after December 1
15 days if accepted on or after February 1
Requests for deferred entrance considered: No
Fee for application: Yes
Amount of fee for application:
In state: $85 Out of state: $85 International: $145
Fee waiver available: Yes

	FIRST DEPOSIT	SECOND DEPOSIT	THIRD DEPOSIT
Required to hold place	Yes	Yes	Yes
Resident amount	$500	$1,000	$1,500
Nonresident amount	$500	$1,000	$1,500
Deposit due	As indicated in admission offer	As indicated in admission offer	As indicated in admission offer
Applied to tuition	Yes	Yes	Yes
Refundable	No	No	Yes
Refundable by			07/15/2014

APPLICATION PROCESS

Participates in Associated American Dental Schools Application Service (AADSAS): Yes
Accepts direct applicants: No
Secondary or supplemental application required: No
Interview is mandatory: Yes
Interview is by invitation: Yes

RESIDENCY

Admissions process distinguishes between in-state/in-province and out-of-state/out-of-province applicants: No
Applications are accepted from non-U.S. citizens/non-U.S. permanent residents: Yes

APPLICATION AND ENROLLMENT	NUMBER OF APPLICANTS	ESTIMATED NUMBER INTERVIEWED	ESTIMATED NUMBER ENROLLED
In-state or province applicants	1,216	212	96
Out-of-state or province applicants	2,247	231	48

Generally and over time, percentage of your first-year enrollment is in-state: 65%

Origin of out-of-state or -province enrollees (U.S.): Arkansas-3, Arizona-4, Colorado-3, Florida-2, Georgia-2, Hawaii-1, Illinois-3, Indiana-1, Maryland-1, Minnesota-1, New Jersey-1, New Mexico-1, New York-3, Pennsylvania-1, Texas-4, Utah-3, Virginia-4

Origin of international enrollees:* Armenia, Canada, India, Iran, North Korea, South Korea, Malaysia, Philippines, Pakistan, Romania, Serbia, Russia, El Salvador, Ukraine, Taiwan, Vietnam

Note: International enrollees include legal U.S. residents, as well as Canadian and South Korean citizens with student visas.

DEMOGRAPHIC DESCRIPTIONS OF APPLICANTS: 2012 ENTERING CLASS

	APPLICANTS		ENROLLEES	
	M	W	M	W
Hispanic/Latino of any race	119	113	3	5
American Indian or Alaska Native	17	14	0	0
Asian	878	837	31	32
Black or African American				
Native Hawaiian or Other Pacific Islander	1	3	0	1
White	897	576	36	31
Two or more races	NA			
Race and ethnicity unknown	NA			
International	NR			

	MINIMUM	MAXIMUM	MEAN
2012 entering class enrollees by age	22	45	26

Number of first-time enrollees over age 30: 18

CURRICULUM

The curricular goals are the following:

1. To use student-centered, inquiry-based methods in all aspects of basic, preclinical, and clinical science instruction throughout all four years that will encourage students to develop lifelong problem-solving and group learning skills;
2. To encourage students to question materials presented and to develop a collegial interaction with the faculty—all areas of instruction occur in a professional atmosphere, and there is no activity that demeans students or creates an atmosphere in which student inquiry is repressed;
3. To vertically integrate the curriculum so that all three sciences and clinical skills are organized to emphasize the direct relevance of basic science learning outcomes to clinical problems;
4. To develop dental graduates who are dedicated to lifelong, self-motivated learning; accomplished in the methods required to solve problems in a clinical setting; and able to effectively understand and respond to changes in the profession

Student research opportunities: Yes

SPECIAL PROGRAMS AND SERVICES

PREDENTAL

Dental Explorers Program (two-week experience for predental and high school students)
Postbaccalaureate programs
Summer enrichment programs

DURING DENTAL SCHOOL

Academic counseling and tutoring
Community service opportunities
Internships, externships, or extramural programs
Personal counseling
Professional- and career-development programming

ACTIVE STUDENT ORGANIZATIONS

American Association of Dental Research Student Research Group
American Association of Women Dentists
American Dental Education Association (ADEA)
American Student Dental Association
Hispanic Dental Association
Student National Dental Association
Student Professional Ethics Club

INTERNATIONAL DENTISTS

Graduates of international dental schools considered for traditional predoctoral program: No
Advanced standing program offered for graduates of international dental schools: Yes
Advanced standing program description: Special two-year program is offered. Application is not through ADEA AADSAS but directly through ADEA Centralized Application for Advanced Placement for International Dentists (ADEA CAAPID).

COMBINED AND ALTERNATE DEGREES

Ph.D.	M.S.	M.P.H.	M.D.	B.A./B.S.	Other
—	—	—	—	—	✓

Other Degree: M.B.A.

COSTS: 2012-13 SCHOOL YEAR

	FIRST YEAR	SECOND YEAR	THIRD YEAR	FOURTH YEAR
Tuition, resident	$74, 838	$74,838	$74,838	$49,892
Tuition, nonresident	$74, 838	$74,838	$74,838	$49,892
Tuition, other				
Fees	$1,435	$1,435	$1,435	$1,363
Instruments, books, and supplies	$12,576	$8,341	$4,541	$2,794
Estimated living expenses	$26,940	$26,940	$26,940	$17,960
Total, resident	$115,789	$115,789	$115,789	$72,009
Total, nonresident	$115,789	$115,789	$115,789	$79,009
Total, other				

The average 2012 graduate indebtedness was $312,000.

FINANCIAL AID

The Ostrow School of Dentistry of USC Financial Aid Office is dedicated to the financial concerns of dental students. We are available Monday through Friday, 8:30 a.m. to 5:00 p.m. Pacific Time, and can be contacted at 213-740-2841 or by email at uscsdfa@usc.edu.

Financial Aid Application Procedures

- The Free Application for Federal Student Aid (FAFSA) can be completed on or after January 1, 2014, online at www.fafsa.ed.gov.
    - USC's School Code is 001328.
    - If you wish to be considered for the Health Professional Student Loan Program (HPSL), you must complete the parental section of the FAFSA.
- After admission into the Ostrow School of Dentistry, complete the online Supplemental Form, which can be found at www.usc.edu/admission/fa/.

After admission and following the financial aid application procedures, the Ostrow School of Dentistry will determine your financial aid eligibility. Notification of eligibility will be emailed beginning in May 2014. Please respond to the notification as instructed therein.

Please visit www.usc.edu/admission/fa/ for more detailed information.

WESTERN UNIVERSITY OF HEALTH SCIENCES
COLLEGE OF DENTAL MEDICINE

Dr. Steven W. Friedrichsen, Dean

GENERAL INFORMATION

Western University of Health Sciences was founded in 1977 and exists as a nonprofit, graduate university for the health professions located on 22 acres in Pomona, California. Pomona is a city of approximately 150,000 residents, located 35 miles east of Los Angeles near the foothills of the San Gabriel Mountains. The mission of Western University of Health Sciences is to produce, in a humanistic tradition, health care professionals and biomedical knowledge that will enhance and extend the quality of life in our communities. The university's emphasis is on the education and preparation of interprofessional primary health care service teams. The university's philosophical perspective focuses on the preparation of highly skilled health care professionals who are also compassionate, humanistic caregivers.

MISSION STATEMENT:

The College of Dental Medicine will realize its vision by educating and training highly competent, diverse groups of clinical practitioners who have the ability to provide complex, integrative, high-quality, evidence-based care for patients, families, and communities. The college will produce graduates who will be ethical, caring lifelong learners; who will collectively engage in clinical oral health care, public health practice, biomedical and health services research, education, and administration; and who will fulfill their professional obligation to improve the oral health of all members of society, especially those most in need. They will embrace scientific and technological advances and understand the connections between oral health and general health. They will be partners in the interprofessional health care delivery systems of the future, as well as leaders of their own oral health care teams, as they enhance and extend the quality of life in their communities.

Type of institution: Private
Year opened: 2009
Term type: Semester
Time to degree in months: 45
Start month: August

Doctoral dental degree offered: D.M.D.
Total predoctoral enrollment: 143
Estimated entering class size: 69
Campus setting: Suburban
Campus housing available: No

PREPARATION

Formal minimum preparation in semester/quarter hours: Semester: 90 Quarter: 135
Baccalaureate degree preferred: Yes
Number of first-year, first-time enrollees whose highest degree is:
- Baccalaureate: 50
- Master's: 5
- Ph.D. or other doctorate: 0

Of first-year, first-time enrollees without baccalaureates, the number with:
- Equivalent of 60 undergraduate credit hours or less: 0
- Equivalent of 61-90 undergraduate credit hours: 0
- Equivalent of 91 or more undergraduate credit hours: 20

PREREQUISITE COURSE	REQUIRED	RECOMMENDED	LAB REQUIRED	CREDITS (SEMESTER/QUARTER)
BCP (biology-chemistry-physics) sciences				
Biology	✓		✓	8/12
Chemistry, general/inorganic	✓		✓	8/12
Chemistry, organic	✓		✓	8/12
Physics	✓		✓	8/12
Additional biological sciences				
Anatomy		✓		4/6
Biochemistry		✓		4/6
Cell biology		✓		4/6

(Prerequisite Courses continued)

CONTACT INFORMATION

http://prospective.westernu.edu/dentistry/welcome.html
309 East Second Street
Pomona, CA 91766
Phone: 909-706-3504
Fax: 909-706-3800

ADMISSIONS
309 East Second Street
Pomona, CA 91766
Phone: 909-469-5335
Email: admissions@westernu.edu
http://prospective.westernu.edu/dentistry/welcome

FINANCIAL AID
309 East Second Street
Pomona, CA 91766
Phone: 909-469-5353
Email: finaid@westernu.edu
http://prospective.westernu.edu/dentistry/financing

STUDENT AFFAIRS
309 East Second Street
Pomona, CA 91766
Phone: 909-469-5340
www.westernu.edu/xp/edu/students/students-servicesoverview.xml

HOUSING
309 East Second Street
Pomona, CA 91766
Phone: 909-469-5605
Email: jhutson@westernu.edu
www.westernu.edu/students-housing-moving

INTERNATIONAL STUDENTS
Kathy Ford
University International Student Advisor
309 East Second Street
Pomona, CA 91766
Phone: 909-469-5542
Email: kford@westernu.edu
http://www.westernu.edu/international-welcome

PREPARATION (CONTINUED)

PREREQUISITE COURSE	REQUIRED	RECOMMENDED	LAB REQUIRED	CREDITS (SEMESTER/QUARTER)
Histology				
Immunology				
Microbiology		✓		4/6
Molecular biology/genetics		✓		4/6
Physiology		✓		4/6
Zoology				
Other				
Calculus		✓		3/4
Psychology		✓		3/4
Conversational Spanish		✓		3/4
College English/composition	✓			6/9

Community college coursework accepted for prerequisites: Yes
Community college coursework accepted for electives: Yes
Limits on community college credit hours: No
Maximum number of community college credit hours: None
Advanced placement (AP) credit accepted for prerequisites: For English only
Advanced placement (AP) credit accepted for electives: No
Job shadowing: Required
Number of hours of job shadowing required or recommended: 30—dental-related work experience (paid or volunteer)

DAT

Mandatory: Yes. Scores valid three years from date of application
Latest DAT for consideration of application: 10/15/2013
Oldest DAT considered: 01/01/2010
When more than one DAT score is reported: Most recent score only is considered
Canadian DAT accepted: No
Application considered before DAT scores are submitted: No

DAT: 2012 ENTERING CLASS

ENROLLEE DAT SCORES	RANGE	MEAN
Academic Average	16-24	19.4
Perceptual Ability	14-26	20.3
Total Science	15-26	19.6

GPA: 2012 ENTERING CLASS

ENROLLEE GPA SCORES	RANGE	MEAN
Science GPA	2.66-3.87	3.24
Total GPA	2.78-3.79	3.32

APPLICATION AND SELECTION

TIMETABLE

Earliest filing date: 06/03/2013
Latest filing date: 12/01/2013
Earliest date for acceptance offers: 12/01/2013
Maximum time in days for applicant's response to acceptance offer:
30 days if accepted on or after December 1
15 days if accepted on or after February 1
Response time lifted if offered after May 15

Requests for deferred entrance considered: In exceptional circumstances only
Fee for application: Yes, submitted with supplemental application
Amount of fee for application:
In state: $60 Out of state: $60 International: $60
Fee waiver available: Check school website for details

	FIRST DEPOSIT	SECOND DEPOSIT	THIRD DEPOSIT
Required to hold place	Yes	Yes	No
Resident amount	$1,000	$1,000	
Nonresident amount	$1,000	$1,000	
Deposit due	As indicated in admission offer	As indicated in admission offer	
Applied to tuition	Yes	Yes	
Refundable	No	No	

APPLICATION PROCESS

Participates in Associated American Dental Schools Application Service (AADSAS): Yes
Accepts direct applicants: No
Secondary or supplemental application required: Yes, to be submitted with $60 fee at same time you submit your AADSAS application
Secondary or supplemental application website: http://prospective.westernu.edu/dentistry/apply
Interview is mandatory: Yes
Interview is by invitation: Yes

RESIDENCY

Admissions process distinguishes between in-state/in-province and out-of-state/out-of-province applicants: No
Applications are accepted from non-U.S. citizens/non-U.S. permanent residents: Yes

APPLICATION AND ENROLLMENT	NUMBER OF APPLICANTS	ESTIMATED NUMBER INTERVIEWED	ESTIMATED NUMBER ENROLLED
In-state or -province applicants	1,121	270	41
Out-of-state or -province applicants	1,557	243	26

Generally and over time, percentage of your first-year enrollment is in-state: 58%

Origin of out-of-state or -province enrollees: Alaska- 1, Arizona- 1, Colorado- 1, Florida- 2, Georgia- 3, Illinois- 1, Maryland- 1, Michigan- 1, North Carolina- 2, New York- 2, Oklahoma- 1, Oregon- 1, Texas- 3, Virginia- 1, Washington- 3, Wisconsin- 1

Origin of international enrollees: South Korea - 1

DEMOGRAPHIC DESCRIPTIONS OF APPLICANTS: 2012 ENTERING CLASS

	APPLICANTS		ENROLLEES	
	M	W	M	W
Hispanic/Latino of any race	99	79	3	3
American Indian or Alaska Native	2	2	0	0
Asian	526	498	12	10
Black or African American	21	28	0	1
Native Hawaiian or Other Pacific Islander	0	0	0	0
White	619	388	11	11
Two or more races	81	84	5	3
Race and ethnicity unknown	48	50	3	2
International	85	61	2	1

Notes: Seven applicants did not report gender.

	MINIMUM	MAXIMUM	MEAN
2012 entering class enrollees by age	21	45	25

Number of first-time enrollees over age 30: 4

CURRICULUM

The College of Dental Medicine will be a premier center for integrative educational innovation; basic and translational research; and high-quality, patient-centered, interprofessional health care, all conducted in a setting that uses advanced technology and promotes individual dignity and potential for personal and professional growth. The overarching themes of the dental curriculum are 1) critical thinking, 2) professionalism, 3) communication and interpersonal skills, 4) health promotion, 5) practice management and informatics, and 6) patient care. Teaching methodologies will include small-group interaction, preclinical simulation laboratory, comprehensive patient-care clinical experience, and community-based clinical care and service.

Student research opportunities: Yes

SPECIAL PROGRAMS AND SERVICES

DURING DENTAL SCHOOL

Academic counseling and tutoring
Community service opportunities
Internships, externships, or extramural programs
Mentoring
Personal counseling
Professional- and career-development programming
Training for those interested in academic careers

ACTIVE STUDENT ORGANIZATIONS

American Student Dental Association
More than 75 diverse clubs and interest groups

INTERNATIONAL DENTISTS

Graduates of international dental schools considered for traditional predoctoral program: Yes
Advanced standing program offered for graduates of international dental schools: No

COMBINED AND ALTERNATE DEGREES					
Ph.D.	M.S.	M.P.H.	M.D.	B.A./B.S.	Other
—	—	—	—	—	—

COSTS: 2012-13 SCHOOL YEAR

	FIRST YEAR	SECOND YEAR	THIRD YEAR	FOURTH YEAR*
Tuition, resident	$60,950	$60,950	$60,950	$56,725
Tuition, nonresident	$60,950	$60,950	$60,950	$56,725
Tuition, other				
Fees	$40	$40	$40	$ 390
Instruments, books, and supplies	$7,974	$6,305	$6,149	$6,264
Estimated living expenses	$24,319	$24,402	$27,940	$27,787
Total, resident	$93,283	$91,697	$95,079	$91,166
Total, nonresident	$93,283	$91,697	$95,079	$91,166
Total, other				

FINANCIAL AID

Students need to complete the Free Application for Federal Student Aid (FAFSA) in order to apply for financial aid. The Financial Aid Office encourages all students to file the FAFSA at www.fafsa.ed.gov after January 1, 2014. Students may estimate their 2013 income in order to complete the FAFSA. The school code for Western University of Health Sciences is 024827. The Financial Aid Office will then be able to determine the student's eligibility for federal aid once the student has submitted the completed FAFSA application. An award letter will be sent electronically to the student's Western University of Health Sciences email address.

For additional information, please visit the Financial Aid website at www.westernu.edu/xp/edu/financial/financial-about.xml or contact their office at 909-469-5353 or finaid@westernu.edu.

THE UNIVERSITY OF COLORADO
SCHOOL OF DENTAL MEDICINE

Dr. Denise K. Kassebaum, Dean

CONTACT INFORMATION

www.ucdenver.edu/sdm
13065 East 17th Avenue, MS F833
Aurora, CO 80045
Phone: 303-724-7122
Fax: 303-724-7109

ADMISSIONS AND STUDENT AFFAIRS

Dr. Randy Kluender
Associate Dean
13065 East 17th Avenue, MS F833
Aurora, CO 80045
Phone: 303-724-7120
www.ucdenver.edu/sdm

STUDENT FINANCIAL AID OFFICE

13120 East 19th Avenue, CB A088
Aurora, CO 80045
Phone: 303-556-2886
www.ucdenver.edu/finaid

OFFICE OF DIVERSITY

Dominic Martinez
Director
13120 East 19th Avenue, MS A049
Aurora, CO 80045
Phone: 303-724-8002
www.ucdenver.edu/about/departments/DiversityandInclusion

HOUSING

Cheryl Gibson
Student Assistance Office
13120 East 19th Avenue, CB A043
Aurora, CO 80045
Phone: 303-724-7684
www.ucdenver.edu/studentassistance

INTERNATIONAL STUDENTS

Dr. Elizabeth Towne
Director
13065 East 17th Avenue, MS 838
Aurora, CO 80045
Phone: 303-724-7060
www.ucdenver.edu/sdm

GENERAL INFORMATION

The University of Colorado School of Dental Medicine enrolled its first class in 1973. Since then, the program has evolved as ongoing research has advanced the field of dentistry. The School of Dental Medicine's mission and progressive vision allow the Doctor of Dental Surgery Degree program to flourish and provide quality educational experiences that are personalized for each of its successful graduates. Recognized as a model institution for developing an innovative inter-professional (IPE) curriculum, the program prepares graduates for future team-based practice.

Predoctoral dental students participate in the School of Dental Medicine's six-semester clinical curriculum. Early clinical experiences include observing and assisting upperclassmen in patient treatment. Following this first year, students begin to treat patients on a limited basis, performing primarily oral diagnosis and periodontal and operative dental procedures. After accumulating a "family" of patients, students are responsible for their complete care. During the semesters that follow, students continue to treat patients and rotate through the Oral Surgery, Emergency, and Pediatric Clinics.

Dental students continue to treat patients in the Comprehensive Care Clinic and simultaneously participate in the Advanced Clinical Training Service (ACTS) program. This service learning program has been nationally recognized. ACTS is a cooperative effort between the School of Dental Medicine and community-based providers.

Students may be found in the simulation laboratory, where they learn dental procedures and the proper ergonomic positions that should be used during treatments. The School of Dental Medicine is set up for clinical functions that include general dentistry, endodontics, orthodontics, periodontics, surgery, radiology, esthetic dentistry, and specialized areas of pediatric care, geriatric care, and special needs care.

MISSION STATEMENT:

The mission of the School of Dental Medicine, as an integral part of The University of Colorado Anschutz Medical Campus, is to provide programs of excellence in teaching, research, patient care, and community and professional service for Colorado and the nation.

VISION:

By 2015, The University of Colorado School of Dental Medicine will be the premier public dental school, recognized for its innovative interprofessional programs of excellence in education, discovery, patient care, and community engagement.

Type of institution: Public
Year opened: 1973
Term type: Semester
Time to degree in months: 46
Start month: August

Doctoral dental degree offered: D.D.S.
Total predoctoral enrollment: 80
Estimated entering class size: 80
Campus setting: Suburban
Campus housing available: No

PREPARATION

Formal minimum preparation in semester/quarter hours: Semester: 90 Quarter: 135
Baccalaureate degree preferred: Yes
Number of first-year, first-time enrollees whose highest degree is:
- Baccalaureate: 77
- Master's: 2
- Ph.D. or other doctorate: 0

Of first-year, first-time enrollees without baccalaureates, the number with:
- Equivalent of 60 undergraduate credit hours or less: 0
- Equivalent of 61-90 undergraduate credit hours: 0
- Equivalent of 91 or more undergraduate credit hours: 1

PREREQUISITE COURSE	REQUIRED	RECOMMENDED	LAB REQUIRED	CREDITS (SEMESTER/QUARTER)
BCP (biology-chemistry-physics) sciences				
Biology	✓		✓	8/12

(Prerequisite Courses continued)

PREPARATION (CONTINUED)

PREREQUISITE COURSE	REQUIRED	RECOMMENDED	LAB REQUIRED	CREDITS (SEMESTER/QUARTER)
Chemistry, general/inorganic	✓		✓	8/12
Chemistry, organic	✓		✓	8/12
Physics	✓		✓	8/12
Additional biological sciences				
Anatomy		✓		4/6
Biochemistry	✓			4/6
Cell biology		✓		4/6
Histology		✓		4/6
Immunology		✓		4/6
Microbiology	✓			4/6
Molecular biology/genetics		✓		4/6
Physiology		✓		4/6
Other				
English composition	✓			4/6

Community college coursework accepted for prerequisites: Yes
Community college coursework accepted for electives: Yes
Limits on community college credit hours: Yes
Maximum number of community college credit hours: 60
Advanced placement (AP) credit accepted for prerequisites: No
Advanced placement (AP) credit accepted for electives: No
Comments regarding AP credit: Granting of advanced standing will be considered on an individual basis.
Job shadowing: Recommended
Number of hours of job shadowing required or recommended: No minimum
Other factors considered in admission: DAT scores, GPAs, interview scores, and letter of recommendations

DAT

Mandatory: Yes
Latest DAT for consideration of application: 02/01/2014
Oldest DAT considered: 02/01/2009
When more than one DAT score is reported: Highest score is considered
Canadian DAT accepted: No
Application considered before DAT scores are submitted: Yes

DAT: 2012 ENTERING CLASS

ENROLLEE DAT SCORES	RANGE	MEAN
Academic Average	17 – 25	19.8
Perceptual Ability	15 – 25	20.0
Total Science	16 – 27	19.6

GPA: 2012 ENTERING CLASS

ENROLLEE GPA SCORES	RANGE	MEAN
Science GPA	2.67 – 4.19	3.57
Total GPA	2.93 – 4.19	3.62

APPLICATION AND SELECTION

TIMETABLE

Earliest filing date: 06/01/2013
Latest filing date: 12/31/2013
Earliest date for acceptance offers: 12/02/2013
Maximum time in days for applicant's response to acceptance offer:
30 days if accepted on or after December 1
15 days if accepted on or after February 1
Requests for deferred entrance considered: In exceptional circumstances only.
Fee for application: Yes, submitted only when requested
Amount of fee for application:
In state: $50 Out of state: $50 International: $175
Fee waiver available: No

	FIRST DEPOSIT	SECOND DEPOSIT	THIRD DEPOSIT
Required to hold place	Yes	No	No
Resident amount	$1,000		
Nonresident amount	$1,000		
Deposit due	As indicated in admission offer		
Applied to tuition	Yes		
Refund	Yes		
Refundable by	60 days prior to matriculation		

APPLICATION PROCESS

Participates in Associated American Dental Schools Application Service (AADSAS): Yes
Accepts direct applicants: No
Secondary or supplemental application required: Yes, only upon request, application fee, residency form, regents questionnaire, and a waiver form
Secondary or supplemental application website: None
Interview is mandatory: Yes
Interview is by invitation: Yes

RESIDENCY

Admissions process distinguishes between in-state/in-province and out-of-state/out-of-province applicants: Yes
Preference given to residents of: Colorado
Reciprocity Admissions Agreement available for legal residents of: None
Applications are accepted from non-U.S. citizens/non-U.S. permanent residents: No

APPLICATION AND ENROLLMENT	NUMBER OF APPLICANTS	ESTIMATED NUMBER INTERVIEWED	ESTIMATED NUMBER ENROLLED
In-state or province applicants	148	109	46
Out-of-state or province applicants	1,342	142	34

Generally and over time, percentage of your first-year enrollment is in-state: 59%

Origin of out-of-state enrollees (U.S.): Arizona-12, Arkansas-1, California-1, Florida-2, Hawaii-2, Idaho-1, Illinois-1, Montana-3, New Mexico-6, North Carolina-1, North Dakota-1, Wyoming-2

Origin of international enrollees: NA

DEMOGRAPHIC DESCRIPTIONS OF APPLICANTS: 2012 ENTERING CLASS

	APPLICANTS		ENROLLEES	
	M	W	M	W
Hispanic/Latino of any race	24	24	5	3
American Indian or Alaska Native	1	2	2	0
Asian	124	117	6	6
Black or African American	9	13	1	1
Native Hawaiian or Other Pacific Islander	0	0	0	0
White	616	373	36	19
Two or more races	71	56	0	0
Race and ethnicity unknown	26	13	1	0
International	—	—	0	0

	MINIMUM	MAXIMUM	MEAN
2012 entering class enrollees by age	21	45	25

Number of first-time enrollees over age 30: 7

CURRICULUM

The goal of the dental curriculum is to graduate a dentist in four years who is capable of entering into dental practice. Graduates of this program will be able to do the following: 1) prevent, diagnose, and treat oral disease; 2) understand biological, physical, and social sciences and apply that knowledge in performing appropriate prevention, diagnosis, and treatment; 3) develop and apply personal and professional skills to practice effectively and relate to patients and colleagues; 4) recognize professional capabilities and judiciously refer patients for specialty care; and 5) continue to acquire knowledge through patterns of lifelong study. Basic science instruction occurs in the first and second years of the program. Basic science information is reinforced by clinical faculty in such courses as systemic disease, and oral and organ pathology, as well as by traditional clinical disciplines as appropriate.

Student research opportunities: Yes

SPECIAL PROGRAMS AND SERVICES

PREDENTAL

Postbaccalaureate programs: One year structured curriculum/underrepresented (by application only)
Summer enrichment programs: The Undergraduate Pre-Health Program (UPP) has shadowing and research opportunities for under-represented minority students.

DURING DENTAL SCHOOL

Academic counseling and tutoring
Community service opportunities
Personal counseling
Transfer applicants considered if space is available

ACTIVE STUDENT ORGANIZATIONS

American Academy of Pediatric Dentistry Student Chapter
American Association of Dental Research
American Association of Public Health Dentistry
American Association of Women Dentists
American Dental Education Association (ADEA)
American Student Dental Association
Hispanic Student Dental Association
Student National Dental Association
Student Chapter of the Academy of LDS Dentists

INTERNATIONAL DENTISTS

Graduates of international dental schools considered for traditional predoctoral program: No
Advanced standing program offered for graduates of international dental schools: Yes
Advanced standing program description: International Student Program

COMBINED AND ALTERNATE DEGREES

Ph.D.	M.S.	M.P.H.	M.D.	B.A./B.S.	Other
—	—	—	—	✓	—

COSTS: 2012-13 SCHOOL YEAR

	FIRST YEAR	SECOND YEAR	THIRD YEAR	FOURTH YEAR
Tuition, resident	$28,868	$28,868	$28,868	$28,868
Tuition, nonresident	$54,171	$54,171	$54,171	$54,171
Tuition, other	NA	NA	NA	NA
Fees	$4,065	$3,850	$3,850	$3,850
Instruments, books, and supplies	$9,660	$5,710	$5,710	$5,710
Estimated living expenses	$20,736	$20,736	$20,736	$15,264
Total, resident	$63,329	$59,164	$59,164	$53,692
Total, nonresident	$88,632	$84,467	$84,467	$78,995
Total, other	NA	NA	NA	NA

FINANCIAL AID

There were 208 recipients of student loans. Amounts were between $172 and $22,768, with an average of $7,926. The average 2012 graduate indebtedness was $100,937.

UNIVERSITY OF CONNECTICUT
SCHOOL OF DENTAL MEDICINE

Dr. R. Lamont MacNeil, Dean

GENERAL INFORMATION

Since its inception in 1968, the University of Connecticut School of Dental Medicine has been a prominent leader in dental education, dental research, and patient care. The predoctoral curriculum focuses on the biological and epidemiological bases of disease and provides strong preparation in the diagnostic and technical skills required for the practice of dentistry in the 21st century. The school shares a basic science curriculum with the School of Medicine and emphasizes an integrative approach to understanding the dynamics of the human body. Upon graduation, up to 80% of the students pursue advanced dental education in either the clinical specialties or general dentistry residency programs. As Connecticut's only dental school and the only public dental school in New England, the school is recognized nationally and internationally for both its predoctoral and advanced dental education/graduate education programs.

MISSION STATEMENT:

The School of Dental Medicine supports the missions of its academic health center and its university through programs in education, patient care, and research, which benefit both public and professional constituencies at all levels. As Connecticut's only public school of dentistry, the School of Dental Medicine is committed to providing predoctoral educational opportunities for qualified applicants who desire to become broadly competent general practitioners of dental medicine, capable of providing for most of the oral health care needs of the state's citizens. The school actively assists its students in achieving their career goals by creating a collegial environment in which academic excellence and the pursuit of scholarship enhance the quality of instruction, advance the understanding of human biology and pathology, and raise the standards of oral health.

Type of institution: Public
Year opened: 1968
Term type: Semester
Time to degree in months: 45
Start month: August

Doctoral dental degree offered: D.M.D.
Total predoctoral enrollment: 165
Estimated entering class size: 40
Campus setting: Suburban
Campus housing available: No

PREPARATION

Formal minimum preparation in semester/quarter hours: Semester: 90 Quarter: 180
Baccalaureate degree preferred: Yes
Number of first-year, first-time enrollees whose highest degree is:
- Baccalaureate: 39
- Master's: 1
- Ph.D. or other doctorate: 0

Of first-year, first-time enrollees without baccalaureates, the number with:
- Equivalent of 60 undergraduate credit hours or less: 0
- Equivalent of 61-90 undergraduate credit hours: 0
- Equivalent of 91 or more undergraduate credit hours: 0

PREREQUISITE COURSE	REQUIRED	RECOMMENDED	LAB REQUIRED	CREDITS (SEMESTER/QUARTER)
BCP (biology-chemistry-physics) sciences				
Biology	✓		✓	8/12
Chemistry, general/inorganic	✓		✓	8/12
Chemistry, organic	✓		✓	8/12
Physics	✓		✓	8/12
Additional biological sciences				
Anatomy				
Biochemistry		✓		4/6

(Prerequisite Courses continued)

CONTACT INFORMATION

http://sdm.uchc.edu
263 Farmington Avenue
Farmington, CT 06030-3915
Phone: 860-679-2808
Fax: 860-679-1330

OFFICE OF ADMISSIONS
Tricia M. Avolt
Admissions Coordinator
263 Farmington Avenue, MC 3905
Farmington, CT 06030-3905
Phone: 860-679-2175
http://sdm.uchc.edu

STUDENT FINANCIAL SERVICE CENTER
Andrea Devereux
Director
263 Farmington Avenue, MC 1827
Farmington, CT 06030-1827
Phone: 860-679-3574
http://sdm.uchc.edu

OFFICE OF DENTAL STUDENT AFFAIRS
263 Farmington Avenue, MC 3905
Farmington, CT 06030-3905
Phone: 860-679-2207
http://sdm.uchc.edu

MINORITY AFFAIRS/DIVERSITY
Dr. Marja Hurley
Associate Dean
263 Farmington Avenue, MC 1850
Farmington, CT 06030-1850
Phone: 860-679-3867

HOUSING
Lisa Francini
Student Affairs and Activities
263 Farmington Avenue, MC 1829
Farmington, CT 06030-1829
Phone: 860-679-2986
Fax: 860-679-6763
http://sdm.uchc.edu

INTERNATIONAL STUDENTS
Tricia M. Avolt
Admissions Coordinator
263 Farmington Avenue, MC 3905
Farmington, CT 06030-3905
Phone: 860-679-2175
http://sdm.uchc.edu

PREPARATION (CONTINUED)

PREREQUISITE COURSE	REQUIRED	RECOMMENDED	LAB REQUIRED	CREDITS (SEMESTER/QUARTER)
Cell biology		✓		4/6
Histology				
Immunology				
Microbiology		✓		4/6
Molecular biology/genetics		✓		4/6
Physiology				
Zoology				

Community college coursework accepted for prerequisites: Yes
Community college coursework accepted for electives: Yes
Limits on community college credit hours: No
Advanced placement (AP) credit accepted for prerequisites: Yes
Advanced placement (AP) credit accepted for electives: Yes
Job shadowing: Required
Number of hours of job shadowing required or recommended: 75

DAT

Mandatory: Yes
Latest DAT for consideration of application: 11/01/2013
Oldest DAT considered: 06/01/2011
When more than one DAT score is reported: Most recent score only is considered
Canadian DAT accepted: Yes
Application considered before DAT scores are submitted: No

DAT: 2012 ENTERING CLASS

ENROLLEE DAT SCORES	RANGE	MEAN
Academic Average	17-25	21
Perceptual Ability	14-26	21
Total Science	19-26	21

GPA: 2012 ENTERING CLASS

ENROLLEE GPA SCORES	RANGE	MEAN
Science GPA	2.68-4.00	3.50
Total GPA	2.78-4.00	3.54

APPLICATION AND SELECTION

TIMETABLE

Earliest filing date: 06/01/2013
Latest filing date: 12/01/2013
Earliest date for acceptance offers: 01/01/2014
Maximum time in days for applicant's response to acceptance offer:
30 days if accepted on or after December 1
15 days if accepted on or after January 1
Requests for deferred entrance considered: In exceptional circumstances only
Fee for application: Yes, submitted at same time as Associated American Dental Schools Application Service (AADSAS) application
Amount of fee for application:
In state: $75 Out of state: $75 International: $75
Fee waiver available: Yes

	FIRST DEPOSIT	SECOND DEPOSIT	THIRD DEPOSIT
Required to hold place	Yes	No	No
Resident amount	$400		
Nonresident amount	$400		
Deposit due	As indicated in admission offer		
Applied to tuition	Yes		
Refundable	No		

APPLICATION PROCESS

Participates in AADSAS: Yes
Accepts direct applicants: Yes
Secondary or supplemental application required: No
Interview is mandatory: Yes
Interview is by invitation: Yes

RESIDENCY

Admissions process distinguishes between in-state/in-province and out-of-state/out-of-province applicants: Yes
Preference given to residents of: Connecticut
Reciprocity Admissions Agreement available for legal residents of: New England
Applications are accepted from non-U.S. citizens/non-U.S. permanent residents: Yes

APPLICATION AND ENROLLMENT	NUMBER OF APPLICANTS	ESTIMATED NUMBER INTERVIEWED	ESTIMATED NUMBER ENROLLED
In-state or province applicants	91	41	25
Out-of-state or province applicants	1,144	125	15

Generally and over time, percentage of your first-year enrollment is in-state: 50%
Origin of out-of-state enrollees (U.S.): Maine-1, Massachusetts-5, Michigan-1, New Hampshire-1, New Jersey-3, New York-2, Rhode Island-1, Washington-1
Origin of international enrollees: NA

DEMOGRAPHIC DESCRIPTIONS OF APPLICANTS: 2012 ENTERING CLASS

	APPLICANTS		ENROLLEES	
	M	W	M	W
Hispanic/Latino of any race	30	43	1	1
American Indian or Alaska Native	0	0	0	0
Asian	153	178	6	1
Black or African American	14	39	0	2
Native Hawaiian or Other Pacific Islander	1	0	0	0
White	328	275	15	10
Two or more races	13	16	0	0
Race and ethnicity unknown	24	21	3	0
International	42	43	0	0

Note: 4 applicants did not report gender and Race/Ethnicity.

	MINIMUM	MAXIMUM	MEAN
2012 entering class enrollees by age	22	40	24

Number of first-time enrollees over age 30: 1

CURRICULUM

The curriculum is designed to provide students with a comprehensive educational experience that allows them to master the knowledge and requisite skills associated with the practice of general dentistry. The goals of the program are to help students gain an understanding of human biology and the behavioral sciences, and to develop their competency in all aspects of clinical dentistry. During the first two years, dental students follow an integrated course of study in the basic sciences along with the medical students. The third- and fourth-year clinical program extends for 22 months and emphasizes comprehensive care, prevention, and the emerging epidemiologic patterns of dental diseases. Students are evaluated through written and practical examinations in the medical, dental, and clinical sciences, and through observation of students' development in patient oral health care delivery. The grading system is on a pass/fail basis.

Student research opportunities: Yes

SPECIAL PROGRAMS AND SERVICES

PREDENTAL

DAT workshops
Passport to Dentistry Program
Postbaccalaureate programs
Summer enrichment programs

DURING DENTAL SCHOOL

Academic counseling and tutoring
Community service opportunities
Internships, externships, or extramural programs
Mentoring
Personal counseling
Professional- and career-development programming
Training for those interested in academic careers

ACTIVE STUDENT ORGANIZATIONS

American Dental Education Association (ADEA)
American Student Dental Association
Hispanic Dental Association
Student National Dental Association

INTERNATIONAL DENTISTS

Graduates of international dental schools considered for traditional predoctoral program: Yes
Advanced standing program offered for graduates of international dental schools: No
Advanced standing program description: NA

COMBINED AND ALTERNATE DEGREES

Ph.D.	M.S.	M.P.H.	M.D.	B.A./B.S.	Other
✓	✓	✓	—	✓	—

Note: An M.S. is offered in Clinical and Translational Research, and an M.P.H. is offered as indicated in the table. These are the only two that are offered to predoctoral students.

COSTS: 2012-13 SCHOOL YEAR

	FIRST YEAR	SECOND YEAR	THIRD YEAR	FOURTH YEAR
Tuition, resident	$22,251	$22,251	$21,395	$21,395
Tuition, nonresident	$51,242	$51,242	$51,242	$51,242
Tuition, New England	$38,939	$38,939	$38,939	$38,939
Fees	$6,360	$6,126	$6,101	$6,101
Instruments, books, and supplies	$7,999	$2,450	$3,603	$1,145
Boards/Clinical exams		$365	$3,400	$420
Transcript fee				$50
Estimated living expenses	$20,925	$21,225	$23,400	$21,900
Total, resident	$57,535	$52,417	$57,899	$51,011
Total, nonresident	$86,526	$81,408	$87,746	$80,858
Total, New England	$74,223	$69,105	$75,443	$68,555

FINANCIAL AID

ENTERING CLASS OF 2012-13 STATISTICS

Incoming students requesting aid	44
Incoming students receiving grants/scholarships	34
Grant/scholarships awards range	$678 - $58,228
Incoming students receiving loans	44
Loan awards range	$708 - $32,000
Average award for all students	$52,126
Average award for all in-state students	$38,745
Average award for all regional students	$65,484
Average award for all out-of-state students	$81,625

GRADUATING CLASS OF 2012 DEBT STATISTICS

Number of graduating students	47
Number of students who entered with debt	20
Average entering debt for class (n=47)	$2,614
Average entering debt for those with debt (n=20)	$2,792
Number of students with dental school debt (n=44)	44
Average dental school debt (n=47)	$126,224
Average dental school debt for those with debt (n=44)	$134,830
Number of students with educational debt	44
Average educational debt (n=47)	$128,838
Average educational debt for those with debt (n=44)	$137,623

To find out more about the financial aid process, please visit http://studentservices.uchc.edu/financial.

HOWARD UNIVERSITY
COLLEGE OF DENTISTRY

Dr. Leo E. Rouse, Dean

GENERAL INFORMATION

The College of Dentistry at Howard University was established in 1881. It is the fifth oldest dental school in the United States. As a teaching and patient care institution, the college has trained thousands of highly skilled dental professionals to serve their communities, particularly the underserved. Our graduates are currently serving communities in 40 states and 53 foreign countries. Our more than 80 faculty members constitute one of the best-trained dental faculties in the world.

MISSION STATEMENT:

The mission of the Howard University College of Dentistry is to provide a dental education of exceptional quality to qualified individuals, with particular emphasis on recruiting promising African Americans and other historically underrepresented students. The college is dedicated to attracting, sustaining, and developing a cadre of faculty who, through teaching, research, and service, is committed to producing distinguished, compassionate, and culturally sensitive graduates. Furthermore, the college is dedicated to providing high-quality oral health care to our patients and in improving the quality of oral health in our local, national, and global communities.

Type of institution: Private
Year opened: 1881
Term type: Semester
Time to degree in months: 42
Start month: August

Doctoral dental degree offered: D.D.S.
Total predoctoral enrollment: 314
Estimated entering class size: 80
Campus setting: Urban
Campus housing available: Yes

PREPARATION

Formal minimum preparation in semester/quarter hours: Semester: 8 Quarter: 12
Baccalaureate degree preferred: Yes, baccalaureate degree is required.
Number of first-year, first-time enrollees whose highest degree is:
- Baccalaureate: 64
- Master's: 17
- Ph.D. or other doctorate: 0

Of first-year, first-time enrollees without baccalaureates, the number with:
- Equivalent of 60 undergraduate credit hours or less: 0
- Equivalent of 61-90 undergraduate credit hours: 0
- Equivalent of 91 or more undergraduate credit hours: 0

PREREQUISITE COURSE	REQUIRED	RECOMMENDED	LAB REQUIRED	CREDITS (SEMESTER/QUARTER)
BCP (biology-chemistry-physics) sciences				
Biology	✓		✓	8/12
Chemistry, general/inorganic	✓		✓	8/12
Chemistry, organic	✓		✓	8/12
Physics	✓		✓	8/12
Anatomy	✓			6/8
Biochemistry	✓			6/8
Additional biological sciences				
Cell biology		✓		4/6
Histology		✓		4/6
Immunology		✓		4/6
Microbiology		✓		4/6
Molecular biology/genetics		✓		4/6
Physiology		✓		6/8

(Prerequisite Courses continued)

CONTACT INFORMATION

www.howard.edu/collegedentistry
600 W Street, NW
Washington, DC 20059
Phone: 202-806-0019
Fax: 202-806-0354

OFFICE OF ADMISSIONS

Deborah Willis
Director of Admissions
Room 126
600 W Street, NW
Washington, DC 20509
Phone: 202-806-0400
www.howard.edu/collegedentistry

FINANCIAL AID

Willie Cartwright
Financial Aid Manager
Room 508
600 W Street, NW
Washington, DC 20059
Phone: 202-806-0375
www.howard.edu/collegedentistry

OFFICE OF STUDENT AFFAIRS

Dr. Cecile E. Skinner
Executive Dean
Room 128
600 W Street, NW
Washington, DC 20509
Phone: 202-806-0443
www.howard.edu/collegedentistry

OFFICE OF THE DEAN

Dr. Leo E. Rouse
Dean
600 W Street, NW
Washington, DC 20059
Phone: 202-806-0019
www.howard.edu/collegedentistry

RESIDENCE LIFE- HOWARD PLAZA

Larry Frelow
Property Manager
2401 4th Street, NW
Washington, DC 20059
Phone: 202-797-7148
www.howard.edu

PREPARATION (CONTINUED)

PREREQUISITE COURSE	REQUIRED	RECOMMENDED	LAB REQUIRED	CREDITS (SEMESTER/QUARTER)
Zoology		✓		4/6
Other				
English Composition		✓		6/8

Community college coursework accepted for prerequisites: No
Community college coursework accepted for electives: No
Limits on community college credit hours: NA
Maximum number of community college credit hours: 0
Advanced placement (AP) credit accepted for prerequisites: No
Advanced placement (AP) credit accepted for electives: No
Comments regarding AP credit: none accepted
Job shadowing: Recommended
Number of hours of job shadowing required or recommended: 100 hours—should be over a period of time.
Other factors considered in admission: Community service, number of hours spent job shadowing, leadership qualities, and interview.

DAT

Mandatory: Yes
Latest DAT for consideration of application: 03/31/2014
Oldest DAT considered: 03/31/2012
When more than one DAT score is reported: Highest score is considered
Canadian DAT accepted: Yes
Application considered before DAT scores are submitted: No

DAT: 2012 ENTERING CLASS

ENROLLEE DAT SCORES	RANGE	MEAN
Academic Average	NR	17.8
Perceptual Ability	NR	17.9
Total Science	NR	17.9

GPA: 2012 ENTERING CLASS

ENROLLEE GPA SCORES	RANGE	MEAN
Science GPA	NR	3.04
Total GPA	NR	3.47

APPLICATION AND SELECTION

TIMETABLE

Earliest filing date: 06/04/2013
Latest filing date: 02/01/2014
Earliest date for acceptance offers: 12/01/2013
Maximum time in days for applicant's response to acceptance offer:
30 days if accepted on or after December 1
15 days if accepted on or after February 1
Requests for deferred entrance considered: In exceptional circumstances only
Fee for application: Yes, nonrefundable, submitted only when requested
Amount of fee for application:
In state: $75 Out of state: $75 International: $75
(Excludes International Dentist Program Applicants)
Fee waiver available: No

	FIRST DEPOSIT	SECOND DEPOSIT	THIRD DEPOSIT
Required to hold place	Yes	No	No
Resident amount	$1,000		
Nonresident amount	$1,000		
Deposit due	As indicated in admission offer		
Applied to tuition	Yes		
Refundable	No		

Participates in Associated American Dental Schools Application Service (AADSAS): Yes
Accepts direct applicants: No
Secondary or supplemental application required: No
Secondary or supplemental application website: www.howard.edu
Interview is mandatory: Yes
Interview is by invitation: Yes

RESIDENCY

Admissions process distinguishes between in-state/in-province and out-of-state/out-of-province applicants: No
Applications are accepted from non-U.S. citizens/non-U.S. permanent residents: Yes

APPLICATION AND ENROLLMENT	NUMBER OF APPLICANTS	ESTIMATED NUMBER INTERVIEWED	ESTIMATED NUMBER ENROLLED
In-state or province applicants	6	2	2
Out-of-state or province applicants	2,378	148	76

Generally and over time, percentage of your first-year enrollment is in-state: 1%
Origin of out-of-state enrollees (U.S.): Arizona-2, California-2, Florida-8, Georgia-4, Illinois-1, Indiana-1, Louisiana-4, Maryland-8, Massachusetts-2, Michigan-1, Minnesota -1, Missouri-2, North Carolina-1, New Jersey-3, New York-3, Pennsylvania-3, Texas-4, Virginia-7
Origin of international enrollees: Antigua-1, Bahamas-2, Gabon-1, Haiti-1, India-1, Iran-1, Jamaica-2, Nigeria-1, South Korea-3, St. Lucia-1, Trinidad and Tobago-2, Venezuela-1

DEMOGRAPHIC DESCRIPTIONS OF APPLICANTS: 2012 ENTERING CLASS

	APPLICANTS		ENROLLEES	
	M	W	M	W
Hispanic/Latino of any race	31	54	3	3
American Indian or Alaska Native	2	2	0	0
Asian	430	470	7	8
Black or African American	167	310	15	30
Native Hawaiian or Other Pacific Islander	1	1	1	0
White	339	239	3	1
Two or more races	117	122	0	7
Race and ethnicity unknown	36	29	0	0
International	194	216	5	11

	MINIMUM	MAXIMUM	MEAN
2012 entering class enrollees by age	20	35	24

Number of first-time enrollees over age 30: 4

CURRICULUM

The primary objective of the curriculum is to educate individuals for the practice of general dentistry. Specific objectives are 1) to provide comprehensive predoctoral dental education such that the dental graduate will be competent in the prevention, diagnosis, and treatment of oral diseases and disorders and 2) to inculcate in our graduates the highest standards of ethical and moral responsibility to the dental profession and to the communities they serve. The foundation courses in the basic biomedical sciences are taught during the first two years followed by clinical courses and clinical experiences in the next two years. However, throughout the four years, the basic science and clinical science curriculum are integrated to prepare the students to be outstanding clinicians.

Student research opportunities: Students participate during the summer in our research lab or at other institutions such as The Johns Hopkins University. They also compete and present scientific research projects nationally.

SPECIAL PROGRAMS AND SERVICES

PREDENTAL

Association of American Medical Colleges/ADEA Summer Medical and Dental Education Program (AAMC/ADEA SMDEP)
Special affiliations with colleges and universities: Howard University - Feeder School
Other summer enrichment programs

DURING DENTAL SCHOOL

Academic counseling and tutoring
Community service opportunities: Community service is part of the curriculum.
Internships, externships, or extramural programs
Mentoring
Personal counseling
Professional- and career-development programming
Training for those interested in academic careers
Transfer applicants considered in the D2 year only if space is available; transferee must be in good academic standing

ACTIVE STUDENT ORGANIZATIONS

American Association of Dental Research Student Research Group
American Association of Women Dentists
American Dental Education Association (ADEA)
American Student Dental Association
Hispanic Dental Association
Student National Dental Association

INTERNATIONAL DENTISTS

Graduates of international dental schools considered for traditional predoctoral program: Yes
Advanced standing program offered for graduates of international dental schools: Yes

COMBINED AND ALTERNATE DEGREES

Ph.D.	M.S.	M.P.H.	M.D.	B.A./B.S.	Other
—	—	—	—	✓	✓

Other Degree: D.D.S./M.B.A.
Note: B.S./D.D.S. offered to Howard undergraduates

COSTS: 2012-13 SCHOOL YEAR

	FIRST YEAR	SECOND YEAR	THIRD YEAR	FOURTH YEAR
Tuition, resident	$37,070	$37,070	$37,070	$37,070
Tuition, nonresident	$37,070	$37,070	$37,070	$37,070
Tuition, other				
Fees	$1,971	$2,756	$2,911	$3,401
Instruments, books, and supplies	$11,952	$6,863	$4,426	$1,644
Estimated living expenses	$19,428	$24,069	$24,069	$24,069
Total, resident	$70,421	$70,758	$68,476	$66,184
Total, nonresident	$70,421	$70,758	$68,476	$66,184
Total, other				

FINANCIAL AID

The priority deadline to apply for financial aid is March15. Scholarships are awarded on the basis of academic merit and financial need. Each year the Jeter Memorial Scholarship is awarded to 10 first-year students who have demonstrated academic excellence in their undergraduate studies and DAT scores. The Trustee Scholarship for full or partial tuition is awarded to continuing students based solely on academic excellence. There is no citizenship requirement for this award.

Several scholarships are also awarded from the National Dental Association Foundation and the American Dental Association. Scholarships for Disadvantaged Students (SDS) are awarded to financially needy students from disadvantaged backgrounds.

Federal student loans were awarded through the William D. Ford Direct Loan Program. Need-based loans total approximately $14,500,564. A small number of alternative private loans were also awarded from various lenders totaling $213,125.

Federal Health Professionals Title VII Student Loans were awarded to financially needy students from disadvantaged backgrounds, totaling approximately $54,348. Approximately 10% of students were awarded loans or scholarships from this program.

The average 2011 graduate indebtedness was $175,000.

LAKE ERIE COLLEGE OF OSTEOPATHIC MEDICINE
SCHOOL OF DENTAL MEDICINE

Dr. Robert F. Hirsch, Dean

CONTACT INFORMATION

www.lecom.edu
4800 Lakewood Ranch Boulevard
Bradenton, FL 34211-4909
Phone: 941-405-1500
Fax: 941-405-1676

OFFICE OF ADMISSIONS AND STUDENT AFFAIRS

5000 Lakewood Ranch Boulevard
Bradenton, FL 34211-4909
Phone: 941-405-1500
Fax: 941-782-5721
Email: dentalfLa@lecom.edu
www.lecom.edu

FINANCIAL AID

5000 Lakewood Ranch Boulevard
Bradenton, FL 34211-4909
Phone: 941-756-0690
Fax: 941-782-5721
Email: bradentonfinaid@lecom.edu
www.lecom.edu

GENERAL INFORMATION

The Lake Erie College of Osteopathic Medicine (LECOM) School of Dental Medicine welcomed its inaugural class of 100 students in July 2012. The dental school is part of LECOM, which has three campuses. LECOM's main campus is located in Erie, Pennsylvania, with additional campuses in Bradenton, Florida, and Greensburg, Pennsylvania. LECOM has a talented leadership team who is creating a unique curriculum that is both innovative and patient centered. As with the College of Medicine's and School of Pharmacy's mission statements for osteopathic physicians and pharmacy practitioners, the mission of LECOM's School of Dental Medicine is to prepare students to become dentists through programs of excellence in education, research, clinical care, and community service to enhance the quality of life through improved health for all humanity. The dental school is housed in a brand new 138,000 square foot building in Bradenton, FL. The simulation and patient clinics are equipped with the latest, state-of-the-art technology. Students will be given the opportunity to have an early clinical experience beginning in their first year and continuing throughout their education. They will provide care to patients at an offsite facility in an undeserved area during the entire 4th year.

MISSION STATEMENT

The primary goal of the LECOM School of Dental Medicine is to prepare dental professionals committed to providing high-quality, ethical, empathetic, and patient-centered care to serve the needs of a diverse population. Through the integration of scientific knowledge, critical thinking, and effective communication skills and an emphasis on best practices in technology use, we will prepare future dentists to be quality caregivers and strong advocates and leaders in their communities, professional associations, and research activities.

Type of institution: Private
Year opened: 2012
Term type: Semester
Time to degree in months: 48
Start month: July

Doctoral dental degree offered: D.M.D.
Total predoctoral enrollment: 400
Estimated entering class size: 100
Campus setting: Suburban
Campus housing available: No

PREPARATION

Formal minimum preparation in semester/quarter hours: Semester: 8 Quarter: 12
Baccalaureate degree preferred: Yes
Number of first-year, first-time enrollees whose highest degree is:
- Baccalaureate: 100
- Master's: 17
- Ph.D. or other doctorate: 0

Of first-year, first-time enrollees without baccalaureates, the number with:
- Equivalent of 60 undergraduate credit hours or less: 0
- Equivalent of 61-90 undergraduate credit hours: 0
- Equivalent of 91 or more undergraduate credit hours: 100

PREREQUISITE COURSE	REQUIRED	RECOMMENDED	LAB REQUIRED	CREDITS (SEMESTER/QUARTER)
BCP (biology-chemistry-physics) sciences				
Biology	✓		✓	8/12
Chemistry, general/inorganic	✓		✓	8/12
Chemistry, organic	✓		✓	8/12
Physics		✓*		4/6
Additional biological sciences				
Anatomy		✓*		3/6
Biochemistry	✓			3/4.5
Cell biology		✓*		

(Prerequisite Courses continued)

PREPARATION (CONTINUED)

PREREQUISITE COURSE	REQUIRED	RECOMMENDED	LAB REQUIRED	CREDITS (SEMESTER/QUARTER)
Histology		✓		
Immunology		✓		
Microbiology		✓*		4/6
Molecular biology/genetics		✓		
Physiology		✓*		4/6
Zoology				
Other				
English composition/technical	✓			6/9

*Strongly recommended

Community college coursework accepted for prerequisites: Yes
Community college coursework accepted for electives: Yes
Limits on community college credit hours: No
Maximum number of community college credit hours: NA
Advanced placement (AP) credit accepted for prerequisites: Yes
Advanced placement (AP) credit accepted for electives: Yes
Comments regarding AP credit: Science scores must be 4 or above. AP credit will be accepted for prerequisite courses only if upper-level (or more advanced) course work is satisfactorily completed.
Job shadowing: Recommended
Number of hours of job shadowing recommended: 100
Other factors considered in admission: Community service, number of hours spent shadowing, leadership qualities, and interview

DAT

Mandatory: Yes
Latest DAT for consideration of application: 02/11/2014
Oldest DAT considered: 02/11/2012
When more than one DAT score is reported: Highest score is considered
Canadian DAT accepted: Yes
Application considered before DAT scores are submitted: No

DAT: 2012 ENTERING CLASS

ENROLLEE DAT SCORES	RANGE	MEAN
Academic Average	15-22	18.5
Perceptual Ability	14-27	18.3
Total Science	15-23	18.4

GPA: 2012 ENTERING CLASS

ENROLLEE GPA SCORES	RANGE	MEAN
Science GPA	2.71-3.83	3.28
Total GPA	2.92-3.88	3.41

APPLICATION AND SELECTION

TIMETABLE

Earliest filing date: 06/01/2013
Latest filing date: 02/01/2014
Earliest date for acceptance offers: 12/01/2013
Maximum time in days for applicant's response to acceptance offer:
30 days if accepted on or after December 1
15 days if accepted on or after February 1
Requests for deferred entrance considered: Exceptional circumstances only
Fee for application: Yes
Amount of fee for application:
Resident: $50 nonrefundable
Nonresident: $50 nonrefundable
Fee waiver available: No

	FIRST DEPOSIT	SECOND DEPOSIT	THIRD DEPOSIT
Required to hold place	$2,000		
Resident amount	$2,000		
Nonresident amount	$2,000		
Deposit due	At indicated in admissions offer		
Applied to tuition	Yes		
Refundable	No		

APPLICATION PROCESS

Participates in Associated American Dental Schools Application Service (AADSAS): Yes
Accepts direct applicants: No
Secondary or supplemental application required: Yes
Secondary or supplemental application website: www.lecom.edu

Interview is mandatory: Yes
Interview is by invitation: Yes

RESIDENCY

Admissions process distinguishes between in-state/in-province and out-of-state/out-of-province applicants: No
Preference given to residents of: None
Reciprocity Admissions Agreement available for legal residents of: None
Applications are accepted from non-U.S. citizens/non-U.S. permanent residents: No

APPLICATION AND ENROLLMENT	NUMBER OF APPLICANTS	ESTIMATED NUMBER INTERVIEWED	ESTIMATED NUMBER ENROLLED
In-state or province applicants	1,442	290	48
Out-of-state or province applicants	1,142	293	52

Generally and over time, percentage of your first-year enrollment is in-state: 48%
Origin of out-of-state enrollees (U.S.): Alabama, Arkansas, Arizona, California, Connecticut, Georgia, Illinois, Indiana, Kansas, Louisiana, Michigan, North Carolina, North Dakota, New Jersey, New York, Ohio, Oklahoma, Pennsylvania, South Carolina, Texas, Virginia, Washington
Origin of international enrollees: NA

DEMOGRAPHIC DESCRIPTIONS OF APPLICANTS: 2012 ENTERING CLASS

	APPLICANTS		ENROLLEES	
	M	W	M	W
Hispanic/Latino of any race	105	94	1	4
American Indian or Alaska Native	5	3	0	1
Asian	349	327	1	7
Black or African American	68	54	0	1
Native Hawaiian or Other Pacific Islander	2	1	0	1
White	499	551	37	39
Two or more races	38	31	2	4
Race and ethnicity unknown	228	201	1	1
International	NA	NA	NA	NA

Notes: Some applicants might not have reported some information, including gender.

	MINIMUM	MAXIMUM	MEAN
2012 entering class enrollees by age	21	26	24

Number of first-time enrollees over age 30: 0

CURRICULUM

Through a unique and innovative curriculum, the School of Dental Medicine prepares students for the practice of general dentistry, specifically for underserved communities. LECOM's evidence-based, quality dental education program will train students to provide patient-centered care; optimal therapeutic and economic outcomes; promote disease prevention; and enhance patient and provider education. LECOM offers the Doctor of Dental Medicine (D.M.D.) degree through a full-time, four-year pathway at the Bradenton campus. The curriculum consists of two years of basic science and preclinical instruction delivered through case-based, small-group Problem-Based Learning (PBL) sessions, as well as lectures, laboratories, and clinical experiences. Years three and four are primarily hands-on, clinical experiences. PBL courses will integrate medical and dental students. Other unique components of the curriculum include faculty-directed self-study of gross anatomy; early exposure to dentistry in the first year by working as dental assistants in local primary care dental clinics; direct comprehensive patient care in the first year (fabrication of full maxillary and mandibular removable prosthesis); a patient-based simulation clinic; and the entire fourth year devoted to primary care clinics in underserved areas of Florida and Erie, Pennsylvania. Faculty members will assess the professional competencies students gain through the program. These competencies empower students with the knowledge and skills necessary to work effectively in interprofessional, interdisciplinary, and multicultural environments.

Student research opportunities: Yes

SPECIAL PROGRAMS AND SERVICES

INTERNATIONAL DENTISTS

Graduates of international dental schools considered for traditional predoctoral program: Yes
Advanced standing program offered for graduates of international dental schools: No

COMBINED AND ALTERNATE DEGREES

Ph.D.	M.S.	M.P.H.	M.D.	B.A./B.S.	Other
—	—	—	—	—	—

COSTS: 2012-13 SCHOOL YEAR

	FIRST YEAR	SECOND YEAR	THIRD YEAR	FOURTH YEAR
Tuition, resident	$48,000	$48,000	$48,000	$48,000
Tuition, nonresident	$48,000	$48,000	$48,000	$48,000
Tuition, other	NA	NA	NA	NA
Fees	$8,500	$8,500	*	*
Instruments, books, and supplies	$11,225	$10,125	*	*
Estimated living expenses	$20,400	$20,400	*	*
Total, resident	$88,125	$87,025	*	*
Total, nonresident	$88,125	$87,025	*	*
Total, other	NA	NA	NA	NA
Total, nonresident	$86,953	$86,953	NA	NA

**Note:* The inaugural class for LECOM's School of Dental Medicine entered in July 2012. Fees and costs other than tuition for the third and fourth years will be announced at a future date.

FINANCIAL AID

Detailed financial aid information, application instructions, and links to application materials may be found on the LECOM School of Dental Medicine website at http://lecom.edu/financial-aid.php under "School of Dental Medicine Tuition & Fees."

If you have any questions, please call the Office of Financial Aid at 941-756-0690 or email bradentonfinaid@lecom.edu.

NOVA SOUTHEASTERN UNIVERSITY
COLLEGE OF DENTAL MEDICINE

Dr. Robert A. Uchin, Dean

GENERAL INFORMATION

Situated on a beautiful, 300-acre campus in Fort Lauderdale, Florida, Nova Southeastern University is the seventh largest not-for-profit university in the southeastern United States and the largest independent institution of higher learning in Florida. The College of Dental Medicine is closely allied with the other colleges that make up the Health Professions Division of Nova Southeastern University. Students in the College of Dental Medicine have the opportunity to socialize and study with students from the colleges of Osteopathic Medicine, Pharmacy, Optometry, Medical Sciences, Health Care Sciences, and Nursing. Courses in basic biomedical sciences and emphasis on integrative clinical thinking, evidence-based treatment options, and application of state-of-the-art technology prepare students to treat patients with quality care. Early introduction into clinical settings, under preceptorship of faculty group practice leaders, enables the student to achieve an understanding of the management and delivery of oral health care and the dynamics of the dentist/patient relationship.

MISSION STATEMENT:

Nova Southeastern University, a private, not-for-profit institution, offers a diverse array of innovative academic programs at the undergraduate, graduate, and professional levels, complementing on-campus educational opportunities and resources with accessible distance learning programs, and fostering intellectual inquiry, leadership, and commitment to community through engagement of students and faculty in a dynamic, life-long learning environment.

Type of institution: Private
Year opened: 1997
Term type: Semester
Time to degree in months: 46
Start month: August

Doctoral dental degree offered: D.M.D.
Total predoctoral enrollment: 492
Estimated entering class size: 120
Campus setting: Suburban
Campus housing available: Yes

PREPARATION

Formal minimum preparation in semester/quarter hours: Semester: 90
Baccalaureate degree preferred: Yes
Number of first-year, first-time enrollees whose highest degree is:
- Baccalaureate: 91
- Master's: 22
- Ph.D. or other doctorate: 1

Of first-year, first-time enrollees without baccalaureates, the number with:
- Equivalent of 60 undergraduate credit hours or less: 0
- Equivalent of 61-90 undergraduate credit hours: 0
- Equivalent of 91 or more undergraduate credit hours: 1

PREREQUISITE COURSE	REQUIRED	RECOMMENDED	LAB REQUIRED	CREDITS (SEMESTER/QUARTER)
BCP (biology-chemistry-physics) sciences				
Biology	✓		✓	8/12
Chemistry, general/inorganic	✓		✓	8/12
Chemistry, organic	✓		✓	8/12
Physics	✓		✓	8/12
Additional biological sciences				
Anatomy		✓		3/5
Biochemistry	✓			3/5
Cell biology		✓		3/5
Histology		✓		3/5
Immunology				3/5
Microbiology	✓			3/5

(Prerequisite Courses continued)

CONTACT INFORMATION

http://dental.nova.edu

Executive Associate Dean of Student Affairs and Admissions
Dr. Hal Lippman
3200 South University Drive
Fort Lauderale, FL 33328
Phone: 954-262-1796
Email: hlippman@nova.edu

Associate Director for Admissions and Financial Aid Services
Joey Jankie
3200 South University Drive
Fort Lauderdale, FL 33328
Phone: 954-262-7249
Email: joey@nova.edu

STUDENT AFFAIRS

Brittney Lyda
Assistant Director of Student Affairs
3200 South University Drive
Fort Lauderdale, FL 33328
Phone: 954-262-7302
Email: bl541@nova.edu

MINORITY AFFAIRS/DIVERSITY

3200 South University Drive
Fort Lauderdale, FL 33328
Phone: 954-262-7338
Email: rgaines@nova.edu

HOUSING, OFFICE OF RESIDENTIAL LIFE

3301 College Avenue
Fort Lauderdale, FL 33314
Phone: 954-262-7052

INTERNATIONAL STUDENTS

3200 South University Drive
Fort Lauderdale, FL 33328
Phone: 954-262-7240
Email: vatral@nova.edu

PREPARATION (CONTINUED)

PREREQUISITE COURSE	REQUIRED	RECOMMENDED	LAB REQUIRED	CREDITS (SEMESTER/QUARTER)
Molecular biology/genetics		✓		3/5
Physiology		✓		3/5

Note: Science classes recommended

Community college coursework accepted for prerequisites: Yes
Community college coursework accepted for electives: Yes
Limits on community college credit hours: Yes
Maximum number of community college credit hours: 60
Advanced placement (AP) credit accepted for prerequisites: Yes
Advanced placement (AP) credit accepted for electives: Yes
Comments regarding AP credit: None
Job shadowing: Recommended
Number of hours of job shadowing required or recommended: 0
Other factors considered in admission: The College of Dental Medicine selects students based on preprofessional academic performance, DAT scores, a personal interview, an application, and letters of evaluation.

DAT

Mandatory: Yes
Latest DAT for consideration of application: 12/30/2013
Oldest DAT considered: 12/31/2011
When more than one DAT score is reported: All scores are evaluated on their merit.
Canadian DAT accepted: Yes
Application considered before DAT scores are submitted: No

DAT: 2012 ENTERING CLASS

ENROLLEE DAT SCORES	RANGE	MEAN
Academic Average	18-26	20.3
Perceptual Ability	16-25	19.6
Total Science	18-26	20.7

GPA: 2012 ENTERING CLASS

ENROLLEE GPA SCORES	RANGE	MEAN
Science GPA	2.94-4.07	3.65
Total GPA	3.06-4.07	3.69

APPLICATION AND SELECTION

TIMETABLE

Earliest filing date: 05/15/2013
Latest filing date: 12/31/2013
Earliest date for acceptance offers: 12/01/2013
Maximum time in days for applicant's response to acceptance offer:
30 days if accepted on or after December 1
15 days if accepted on or after February 1
Requests for deferred entrance considered: In exceptional circumstances only.
Fee for application: Yes, submitted only when requested.
Amount of fee for application:
In state: $50 Out of state: $50 International: $50
Fee waiver available: No

	FIRST DEPOSIT	SECOND DEPOSIT	THIRD DEPOSIT
Required to hold place	Yes	Yes	No
Resident amount	$1,000	$1,000	
Nonresident amount	$1,000	$1,000	
Deposit due	As indicated in admission offer	As indicated in admission offer	
Applied to tuition	Yes	Yes	
Refundable	No	No	

APPLICATION PROCESS

Participates in Associated American Dental Schools Application Service (AADSAS): Yes
Accepts direct applicants: No
Secondary or supplemental application required: Yes
Secondary or supplemental application website: www.nova.edu
Interview is mandatory: Yes
Interview is by invitation: Yes

RESIDENCY

Admissions process distinguishes between in-state/in-province and out-of-state/out-of-province applicants: No
Applications are accepted from non-U.S. citizens/non-U.S. permanent residents: Yes

APPLICATION AND ENROLLMENT	NUMBER OF APPLICANTS	ESTIMATED NUMBER INTERVIEWED	ESTIMATED NUMBER ENROLLED
In-state or province applicants	1,847	280	75
Out-of-state or province applicants	1,086	280	48

Generally and over time, percentage of your first-year enrollment is in-state: 60%
Origin of out-of-state enrollees (U.S.): California-6, Colorado-1, Georgia-3, Idaho-1, Illinois-2, Maryland-1, Michigan-2, Missouri- 1, Nevada-1, New Jersey- 2, New York-2, North Dakota- 1, Oklahoma-1, Pennsylvania-1, South Carolina- 1, Tennessee- 1, Texas-2, Utah-4, Virginia-2
Origin of international enrollees: Canada-9, China-1, France-1, South Korea-2

DEMOGRAPHIC DESCRIPTIONS OF APPLICANTS: 2012 ENTERING CLASS

	APPLICANTS		ENROLLEES	
	M	W	M	W
Hispanic/Latino of any race	NR	NR	6	15
American Indian or Alaska Native	NR	NR	0	0
Asian	NR	NR	16	17
Black or African American	NR	NR	2	2
Native Hawaiian or Other Pacific Islander	NR	NR	0	0
White	NR	NR	36	26
Two or more races	NR	NR	0	0
Race and ethnicity unknown	NR	NR	0	3
International	NR	NR	0	0

	MINIMUM	MAXIMUM	MEAN
2012 entering class enrollees by age	19	35	24

Number of first-time enrollees over age 30: 5

CURRICULUM

The College of Dental Medicine's mission is to educate and train students to ensure their competency to practice the art and science of the dental profession. This competency requires graduates to be biologically knowledgeable, technically skilled, compassionate, and sensitive to the needs of all patients and the community. The college fosters excellence in dental education through innovative teaching, research, and community service.

Student research opportunities: Yes

SPECIAL PROGRAMS AND SERVICES

PREDENTAL

Postbaccalaureate programs
Special affiliations with colleges and universities: Shaw University - Fast track 3-4 program; St. Leo College - Fast track 3-4 program; Nova Southeastern University - Fast track 3-4 program and 4-4 program; Talladega University - 3-4 program; University of Pennsylvania (LPS) Post-baccalaureate Pre-Health Program

DURING DENTAL SCHOOL

Academic counseling and tutoring
Community service opportunities
Internships, externships, or extramural programs
Mentoring
Personal counseling
Professional- and career-development programming
Training for those interested in academic careers
Transfer applicants considered if space is available

ACTIVE STUDENT ORGANIZATIONS

American Academy of Pediatric Dentistry
American Student Dental Education Association
Class Councils
Hispanic Dental Student Association
Omicron Kappa Upsilon
Psi Omega
Student Government Association
Student National Dental Association
Women's Dental Society Student Organization

INTERNATIONAL DENTISTS

Graduates of international dental schools considered for traditional predoctoral program: Yes
Advanced standing program offered for graduates of international dental schools: Yes
Advanced standing program description: Program awarding a dental degree

COMBINED AND ALTERNATE DEGREES

Ph.D.	M.S.	M.P.H.	M.D.	B.A./B.S.	Other
—	✓	✓	—	—	✓

Other Degree: D.O./D.M.D.

COSTS: 2012-13 SCHOOL YEAR

	FIRST YEAR	SECOND YEAR	THIRD YEAR	FOURTH YEAR
Tuition, resident	$53,175	$53,175	$53,175	$53,175
Tuition, nonresident	$54,774	$54,774	$54,774	$54,774
Tuition, other (IDG*)	NA	$57,888	$57,888	$57,888
Fees	$1,620	$1,620	$1,620	$1,620
Instruments, books, and supplies	$17,550	$14,550	$10,050	$12,552
Estimated living expenses	$24,297	$24,297	$24,297	$24,297
Total, resident	$96,642	$93,642	$89,142	$91,644
Total, nonresident	$98,241	$95,241	$90,741	$93,243
Total, other (IDG*)	NA	$98,154	$94,257	$98,253

**Note:* International Dental Graduate

FINANCIAL AID

Information regarding the financial award process and deadlines, as well as links to applications materials, can be found on our website at www.nova.edu/financialaid/process.

For additional information on financial aid, please call 954-262-3380 or 800-806-3680.

UNIVERSITY OF FLORIDA
COLLEGE OF DENTISTRY

Dr. Teresa A. Dolan, Dean

GENERAL INFORMATION

The University of Florida College of Dentistry is one of the top dental schools in the United States. The college is part of a large health science center with a major teaching hospital and five other health colleges: Medicine, Nursing, Pharmacy, Public Health and Health Professions, and Veterinary Medicine.

The University of Florida Health Science Center is part of the comprehensive University of Florida campus, which offers rich educational and cultural opportunities, nationally ranked sports teams, and everything a large university system has to offer. Students, faculty, staff, and residents in the community represent a very diverse, highly educated population, who come to live, study, and work from across the state, nation, and from all over the world.

MISSION STATEMENT

The mission of the College of Dentistry is to achieve excellence in the art and science of dentistry through teaching, research, and service.

Type of institution: Public
Year opened: 1971
Term type: Semester
Time to degree in months: 45
Start month: August

Doctoral dental degree offered: D.M.D.
Total predoctoral enrollment: 330
Estimated entering class size: 83
Campus setting: Suburban
Campus housing available: Yes

PREPARATION

Formal minimum preparation in semester/quarter hours: Semester: 90 Quarter: 120
Baccalaureate degree preferred: Yes. A baccalaureate degree is strongly recommended.
Number of first-year, first-time enrollees whose highest degree is:
- Baccalaureate: 75
- Master's: 8
- Ph.D. or other doctorate: 0

Of first-year, first-time enrollees without baccalaureates, the number with:
- Equivalent of 60 undergraduate credit hours or less: 0
- Equivalent of 61-90 undergraduate credit hours: 0
- Equivalent of 91 or more undergraduate credit hours: 0

PREREQUISITE COURSE	REQUIRED	RECOMMENDED	LAB REQUIRED	CREDITS (SEMESTER/QUARTER)
BCP (biology-chemistry-physics) sciences				
Biology	✓		✓	8/12
Chemistry, general/inorganic	✓		✓	8/12
Chemistry, organic	✓		✓	8/12
Physics	✓		✓	8/12
Additional biological sciences				
Anatomy		✓		4/6
Biochemistry	✓		✓	4/6
Cell biology		✓		
Histology		✓		
Immunology		✓		
Microbiology	✓		✓	4/6
Molecular biology/genetics	✓		✓	4/6
Physiology		✓		
Zoology		✓		

(Prerequisite Courses continued)

CONTACT INFORMATION

www.dental.ufl.edu
P.O. Box 100445
Gainesville, FL 32610-0445
Phone: 352-273-5955
Fax: 352-846-0311

OFFICE OF ADMISSIONS

Dr. Pamela L. Sandow
Assistant Dean for Admissions & Financial Aid
P.O. Box 100445
Gainesville, FL 32610-0445
Phone: 352-273-5955
www.dental.ufl.edu

OFFICE OF FINANCIAL AID

S. Thomas Kolb
Student Financial Aid Coordinator
P.O. Box 100445
Gainesville, FL 32610-0445
Phone: 352-273-5999
www.dental.ufl.edu

STUDENT AND MULTICULTURAL AFFAIRS

Patricia Xirau-Probert
Director, Student and Multicultural Affairs
P.O. Box 100445
Gainesville, FL 32610-0445
Phone: 352-273-5954
www.dental.ufl.edu

HOUSING

SW 13th Street and Museum Road
P.O. Box 112100
Gainesville, FL 32611-2100
Phone: 352-392-2161
Email: houinfo@housing.ufl.edu
www.housing.ufl.edu/housing

INTERNATIONAL STUDENTS

Dr. Pamela L. Sandow
Assistant Dean for Admissions & Financial Aid
P.O. Box 100445
Gainesville, FL 32610-0445
Phone: 352-273-5955
www.dental.ufl.edu

PREPARATION (CONTINUED)

PREREQUISITE COURSE	REQUIRED	RECOMMENDED	LAB REQUIRED	CREDITS (SEMESTER/QUARTER)
Other				
General Psychology	✓			3/6
English grammar and composition	✓			6/6

Community college coursework accepted for prerequisites: Yes
Community college coursework accepted for electives: Yes
Limits on community college credit hours: No
Maximum number of community college credit hours: None
Advanced placement (AP) credit accepted for prerequisites: Yes
Advanced placement (AP) credit accepted for electives: Yes
Comments regarding AP credit: Applicants are strongly encouraged to take prerequisite courses at the university level for which they have earned AP/International Baccalaureate (IB) or other credit.
Job shadowing: Strongly recommended

DAT

Mandatory: Yes
Latest DAT for consideration of application: 01/01/2014
Oldest DAT considered: Varies
When more than one DAT score is reported: Highest set of scores is considered
Canadian DAT accepted: Yes
Application considered before DAT scores are submitted: No

DAT: 2012 ENTERING CLASS

ENROLLEE DAT SCORES	RANGE	MEAN
Academic Average	16-24	20
Perceptual Ability	16-26	20
Total Science	16-25	20

GPA: 2012 ENTERING CLASS

ENROLLEE GPA SCORES	RANGE	MEAN
Science GPA	2.58-4.00	3.52
Total GPA	2.81-4.00	3.61

APPLICATION AND SELECTION

TIMETABLE

Earliest filing date: 06/01/2013
Latest filing date: 12/01/2013
Earliest date for acceptance offers: 12/01/2013
Maximum time in days for applicant's response to acceptance offer:
30 days if accepted on or after December 1
15 days if accepted on or after February 1
Requests for deferred entrance considered in exceptional circumstances only
Fee for application: Yes, submitted only when requested
Amount of fee for application:
In state: $30 Out of state: $30 International: $30
Fee waiver available: Check school website for details.

	FIRST DEPOSIT	SECOND DEPOSIT	THIRD DEPOSIT
Required to hold place	Yes	No	No
Resident amount	$200		
Nonresident amount	$200		
Deposit due	As indicated in admission offer		
Applied to tuition	Yes		
Refundable	No		

APPLICATION PROCESS

Participates in Associated American Dental Schools Application Service (AADSAS): Yes
Accepts direct applicants: No
Secondary or supplemental application required: Yes. Secondary application by invitation.
Secondary or supplemental application website: Website address given when invited to complete a supplemental application.
Interview is mandatory: Yes
Interview is by invitation: Yes

RESIDENCY

Admissions process distinguishes between in-state/in-province and out-of-state/out-of-province applicants: Yes
Preference given to residents of: Florida
Reciprocity Admissions Agreement available for legal residents of: None
Applications are accepted from non-U.S. citizens/non-U.S. permanent residents: No

APPLICATION AND ENROLLMENT	NUMBER OF APPLICANTS	ESTIMATED NUMBER INTERVIEWED	ESTIMATED NUMBER ENROLLED
In-state or province applicants	622	343	78
Out-of-state or province applicants	904	53	5

Generally and over time, percentage of your first-year enrollment is in-state: 90%
Origin of out-of-state enrollees (U.S.): Georgia-3, Maryland-1, Oklahoma-1
Origin of international enrollees: NA

DEMOGRAPHIC DESCRIPTIONS OF APPLICANTS: 2012 ENTERING CLASS

	APPLICANTS		ENROLLEES	
	M	W	M	W
Hispanic/Latino of any race	84	157	1	12
American Indian or Alaska Native	1	2	0	0
Asian	152	183	5	9
Black or African American	25	52	4	4
Native Hawaiian or Other Pacific Islander	1	0	0	0
White	420	324	22	22
Two or more races	24	21	2	0
Race and ethnicity unknown	24	19	2	0
International	11	13	NA	NA

	MINIMUM	MAXIMUM	MEAN
2012 entering class enrollees by age	21	36	24

Number of first-time enrollees over age 30: 6

CURRICULUM

The College of Dentistry has a dynamic curriculum relevant to the educational needs of the present and adaptable to those of the future. This curriculum applies instructional technology to enhance learning effectiveness in the classroom, preclinical simulation laboratory, and clinics. Graduates will be well-prepared to practice competently, implement current dental concepts, guide the work of others, and manage a dental office. The curriculum is organized as follows: Year 1: Basic science, preclinical technique, and introduction to clinics. Year 2: Completion of basic sciences, preclinical technical courses, and beginning of comprehensive patient care. Year 3: Clinical rotations and comprehensive patient care. Year 4: Comprehensive patient care, extramural rotations, and experience in private practice concepts. Community service is incorporated into all four years of the curriculum. A D.M.D/Ph.D. program is now available. Students accepted to the D.M.D. program can apply for admissions to the D.M.D./Ph.D. program any time prior to their eighth consecutive semester after beginning the D.M.D. degree program.

Student research opportunities: A summer research program for entering first-year students is available. Research track and research honors at graduation available.

SPECIAL PROGRAMS AND SERVICES

PREDENTAL

Summer enrichment programs: A Summer Learning Program for first- and second-year undergraduate students is available.

DURING DENTAL SCHOOL

Academic counseling and tutoring
Community service opportunities: Community service is integral to the curriculum.
Internships, externships, or extramural programs
Mentoring
Opportunity to study for credit at institution abroad
Personal counseling
Professional- and career-development programming
Training for those interested in academic careers
Transfer applicants considered if space is available

ACTIVE STUDENT ORGANIZATIONS

American Association of Dental Research Student Research Group
American Association of Pediatric Dentistry
American Association of Women Dentists
American Dental Education Association (ADEA)
American Student Dental Association
Hispanic Student Dental Association
Psi Omega Dental Fraternity
Student National Dental Association

INTERNATIONAL DENTISTS

Graduates of international dental schools considered for traditional predoctoral program: No
Advanced standing program offered for graduates of international dental schools: No
Advanced standing program description: We offer a four-year D.M.D. program and a two-year Advanced Education in General Dentistry (AEGD) certificate program for internationally educated dentists. For information, please visit www.dental.ufl.edu/Offices/Admissions/IEDP.

COMBINED AND ALTERNATE DEGREES					
Ph.D.	M.S.	M.P.H.	M.D.	B.A./B.S.	Other
—	—	—	—	—	✓

Other Degree: Honors Combined B.S./D.M.D. Program. Combined D.M.D./Ph.D Program.

COSTS: 2012-13 SCHOOL YEAR

	FIRST YEAR	SECOND YEAR	THIRD YEAR	FOURTH YEAR
Tuition, resident	$40,326	$40,326	$40,326	$40,326
Tuition, nonresident	$66,808	$66,808	$66,808	$66,808
Tuition, other				
Fees*	NA	NA	NA	NA
Instruments, books, and supplies	$10,041	$10,041	$10,041	$10,041
Estimated living expenses	$19,380	$19,380	$19,380	$19,380
Total, resident	$69,747	$69,747	$69,747	$69,747
Total, nonresident	$96,229	$96,229	$96,229	$96,229
Total, other				

*Fees are included in the tuition costs indicated.

FINANCIAL AID

There were 27 recipients of scholarships and grants in the 2011 entering class. Amounts ranged from $2,000 to $10,000. There were 79 students who received student loans ranging from $8,500 to $92,188. The average 2011 indebtedness was $150,457.

*Disclaimer: Program information is likely to change in the upcoming years. Please refer to our website for the most up-to-date information: http://dental.ufl.edu/admissions/dmd-program/.

GEORGIA REGENTS UNIVERSITY
COLLEGE OF DENTAL MEDICINE

Dr. Connie L. Drisko, Dean

GENERAL INFORMATION

Since enrolling its first class in 1969, the Georgia Regents University College of Dental Medicine has had the improvement of the oral health of the citizens of Georgia as its primary mission. The school remains committed to this goal with programs for education, research, and public service through patient care. The College of Dental Medicine is part of the Georgia Regents University, one of 34 autonomous institutions within the University System of Georgia. In addition to dentistry, the institution includes schools of allied health, graduate studies, medicine, and nursing and is adjacent to a large complex of health care facilities, providing a diverse and stimulating environment for its students on the fringe of downtown Augusta, Georgia.

MISSION STATEMENT:

The mission of the Georgia Regents University College of Dental Medicine is to educate dentists in order to improve overall health and to reduce the burden of illness in society through the discovery and application of knowledge that embraces craniofacial health and disease prevention.

Type of institution: Public
Year opened: 1969
Term type: Semester
Time to degree in months: 46
Start month: August

Doctoral dental degree offered: D.M.D.
Total predoctoral enrollment: 295
Estimated entering class size: 80
Campus setting: Urban
Campus housing available: Yes

PREPARATION

Formal minimum preparation in semester/quarter hours: Semester: 90 Quarter: 120
Baccalaureate degree preferred: Yes
Number of first-year, first-time enrollees whose highest degree is:
- Baccalaureate: 69
- Master's: 11
- Ph.D. or other doctorate: 0

Of first-year, first-time enrollees without baccalaureates, the number with:
- Equivalent of 60 undergraduate credit hours or less: 0
- Equivalent of 61-90 undergraduate credit hours: 0
- Equivalent of 91 or more undergraduate credit hours: 0

PREREQUISITE COURSE	REQUIRED	RECOMMENDED	LAB REQUIRED	CREDITS (SEMESTER/QUARTER)
BCP (biology-chemistry-physics) sciences				
Biology	✓		✓	8/12
Chemistry, general/inorganic	✓		✓	8/12
Chemistry, organic	✓		✓	8/12
Physics	✓		✓	4/6
Additional biological sciences				
Anatomy		✓		4/6
Biochemistry		✓		4/6
Cell biology		✓		3/5
Histology		✓		3/5
Immunology		✓		3/5
Microbiology		✓		3/5
Molecular biology/genetics		✓		3/5
Physiology				
Zoology				

(Prerequisite Courses continued)

CONTACT INFORMATION

www.georgiahealth.edu/dentalmedicine
1120 15th Street
Augusta, GA 30912
Phone: 706-721-2117
Fax: 706-721-6276

ADMISSIONS

Dr. Carole Hanes
Associate Dean for Students, Admissions and Alumni
1430 John Wesley Gilbert Drive
Augusta, GA 30912
Phone: 706-721-3587

FINANCIAL AID

Edith Marshall
Assistant Director of Financial Aid
1120 15th Street
Augusta, GA 30912
Phone: 706-721-4901
Email: emarshall@gru.edu
http://www.gru.edu/finaid/

STUDENT AFFAIRS

Dr. Carole Hanes
Associate Dean for Students, Admissions and Alumni
1430 John Wesley Gilbert Drive
Augusta, GA 30912
Phone: 706-721-2813

OFFICE OF STUDENT DIVERSITY

Beverly Tarver
Director of Student Diversity and International
1120 15th Street
Augusta, GA 30912
Phone: 706-721-2821

HOUSING

Dale Hartenburg
Director of Residence Life
1120 15th Street
Augusta, GA 30912
Phone: 706-721-3471
Email: tfitts@gru.edu

INTERNATIONAL STUDENTS

Beverly Tarver
Director of Student Diversity and International
1120 15th Street
Augusta, GA 30912
Phone: 706-721-2821
Email: btarver@gru.edu

PREPARATION (CONTINUED)

PREREQUISITE COURSE	REQUIRED	RECOMMENDED	LAB REQUIRED	CREDITS (SEMESTER/QUARTER)
Other				
English	✓			6/10
Drafting/Pottery		✓		3/5
Psychology		✓		3/5

Community college coursework accepted for prerequisites: Yes
Community college coursework accepted for electives: Yes
Limits on community college credit hours: Yes
Maximum number of community college credit hours: 90
Advanced placement (AP) credit accepted for prerequisites: Yes
Advanced placement (AP) credit accepted for electives: Yes
Job shadowing: Required
Number of hours of job shadowing required or recommended: At least 30 hours is recommended.
Other factors considered in admission: Leadership roles, community service, home county, and experience related to dentistry.

DAT

Mandatory: Yes
Latest DAT for consideration of application: 09/30/2013
Oldest DAT considered: 06/01/2011
When more than one DAT score is reported: Highest score is considered
Canadian DAT accepted: No
Application considered before DAT scores are submitted: Yes

DAT: 2012 ENTERING CLASS

ENROLLEE DAT SCORES	RANGE	MEAN
Academic Average	15-23	19
Perceptual Ability	15-27	20
Total Science	15-24	19

GPA: 2012 ENTERING CLASS

ENROLLEE GPA SCORES	RANGE	MEAN
Science GPA	2.76 – 4.00	3.50
Total GPA	2.69 – 4.00	3.52

APPLICATION AND SELECTION

TIMETABLE

Earliest filing date: 06/01/2013
Latest filing date: 09/30/2013
Earliest date for acceptance offers: 12/01/2013
Maximum time in days for applicant's response to acceptance offer: 30 days
Requests for deferred entrance considered: In exceptional circumstances only.
Fee for application: Yes
Amount of fee for application:
In state: $30 Out of state: $30 International: NA
Fee waiver available: No

	FIRST DEPOSIT	SECOND DEPOSIT	THIRD DEPOSIT
Required to hold place	Yes	No	No
Resident amount	$200		
Nonresident amount	$200		
Deposit due	As indicated in acceptance		
Applied to tuition	Yes		
Refundable	Yes		
Refundable by	07/01/2013		

APPLICATION PROCESS

Participates in Associated American Dental Schools Application Service (AADSAS): Yes
Accepts direct applicants: No
Secondary or supplemental application required: No, only if residency is at issue.
Interview is mandatory: Yes
Interview is by invitation: Yes

RESIDENCY

Admissions process distinguishes between in-state/in-province and out-of-state/out-of-province applicants: Yes
Preference given to residents of: Georgia
Reciprocity Admissions Agreement available for legal residents of: None
Applications are accepted from non-U.S. citizens/non-U.S. permanent residents: No

APPLICATION AND ENROLLMENT	NUMBER OF APPLICANTS	ESTIMATED NUMBER INTERVIEWED	ESTIMATED NUMBER ENROLLED
In-state or -province applicants	299	180	76
Out-of-state or -province applicants	37	12	4

Generally and over time, percentage of your first-year enrollment is in-state or in-province: 95%
Origin of out-of-state or out-of-province enrollees: South Carolina-1, Texas-1, Utah-1, Virginia-1
Origin of international enrollees: NA

DEMOGRAPHIC DESCRIPTIONS OF APPLICANTS: 2012 ENTERING CLASS

	APPLICANTS		ENROLLEES	
	M	W	M	W
Hispanic/Latino of any race	8	17	2	3
American Indian or Alaska Native	0	0	0	0
Asian	24	40	2	6
Black or African American	11	25	6	6
Native Hawaiian or Other Pacific Islander	0	0	0	0
White	119	69	34	18
Two or more races	3	3	1	1
Race and ethnicity unknown	13	4	2	1
International	0	0	0	0

	MINIMUM	MAXIMUM	MEAN
2012 entering class enrollees by age	20	37	25

Number of first-time enrollees over age 30: 12

CURRICULUM

The College of Dental Medicine awards the D.M.D. degree. The program of study consists of 11 semesters spread over approximately 45 months. Students are enrolled for eight regular semesters (fall and spring) of 15 weeks and for summer semesters of eight, 13, and 14 weeks after the first, second, and third years, respectively. Clinical and basic science courses are taught throughout the eight regular semesters, and elementary clinical treatment of patients, including restorative dentistry, begins in the second year. The placement of clinical experiences in the first year shifts some basic science courses to the third year.

Student research opportunities: Yes

SPECIAL PROGRAMS AND SERVICES

PREDENTAL

Summer Educational Enrichment Program

DURING DENTAL SCHOOL

Academic counseling and tutoring
Community service opportunities
Internships, externships, or extramural programs
Mentoring
Personal counseling
Professional- and career-development programming
Training for those interested in academic careers

ACTIVE STUDENT ORGANIZATIONS

American Association of Dental Research Student Research Group
American Association of Pediatric Dentistry
American Student Dental Association
Serving All Health Care Needs of Hispanics (SANO)
Student National Dental Association
Hispanic Student Dental Association
Give a Smile Foundation
Operation Smile

INTERNATIONAL DENTISTS

Graduates of international dental schools considered for traditional predoctoral program: No
Advanced standing program offered for graduates of international dental schools: No

COMBINED AND ALTERNATE DEGREES

Ph.D.	M.S.	M.P.H.	M.D.	B.A./B.S.	Other
✓	✓	—	—	—	—

COSTS: 2012-13 SCHOOL YEAR

	FIRST YEAR	SECOND YEAR	THIRD YEAR	FOURTH YEAR
Tuition, resident	$22,872	$22,872	$22,872	$15,248
Tuition, nonresident	$68,610	$68,610	$68,610	$45,740
Tuition, other				
Fees	$9,659	$8,671	$8,671	$6,517
Instruments, books, and supplies	$3,906	$540	$823	$825
Estimated living expenses	$24,618	$24,618	$24,618	$20,515
Total, resident	$61,055	$56,701	$56,984	$43,105
Total, nonresident	$106,793	$102,439	$102,722	$73,597
Total, other				

FINANCIAL AID

After January 1 of each year, students complete the Free Application for Federal Student Aid (FAFSA) located at www.fafsa.ed.gov. Once students have been admitted to the Georgia Regents University (GRU), their information is accessed electronically by our office via a data-load process. After February 1 of each year (and after they have been admitted), students complete the GRU Financial Aid Application, an online application accessible at www.georgiahealth.edu/students/finaid. The GRU application gives us specific, detailed information about each student, the degree he or she is seeking, his or her intention for level of enrollment, and the amount and type of funding he or she is requesting.

If the above information is received at least eight weeks prior to the start of his or her term, funds arrive and are disbursed into the student's account by their tuition due date. Any funds over and beyond what students owe for tuition and fees are refunded to them for living expenses. The process of receiving funds, disbursement, and refund of funds happens once each semester for which the student is enrolled.

In the 2011 entering class there were 40 recipients of scholarships or grants ranging from $500 to $19,614. There were 288 recipients of student loans.

MIDWESTERN UNIVERSITY
COLLEGE OF DENTAL MEDICINE-ILLINOIS

Dr. Lex MacNeil, Dean

CONTACT INFORMATION

www.midwestern.edu
555 31st Street
Downers Grove, IL 60515-1235
Phone: 630-515-7350
Fax: 630-515-7290

OFFICE OF ADMISSIONS

Office of Admissions
555 31st Street
Downers Grove, IL 60515-1235
Phone: 800-458-6253 or 630-515-7200
Fax: 630-971-6086
Email: admissil@midwestern.edu

FINANCIAL AID

Phone: 630-515-6101

STUDENT AFFAIRS

Phone: 630-515-6470

MINORITY AFFAIRS/DIVERSITY

Phone: 630-515-6470

HOUSING

Phone: 630-971-6400

GENERAL INFORMATION

At Midwestern University-Illinois, health care education is what we do. We are an established leader with an exciting vision for the future. Midwestern University-Illinois offers programs that give you solid footing in the sciences, extensive hands-on experience in outstanding clinical rotations, and a compassionate perspective toward your patients. You will learn side-by-side with students in other health professions, modeling the team approach to 21st century health care practice. And you will learn from faculty mentors who are dedicated to preparing their future colleagues for the realities of patient care. Our graduates are found in leading hospitals, private practices, laboratories, pharmacies, and health care facilities across the United States. The new College of Dental Medicine-Illinois utilizes state-of-the-art technology to provide high-quality, integrated dental education.

MISSION STATEMENT:

The Midwestern University College of Dental Medicine–Illinois is dedicated to the education of dentists who will demonstrate excellence in comprehensive oral health care and the discovery and dissemination of knowledge.

Type of institution: Private
Year opened: 2011
Term type: Quarter
Time to degree in months: 46
Start month: August
Doctoral dental degree offered: D.M.D.
Total predoctoral enrollment: 500 when fully enrolled
Estimated entering class size: 125
Campus setting: Suburban
Campus housing available: Yes

PREPARATION

Formal minimum preparation in semester/quarter hours: Semester: 120 Quarter: 180
Baccalaureate degree preferred: Yes. Bachelor's degree required.
Number of first-year, first-time enrollees whose highest degree is:
- Baccalaureate: 115
- Master's: 16
- Ph.D. or other doctorate: 0

Of first-year, first-time enrollees without baccalaureates, the number with:
- Equivalent of 60 undergraduate credit hours or less: 0
- Equivalent of 61-90 undergraduate credit hours: 0
- Equivalent of 91 or more undergraduate credit hours: 0

PREREQUISITE COURSE	REQUIRED	RECOMMENDED	LAB REQUIRED	CREDITS (SEMESTER/QUARTER)
BCP (biology-chemistry-physics) sciences				
Biology	✓	✓	✓	8/12
Chemistry, general/inorganic	✓	✓	✓	8/12
Chemistry, organic	✓	✓	✓	4/6
Physics	✓	✓	✓	8/12
Additional biological sciences				
Anatomy	✓		✓	3/4
Biochemistry	✓			2/3
Cell biology				
Histology		✓		
Immunology		✓		
Microbiology	✓		✓	3/4
Molecular biology/genetics		✓		

(Prerequisite Courses continued)

PREPARATION (CONTINUED)

PREREQUISITE COURSE	REQUIRED	RECOMMENDED	LAB REQUIRED	CREDITS (SEMESTER/QUARTER)
Physiology	✓			3/4
Zoology		✓		
Other				
English composition/ technical writing	✓			6/9

Community college coursework accepted for prerequisites: Yes
Community college coursework accepted for electives: Yes
Limits on community college credit hours: No
Maximum number of community college credit hours: Not specified
Advanced placement (AP) credit accepted for prerequisites: Yes
Advanced placement (AP) credit accepted for electives: Yes
Comments regarding AP credit: Reviewed by Admissions Office
Job shadowing: Recommended
Number of hours of job shadowing required or recommended: Not specified
Other factors considered in admission: Demonstration of a sincere understanding of, and interest in, the humanitarian ethos of health care and, particularly, dental medicine

DAT

Mandatory: Yes
Latest DAT for consideration of application: 12/01/2013
Oldest DAT considered: 01/01/2011
When more than one DAT score is reported: Most recent score is considered
Canadian DAT accepted: Yes
Application considered before DAT scores are submitted: No

DAT: 2012 ENTERING CLASS

ENROLLEE DAT SCORES	RANGE	MEAN
Academic Average	16-23	19
Perceptual Ability	15-25	20
Total Science	15-24	18

GPA: 2012 ENTERING CLASS

ENROLLEE GPA SCORES	RANGE	MEAN
Science GPA	2.76-3.86	3.30
Total GPA	2.97-3.9	3.44

APPLICATION AND SELECTION

TIMETABLE

Earliest filing date: 06/01/2013
Latest filing date: 01/01/2014
Earliest date for acceptance offers: 12/01/2013
Maximum time in days for applicant's response to acceptance offer:
30 days if accepted on or after December 1
15 days if accepted on or after February 1
Requests for deferred entrance considered: In exceptional circumstances
Fee for application: Yes, submit only when requested
Amount of fee for application:
In state: $50 Out of state: $50 International: $50
Fee waiver available: No

	FIRST DEPOSIT	SECOND DEPOSIT	THIRD DEPOSIT
Required to hold place	Yes	No	NO
Resident amount	$1,000		
Nonresident amount	$1,000		
Deposit due	NR		
Applied to tuition	Yes		
Refundable	Partially		
Refundable by	NR		

APPLICATION PROCESS

Participates in Associated American Dental Schools Application Service (AADSAS): Yes
Accepts direct applicants: No
Secondary or supplemental application required: Yes
Secondary or supplemental application website: Sent from Office of Admissions if qualified
Interview is mandatory: Yes
Interview is by invitation: Yes

RESIDENCY

Admissions process distinguishes between in-state/in-province and out-of-state/out-of-province applicants: No
Preference given to residents of: None
Reciprocity Admissions Agreement available for legal residents of: None
Applications are accepted from non-U.S. citizens/non-U.S. permanent residents: Yes

APPLICATION AND ENROLLMENT	NUMBER OF APPLICANTS	ESTIMATED NUMBER INTERVIEWED	ESTIMATED NUMBER ENROLLED
In-state or province applicants	381	111	47
Out-of-state or province applicants	2,039	295	83

Generally and over time, percentage of your first-year enrollment is in-state: 35-40 %
Origin of out-of-state enrollees (U.S.): Arkansas-1, Arizona-4, California-10, Colorado-1, Florida-2, Georgia-3, Idaho-2, Indiana-7, Iowa-2, Kansas-2, Louisiana-1, Maine-1, Massachusetts-2, Michigan-5, Minnesota-3, Missouri-1, Nebraska-1, New Jersey-2, New York-2, North Carolina-1, Ohio-4, Oklahoma-1, Pennsylvania-3, South Carolina-1, South Dakota-1, Texas-8, Virginia-2, Washington-2, Wisconsin-8
Origin of international enrollees: NA

DEMOGRAPHIC DESCRIPTIONS OF APPLICANTS: 2012 ENTERING CLASS

	APPLICANTS		ENROLLEES	
	M	W	M	W
Hispanic/Latino of any race	37	46	4	2
American Indian or Alaska Native	1	0	0	0
Asian	374	338	15	13
Black or African American	25	19	1	0
Native Hawaiian or Other Pacific Islander	3	6	0	0
White	637	454	53	40
Two or more races	28	19	0	1
Race and ethnicity unknown	203	205	1	0
International	0	0	0	0

Note: Twenty-five applicants did not specify a gender

	MINIMUM	MAXIMUM	MEAN
2012 entering class enrollees by age	20	37	24

Number of first-time enrollees over age 30: 5

CURRICULUM

The Midwestern University College of Dental Medicine-Illinois provides an integrated, clinically based, interactive learning environment that incorporates the clinical, behavioral, and basic sciences. In the fourth year of the program students will spend approximately 10% of their time in community health situations.

Student research opportunities: Yes

SPECIAL PROGRAMS AND SERVICES

DURING DENTAL SCHOOL

Academic counseling and tutoring
Community service opportunities
Internships, externships, and extramural programs
Mentoring
Personal counseling
Professional- and career-development programming
Training for those interested in academic careers

ACTIVE STUDENT ORGANIZATIONS

American Association of Dental Research Student Research Group
American Association of Pediatric Dentistry
American Association of Women Dentists
American Dental Education Association (ADEA)
American Student Dental Association
Hispanic Dental Association
Student National Dental Association

INTERNATIONAL DENTISTS

Graduates of international dental schools considered for traditional predoctoral program: Yes
Advanced standing program offered for graduates of international dental schools: No

COMBINED AND ALTERNATE DEGREES

Ph.D.	M.S.	M.P.H.	M.D.	B.A./B.S.	Other
—	✓	—	—	—	✓

Other: D.M.D./Master's in Biomedical Science

COSTS: 2012-13 SCHOOL YEAR

	FIRST YEAR	SECOND YEAR	THIRD YEAR	FOURTH YEAR
Tuition, resident	$60,774	$60,774	NR	NR
Tuition, nonresident	$60,774	$60,774	NR	NR
Tuition, other	NA	NA	NR	NR
Fees	$12,489	$10,414	NR	NR
Instruments, books, and supplies	$5,096	$5,096	NR	NR
Estimated living expenses	$9,420	$9,420	NR	NR
Total, on campus	$97,908	$95,833	NR	NR
Total, off campus	$103,312	$101,237	NR	NR
Total, with parents	$91,387	$89,312	NR	NR

FINANCIAL AID

The Office of Student Financial Services at Midwestern University-Illinois offers a convenient five-step online application process to all financial aid applicants.

FOR NEWLY ACCEPTED STUDENTS:

Once you have been accepted, the Office of Admissions will send you your matriculation agreement and access to the online site to make your matriculation deposit. When your first deposit is received, we will give you access to the online site. Our office will also send you a message through your Midwestern University-Illinois email account with brief instructions for the online financial aid application process. After you complete the online application process, the Office of Student Financial Services will take the following steps to finish the financial aid process:

The Office of Student Financial Services begins the financial aid award process using a priority system we call "packaging." The process commences with the consideration of gift assistance, student loans, and work study. When the packaging process has been completed, prior to the beginning of the award year, we send an award letter electronically to each student via the university email system. The award letter provides the following information: (1) It lists the maximum amount of aid from each federal, state, and institutional program the student may receive, and (2) it indicates the approximate amount of funds the student will receive each quarter.

Financial aid funds generally are sent from the lender or sponsor directly to the University Accounts Receivable Office by check or by electronic funds transfer (EFT). Checks are held for student endorsement and then credited to the student's tuition account one week after the beginning of each quarter. A portion of the proceeds of each financial aid program will arrive at the university each quarter. Any excess funds are refunded to the student in the form of a check or direct deposit.

The financial aid deadline date for first-year students is in mid-April 2013. Additional information can be found on our website at www.midwestern.edu.

SOUTHERN ILLINOIS UNIVERSITY
SCHOOL OF DENTAL MEDICINE

Dr. Bruce E. Rotter, Dean

GENERAL INFORMATION

Southern Illinois University (SIU), a state-supported institution, established the School of Dental Medicine (SDM) in 1969. The dental school is located on the campus of the former Shurtleff College in Alton, 15 miles from the Edwardsville campus. Situated within the metropolitan St. Louis area, SIU-SDM offers the social and cultural attractions of an urban environment while it identifies with predominantly rural southern Illinois. This unique circumstance enables SDM students to apply their knowledge and skills in the treatment of the broadest spectrum of oral health care needs.

MISSION STATEMENT:

The mission of the Southern Illinois University School of Dental Medicine is to improve the oral health of the region through education and patient care, in conjunction with scholarship/research and service.

Type of institution: Public
Year opened: 1972
Term type: Semester
Time to degree in months: 44
Start month: August

Doctoral dental degree offered: D.M.D.
Total predoctoral enrollment: 198
Estimated entering class size: 51
Campus setting: Suburban
Campus housing available: No

PREPARATION

Formal minimum preparation in semester/quarter hours: Semester: 90 Quarter: 120
Baccalaureate degree preferred: Yes
Number of first-year, first-time enrollees whose highest degree is:
- Baccalaureate: 42
- Master's: 1
- Ph.D. or other doctorate: 0

Of first-year, first-time enrollees without baccalaureates, the number with:
- Equivalent of 60 undergraduate credit hours or less: 0
- Equivalent of 61-90 undergraduate credit hours: 0
- Equivalent of 91 or more undergraduate credit hours: 8

PREREQUISITE COURSE	REQUIRED	RECOMMENDED	LAB REQUIRED	CREDITS (SEMESTER/QUARTER)
BCP (biology-chemistry-physics) sciences				
Biology	✓		✓	8/12
Chemistry, general/inorganic	✓		✓	8/12
Chemistry, organic	✓		✓	8/12
Physics	✓		✓	6/9
Additional biological sciences				
Anatomy		✓		3/5
Biochemistry	✓			3/5
Cell biology		✓		3/5
Histology		✓		3/5
Immunology		✓		3/5
Microbiology		✓		3/5
Molecular biology/genetics		✓		3/5
Physiology		✓		3/5
Zoology		✓		3/5

(Prerequisite Courses continued)

CONTACT INFORMATION

www.siue.edu/dentalmedicine
2800 College Avenue
Alton, IL 62002
Phone: 618-474-7120
Fax: 618-474-7249

ADMISSIONS OFFICE

2800 College Avenue
Building 273
Room 2300
Alton, IL 62002
Phone: 618-474-7170

FINANCIAL AID

2800 College Avenue
Alton, IL 62002
Phone: 618-474-7175
www.siue.edu/dentalmedicine

STUDENT SERVICES

Phone: 618-474-7170

MINORITY SERVICES/DIVERSITY

2800 College Ave
Alton, IL 62002
Phone: 618-474-7170
www.siue.edu/dentalmedicine

HOUSING

Phone: 618-474-7170

PREPARATION (CONTINUED)

PREREQUISITE COURSE	REQUIRED	RECOMMENDED	LAB REQUIRED	CREDITS (SEMESTER/QUARTER)
Other				
English	✓			6/9
Statistics		✓		3/5

Community college coursework accepted for prerequisites: Yes
Community college coursework accepted for electives: Yes
Limits on community college credit hours: Yes
Maximum number of community college credit hours: 60
Advanced placement (AP) credit accepted for prerequisites: No
Advanced placement (AP) credit accepted for electives: Yes
Comments regarding AP credit: None
Job shadowing: Recommended
Number of hours of job shadowing required or recommended: 30

DAT

Mandatory: Yes
Latest DAT for consideration of application: 04/01/2014
Oldest DAT considered: 08/01/2011
When more than one DAT score is reported: Most recent score only is considered
Canadian DAT accepted: Yes
Application considered before DAT scores are submitted: No

DAT: 2012 ENTERING CLASS

ENROLLEE DAT SCORES	RANGE	MEAN
Academic Average	17-24	19.4
Perceptual Ability	16-26	19.7
Total Science	16-25	19.0

GPA: 2012 ENTERING CLASS

ENROLLEE GPA SCORES	RANGE	MEAN
Science GPA	2.66-4.00	3.52
Total GPA	2.96-4.00	3.64

APPLICATION AND SELECTION

TIMETABLE

Earliest filing date: 06/01/2013
Latest filing date: 02/01/2014
Earliest date for acceptance offers: 12/01/2013
Maximum time in days for applicant's response to acceptance offer:
30 days if accepted on or after December 1
15 days if accepted on or after February 1
Requests for deferred entrance considered: No
Fee for application: Yes, submitted at same time as AADSAS application
Amount of fee for application:
In state: $20 Out of state: $20 International: NA
Fee waiver available: No

	FIRST DEPOSIT	SECOND DEPOSIT	THIRD DEPOSIT
Required to hold place	Yes	No	No
Resident amount	$300		
Nonresident amount	$300		
Deposit due	As indicated in admission offer		
Applied to tuition	Yes		
Refundable	No		

APPLICATION PROCESS

Participates in Associated American Dental Schools Application Service (AADSAS): Yes
Accepts direct applicants: No
Secondary or supplemental application required: Yes
Secondary or supplemental application website: www.siue.edu/dentalmedicine/prospective/app_process.shtml
Interview is mandatory: Yes
Interview is by invitation: Yes

RESIDENCY

Admissions process distinguishes between in-state/in-province and out-of-state/out-of-province applicants: Yes
Preference given to residents of: Illinois
Reciprocity Admissions Agreement available for legal residents of: None
Applications are accepted from non-U.S. citizens/non-U.S. permanent residents: No

APPLICATION AND ENROLLMENT	NUMBER OF APPLICANTS	ESTIMATED NUMBER INTERVIEWED	ESTIMATED NUMBER ENROLLED
In-state or province applicants	327	103	51
Out-of-state or province applicants	235	5	0

Generally and over time, percentage of your first-year enrollment is in-state: 100%
Origin of out-of-state enrollees (U.S.): NA
Origin of international enrollees: NA

DEMOGRAPHIC DESCRIPTIONS OF APPLICANTS: 2012 ENTERING CLASS

	APPLICANTS		ENROLLEES	
	M	W	M	W
Hispanic/Latino of any race	5	4	1	1
American Indian or Alaska Native	0	1	0	0
Asian	77	82	4	2
Black or African American	14	20	0	0
Native Hawaiian or Other Pacific Islander	0	0	0	0
White	159	142	25	17
Two or more races	13	28	0	0
Race and ethnicity unknown	7	10	1	0
International	0	0	0	0

	MINIMUM	MAXIMUM	MEAN
2012 entering class enrollees by age	20	37	23

Number of first-time enrollees over age 30: 1

CURRICULUM

The School of Dental Medicine's curriculum develops the critical thinking and intellectual curiosity necessary for its students to maintain a state of continuous self-improvement. The program is divided into four academic years consisting of biomedical sciences, clinical sciences, and behavioral sciences, as well as study and consultation time.

Student research opportunities: Yes

SPECIAL PROGRAMS AND SERVICES

DURING DENTAL SCHOOL

Academic counseling and tutoring
Community service opportunities
Personal counseling
Research opportunities

ACTIVE STUDENT ORGANIZATIONS

American Dental Education Association (ADEA)
American Student Dental Association
Illinois State Dental Society

INTERNATIONAL DENTISTS

Graduates of international dental schools considered for traditional predoctoral program: No
Advanced standing program offered for graduates of international dental schools: No
Advanced standing program description: NA

COMBINED AND ALTERNATE DEGREES

Ph.D.	M.S.	M.P.H.	M.D.	B.A./B.S.	Other
—	—	—	—	—	—

COSTS: 2012-13 SCHOOL YEAR

	FIRST YEAR	SECOND YEAR	THIRD YEAR	FOURTH YEAR
Tuition, resident	$27,720	$33,880	$33,880	$27,720
Tuition, nonresident	$83,160	$101,640	$101,640	$83,160
Tuition, other				
Fees	$4,989	$6,349	$6,349	$4,989
Instruments, books, and supplies	$8,089	$7,781	$2,164	$3,661
Estimated living expense	$15,500	$15,500	$15,500	$15,500
Total, resident	$56,298	$63,510	$57,893	$51,870
Total, nonresident	$111,738	$131,270	$125,653	$107,310
Total, other				

FINANCIAL AID

In the 2011 entering class, there were 9 recipients of scholarships and tuition waivers and 46 recipients of student loans. Scholarship and waiver awards ranged between $500 and $18,309, with an average of $10,870. Students received loan amounts between $500 and $52,262, with the average student borrowing $51,360.

The average 2012 graduate indebtedness was $149,491.

UIC College of Dentistry

UNIVERSITY OF ILLINOIS AT CHICAGO
COLLEGE OF DENTISTRY

Dr. Bruce S. Graham, Dean

GENERAL INFORMATION

Located on the urban academic health center campus of the University of Illinois at Chicago, in the home city of organized dentistry, the UIC College of Dentistry collaborates with America's largest medical college and nationally recognized colleges of Nursing, Pharmacy, Engineering, and Public Health. With a faculty dedicated to excellence and innovation in education and research, and the strong support of the University of Illinois, the College of Dentistry is preparing its graduates for leadership roles in every aspect of their chosen profession. The UIC College of Dentistry also offers advanced dental education programs in Endodontics, Oral and Maxillofacial Surgery, Orthodontics, Pediatric Dentistry, Periodontics, and Prosthodontics. Programs leading to the M.S. and Ph. D. degrees are also available through the Graduate College.

MISSION STATEMENT:

The mission of the UIC College of Dentistry is to promote optimum oral and general health to the people of the state of Illinois and worldwide through excellence in education, patient care, research, and service. The college identifies the following goals to meet this mission: to prepare highly qualified health care professionals, educators, and scientists in the basic and oral health sciences; to provide patient-centered care that is comprehensive and compassionate for a culturally diverse population; to provide student-oriented education programs that prepare individuals for the thoughtful, ethical practice of dentistry and lifelong learning; to foster collaborative research and develop specialized centers for innovated research in areas of health and disease; to address community and regional health care needs through outreach initiatives, educational programs, and consultative and referral services.

Type of institution: Public
Year opened: 1891
Term type: Semester
Time to degree in months: 44
Start month: August

Doctoral dental degree offered: D.M.D.
Total predoctoral enrollment: 271
Estimated entering class size: 55
Campus setting: Urban
Campus housing available: Yes

PREPARATION

Formal minimum preparation in semester/quarter hours: UIC requires that applicants have a minimum of a bachelor's degree conferred no later than June of the matriculation year from a United States institution.

Number of first-year, first-time enrollees whose highest degree is:
- Baccalaureate: 63
- Master's: 5
- Ph.D. or other doctorate: 0

PREREQUISITE COURSE	REQUIRED	RECOMMENDED	LAB REQUIRED	CREDITS (SEMESTER/QUARTER)
BCP (biology-chemistry-physics) sciences				
Biology	✓		✓	6/10
Chemistry, general/inorganic	✓		✓	10/16
Chemistry, organic	✓		✓	4/6
Physics	✓		✓	6/10
Additional biological sciences				
Anatomy*		✓		
Biochemistry*		✓		
Cell biology		✓		
Genetics		✓		

(Prerequisite Courses continued)

CONTACT INFORMATION

http://dentistry.uic.edu
801 South Paulina Street, MC 621
Chicago, IL 60612
Phone: 312-996-1020
Fax: 312-413-9050

OFFICE OF STUDENT & DIVERSITY

Dr. Darryl D. Pendleton
Associate Dean for Student and Diversity Affairs
801 South Paulina Street, MC 621
Chicago, IL 60612
Phone: 312-355-1670
http://dentistry.uic.edu

Millie Mendez
Director of Student Services
801 S. Paulina Street, MC 621
Chicago, IL 60612
Phone: 312-413-1209
http://dentistry.uic.edu

OFFICE OF ADMISSIONS

Braulia Espinosa
Assistant Director of Admissions
801 South Paulina Street, MC 621
Chicago, IL 60612
Phone: 312-355-0320
http://dentistry.uic.edu

Carolyn Feller
Assistant Director of Admissions
801 South Paulina Street, MC 621
Chicago, IL 60612
Phone: 312-996-2873
http://dentistry.uic.edu

OFFICE OF STUDENT FINANCIAL AID

1800 Student Services Building
1200 West Harrison, MC 334
Chicago, IL 60612
Phone: 312-996-3126
www.uic.edu/depts/financialaid

CAMPUS HOUSING

Campus Housing
818 South Wolcott Street, MC 579
Chicago, IL 60612
Phone: 312-355-6300
www.housing.uic.edu

PREPARATION (CONTINUED)

PREREQUISITE COURSE	REQUIRED	RECOMMENDED	LAB REQUIRED	CREDITS (SEMESTER/QUARTER)
Histology		✓		
Immunology		✓		
Microbiology*		✓		
Molecular biology/genetics		✓		
Physiology*		✓		
Other				
English	✓			6/10

*STRONGLY RECOMMENDED

Disclaimer: Please continue to check the UIC College of Dentistry website for any updates or changes to school requirements.

Community college coursework accepted for prerequisites: Yes
Community college coursework accepted for electives: Yes
Limits on community college credit hours: No
Maximum number of community college credit hours: None
Advanced placement (AP) credit accepted for prerequisites: No
Advanced placement (AP) credit accepted for electives: Yes
Job shadowing: Recommended
Number of hours of job shadowing required or recommended: 100

DAT

Mandatory: Yes
Latest DAT for consideration of application: 12/01/2013
Oldest DAT considered: 01/01/2012
When more than one DAT score is reported: Highest score is considered
Canadian DAT accepted: No
Application considered before DAT scores are submitted: No

DAT: 2012 ENTERING CLASS

ENROLLEE DAT SCORES	RANGE	MEAN
Academic Average	13-23	20
Perceptual Ability	12-27	20
Total Science	13-24	20

GPA: 2012 ENTERING CLASS

ENROLLEE GPA SCORES	RANGE	MEAN
Science GPA	2.95 – 4.28	3.5
Total GPA	3.10 – 4.29	3.6

APPLICATION AND SELECTION

TIMETABLE

Earliest filing date: 06/01/2013
Latest filing date: 12/01/2013
Earliest date for acceptance offers: 12/01/2013
Maximum time in days for applicant's response to acceptance offer:
30 days if accepted on or after December 1
15 days if accepted on or after February 1
Requests for deferred entrance considered: In exceptional circumstances only
Fee for application: Yes, submitted only when requested
Amount of fee for application:
In state: $85 Out of state: $85 International: NA
Fee waiver available: No

	FIRST DEPOSIT	SECOND DEPOSIT	THIRD DEPOSIT
Required to hold place	Yes	No	No
Resident amount	$300		
Nonresident amount	$1,500		
Deposit due	As indicated in admission offer		
Applied to tuition	Yes		
Refundable	No		

APPLICATION PROCESS

Participates in Associated American Dental Schools Application Service (AADSAS): Yes. Letters of recommendation are accepted electronically via AADSAS only.
Accepts direct applicants: No
Secondary or supplemental application required: No
Interview is mandatory: Yes
Interview is by invitation: Yes

RESIDENCY

Effective June 1, 2013, the University of Illinois at Chicago (UIC) College of Dentistry (COD) will be unable to accept applications for the D.M.D. program from out-of-state candidates. UIC COD will only accept and process applications from in-state candidates.
Admissions process distinguishes between in-state/in-province and out-of-state/out-of-province applicants: Yes
Preference given to residents of: Illinois
Reciprocity Admissions Agreement available for legal residents of: None
Applications are accepted from non-U.S. citizens/non-U.S. permanent residents: No

APPLICATION AND ENROLLMENT	NUMBER OF APPLICANTS	ESTIMATED NUMBER INTERVIEWED	ESTIMATED NUMBER ENROLLED
In-state or province applicants	459	173	62
Out-of-state or province applicants	1,181	31	6

Generally and over time, percentage of your first-year enrollment is in-state: 91%
Origin of out-of-state enrollees (U.S.): California-1, Florida-1, Indiana-1, Michigan-1, Missouri-1, Wisconsin-1
Origin of international enrollees: NA

DEMOGRAPHIC DESCRIPTIONS OF APPLICANTS: 2012 ENTERING CLASS

	APPLICANTS		ENROLLEES	
	M	W	M	W
Hispanic/Latino of any race	13	26	1	5
American Indian or Alaska Native	1	2	0	0
Asian	229	275	8	16
Black or African American	36	49	3	1
Native Hawaiian or Other Pacific Islander	0	0	0	0
White	436	402	24	10
Two or more races	45	61	0	0
Race and ethnicity unknown	23	27	0	0
International	0	0	0	0

Note: 14 applications did not report gender. Due to individual school reporting procedures, sum of applicants by race/ethnicity may not total applicants by residency.

	MINIMUM	MAXIMUM	MEAN
2012 entering class enrollees by age	20	35	23

Number of first-time enrollees over age 30: 4

CURRICULUM

The UIC College of Dentistry curriculum, supported by innovative information technologies, provides an interdisciplinary, collaborative learning environment in which students achieve the competencies for oral health care in the context of patient management for the 21st century. The curriculum features small-group and independent learning, combined with experiential laboratory activities in biomedical, clinical, and behavioral sciences, and extensive time in community clinical experiences. Biomedical, clinical, and behavioral education all span the entire four years of the curriculum, from the first week of the D1 year until graduation. The college prides itself on its student and faculty culture of collegiality, intellectual rigor, high standards of competence and ethical behavior, commitment to improve access to care, and service to diverse communities.

Student research opportunities: Yes

SPECIAL PROGRAMS AND SERVICES

PREDENTAL

DAT workshops
Illinois Predental Consortium
Postbaccalaureate programs
Summer enrichment programs

DURING DENTAL SCHOOL

Academic counseling and tutoring
Community service opportunities
Internships, externships, or extramural programs
Mentoring
Personal counseling
Professional- and career-development programming
Training for those interested in academic careers

ACTIVE STUDENT ORGANIZATIONS

Alpha Omega
American Association of Pediatric Dentistry
American Association of Public Health
American Association of Women Dentists
American Dental Education Association (ADEA)
American Student Dental Association
Association of Muslim Dental Students
Christian Medical and Dental Association
Chinese American Student Dental Association
Dental Student Council
Hispanic Dental Association
Illinois Academy of General Dentistry
Korean American Student Dental Association
Middle Eastern Dental Student Association
Student National Dental Association
Student Research Group

INTERNATIONAL DENTISTS

Graduates of international dental schools considered for traditional predoctoral program: No
Advanced standing program offered for graduates of international dental schools: Yes
Advanced standing program description: Program awarding a dental degree

COMBINED AND ALTERNATE DEGREES

Ph.D.	M.S.	M.P.H.	M.D.	B.A./B.S.	Other
✓	✓	—	—	—	—

COSTS: 2012-13 SCHOOL YEAR

	FIRST YEAR	SECOND YEAR	THIRD YEAR	FOURTH YEAR
Tuition, resident	$29,360	$44,040	$44,040	$44,040
Tuition, nonresident	$53,898	$80,847	$80,847	$80,847
Tuition, other	$6,906	$10,359	$10,359	$9,870
Fees	$3,700	$4,867	$4,867	$4,867
Instruments, books, and supplies	$2,000	$2,000	$2,000	$2,000
Estimated living expenses	$20,000	$20,000	$20,000	$20,000
Total, resident	$61,966	$81,266	$81,266	$80,777
Total, nonresident	$86,504	$118,073	$118,073	$117,584
Total, other				

Comments: Fees include clinic education fee. Loupes are not included.

FINANCIAL AID

Although the cost of an education at the UIC is moderate, it is still beyond the financial resources of many students and their families. The UIC Office of Student Financial Aid provides a wide range of financial services designed to help students and their families meet the cost of attending the university. Financial aid is available for those students who need assistance with their education-related expenses (i.e., tuition, fees, books, supplies, childcare, rental, and miscellaneous expenses). To be considered for various types of aid, students must complete the Free Application for Federal Student Aid (FAFSA) application.

INDIANA UNIVERSITY
SCHOOL OF DENTISTRY

Dr. John N. Williams, Dean

GENERAL INFORMATION

The School of Dentistry is an integral part of Indiana University's Medical Center in Indianapolis, which includes a medical school, a school of nursing, and a complex of hospitals with a total of over 600 beds. Clinical facilities are excellent, and patients are drawn from a population area of more than one million persons. The school maintains dental clinics in the Riley Hospital for Children at Indiana University (IU) Health, the Regenstrief Institute, and the IU Health University Hospital on the Medical Center campus. The School of Dentistry was established as a private school in 1879 and has been a part of Indiana University since 1925. Approximately 100 students are accepted for each freshman class. Graduate students are candidates for either M.S. or M.S.D. degrees in most departments in the dental school; a limited number of Ph.D. programs are offered as well as dental auxiliary programs in dental hygiene and dental assisting. A dual D.D.S./M.P.H. option is available.

MISSION STATEMENT:

Indiana University School of Dentistry (IUSD) strives to promote optimal oral and general health of Indiana's citizens and others through educational, research, patient-care, and service programs. The IUSD Indiana Model of Dental Education program prepares students to become competent, critically thinking, ethical, and socially responsible practitioners who become outstanding practitioners and who demand career-long learning through continuing education. The IUSD Research Program strives to increase the knowledge base in all areas related to oral health. Patient care at IUSD provides a broad spectrum of high-quality patient services for reasonable fees to furnish clinical educational opportunities for students and to maintain a clinical education system that simulates as closely as possible a contemporary, high-quality practice of general dentistry. Service at IUSD interacts with the community through school-based outreach services and health-education programs.

Type of institution: Public
Year opened: 1879
Term type: Semester
Time to degree in months: 48
Start month: July

Doctoral dental degree offered: D.D.S.
Total predoctoral enrollment: 400
Estimated entering class size: 100
Campus setting: Urban
Campus housing available: Yes

PREPARATION

Formal minimum preparation in semester/quarter hours: Semester: 90 Quarter: 135
Baccalaureate degree preferred: Yes; preferred but not required
Number of first-year, first-time enrollees whose highest degree is:
- Baccalaureate: 79
- Master's: 17
- Ph.D. or other doctorate: 0

Of first-year, first-time enrollees without baccalaureates, the number with:
- Equivalent of 60 undergraduate credit hours or less: 0
- Equivalent of 61-90 undergraduate credit hours: 0
- Equivalent of 91 or more undergraduate credit hours: 7

PREREQUISITE COURSE	REQUIRED	RECOMMENDED	LAB REQUIRED	CREDITS (SEMESTER/QUARTER)
BCP (biology-chemistry-physics) sciences				
Biology	✓		✓	8/12
Chemistry, general/inorganic	✓		✓	8/12
Chemistry, organic	✓		✓	4/6
Physics	✓		✓	8/12
Additional biological sciences				
Anatomy	✓		✓	4/6
Biochemistry	✓			3/5
Cell biology		✓		

(Prerequisite Courses continued)

CONTACT INFORMATION

www.iusd.iupui.edu
1121 West Michigan Street
Indianapolis, IN 46202
Phone: 317-274-8173
Fax: 317-278-9066

RECORDS & ADMISSIONS OFFICE
Dr. Melanie Peterson
Assistant Dean of Admissions and Student Affairs
1121 West Michigan Street
Indianapolis, IN 46202
Phone: 317-274-5117
www.iusd.iupui.edu/prospective-students

OFFICE OF STUDENT FINANCIAL AID
Jennifer Vines
Assistant Director of Financial Aid
1121 West Michigan Street
DS 125A
Indianapolis, IN 46202
Phone: 317-278-1549

STUDENT AFFAIRS
1121 West Michigan Street
Indianapolis, IN 46202
Phone: 317-274-5117
Email: rkasberg@iupui.edu

DIVERSITY OFFICE
Dr. Pamella P. Shaw
Associate Dean for Diversity, Equity, and Inclusion
1121 West Michigan Street
Indianapolis, IN 46202-5186
Phone: 317-274-6573
Fax: 317-278-9066
Email: ppshaw@iupui.edu

HOUSING
Hayward Guenard
Director of Housing and Residence Life
405 Porto Alegre Street
Indianapolis, IN 46202
Phone: 317-274-7457
www.life.iupui.edu/housing

INTERNATIONAL STUDENTS
Office of International Affairs
902 West New York Street
ES 2126
Indianapolis, IN 46202
Phone: 317-274-7000

PREPARATION (CONTINUED)

PREREQUISITE COURSE	REQUIRED	RECOMMENDED	LAB REQUIRED	CREDITS (SEMESTER/QUARTER)
Histology		✓		
Immunology		✓		
Microbiology		✓		
Molecular biology/genetics		✓		
Physiology	✓			3/5
Zoology				
Other				
English composition	✓			3/5
Psychology	✓			3/5
Spanish		✓		
Social science		✓		
Humanities		✓		

Community college coursework accepted for prerequisites: Yes; prefer science prerequisites from four-year colleges
Community college coursework accepted for electives: Yes
Limits on community college credit hours: Yes; science classes should be from a four-year college.
Maximum number of community college credit hours: 60
Advanced placement (AP) credit accepted for prerequisites: No
Advanced placement (AP) credit accepted for electives: Yes
Job shadowing: Required
Number of hours of job shadowing required or recommended: 40—must shadow general practice dentists in private practice settings
Other factors considered in admission: Community service, campus involvement, volunteerism, communication skills, and manual dexterity skills

DAT

Mandatory: Yes
Latest DAT for consideration of application: 01/15/2013
Oldest DAT considered: 12/31/2008
When more than one DAT score is reported: Most recent score only is considered
Canadian DAT accepted: Yes
Application considered before DAT scores are submitted: No

DAT: 2012 ENTERING CLASS

ENROLLEE DAT SCORES	RANGE	MEAN
Academic Average	14-25	19
Perceptual Ability	14-25	19
Total Science	15-26	19

GPA: 2012 ENTERING CLASS

ENROLLEE GPA SCORES	RANGE	MEAN
Science GPA	2.13 – 4.17	3.42
Total GPA	2.41 – 4.16	3.50

APPLICATION AND SELECTION

TIMETABLE

Earliest filing date: 06/01/2013
Latest filing date: 11/01/2013
Earliest date for acceptance offers: 12/01/2013
Maximum time in days for applicant's response to acceptance offer:
30 days if accepted on or after December 1
15 days if accepted on or after February 1
Requests for deferred entrance considered: In exceptional circumstances only
Fee for application: Yes
Amount of fee for application:
In state: $50 Out of state: $50 International: $60
Fee waiver available: No

	FIRST DEPOSIT	SECOND DEPOSIT	THIRD DEPOSIT
Required to hold place	Yes	No	No
Resident amount	$1,000		
Nonresident amount	$1,000		
Deposit due	As indicated in admission offer		
Applied to tuition	Yes		
Refundable	No		

APPLICATION PROCESS

Participates in Associated American Dental Schools Application Service (AADSAS): Yes
Accepts direct applicants: No
Secondary or supplemental application required: Yes
Interview is mandatory: Yes
Interview is by invitation: Yes

RESIDENCY

Admissions process distinguishes between in-state/in-province and out-of-state/out-of-province applicants: Yes
Preference given to residents of: None
Reciprocity Admissions Agreement available for legal residents of: None

Applications are accepted from non-U.S. citizens/non-U.S. permanent residents: Yes

APPLICATION AND ENROLLMENT	NUMBER OF APPLICANTS	ESTIMATED NUMBER INTERVIEWED	ESTIMATED NUMBER ENROLLED
In-state or province applicants	233	164	77
Out-of-state or province applicants	1,429	202	27

Generally and over time, percentage of your first-year enrollment is in-state: 70%

Origin of out-of-state enrollees (U.S.): Arizona-1, California-1, Florida-3, Georgia-2, Illinois-8, Michigan-2, Minnesota-1, New York-1, Ohio-1, Tennessee-1, Texas-1

Origin of international enrollees: Canada-5

DEMOGRAPHIC DESCRIPTIONS OF APPLICANTS: 2012 ENTERING CLASS

	APPLICANTS		ENROLLEES	
	M	W	M	W
Hispanic/Latino of any race	33	33	0	2
American Indian or Alaska Native	9	7	0	0
Asian	258	248	3	8
Black or African American	23	39	4	4
Native Hawaiian or Other Pacific Islander	1	5	0	0
White	543	389	32	42
Two or more races	47	49	0	4
Race and ethnicity unknown	27	25	3	1
International	81	46	2	3

	MINIMUM	MAXIMUM	MEAN
2012 entering class enrollees by age	21	34	25

Number of first-time enrollees over age 30: 6

CURRICULUM

Launched in 1997, the Indiana Model of Dental Education offers a dynamic blend of contemporary and traditional learning environments designed and continually refined so as to maximally promote the principles of student centeredness, critical thinking, problem solving, evidence-based decision making, competency-based clinical care, and lifelong learning.

Student research opportunities: Yes

SPECIAL PROGRAMS AND SERVICES

DURING DENTAL SCHOOL

Academic counseling and tutoring
Community service opportunities: Division of Community Dentistry—Dr. Karen Yoder
Internships, externships, or extramural programs
Mentoring
Personal counseling
Professional- and career-development programming
Training for those interested in academic careers

ACTIVE STUDENT ORGANIZATIONS

Academy of General Dentistry
American Association of Dental Research Student Research Group
American Association of Pediatric Dentistry
American Association of Public Health
American Association of Women Dentists
American Dental Education Association (ADEA)
American Student Dental Association
Christian Student Association
Delta Sigma Delta
Hispanic Dental Association
Latter-day Saint Student Association
Muslim Students Association
Student National Dental Association

INTERNATIONAL DENTISTS

Graduates of international dental schools considered for traditional predoctoral program: Yes

Advanced standing program offered for graduates of international dental schools: No

COMBINED AND ALTERNATE DEGREES

Ph.D.	M.S.	M.P.H.	M.D.	B.A./B.S.	Other
✓	✓	✓	—	—	✓

Other Degrees: M.S.D. programs in most areas

COSTS: 2012-13 SCHOOL YEAR

	FIRST YEAR	SECOND YEAR	THIRD YEAR	FOURTH YEAR
Tuition, resident	$30,324	$30,324	$30,324	$30,324
Tuition, nonresident	$63,472	$63,472	$63,472	$63,472
Fees	$3,120	$3,120	$3,120	$3,120
Fees, other: Board expenses		$ 345		$390
Instruments, books, and supplies	$11,998	$12,665	$4,384	$2,833
Estimated living expenses	$20,256	$20,256	$20,256	$20,256
Total, resident	$65,698	$66,365	$58,084	$56,533
Total, nonresident	$98,846	$99,858	$91,232	$90,071
Total, other				

FINANCIAL AID

For the 2011-12 academic year, there were 89 first-year dental students who received some type of financial assistance (scholarship/loans/fee remission). All of these students received at least one federal student loan (e.g., Federal Stafford Loan, Federal Graduate PLUS loan, Health Profession Student Loan program). Three of the first-year dental students received a four-year military scholarship through the Health Professions Scholarship Program (HPSP). Six first-year dental students received a $25,000 dental school scholarship award from IUSD. Of the total class of 104 students, 15 students did not request or receive financial assistance.

The average indebtedness for the Class of 2011 was $210,510. The average indebtedness for the in-state graduates was $184,487 and the average indebtedness for the non-resident graduates was $294,234.

UNIVERSITY OF IOWA
COLLEGE OF DENTISTRY

Dr. David C. Johnsen, Dean

CONTACT INFORMATION

www.dentistry.uiowa.edu
University of Iowa College of Dentistry
801 Newton Road
Iowa City, IA 52242
Phone: 319-335-9650
Fax: 319-335-7155

OFFICE OF ADMISSIONS

Elaine Brown
Director, Dental Admissions
311 Dental Science Building N
Iowa City, IA 52242-1010
Phone: 319-335-7157
www.dentistry.uiowa.edu

OFFICE FOR STUDENT FINANCIAL AID

Calvin Hall
Iowa City, IA 52242
Phone: 319-335-1450
www.dentistry.uiowa.edu

STUDENT AFFAIRS

Catherine M. Solow
Associate Dean for Student Affairs
311 Dental Science Building N
Iowa City, IA 52242-1010
Phone: 319-335-7164
www.dentistry.uiowa.edu

MINORITY AFFAIRS/FINANCIAL AID/ADMISSIONS

311 Dental Science Building N
Iowa City, IA 52242-1010
Phone: 319-335-7164
www.dentistry.uiowa.edu

HOUSING

Housing Service Building
Iowa City, IA 52242
Phone: 319-335-9199
www.uiowa.edu

INTERNATIONAL STUDENTS

www.dentistry.uiowa.edu

GENERAL INFORMATION

The University of Iowa (UI) is a state-supported institution with an enrollment of more than 30,000, located on a 1,700-acre campus spanning the Iowa River Valley and merging with the business center of Iowa City, a community of 60,000. The College of Dentistry, founded in 1882, has an enrollment of about 320 dental students and a faculty of 90. The Dental Science Building includes patient care clinics, academic classrooms, a simulation clinic, and preclinical research laboratories. In addition to the D.D.S. program, the College of Dentistry is the only dental school that offers advanced dental education programs in all dental specialties recognized by the American Dental Association (ADA). The college also offers additional outstanding programs and residencies with study toward master's and Ph.D. degrees.

MISSION STATEMENT:

The College of Dentistry is an integral part of the University of Iowa. Its mission embraces the academic values of a university as well as the ethical responsibilities implicit in the education of future members of a health care profession. The mission rests upon a tripartite foundation reflecting the full spectrum of collegiate activity: to educate dentists and specialists for the state and beyond, advance oral health care through excellence in scholarly research activity, deliver high-quality oral health care to Iowa and the region, and serve as a resource to the state and the profession.

Type of institution: Public
Year opened: 1882
Term type: Semester
Time to degree in months: 48
Start month: August

Doctoral dental degree offered: D.D.S.
Total predoctoral enrollment: 320
Estimated entering class size: 80
Campus setting: Urban
Campus housing available: Yes

PREPARATION

Formal minimum preparation in semester/quarter hours: Semester: 90
Baccalaureate degree preferred: Yes
Number of first-year, first-time enrollees whose highest degree is:
- Baccalaureate: 77
- Master's: 1
- Ph.D. or other doctorate: 1

Of first-year, first-time enrollees without baccalaureates, the number with:
- Equivalent of 60 undergraduate credit hours or less: 0
- Equivalent of 61-90 undergraduate credit hours: 0
- Equivalent of 91 or more undergraduate credit hours: 1

PREREQUISITE COURSE	REQUIRED	RECOMMENDED	LAB REQUIRED	CREDITS (SEMESTER/QUARTER)
BCP (biology-chemistry-physics) sciences				
Biology	✓			8
Chemistry, general/inorganic	✓			8
Chemistry, organic	✓			8
Physics	✓			8
Additional biological sciences				
Anatomy		✓		
Biochemistry	✓			3
Cell biology		✓		
Histology		✓		
Immunology		✓		
Microbiology		✓		

(Prerequisite Courses continued)

PREPARATION (CONTINUED)

PREREQUISITE COURSE	REQUIRED	RECOMMENDED	LAB REQUIRED	CREDITS (SEMESTER/QUARTER)
Molecular biology/genetics		✓		
Physiology		✓		
Zoology		✓		

Community college coursework accepted for prerequisites: Yes
Community college coursework accepted for electives: Yes
Limits on community college credit hours: Yes
Maximum number of community college credit hours: 60
Advanced placement (AP) credit accepted for prerequisites: Yes
Advanced placement (AP) credit accepted for electives: Yes
Comments regarding AP credit: AP credit in math and physics is acceptable; prefer biology and chemistry be taken at a four-year institution
Job shadowing: Recommended (hours not specified)
Other factors considered in admission: Personal essay, letters of recommendation, diversity, community service, leadership qualities, college attended, and course load

DAT

Mandatory: Yes
Latest DAT for consideration of application: 08/31/2013
Oldest DAT considered: 08/01/2008
When more than one DAT score is reported: Most recent score only is considered
Canadian DAT accepted: Yes
Application considered before DAT scores are submitted: No

DAT: 2012 ENTERING CLASS

ENROLLEE DAT SCORES	RANGE	MEAN
Academic Average	16-27	20
Perceptual Ability	15-25	20
Total Science	16-30	20

GPA: 2012 ENTERING CLASS

ENROLLEE GPA SCORES	RANGE	MEAN
Science GPA	2.90 – 4.18	3.68
Total GPA	3.18 – 4.13	3.75

APPLICATION AND SELECTION

TIMETABLE

Earliest filing date: 06/04/2013
Latest filing date: 10/01/2013
Earliest date for acceptance offers: 12/01/2013
Maximum time in days for applicant's response to acceptance offer:
30 days if accepted on or after December 1
15 days if accepted on or after February 1
Requests for deferred entrance considered: Yes
Fee for application: Yes, submitted only when requested.
Amount of fee for application:
In state: $60 Out of state: $60 International: $100
Fee waiver available: Yes

	FIRST DEPOSIT	SECOND DEPOSIT	THIRD DEPOSIT
Required to hold place	Yes	No	No
Resident amount	$500		
Nonresident amount	$500		
Deposit due	As indicated in admission offer		
Applied to tuition	Yes		
Refundable	No		

APPLICATION PROCESS

Participates in Associated American Dental Schools Application Service (AADSAS): Yes
Accepts direct applicants: No
Secondary or supplemental application required: Yes
Secondary or supplemental application website: www.dentistry.uiowa.edu
Interview is mandatory: Yes
Interview is by invitation: Yes

RESIDENCY

Admissions process distinguishes between in-state/in-province and out-of-state/out-of-province applicants: Yes
Preference given to residents of: Iowa
Reciprocity Admissions Agreement available for legal residents of: None
Applications are accepted from non-U.S. citizens/non-U.S. permanent residents: Yes

APPLICATION AND ENROLLMENT	NUMBER OF APPLICANTS	ESTIMATED NUMBER INTERVIEWED	ESTIMATED NUMBER ENROLLED
In-state or province applicants	125	89	57
Out-of-state or province applicants	814	144	23

Generally and over time, percentage of your first-year enrollment is in-state: 71%
Origin of out-of-state enrollees (U.S.): Colorado-1, Hawaii-1, Idaho-1, Illinois-7, Minnesota -3, Oklahoma-1, Pennsylvania-1, Utah-2, Virginia-1, Washington-1, Wisconsin-3
Origin of international enrollees: Canada-1

DEMOGRAPHIC DESCRIPTIONS OF APPLICANTS: 2012 ENTERING CLASS

	APPLICANTS		ENROLLEES	
	M	W	M	W
Hispanic/Latino of any race	19	22	0	3
American Indian or Alaska Native	0	0	0	0
Asian	76	89	2	6
Black or African American	15	20	1	0
Native Hawaiian or Other Pacific Islander	0	0	0	0
White	402	249	43	24
Two or more races	8	14	0	0
Race and ethnicity unknown	8	8	0	0
International	5	6	0	1

	MINIMUM	MAXIMUM	MEAN
2012 entering class enrollees by age	20	35	23

Number of first-time enrollees over age 30: 2

CURRICULUM

The University of Iowa College of Dentistry is committed to providing a high-quality dental education to aspiring dentists to help them meet the health needs of a large and diverse population.

Year 1: Basic sciences, laboratory and technique courses, and an introduction to clinical experiences

Year 2: Continuation of basic sciences and technical courses, plus definitive clinical patient treatment

Year 3: Rotation through a series of clerkships in each of the seven clinical disciplines

Year 4: Delivery of comprehensive dental care under conditions approximating those in private practice; seniors' participation in extramural programs in locations primarily throughout the Midwest

Student research opportunities: Yes

SPECIAL PROGRAMS AND SERVICES

PREDENTAL

Summer enrichment programs

DURING DENTAL SCHOOL

Academic counseling and tutoring
Community service opportunities
Internships, externships, or extramural programs
Mentoring
Opportunity to study for credit at institution abroad
Personal counseling
Professional- and career-development programming
Training for those interested in academic careers

ACTIVE STUDENT ORGANIZATIONS

American Association of Dental Research Student Research Group
American Association of Pediatric Dentistry
American Association of Public Health Dentistry
American Association of Women Dentists
American Dental Education Association (ADEA)
American Society for Geriatric Dentistry
American Student Dental Association
Christian Dental Association
Dentistry Gay Straight Alliance
Hispanic Dental Association
Military Dental Student Association
Student National Dental Association

INTERNATIONAL DENTISTS

Graduates of international dental schools considered for traditional predoctoral program: Yes

Advanced standing program offered for graduates of international dental schools: No

COMBINED AND ALTERNATE DEGREES

Ph.D.	M.S.	M.P.H.	M.D.	B.A./B.S.	Other
—	✓	✓	—	—	✓

Other: The opportunity exists for students to complete a defined set of requirements of the M.S. in Public Health program while in dental school and have advanced standing in the M.S. program at the completion of the D.D.S.

COSTS: 2012-13 SCHOOL YEAR

	FIRST YEAR	SECOND YEAR	THIRD YEAR	FOURTH YEAR
Tuition, resident	$36,195	$36,195	$36,195	$36,195
Tuition, nonresident	$58,377	$58,377	$58,377	$58,377
Tuition, other				
Fees				
Instruments, books, and supplies	$16,124	$10,946	$6,588	$5,500
Estimated living expenses	$16,606	$16,606	$18,266	$18,266
Total, resident	$68,925	$63,747	$61,049	$59,961
Total, nonresident	$91,107	$85,929	$83,231	$82,143
Total, other				

FINANCIAL AID

Major sources of support include parental assistance, part-time jobs, accumulated savings, scholarships, loans, teaching/research awards, and the income of working spouses. Students are not encouraged to have jobs during the first two years due to the intensity of their course of study. Eligibility for financial aid is based on need established by completion of the Free Application for Federal Student Aid (FAFSA). Eligible dental students may receive Health Professions Student Loans, Federal Perkins loans, Stafford loans, and PLUS loans. Interest on these loans accrues at a comparatively low rate, and the loans are repayable over an extended period of time after you complete your course of study. In addition, some loans are available from the American Dental Association (ADA) and sources within the University of Iowa College of Dentistry. Information on the scholarships and loans available to dentistry students may be obtained from the Office of Student Financial Aid, 208 Calvin Hall.

In 2011, 29 incoming students received scholarships or grants between $10,000 and $15,000. The average award for residents was $10,000 and $15,000 for nonresidents.

UNIVERSITY OF KENTUCKY
COLLEGE OF DENTISTRY

Dr. Sharon P. Turner, Dean

CONTACT INFORMATION

www.mc.uky.edu/dentistry
M-134 Chandler Medical Center
Lexington, KY 40536
Phone: 859-323-1884

OFFICE OF ADMISSIONS AND STUDENT AFFAIRS

Christine Harper
Assistant Dean Academic and Student Affairs

Missy Lockard
Admissions Coordinator

Becky Sauer
Staff Assistant
Admissions and Student Affairs
M-134 Chandler Medical Center
Lexington, KY 40536
Phone: 859-323-6071
basaue2@uky.edu
www.mc.uky.edu/dentistry

FINANCIAL AID

Don Brown
Financial Aid Coordinator
D-155 Chandler Medical Center
Lexington, KY 40536
Phone: 859-323-5280

ACADEMIC AFFAIRS

M-134 Chandler Medical Center
Lexington, KY 40536
Phone: 859-323-5656
www.mc.uky.edu/dentistry

GENERAL INFORMATION

The College of Dentistry, a public institution with a statewide mission, is located on the main campus of the University of Kentucky. The university has a suburban setting in Lexington, a city with a population of 297,000 and situated in the heart of the scenic bluegrass region of Kentucky. Along with the Doctor of Dental Medicine (D.M.D.) program, advanced dental education programs are offered in oral and maxillofacial surgery, orthodontics, pediatric dentistry, periodontics, general practice dentistry, and orofacial pain. In addition to strong research and continuing education programs, the college conducts many public service activities throughout Kentucky, especially with pediatric patients. The College of Dentistry admitted its first class in 1962. Today it has an enrollment of 227 student dentists and 58 advanced dental education students. There are 70 full-time faculty in the college for an excellent student/faculty ratio of three to one.

MISSION STATEMENT:

The mission of the College of Dentistry reflects the mission of the university, and its purpose is to promote oral health within Kentucky and beyond by providing a high-quality education for students in the doctoral and specialty programs; meaningful research in oral health and related areas that is disseminated to communities of interest; and service to the university, community, the commonwealth, and the profession.

Type of institution: Public
Year opened: 1962
Term type: Semester
Time to degree in months: 43
Start month: August

Doctoral dental degree offered: D.M.D.
Total predoctoral enrollment: 227
Estimated entering class size: 65
Campus setting: Urban
Campus housing available: Yes

PREPARATION

Formal minimum preparation in semester/quarter hours: Semester: 120
Baccalaureate degree preferred: Yes
Number of first-year, first-time enrollees whose highest degree is:
- Baccalaureate: 55
- Master's: 1
- Ph.D. or other doctorate: 1

Of first-year, first-time enrollees without baccalaureates, the number with:
- Equivalent of 60 undergraduate credit hours or less: 0
- Equivalent of 61-90 undergraduate credit hours: 0
- Equivalent of 91 or more undergraduate credit hours: 0

PREREQUISITE COURSE	REQUIRED	RECOMMENDED	LAB REQUIRED	CREDITS (SEMESTER/QUARTER)
BCP (biology-chemistry-physics) sciences				
Biology	✓		✓	2 semesters
Chemistry, general/inorganic	✓		✓	2 semesters
Chemistry, organic	✓		✓	2 semesters
Physics	✓		✓	1 semester
Additional biological sciences				
Anatomy		✓		
Biochemistry	✓			1 semester
Cell biology		✓		
Histology		✓		
Immunology		✓		
Microbiology	✓			1 semester

(Prerequisite Courses continued)

PREPARATION (CONTINUED)

PREREQUISITE COURSE	REQUIRED	RECOMMENDED	LAB REQUIRED	CREDITS (SEMESTER/QUARTER)
Molecular biology/genetics		✓		
Physiology		✓		
Zoology				

Community college coursework accepted for prerequisites: Yes
Community college coursework accepted for electives: No
Limits on community college credit hours: Yes
Maximum number of community college credit hours: 60
Advanced placement (AP) credit accepted for prerequisites: Yes
Advanced placement (AP) credit accepted for electives: No
Job shadowing: Required
Number of hours of job shadowing required or recommended: 20 hours minimum
Other factors considered in admission: Noncognitive factors

DAT

Mandatory: Yes
Latest DAT for consideration of application: 12/01/2013
Oldest DAT considered: 01/01/2010
When more than one DAT score is reported: Highest score is considered
Canadian DAT accepted: Yes
Application considered before DAT scores are submitted: No

DAT: 2012 ENTERING CLASS

ENROLLEE DAT SCORES	RANGE	MEAN
Academic Average	16-22	18.3
Perceptual Ability	15-26	18.8
Total Science	16-22	18.1

GPA: 2012 ENTERING CLASS

ENROLLEE GPA SCORES	RANGE	MEAN
Science GPA	2.25-3.94	3.34
Total GPA	2.66-3.95	3.46

APPLICATION AND SELECTION

TIMETABLE

Earliest filing date: 06/01/2013
Latest filing date: 12/01/2013
Earliest date for acceptance offers: 12/01/2013
Maximum time in days for applicant's response to acceptance offer:
30 days if accepted on or after December 1
15 days if accepted on or after February 1
Requests for deferred entrance considered: In exceptional circumstances only
Fee for application: Yes, submitted only when requested
Amount of fee for application:
In state: $75 Out of state: $75 International: $75
Fee waiver available: No

	FIRST DEPOSIT	SECOND DEPOSIT	THIRD DEPOSIT
Required to hold place	Yes	No	No
Resident amount	$250		
Nonresident amount	$1,000		
Deposit due	As indicated in admission offer		
Applied to tuition	Yes		
Refundable	No		

APPLICATION PROCESS

Participates in Associated American Dental Schools Application Service (AADSAS): Yes
Accepts direct applicants: No
Secondary or supplemental application required: Yes, only when contacted
Secondary or supplemental application website: No
Interview is mandatory: Yes
Interview is by invitation: Yes

RESIDENCY

Admissions process distinguishes between in-state/in-province and out-of-state/out-of-province applicants: Yes
Preference given to residents of: Kentucky
Reciprocity Admissions Agreement available for legal residents of: None
Applications are accepted from non-U.S. citizens/non-U.S. permanent residents: Yes

APPLICATION AND ENROLLMENT	NUMBER OF APPLICANTS	ESTIMATED NUMBER INTERVIEWED	ESTIMATED NUMBER ENROLLED
In-state or province applicants	166	80	39
Out-of-state or province applicants	1,507	65	18

Generally and over time, percentage of your first-year enrollment is in-state: 70%
Origin of out-of-state enrollees (U.S.): California-1, Connecticut-1, Florida-3, Georgia-1, Idaho-1, Indiana-1, Missouri-1, Maryland-1, Ohio-4, Pennsylvania-1, Tennessee -2, West Virginia-1
Origin of international enrollees: South Korea-1

DEMOGRAPHIC DESCRIPTIONS OF APPLICANTS: 2012 ENTERING CLASS

	APPLICANTS		ENROLLEES	
	M	W	M	W
Hispanic/Latino of any race	8	12	1	1
American Indian or Alaska Native	1	1	0	0
Asian	118	134	3	0
Black or African American	27	33	0	1
Native Hawaiian or Other Pacific Islander	0	0	0	0
White	623	422	23	24
Two or more races	52	44	2	1
Race and ethnicity unknown	19	14	0	0
International	83	70	1	0

	MINIMUM	MAXIMUM	MEAN
2012 entering class enrollees by age	21	34	23

Number of first-time enrollees over age 30: 2

CURRICULUM

The College of Dentistry's program integrates basic science, preclinical lab, technique, clinical, and related courses throughout the curriculum. Basic science courses begin at enrollment. Clinical course time and patient contact start early in the first year and expand as the basic science and preclinical curriculum decreases. The dental curriculum has four primary areas of study: basic sciences, behavioral sciences, preclinical dentistry, and clinical dentistry. The basic sciences, such as anatomy, biochemistry, and pharmacology, as well as the didactic portion of the preclinical courses, are taught mainly by lecture, seminar, some self-instruction, or any combination of these teaching methods. The technical skills of the preclinical subjects, such as restorations, denture construction, and periodontal therapy are taught in laboratory and clinical settings.

Student research opportunities: Yes

SPECIAL PROGRAMS AND SERVICES

PREDENTAL

Advising
DAT workshops
Personal Statement Workshop
Summer enrichment programs

DURING DENTAL SCHOOL

Academic counseling and tutoring
Community service opportunities
Internships, externships, or extramural programs
Mentoring
Professional- and career-development programming
Summer enrichment program

ACTIVE STUDENT ORGANIZATIONS

American Association of Women Dentists
American Association of Public Health Dentistry
American Dental Education Association (ADEA)
American Student Dental Association
Hispanic Dental Association
Student National Dental Association
Student Professionalism and Ethics Association
American Association for Dental Research Student Research Group

INTERNATIONAL DENTISTS

Graduates of international dental schools considered for traditional predoctoral program: Yes

Advanced standing program offered for graduates of international dental schools: No

COMBINED AND ALTERNATE DEGREES

Ph.D.	M.S.	M.P.H.	M.D.	B.A./B.S.	Other
✓	✓	—	—	—	—

COSTS: 2012-13 SCHOOL YEAR

	FIRST YEAR	SECOND YEAR	THIRD YEAR	FOURTH YEAR
Tuition, resident	$27,217	$27,217	$27,217	$27,217
Tuition, nonresident	$56,845	$56,845	$56,845	$56,845
Tuition, other	NA	NA	NA	NA
Fees	$2,845	$3,393	$2,873	$6,043
Instruments, books, and supplies	$8,844	$10,588	$3,152	$570
Estimated living expenses	$21,250	$21,250	$21,250	$21,250
Total, resident	$60,156	$62,448	$54,492	$55,080
Total, nonresident	$89,784	$92,076	$84,120	$84,708
Total, other	NA	NA	NA	NA

FINANCIAL AID

There were 24 recipients of scholarships and grants in the 2012 entering class. Awards were between $3,000 and $10,000. The average award for residents was $4,820 and $4,500 for nonresidents. Fifty-two students received student loans between $3,000 and $88,970. The average loan for residents was $45,181 and $61,977 for nonresidents.

The average 2012 graduate indebtedness was $174,193.

UNIVERSITY OF LOUISVILLE
SCHOOL OF DENTISTRY

Dr. John J. Sauk, Dean

GENERAL INFORMATION

Offering outstanding clinical education through state-of-the art simulation education and technology and leading biomedical research, the University of Louisville School of Dentistry (ULSD) continues its quest to provide quality education and unique opportunities. The philosophy of the school is to consider students partners in learning and to provide them with the knowledge and skills to meet the challenges of today's diverse dental profession. Many ULSD graduates choose to practice general dentistry, while others continue their education in a specialty, engage in dental research, or prepare for a career in education. The school is a state-supported institution located within the University Health Sciences Center (HSC) in downtown Louisville (metropolitan area population of more than one million). Founded in 1887, the school is housed in a building that opened in 1970 as part of the HSC. A total renovation of the clinics and classrooms, including the addition of state-of-the-art technology, was completed in fall 2011. The school is celebrating its 125th year in dental education. We also welcome the addition of our seventh post graduate doctoral residency program, Advanced Education in Prosthodontics.

MISSION STATEMENT:

The University of Louisville School of Dentistry, through excellence in teaching and research, will educate competent dental professionals. The school will provide quality dental care and will serve the community to fulfill our urban and statewide missions.

Type of institution: Public
Year opened: 1887
Term type: Semester
Time to degree in months: 40
Start month: July

Doctoral dental degree offered: D.M.D.
Total predoctoral enrollment: 439
Entering class size: 120
Campus setting: Urban
Campus housing available: Yes

PREPARATION

Formal minimum preparation in semester/quarter hours: Semester: 6 Quarter: 10
Baccalaureate degree preferred: Yes
Number of first-year, first-time enrollees whose highest degree is:
- Baccalaureate: 109
- Master's: 10
- Ph.D. or other doctorate: 1

Of first-year, first-time enrollees without baccalaureates, the number with:
- Equivalent of 60 undergraduate credit hours or less: 0
- Equivalent of 61-90 undergraduate credit hours: 0
- Equivalent of 91 or more undergraduate credit hours: 0

PREREQUISITE COURSE	REQUIRED	RECOMMENDED	LAB REQUIRED	CREDITS (SEMESTER/QUARTER)
BCP (biology-chemistry-physics) sciences				
Biology	✓		✓	16/24
Chemistry, general/inorganic	✓		✓	8/12
Chemistry, organic	✓		✓	8/12
Physics	✓			3/5
Additional biological sciences				
Anatomy		✓	✓	4/6
Biochemistry		✓	✓	4/6
Cell biology		✓	✓	4/6
Histology		✓	✓	4/6
Immunology		✓	✓	4/6

(Prerequisite Courses continued)

CONTACT INFORMATION

www.dental.louisville.edu/dental
501 S. Preston Street
Louisville, KY 40202
Phone: 502-852-5081

ADMISSIONS

Robin R. Benningfield
Admissions Counselor
Room 234, School of Dentistry
501 S. Preston Street
Louisville, KY 40202
Phone: 502-852-5081
Email: dmdadms@louisville.edu
www.louisville.edu/dental

FINANCIAL AID

Barbara Dagnan
Financial Aid Coordinator
Room 230, HSC Instructional Building
Louisville, KY 40202
Phone: 502-852-5076
Email: dmdadms@louisville.edu
www.louisville.edu/dental

STUDENT AFFAIRS

Dianne Foster
Assistant Dean for Student Affairs
Room 234, School of Dentistry
501 S. Preston Street
Louisville, KY 40202
Phone: 502-852-5081
Email: dmdadms@louisville.edu
www.louisville.edu/dental

MINORITY AFFAIRS

Dr. Sherry Babbage
Minority Affairs Coordinator
Room 234, School of Dentistry
501 S. Preston Street
Louisville, KY 40202
Phone: 502-852-5081
Email: dmdadms@louisville.edu
www.louisville.edu/dental

HOUSING

Shannon Staten
Director of Residence Administration
Phone: 502-852-6636
Email: shannon.staten@louisville.edu
http://campuslife.louisville.edu/housing

INTERNATIONAL CENTER

Sharolyn Pepper
International Student Coordinator
Phone: 502-852-6602
Email: pepper@louisville.edu
www.louisville.edu/internationalcenter

PREPARATION (CONTINUED)

PREREQUISITE COURSE	REQUIRED	RECOMMENDED	LAB REQUIRED	CREDITS (SEMESTER/QUARTER)
Microbiology		✓	✓	4/6
Molecular biology/genetics		✓	✓	4/6
Physiology		✓	✓	4/6
Zoology		✓	✓	4/6

Community college coursework accepted for prerequisites: Yes
Community college coursework accepted for electives: Yes
Limits on community college credit hours: Yes
Maximum number of community college credit hours: 60
Advanced placement (AP) credit accepted for prerequisites: Yes
Advanced placement (AP) credit accepted for electives: Yes
Comments regarding AP credit: Accepted by ULSD if accepted by institution granting undergraduate degree
Job shadowing: Highly recommended shadowing in general dentistry
Number of hours of job shadowing required or recommended: Minimum of 40 hours highly recommended
Other factors considered in admission: Social awareness, volunteerism, and community service

DAT

Mandatory: Yes
Latest DAT for consideration of application: 06/01/2014
Oldest DAT considered: 06/01/2011
When more than one DAT score is reported: Highest set of scores is considered.
Canadian DAT accepted: Yes
Application considered before DAT scores are submitted: No

DAT: 2012 ENTERING CLASS

ENROLLEE DAT SCORES	RANGE	MEAN
Academic Average	15-23	19.3
Perceptual Ability	14-27	19.5
Total Science	14-23	19.1

GPA: 2012 ENTERING CLASS

ENROLLEE GPA SCORES	RANGE	MEAN
Science GPA	2.38 – 4.00	3.44
Total GPA	2.63 – 4.00	3.56

APPLICATION AND SELECTION

TIMETABLE

Earliest filing date: 06/01/2013
Latest filing date: 12/15/2013
Earliest date for acceptance offers: 12/01/ 2013
Maximum time in days for applicant's response to acceptance offer:
30 days if accepted on or after December 1
15 days if accepted on or after February 1
Requests for deferred entrance considered: In exceptional circumstances only.
Fee for application: Yes, submitted only after email request is sent from ULSD.
Amount of fee for application:
In state: $65 Out of state: $65 International: $65
Fee waiver available: No

	FIRST DEPOSIT	SECOND DEPOSIT	THIRD DEPOSIT
Required to hold place	Yes	No	No
Resident amount	$200		
Nonresident amount	$1,000		
Deposit due	As indicated in admission offer		
Applied to tuition	Yes		
Refundable	No		

APPLICATION PROCESS

Participates in Associated American Dental Schools Application Service (AADSAS): Yes
Accepts direct applicants: No
Secondary or supplemental application required: No
Interview is mandatory: Yes
Interview is by invitation: Yes

RESIDENCY

Admissions process distinguishes between in-state/in-province and out-of-state/out-of-province applicants: Yes
Preference given to residents of: Arkansas, Kentucky
Reciprocity Admissions Agreement available for legal residents of: Arkansas
Applications are accepted from non-U.S. citizens/non-U.S. permanent residents: Yes

APPLICATION AND ENROLLMENT	NUMBER OF APPLICANTS	ESTIMATED NUMBER INTERVIEWED	ESTIMATED NUMBER ENROLLED
In-state or province applicants	169	117	44
Out-of-state or province applicants	2,862	341	76

Generally and over time, percentage of your first-year enrollment is in-state: 41%
Origin of out-of-state enrollees (U.S.): Alabama-2, Arkansas-2, Florida-9, Georgia-5, Idaho-3, Illinois-3, Indiana-15, Michigan-3, New Jersey-1, North Carolina-4, Ohio-1, Pennsylvania-1, South Carolina-3, Tennessee-7, Texas-1, Utah-7, Virginia- 3, Wisconsin-4, Active-duty military with no state-1
Origin of international enrollees: Canada-1

DEMOGRAPHIC DESCRIPTIONS OF APPLICANTS: 2012 ENTERING CLASS

	APPLICANTS		ENROLLEES	
	M	W	M	W
Hispanic/Latino of any race	15	24	0	0
American Indian or Alaska Native	0	3	0	0
Asian	267	261	6	5
Black or African American	44	80	3	4
Native Hawaiian or Other Pacific Islander	0	0	0	0
White	1,131	679	55	37
Two or more races	108	75	7	2
Race and ethnicity unknown	44	27	1	0
International	138	107	0	0

Note: Totals differ from table above because some applicants did not report ethnicity or gender.

	MINIMUM	MAXIMUM	MEAN
2012 entering class enrollees by age	21	40	24

Number of first-time enrollees over age 30: 7

CURRICULUM

The curriculum of the School of Dentistry is designed to develop practitioners who are competent to enter the dental profession as lifelong learners who may practice general dentistry or to proceed into advanced training. The first two years of the curriculum focus on the basic sciences and preclinical techniques as well as the strengthening of professional values. Students utilize the Simulation Clinic to gain experience in diagnosis and preclinical procedures. The third- and fourth-year curricula are primarily patient care augmented by continued education in all clinical disciplines. Students deliver care to patients through a comprehensive general practice clinic and through rotations, such as pediatric dentistry, oral surgery, radiography, endodontics, special needs clinics, etc. An extramural experience with dental practitioners improves students' abilities to provide care to racially, ethnically, and culturally diverse groups. Extramural experience may also include service through agencies such as the U.S. Public Health Service and the Indian Health Service. Elective courses offered during the fourth year permit students to explore many different aspects of the profession.

Student research opportunities: Yes

SPECIAL PROGRAMS AND SERVICES

PREDENTAL

Association of American Medical Colleges/ADEA Summer Medical and Dental Education Program (AAMC/ADEA SMDEP)
DAT workshops
Other summer enrichment programs

DURING DENTAL SCHOOL

Academic counseling and tutoring
Community service opportunities
Internships, externships, or extramural programs
Mentoring
Personal counseling
Professional- and career-development programming
Transfer applicants considered if space is available

ACTIVE STUDENT ORGANIZATIONS

Alpha Omega
American Association of Women Dentists
American Dental Education Association (ADEA)
American Student Dental Association
Christian Medical and Dental Society
Hispanic Student Dental Association
Omicron Kappa Upsilon
Psi Omega
Student National Dental Association
Student Remote Area Medical Association

INTERNATIONAL DENTISTS

Graduates of international dental schools considered for traditional predoctoral program: Yes

Advanced standing program offered for graduates of international dental schools: Advanced Standing admission option

Advanced standing program description: The University of Louisville School of Dentistry (ULSD) offers advanced standing admission to the traditional D.M.D. program for selected individuals who have received their dental degree from an institution outside the United States or Canada. Advanced standing admission is dependent upon the school's available resources.

COMBINED AND ALTERNATE DEGREES

Ph.D.	M.S.	M.P.H.	M.D.	B.A./B.S.	Other
✓	✓	—	—	—	—

COSTS: 2012-13 SCHOOL YEAR

	FIRST YEAR	SECOND YEAR	THIRD YEAR	FOURTH YEAR
Tuition, resident	$26,430	$26,430	$26,430	$26,430
Tuition, nonresident	$55,606	$55,606	$55,606	$55,606
Tuition, other	NA	NA	NA	NA
Fees & Mandatory Health Insurance	$2,528	$2,367	$2,367	$2,367
Instruments, books, and supplies	$8,500	$8,266	$8,000	$6,566
Estimated living expenses	$20,400	$20,400	$17,000	$17,000
Total, resident	$57,858	$57,463	$57,197	$52,363
Total, nonresident	$87,034	$86,639	$86,373	$81,539
Total, other	NA	NA	NA	NA

FINANCIAL AID

Approximately 90% of all dental students receive some form of financial aid. Both scholarships and loans are offered, although the majority of financial aid comes in the form of student loans. Most financial aid is federally based and is available only to U.S. citizens or qualified nonresidents. International students (F visas) are not eligible for federal student aid. All applicants for federal student aid must annually submit a Free Application for Federal Student Aid (FAFSA) or a renewal application. A student's financial aid award cannot exceed the cost of attendance. Cost of attendance is a standard figure computed for each category of student (i.e., all first-year, out-of-state students have the same cost of attendance budget) and includes:

- tuition and fees
- dental instrument rental
- books and supplies
- personal and living expenses

Federal regulations require that cost of attendance be based on the student only and not include the student's family. We are unable to consider larger cost of living expenses because a student is married or has dependents. However, child care costs for dependents can be added to the student's cost of attendance when documentation is provided.

The University of Louisville School of Dentistry is dedicated to providing financial literacy for our students. All students participate in mandatory and volunteer financial literacy workshops while enrolled in the D.M.D. program. The workshops include: money behavior habits, budgets, credit, tax guidance, debt management, repayment strategies of student loans, and practice management. The school values these workshops as an investment in our future alumni.

LOUISIANA STATE UNIVERSITY
SCHOOL OF DENTISTRY

Dr. Henry A. Gremillion, Dean

CONTACT INFORMATION

www.lsusd.lsuhsc.edu
1100 Florida Avenue
New Orleans, LA 70119
Phone: 504-941-8124
Fax: 504-941-8123

OFFICE OF ADMISSIONS

Dr. Toby Cheramie
Director of Admissions
1100 Florida Avenue, Box 228
New Orleans, LA 70119
Phone: 504-941-8124
Email: tchera@lsuhsc.edu
Fax: 504-941-8123

OFFICE OF FINANCIAL AID

Kimberly Bruno
Assistant Director of Financial Aid
Louisiana State University Health Sciences Center in New Orleans
433 Bolivar Street, Room 215
New Orleans, LA 70112-2223
Phone: 504-568-4820

STUDENT AFFAIRS

Darlene Brunet
Director of Student Affairs
1100 Florida Avenue, Box 228
New Orleans, LA 70119
Phone: 504-941-8122

DIVERSITY AND MINORITY AFFAIRS

Dr. Stephen Brisco
Director of Diversity and Minority Affairs
1100 Florida Avenue, Box 137
New Orleans, LA 70119
Phone: 504-941-8253
Email: sbrisc1@lsuhsc.edu
Fax: 504-941-8218

GENERAL INFORMATION

The Louisiana State University School of Dentistry (LSUSD) admitted its first class in September 1968. The $16 million dental school building was dedicated in 1972. The dental school complex provides excellent basic sciences, preclinical, and clinical facilities. The School of Dentistry is a public, state-supported institution and is an integral part of the Louisiana State University (LSU) Health Sciences Center in New Orleans. The school serves as a center for education, research, and service related to oral health for the state of Louisiana and, as such, offers a variety of educational opportunities, including advanced education and programs in dental hygiene and laboratory technology.

MISSION STATEMENT:

The mission of the LSUSD is to serve the needs of the citizens of the state of Louisiana by educating future general dentists, specialists, and allied dental professionals to provide excellent and current health care; providing a leadership role in research through investigating new approaches to the prevention and management of disease, developing innovative treatment modalities, expediting the transfer of knowledge for clinical use, and enhancing health care delivery; providing health care services to the public; and disseminating information to the dental community on a local, national, and international level.

Type of institution: Public
Year opened: 1968
Term type: Academic Year
Time to degree in months: 48
Start month: July

Doctoral dental degree offered: D.D.S.
Total predoctoral enrollment: 262
Estimated entering class size: 65
Campus setting: Urban
Campus housing available: Yes

PREPARATION

Formal minimum preparation in semester/quarter hours: Semester: 90
Baccalaureate degree preferred: Yes
Number of first-year, first-time enrollees whose highest degree is:
- Baccalaureate: 60
- Master's: 3
- Ph.D. or other doctorate: 0

Of first-year, first-time enrollees without baccalaureates, the number with:
- Equivalent of 60 undergraduate credit hours or less: 0
- Equivalent of 61-90 undergraduate credit hours: 0
- Equivalent of 91 or more undergraduate credit hours: 2

PREREQUISITE COURSE	REQUIRED	RECOMMENDED	LAB REQUIRED	CREDITS (SEMESTER/QUARTER)
BCP (biology-chemistry-physics) sciences				
Biology	✓		✓	12/18
Chemistry, general/inorganic	✓		✓	8/12
Chemistry, organic	✓		✓	8/12
Physics	✓		✓	8/12
Additional biological sciences				
Anatomy		✓		4/6
Biochemistry		✓		4/6
Cell biology		✓		4/6
Histology		✓		4/6
Immunology		✓		4/6
Microbiology		✓		4/6

(Prerequisite Courses continued)

PREPARATION (CONTINUED)

PREREQUISITE COURSE	REQUIRED	RECOMMENDED	LAB REQUIRED	CREDITS (SEMESTER/QUARTER)
Molecular biology/genetics		✓		4/6
Physiology		✓		4/6
Zoology		✓		4/6
Other				
English	✓			9 hours

Community college coursework accepted for prerequisites: Yes
Community college coursework accepted for electives: Yes
Limits on community college credit hours: No
Advanced placement (AP) credit accepted for prerequisites: Yes
Advanced placement (AP) credit accepted for electives: Yes
Job shadowing: Required
Number of hours of job shadowing required or recommended: Minimum of 30 hours. Fifteen hours each at two different general dentists' offices.

DAT

Mandatory: Yes
Latest DAT for consideration of application: 10/01/2013
Oldest DAT considered: 11/01/2009
When more than one DAT score is reported: Highest score is considered
Canadian DAT accepted: Yes
Application considered before DAT scores are submitted: No

DAT: 2012 ENTERING CLASS

ENROLLEE DAT SCORES	RANGE	MEAN
Academic Average	17-23	19.6
Perceptual Ability	16-25	19.6
Total Science	17-23	19.6

GPA: 2012 ENTERING CLASS

ENROLLEE GPA SCORES	RANGE	MEAN
Science GPA	2.98-4.00	3.60
Total GPA	3.00-4.00	3.67

APPLICATION AND SELECTION

TIMETABLE

Earliest filing date: 06/01/2013
Latest filing date: 11/01/2013
Earliest date for acceptance offers: 12/01/2013
Maximum time in days for applicant's response to acceptance offer:
30 days if accepted on or after December 1
15 days if accepted on or after February 1
Requests for deferred entrance considered: No
Fee for application: Yes
Amount of fee for application:
In state: $50 Out of state: $50 International: NA
Fee waiver available: No

	FIRST DEPOSIT	SECOND DEPOSIT	THIRD DEPOSIT
Required to hold place	Yes	No	No
Resident amount	$200		
Nonresident amount	$200		
Deposit due	As indicated in admission offer		
Applied to tuition	Yes		
Refundable	No		

APPLICATION PROCESS

Participates in Associated American Dental Schools Application Service (AADSAS): Yes
Accepts direct applicants: No
Secondary or supplemental application required: Yes, by invitation only
Secondary or supplemental application website: Sent by Admissions Office
Interview is mandatory: Yes
Interview is by invitation: Yes

RESIDENCY

Admissions process distinguishes between in-state/in-province and out-of-state/out-of-province applicants: Yes
Preference given to residents of: Louisiana
Reciprocity Admissions Agreement available for legal residents of: Arkansas
Applications are accepted from non-U.S. citizens/non-U.S. permanent residents: No

APPLICATION AND ENROLLMENT	NUMBER OF APPLICANTS	ESTIMATED NUMBER INTERVIEWED	ESTIMATED NUMBER ENROLLED
In-state or province applicants	185	80	56
Out-of-state or province applicants	542	37	9

Generally and over time, percentage of your first-year enrollment is in-state: 86%
Origin of out-of-state enrollees (U.S.): Arkansas-4, Florida-1, Mississippi-1, North Carolina-1, Texas-1, Utah-1
Origin of international enrollees: NA

DEMOGRAPHIC DESCRIPTIONS OF APPLICANTS: 2012 ENTERING CLASS

	APPLICANTS		ENROLLEES	
	M	W	M	W
Hispanic/Latino of any race	7	6	0	1
American Indian or Alaska Native	0	1	0	0
Asian	68	78	2	7
Black or African American	17	37	3	1
Native Hawaiian or Other Pacific Islander	0	1	0	1
White	243	177	16	27
Two or more races	38	35	0	0
Race and ethnicity unknown	8	11	0	7
International	0	0	0	0

Notes: Louisiana State University School of Dentistry includes the category "Unsure," which this table does not include.

	MINIMUM	MAXIMUM	MEAN
2012 entering class enrollees by age	21	33	24

Number of first-time enrollees over age 30: 1

CURRICULUM

LSUSD follows a diagonal curriculum providing a blend of basic, clinical, and behavioral sciences and practice management. This approach allows early introduction to clinical experience and integration of basic science material into the clinical curriculum.

Year 1: Basic sciences, preclinical technical courses, and behavioral science with limited clinical experience

Year 2: Continuation of basic sciences and preclinical technical courses with clinical patient treatment in operative dentistry, oral diagnosis, and periodontics

Year 3: Clinical didactic courses and clinical patient treatment in a comprehensive care format, which includes operative dentistry, fixed and removable prosthodontics, pediatric dentistry, periodontics, oral and maxillofacial surgery, orthodontics, oral diagnosis, and endodontics

Year 4: Total comprehensive patient care in general dentistry; elective courses available in many departments

Student research opportunities: Yes, optional

SPECIAL PROGRAMS AND SERVICES

PREDENTAL

Predental 101-College Workshop
Summer enrichment programs

DURING DENTAL SCHOOL

Academic counseling and tutoring
Community service opportunities
Internships, externships, or extramural programs
Personal counseling
Transfer applicants considered if space is available

ACTIVE STUDENT ORGANIZATIONS

American Association of Dental Research Student Research Group
American Dental Education Association (ADEA)
American Student Dental Association
Delta Sigma Delta Fraternity
Student National Dental Association

INTERNATIONAL DENTISTS

Graduates of international dental schools considered for traditional predoctoral program: No

Advanced standing program offered for graduates of international dental schools: No

COMBINED AND ALTERNATE DEGREES

Ph.D.	M.S.	M.P.H.	M.D.	B.A./B.S.	Other
✓	—	—	—	—	—

COSTS: 2012-13 SCHOOL YEAR

	FIRST YEAR	SECOND YEAR	THIRD YEAR	FOURTH YEAR
Tuition, resident	$16,768	$16,768	$16,768	$16,768
Tuition, nonresident	$36,405	$36,405	$36,405	$36,405
Tuition, other	$9,623	$7,237	$7,996	$8,730
Fees	NA	NA	NA	NA
Instruments, books, and supplies	$4,550	$2,850	$1,200	$150
Estimated living expenses	NA	NA	NA	NA
Total, resident	$30,941	$26,855	$25,964	$25,648
Total, nonresident	$50,578	$46,492	$45,601	$45,285
Total, other	NA	NA	NA	NA

FINANCIAL AID

THE THREE-STEP APPLICATION PROCESS

1. File your 2012-13 Free Application for Federal Student Aid (FAFSA) at www.fafsa.ed.gov. School Code 002014 must be included or added to an existing FAFSA for Louisiana State University Health Science Center – New Orleans (LSUHSC-NO) to receive the results.
2. Recently passed federal legislation discontinues the Federal Family Educational Loan (FFEL) program, which was based on lending through banks and other lenders. All federal Stafford and PLUS borrowers and schools must utilize the Federal Direct Loan Program beginning with the 2010-11 academic year. Therefore, ALL student loan borrowers at LSUHSC-NO must file Federal Loan Direct Master Promissory Notes (MPN).

   Please complete your MPN at https://studentloans.gov/myDirectLoan/index.action. The PIN required is the same PIN you use to file the Free Application for Federal Student Aid (FAFSA). Select "LOUISIANA STATE UNIVERSITY HEALTH SCIENCES CENTER – NEW ORLEANS" from the school selection pull-down menu. DO NOT select "LOUISIANA STATE UNIVERSITY HEALTH SCIENCES CENTER – SCH. OF DENTISTRY" even if you are a student at the School of Dentistry.

   Students who borrowed federal Stafford loans at LSUHSC-NO in 2010-11 do not need to complete the online counseling session discussed below. Most borrowers will obtain sufficient funding through the federal Stafford program. Some may need to seek additional funding through Graduate PLUS, Undergraduate PLUS (for parents of dependent undergraduates), or private alternative loans.
3. Complete the Federal Stafford Loan online entrance counseling session at https://studentloans.gov/myDirectLoan/index.action.

UNIVERSITY OF NEW ENGLAND
COLLEGE OF DENTAL MEDICINE

Dr. James J. Koelbl, Dean

CONTACT INFORMATION

www.une.edu/dentalmedicine
716 Stevens Avenue
Portland, ME 04103
Phone: 207-221-4700
Fax: 207-523-1915

GRADUATE & PROFESSIONAL ADMISSIONS

Isaac Stickney
Graduate Admissions Counselor
716 Stevens Avenue
Portland, ME 04103
Phone: 207-221-4480
Fax: 207-523-1925
Email: gradadmissions@une.edu
www.une.edu/dentalmedicine/admissions

FINANCIAL AID

Kendra St. Gelais
Assistant Director of Financial Aid
716 Stevens Avenue
Portland, ME 04103
Phone: 207-602-2342
Fax: 207-221-4890
Email: finaid@une.edu
www.une.edu/financialaid

GRADUATE & PROFESSIONAL STUDENT AFFAIRS

Ray Handy
Assistant Dean of Students
716 Stevens Avenue
Portland, ME 04103
Phone: 207-221-4213
Fax: 207-523-1903
Email: rhandy@une.edu
www.une.edu/studentlife/portland

MINORITY AFFAIRS/DIVERSITY

Donna Gaspar
Director of Multicultural Affairs
11 Hills Beach Road
Biddeford, ME 04005
Phone: 207-602-2461
Fax: 207-602-5980
Email: dgaspar@une.edu
www.une.edu/studentlife/multicultural

HOUSING

Travis Erikson
Director, Student and Community Life
716 Stevens Avenue
Portland, ME 04103
Phone: 207-221-4213
Fax: 207-523-1903
Email: terickson@une.edu
www.une.edu/studentlife/portland

GENERAL INFORMATION

The University of New England College of Dental Medicine is a new dental school whose inaugural class will begin in August 2013. The University of New England is a top-ranked independent, coeducational, nonprofit university with two distinctive campuses located in the coastal communities of Portland and Biddeford, Maine. It has over 6,000 students and offers more than 40 undergraduate, graduate, and professional degree programs. The institution is the leading provider of health care professionals in the state of Maine, and has recognized strengths in osteopathic medicine; health sciences; biological, marine, and environmental sciences; and other select areas of excellence in the liberal arts.

The institution upholds the proud traditions and spirit of the original colleges that merged to become the University of New England: St. Francis College, The New England College of Osteopathic Medicine, and Westbrook College, with a history dated to 1831. The six academic units within the University are the College of Osteopathic Medicine and College of Arts and Sciences (Biddeford campus) and the Westbrook College of Health Professions, Center for Public and Community Health, College of Pharmacy and the College of Dental Medicine (Portland campus). As the newest academic unit, the College of Dental Medicine will welcome its first class of dental students in 2013. The College of Dental Medicine will offer a D.M.D. degree.

MISSION STATEMENT:

The mission of the University of New England College of Dental Medicine is to improve the health of Northern New England and shape the future of dentistry through excellence in education, discovery, and service.

Type of institution: Private
Year opened: 2013
Term type: Trimester
Time to degree in months: 46
Start month: August

Doctoral dental degree offered: D.M.D.
Total predoctoral enrollment: 184 when fully enrolled
Estimated entering class size: 48
Campus setting: Suburban
Campus housing available: No

PREPARATION

Formal minimum preparation in semester/quarter hours: Semester: 90 Quarter: 135
Baccalaureate degree preferred: Yes
Number of first-year, first-time enrollees whose highest degree is:
- Baccalaureate: NA
- Master's: NA
- Ph.D. or other doctorate: NA

Of first-year, first-time enrollees without baccalaureates, the number with:
- Equivalent of 60 undergraduate credit hours or less: NA
- Equivalent of 61-90 undergraduate credit hours: NA
- Equivalent of 91 or more undergraduate credit hours: NA

PREREQUISITE COURSE	REQUIRED	RECOMMENDED	LAB REQUIRED	CREDITS (SEMESTER/QUARTER)
BCP (biology-chemistry-physics) sciences				
Biology	✓		✓	4/6
Chemistry, general/inorganic	✓		✓	4/6
Chemistry, organic	✓		✓	4/6
Physics		✓		
Additional biological sciences				
Anatomy		✓		
Biochemistry	✓			3/4
Cell biology		✓		

(Prerequisite Courses continued)

PREPARATION (CONTINUED)

PREREQUISITE COURSE	REQUIRED	RECOMMENDED	LAB REQUIRED	CREDITS (SEMESTER/QUARTER)
Histology		✓		
Immunology				
Microbiology	✓		✓	4/6
Molecular biology/genetics		✓		
Physiology		✓		
Zoology				
Other				
Additional biology, chemistry, and/or physics courses	✓			16/24
English composition/technical writing	✓			3/4
Business		✓		
Computers		✓		
3-Dimensional art		✓		
Communications		✓		
Ethics		✓		

Community college coursework accepted for prerequisites: Yes
Community college coursework accepted for electives: Yes
Limits on community college credit hours: No
Maximum number of community college credit hours: NA
Advanced placement (AP) credit accepted for prerequisites: No
Advanced placement (AP) credit accepted for electives: No
Comments regarding AP credit: None
Job shadowing: Required
Number of hours of job shadowing required or recommended: 30
Other factors considered in admission: Demonstrated Community Service—Applicants must demonstrate community service through volunteerism or service-oriented employment.

DAT

Mandatory: Yes
Latest DAT for consideration of application: 10/15/2013
Oldest DAT considered: NA
When more than one DAT score is reported: Most recent score only is considered
Canadian DAT accepted: Yes
Application considered before DAT scores are submitted: No

APPLICATION AND SELECTION

TIMETABLE

Earliest filing date: 06/01/2013
Latest filing date: 11/01/2013
Earliest date for acceptance offers: 12/01/2013
Maximum time in days for applicant's response to acceptance offer: 30
Requests for deferred entrance considered: No
Fee for application: Yes
Amount of fee for application:
In state: $55 Out of state: $55 International: $55
Fee waiver available: No

	FIRST DEPOSIT	SECOND DEPOSIT	THIRD DEPOSIT
Required to hold place	$500	$1,500	No
Resident amount	$500	$1,500	
Nonresident amount	$500	$1,500	
Deposit due	30 days	03/15/2014	No
Applied to tuition	Yes	Yes	
Refundable	No	No	

APPLICATION PROCESS

Participates in Associated American Dental Schools Application Service (AADSAS): Yes
Accepts direct applicants: No
Secondary or supplemental application required: Yes
Secondary or supplemental application website: TBD
Interview is mandatory: Yes
Interview is by invitation: Yes

RESIDENCY

Admissions process distinguishes between in-state/in-province and out-of-state/out-of-province applicants: No
Preference given to residents of: Maine, New Hampshire, Vermont
Reciprocity Admissions Agreement available for legal residents of: NA
Applications are accepted from non-U.S. citizens/non-U.S. permanent residents: Yes

CURRICULUM

Overall, along with early and extensive clinical experiences, the program will utilize various methods of teaching and learning (e.g., lectures, small group sessions, online courses, self-directed learning, etc.) to deliver curriculum grounded in the biomedical and behavioral sciences. Because the University of New England College of Dental Medicine considers the students as members of the profession from day one, the school focuses particular attention on professionalism and ethics throughout the program. Learning objectives focus on the knowledge, skills, and values necessary to provide culturally competent, comprehensive, patient-centered care.

Throughout its duration, the program emphasizes reinforcing the linkages between basic, behavioral, and clinical sciences and the clinical practice of dentistry, including principles of community and public health. The D.M.D. program will provide dental students with an extensive clinical education in the university's main dental clinic, as well as in a network of community-based clinics and practices.

Students will begin their clinical experiences by treating "patients" in the state-of-the-art simulation clinic. These simulated patients will present with electronic patient records and digital images. Students will learn to evaluate health histories and develop and implement comprehensive treatment plans on a variety of simulated patients. Students will work in teams to learn and practice hands-on diagnosis and assessment skills on each other in the newly constructed comprehensive care clinic.

It is anticipated that students will:

- Begin to provide care to clinical patients in the latter part of the second year;
- Further develop their clinical knowledge and skills through the third year in the campus teaching clinic; and
- Spend the majority of time in the fourth year providing oral health care in community-based clinics and practices throughout northern New England.

Faculty-led group practices will include student "associates" from each of the four years of the program. Students will also participate in electives and research.

Student research opportunities: Yes

SPECIAL PROGRAMS AND SERVICES

PREDENTAL

Summer enrichment programs

DURING DENTAL SCHOOL

Academic counseling and tutoring
Community service opportunities (extensive)
Internships, externships, or extramural programs
Mentoring
Opportunity to study for credit at institution abroad
Personal counseling
Professional- and career-development programming
Training for those interested in academic careers
Transfer applicants considered if space is available
Research opportunities

ACTIVE STUDENT ORGANIZATIONS

NA

INTERNATIONAL DENTISTS

Graduates of international dental schools considered for traditional predoctoral program: Yes
Advanced standing program offered for graduates of international dental schools: No

COMBINED AND ALTERNATE DEGREES

Ph.D.	M.S.	M.P.H.	M.D.	B.A./B.S.	Other
—	—	—	—	—	—

ESTIMATED COSTS: 2013-14 SCHOOL YEAR

	FIRST YEAR	SECOND YEAR	THIRD YEAR	FOURTH YEAR
Tuition, resident	$56,950			
Tuition, nonresident	$56,950			
Tuition, other				
Fees	$580			
Program fee (instruments, books, and supplies, etc.)	$11,500			
Personal expenses	$5,800			
Estimated living expenses	$16,290			
Total, resident	$91,175			
Total, nonresident	$91,175			
Total, other				

FINANCIAL AID

Students need to complete the Free Application for Federal Student Aid (FAFSA) in order to apply for financial aid. The Financial Aid Office encourages all students to file the FAFSA via the web at www.fafsa.ed.gov after January 1 of the admission year. Students may estimate their income for the previous year in order to complete the FAFSA. The school code for the University of New England is 002050. Once the student has submitted the completed FAFSA application, the Financial Aid Office will be able to determine the student's eligibility for federal aid. An award letter will be sent electronically to the student's University of New England email address. For additional information, please contact finaid@une.edu.

UNIVERSITY OF MARYLAND
SCHOOL OF DENTISTRY

Dr. Christian S. Stohler, Dean

GENERAL INFORMATION

The University of Maryland School of Dentistry is a public institution that began as the Baltimore College of Dental Surgery, the first school in history to offer a course in dental education. Founded in 1840, the college was later consolidated with the Maryland Dental College and in 1923 merged with the Dental Department of the University of Maryland. The first dental college in the world, the University of Maryland School of Dentistry has maintained its position as a leader in dental education. The school offers a very strong curriculum, supported by well-trained, highly committed faculty. Faculty in the biological and clinical sciences are recognized as leaders in education, research, and service. The School of Dentistry enjoys the advantages of sharing an urban campus with the schools of Medicine, Law, Pharmacy, Nursing, and Social Work, and the Veterans Administration and University Medical Centers. The new dental school facility was completed and became operational in the fall of 2006, is located in Baltimore's famous revitalized downtown center.

MISSION STATEMENT:

The University of Maryland School of Dentistry is the direct descendant of the world's first dental college, the Baltimore College of Dental Surgery, which was chartered by an act of the Maryland General Assembly in 1840. It has successfully upheld the aspirations of its founders, Drs. Horace H. Hayden and Chapin A. Harris. The School of Dentistry is an exciting place to be, a place with unique history and tradition in our profession, yet eager to embrace a future that assuredly will be different. The school's mission is to improve the quality of life in Maryland through education, research, and service related to health, with special emphasis on improving dental, oral, and craniofacial health through comprehensive education, research, and service programs.

Type of institution: Public
Year opened: 1840
Term type: Semester
Time to degree in months: 46
Start month: August

Doctoral dental degree offered: D.D.S.
Total predoctoral enrollment: 520
Estimated entering class size: 130
Campus setting: Urban
Campus housing available: Yes

PREPARATION

Formal minimum preparation in semester/quarter hours: Semester: 90 Quarter: 135
Baccalaureate degree preferred: Yes, baccalaureate degree strongly preferred
Number of first-year, first-time enrollees whose highest degree is:
- Baccalaureate: 116
- Master's: 14
- Ph.D. or other doctorate: 0

Of first-year, first-time enrollees without baccalaureates, the number with:
- Equivalent of 60 undergraduate credit hours or less: 0
- Equivalent of 61-90 undergraduate credit hours: 0
- Equivalent of 91 or more undergraduate credit hours: 0

PREREQUISITE COURSE	REQUIRED	RECOMMENDED	LAB REQUIRED	CREDITS (SEMESTER/QUARTER)
BCP (biology-chemistry-physics) sciences				
Biology	✓		✓	8/12
Chemistry, general/inorganic	✓		✓	8/12
Chemistry, organic	✓		✓	8/12
Physics	✓		✓	8/12
Additional biological sciences				
Anatomy		✓		
Biochemistry	✓			3/5
Cell biology		✓		

(Prerequisite Courses continued)

CONTACT INFORMATION

www.dental.umaryland.edu
650 West Baltimore Street, 6-South
Baltimore, MD 21201

ADMISSIONS
Dr. Patricia E. Meehan
Assistant Dean of Admissions and Recruitment
650 West Baltimore Street, 6-South
Room 6410
Baltimore, MD 21201
Phone: 410-706-7472
www.dental.umaryland.edu

STUDENT AFFAIRS
Dr. Carroll Ann Trotman
Associate Dean for Academic and Student Affairs
650 West Baltimore Street, 6-South
Room 6408
Baltimore, MD 21201

RECRUITMENT AND STUDENT ADVOCACY
Dr. Andrea Morgan
Dental Recruitment Coordinator
Director of Student Advocacy and Cultural Affairs
650 West Baltimore Street
Room 6410
Baltimore, MD 21201
Phone: 410-706-7472

STUDENT FINANCIAL ASSISTANCE AND EDUCATION
601 West Lombard Street
Suite 221
Baltimore, MD 21201
Phone: 410-706-7347
Email: Aidtalk@umaryland.edu

HOUSING
518 West Fayette Street
Baltimore, MD 21201
Phone: 410-706-5523
Email: umbhousing@umaryland.edu
www.housing.umaryland.edu

PREPARATION (CONTINUED)

PREREQUISITE COURSE	REQUIRED	RECOMMENDED	LAB REQUIRED	CREDITS (SEMESTER/QUARTER)
Histology		✓		
Immunology		✓		
Microbiology		✓		
Molecular biology/genetics		✓		
Physiology		✓		
Zoology		✓		
Other				
English composition	✓			6/9

Community college coursework accepted for prerequisites: Yes
Community college coursework accepted for electives: Yes
Limits on community college credit hours: Yes
Maximum number of community college credit hours: 60
Advanced placement (AP) credit accepted for prerequisites: Yes
Advanced placement (AP) credit accepted for electives: Yes
Comments regarding AP credit: AP credits for prerequisites will be reviewed by the Admissions Committee.
Job shadowing: Highly recommended
Number of hours of job shadowing required or recommended: Minimum recommended is 50 hours
Other factors considered in admission: Academic performance, performance on the DAT, knowledge of the profession, personal statement, letters of recommendation, extracurricular activities including leadership and community service, the personal interview, and personal factors

DAT

Mandatory: Yes
Latest DAT for consideration of application: 12/01/2013
Oldest DAT considered: 01/01/2011
When more than one DAT score is reported: Most recent score only is considered
Canadian DAT accepted: Yes
Application considered before DAT scores are submitted: No

DAT: 2012 ENTERING CLASS

ENROLLEE DAT SCORES	RANGE	MEAN
Academic Average	17-24	20
Perceptual Ability	15-26	20
Total Science	17-26	20

GPA: 2012 ENTERING CLASS

ENROLLEE GPA SCORES	RANGE	MEAN
Science GPA	2.9-4.0	3.5
Total GPA	3.0-4.0	3.6

APPLICATION AND SELECTION

TIMETABLE

Earliest filing date: 06/04/2013
Latest filing date: 01/01/2014
Earliest date for acceptance offers: 12/01/2013
Maximum time in days for applicant's response to acceptance offer:
30 days if accepted on or after December 1
15 days if accepted on or after February 1

Requests for deferred entrance considered: In exceptional circumstances only.
Fee for application: Yes, submitted at same time as Associated American Dental Schools Application Service (AADSAS) application.
Amount of fee for application:
In state: $85 Out of state: $85 International: $85
Fee waiver available: No

	FIRST DEPOSIT	SECOND DEPOSIT	THIRD DEPOSIT
Required to hold place	Yes	Yes	No
Resident amount	$750	$1,000	
Nonresident amount	$750	$1,000	
Deposit due	As indicated in offer letter	04/01/2014	No
Applied to tuition	Yes	Yes	
Refundable	No	No	

APPLICATION PROCESS

Participates in AADSAS: Yes
Accepts direct applicants: No
Secondary or supplemental application required: Yes, by invitation
Secondary or supplemental application website: NA
Interview is mandatory: Yes
Interview is by invitation: Yes

RESIDENCY

Admissions process distinguishes between in-state/in-province and out-of-state/out-of-province applicants: Yes
Preference given to residents of: Maryland
Reciprocity Admissions Agreement available for legal residents of: None
Applications are accepted from non-U.S. citizens/non-U.S. permanent residents: Yes

APPLICATION AND ENROLLMENT	NUMBER OF APPLICANTS	ESTIMATED NUMBER INTERVIEWED	ESTIMATED NUMBER ENROLLED
In-state or province applicants	210	130	70
Out-of-state or province applicants	2,640	330	60

Generally and over time, percentage of your first-year enrollment is in-state: NR

Origin of out-of-state enrollees (U.S.): Alabama-1, California-3, Connecticut-3, District of Columbia- 1, Florida-10, Georgia-1, Illinois-1, Indiana - 1, Massachusets-1, Michigan - 4, New Hampshire-2, New Jersey-4, New York-5, North Carolina-2, Ohio-1, Pennsylvania-13 Virginia-9, Washington-1

Origin of international enrollees: NA

DEMOGRAPHIC DESCRIPTIONS OF APPLICANTS: 2012 ENTERING CLASS

	APPLICANTS		ENROLLEES	
	M	W	M	W
Hispanic/Latino of any race	22	24	5	6
American Indian or Alaska Native	11	8	2	0
Asian	501	512	13	15
Black or African American	49	107	2	10
Native Hawaiian or Other Pacific Islander	0	1	0	0
White	754	578	42	28
Two or more races	94	95	3	2
Race and ethnicity unknown	57	37	0	2
International	NR	NR	NR	NR

	MINIMUM	MAXIMUM	MEAN
2012 entering class enrollees by age	21	37	24

Number of first-time enrollees over age 30: 7

CURRICULUM

The D.D.S. program combines a strong base of biological sciences and an outstanding clinical education, with a focus on application of latest research findings. Working in a highly collegial manner, nationally recognized faculty provide excellent educational services for students. Students have the opportunity to utilize innovative educational methodologies, including online learning activities. The outstanding clinical education program, featuring patient-centered and student-centered general practices, simulates the structure of a dental practice. Various cooperative efforts with local, state, and federal agencies also provide dental services for special-needs populations. Additionally, the University of Maryland School of Dentistry-Perryville is a satellite school staffed by faculty and students providing contemporary dental care to an underserved population in Cecil County and surrounding areas. This 26-chair facility is equipped with state-of-the-art equipment. Students engage in service learning experiences at this facility under the supervision of faculty. Dental graduates are well prepared to enter advanced dental education programs and to practice their professions in a wide range of private practice, public service, and academic settings.

Student research opportunities: Yes

SPECIAL PROGRAMS AND SERVICES

PREDENTAL

Summer enrichment programs

DURING DENTAL SCHOOL

Academic counseling and tutoring
Community service opportunities
Internships, externships, or extramural programs
Transfer applicants considered if space is available

ACTIVE STUDENT ORGANIZATIONS

American Association of Dental Research Student Research Group
American Association of Pediatric Dentistry
American Association of Women Dentists
American Dental Education Association (ADEA)
American Student Dental Association
Hispanic Dental Association
Student National Dental Association

INTERNATIONAL DENTISTS

Graduates of international dental schools considered for traditional predoctoral program: No

Advanced standing program offered for graduates of international dental schools: Yes

Advanced standing program description: The University of Maryland School of Dentistry does not have a specific program designed for candidates seeking admission to the Doctor of Dental Surgery (D.D.S.) program with advanced standing. However, it may be possible for exceptionally talented graduates of non-U.S./non-Canadian dental schools or dental students currently enrolled in U.S./Canadian dental schools to gain admission to the University of Maryland's D.D.S. program with advanced standing.

COMBINED AND ALTERNATE DEGREES

Ph.D.	M.S.	M.P.H.	M.D.	B.A./B.S.	Other
✓	✓	✓	—	—	✓

Other Degree: Master of Science in Clinical Research

COSTS: 2012-13 SCHOOL YEAR

	FIRST YEAR	SECOND YEAR	THIRD YEAR	FOURTH YEAR
Tuition, resident	$26,314	$26,314	$26,314	$26,314
Tuition, nonresident	$57,515	$54,276	$54,276	$54,276
Tuition, other				
Fees	$11,662	$11,390	$11,988	$12,791
Instruments, books, and supplies	$7,571	$7,319	$3,393	$2,663
Estimated living expenses	$23,500	$21,350	$25,650	$27,800
Total, resident	$69,047	$63,900	$65,872	$68,095
Total, nonresident	$102,761	$97,626	$99,569	$101,792
Total, other				

FINANCIAL AID

The University of Maryland requires the Free Application for Federal Student Aid (FASFA) to determine a student's eligibility for federal, state, and institutional financial aid. To receive consideration for all types of financial aid, applicants are strongly encouraged to complete the FAFSA prior to March 1, 2013. Applicants can complete the FAFSA online at www.fafsa.ed.gov. The school code is 002104. We also encourage students to include parental income and signatures on the initial FAFSA for consideration of the Health Professions Student Loan (HPSL) program. Notification of financial aid awards are emailed to students in early May 2013. For additional information, please visit the website for Student Financial Assistance & Education—www.umaryland.edu/fin. Applicants may also email us at aidtalk@umaryland.edu or call 401-706-7347.

BOSTON UNIVERSITY
HENRY M. GOLDMAN SCHOOL OF DENTAL MEDICINE

Dr. Jeffrey W. Hutter, Dean

GENERAL INFORMATION

The Boston University Henry M. Goldman School of Dental Medicine (GSDM) is a forward-thinking educational institution that produces a highly competent dentist in a challenging and exciting environment. A comfortable class size combined with a dedicated, talented faculty provides an exceptionally stimulating educational experience. The curriculum successfully integrates the biomedical sciences with the clinical care of patients both within the school and in selected extramural sites. The Extramural Program, composed of an Applied Professional Experience (APEX) Program in the first year and an externship during the fourth year, provides students with practical clinical experience in preparation for their professional careers upon graduation.

MISSION STATEMENT:

The Boston University GSDM will be the premier academic dental institution promoting excellence in dental education, research, oral health care, and community service to improve the overall health of the global population. We will provide outstanding service to a diverse group of students, patients, faculty, staff, alumni, and health care professionals within our facilities, our community, and the world. We will shape the future of the profession through scholarship, creating and disseminating new knowledge, developing and using innovative technologies and educational methodologies, and by promoting critical thinking and lifelong learning. We will do so in an ethical, supportive environment, consistent with our core values of respect, truth, responsibility, fairness, and compassion, and our operational values of excellence, service, and effective communication in synergy with the strategic plan of Boston University. We will support this mission using responsible financial policies and philanthropy.

Type of institution: Private
Year opened: 1972
Term type: Semester
Time to degree in months: 48
Start month: July

Doctoral dental degree offered: D.M.D.
Total predoctoral enrollment: 460
Estimated entering class size: 115
Campus setting: Urban
Campus housing available: Yes

PREPARATION

Formal minimum preparation in semester/quarter hours: Semester: 120 Quarter: 200
Baccalaureate degree preferred: Yes, required
Number of first-year, first-time enrollees whose highest degree is:
- Baccalaureate: 86
- Master's: 25
- Ph.D. or other doctorate: 3

Of first-year, first-time enrollees without baccalaureates, the number with:
- Equivalent of 60 undergraduate credit hours or less: 0
- Equivalent of 61-90 undergraduate credit hours: 0
- Equivalent of 91 or more undergraduate credit hours: 1 enrolled in Boston University 7-year B.A./D.M.D. program

PREREQUISITE COURSE	REQUIRED	RECOMMENDED	LAB REQUIRED	CREDITS (SEMESTER/QUARTER)
BCP (biology-chemistry-physics) sciences				
Biology	✓		✓	12/18
Chemistry, general/inorganic	✓		✓	8/12

(Prerequisite Courses continued)

CONTACT INFORMATION

www.bu.edu/dental
Boston University Henry M. Goldman
School of Dental Medicine
100 East Newton Street, G-305
Boston, MA 02118
Phone: 617-638-4787
Fax: 617-638-4798

ADMISSIONS
Catherine Sarkis
Assistant Dean for Admissions
Boston University Henry M. Goldman
School of Dental Medicine
100 East Newton Street, G-305
Boston, MA 02118
Phone: 617-638-4787
www.bu.edu/dental/admissions

STUDENT FINANCIAL SERVICES
Elayne Peloquin
Executive Director
Boston University Medical Campus
72 East Concord Street, A-303
Boston, MA 02118
Phone: 617-638-5130
www.bumc.bu.edu/osfs

STUDENT AFFAIRS
Dr. Joseph Calabrese
Assistant Dean of Students
Boston University Henry M. Goldman
School of Dental Medicine
100 East Newton Street, G-305
Boston, MA 02118
Phone: 617-638-4790
http://www.bu.edu/dental/about/offices/student-affairs/

MINORITY AFFAIRS/DIVERSITY
Dr. Larry G. Dunham
Director of Diversity and Multicultural Affairs
Boston University Henry M. Goldman
School of Dental Medicine
100 East Newton Street, G-305
Boston, MA 02118
Phone: 617-638-4738
www.bu.edu/dental/admissions

HOUSING RESOURCES
Barbara Attianese
Housing Resources Advisor
Boston University Medical Campus
Office of Housing Resources
72 East Concord Street, A-303
Boston, MA 02118
Phone: 617-638-5125
www.bumc.bu.edu/ohr

INTERNATIONAL STUDENTS AND SCHOLARS OFFICE
Jeanne Kelley
Director
Boston University ISSO
888 Commonwealth Avenue
Boston, MA 02215
Phone: 617-353-3565
www.bu.edu/isso

PREPARATION (CONTINUED)

PREREQUISITE COURSE	REQUIRED	RECOMMENDED	LAB REQUIRED	CREDITS (SEMESTER/QUARTER)
Chemistry, organic	✓		✓	8/12
Physics	✓		✓	8/12
Additional biological sciences				
Anatomy		✓		4/6
Biochemistry		✓		4/6
Cell biology		✓		4/6
Histology		✓		4/6
Immunology		✓		4/6
Microbiology		✓		4/6
Molecular biology/genetics		✓		4/6
Physiology		✓		4/6
Zoology		✓		4/6
Other				
Math with calculus	✓			8/12
English or composition	✓			8/12
Social sciences selections		✓		20/26
Economics, business		✓		

Community college coursework accepted for prerequisites: No. Prerequisites only from four-year accredited U.S./Canada colleges.
Community college coursework accepted for electives: Yes
Limits on community college credit hours: Yes
Maximum number of community college credit hours: 30
Advanced placement (AP) credit accepted for prerequisites: No
Advanced placement (AP) credit accepted for electives: Yes
Comments regarding AP credit: Applicants with AP in prerequisites should take upper-level courses. Credits from an accredited four-year U.S./Canada college or university should match or exceed the prerequisite requirement in the subject.
Job shadowing: Recommended
Other factors considered in admission: Undergraduate record, quality and difficulty of courses taken, demonstrated leadership ability, motivation for the study of dentistry, references, DAT, extracurricular endeavors, and communication skills

DAT

Mandatory: Yes
Latest DAT for consideration of application: 12/03/2013
Oldest DAT considered: 06/01/2011
When more than one DAT score is reported: Highest score is considered.
Canadian DAT accepted: Yes
Application considered before DAT scores are submitted: No

DAT: 2012 ENTERING CLASS

ENROLLEE DAT SCORES	RANGE	MEAN
Academic Average	17-23	20
Perceptual Ability	15-30	20
Total Science	16-24	20

GPA: 2012 ENTERING CLASS

ENROLLEE GPA SCORES	RANGE	MEAN
Science GPA	2.90-4.00	3.40
Total GPA	2.97-3.99	3.45

APPLICATION AND SELECTION

TIMETABLE

Earliest filing date: 06/01/2013
Latest filing date: 12/01/2013
Earliest date for acceptance offers: 12/03/2013
Maximum time in days for applicant's response to acceptance offer:
30 days if accepted on or after December 1
15 days if accepted on or after February 1
Requests for deferred entrance considered: Yes
Fee for application: Yes, submitted only when requested
Amount of fee for application:
In state: $75 Out of state: $75 International: $105
Fee waiver available: Yes

	FIRST DEPOSIT	SECOND DEPOSIT	THIRD DEPOSIT
Required to hold place	Yes	No	No
Resident amount	$3,000		
Nonresident amount	$3,000		
Deposit due	As indicated in admission offer		
Applied to tuition	Yes		
Refundable	No		

APPLICATION PROCESS

Participates in Associated American Dental Schools Application Service (AADSAS): Yes
Accepts direct applicants: No
Secondary or supplemental application required: Yes
Interview is mandatory: Yes
Interview is by invitation: Yes

RESIDENCY

Admissions process distinguishes between in-state/in-province and out-of-state/out-of-province applicants: No
Preference given to residents of: None
Applications are accepted from non-U.S. citizens/non-U.S. permanent residents: Yes

APPLICATION AND ENROLLMENT	NUMBER OF APPLICANTS	ESTIMATED NUMBER INTERVIEWED	ESTIMATED NUMBER ENROLLED
In-state or province applicants	168	82	30
Out-of-state or province applicants	4,422	302	85

Generally and over time, percentage of your first-year enrollment is in-state: 25%

Origin of out-of-state enrollees (U.S.): California-5, Connecticut-5, Florida-8, Georgia-3, Maine-2, Maryland-1, Michigan-2, Minnesota-1, New Jersey-2, New York-6, Pennsylvania-1, Rhode Island-4, Texas-5, Vermont-2, Virginia-3, Wisconsin-2

Origin of international enrollees: Canada-24, South Korea-8, Kuwait-1

DEMOGRAPHIC DESCRIPTIONS OF APPLICANTS: 2012 ENTERING CLASS

	APPLICANTS		ENROLLEES	
	M	W	M	W
Hispanic/Latino of any race	127	154	4	3
American Indian or Alaska Native	10	16	0	0
Asian	727	789	14	14
Black or African American	43	68	0	1
Native Hawaiian or Other Pacific Islander	1	1	0	0
White	1,026	763	22	20
Two or more races	52	60	4	0
Race and ethnicity unknown	69	57	0	0
International	292	279	16	17

Note: Additional applicants, gender not reported: Hispanic/Latino- 4; Asian-21; Black or African American-2; White- 5; Two or more races-2; Race and ethnicity unknown-13; International-9.

	MINIMUM	MAXIMUM	MEAN
2012 entering class enrollees by age	21	34	24

Number of first-time enrollees over age 30: 2

CURRICULUM

Integrated learning experiences provide the student with the ability to ultimately deliver the highest level of oral health care. Year 1 starts with biomedical science courses and an introduction to general dentistry. It continues with simulated dental experiences and culminates with APEX, an internship experience in a dental practice. Year 2 continues with biomedical and behavioral sciences, simulated dental experiences, and clinical sciences. Emphasis is on integrating biomedical and behavioral sciences with clinical sciences. Years 3 and 4 focus on comprehensive patient care. Faculty mentors oversee clinical activities of students. A 10-week externship experience in Year 4 serves as a capstone activity that fosters students' development into independent clinical practitioners.

Student research opportunities: Yes

SPECIAL PROGRAMS AND SERVICES

PREDENTAL

Postbaccalaureate programs
Special affiliations with colleges and universities: Boston University School of Medicine Division of Graduate Medical Sciences - Master of Arts in Medical Sciences Concentration in Oral Health Sciences; Boston University College of Liberal Arts - 7 Year B.A./D.M.D.; Boston University Metropolitan College Postbaccalaureate Certificate in Premedical Studies

DURING DENTAL SCHOOL

Academic counseling and tutoring
Community service opportunities
Internships, externships, or extramural programs
Mentoring
Personal counseling
Professional- and career-development programming
Training for those interested in academic careers

ACTIVE STUDENT ORGANIZATIONS

Alpha Omega
American Association of Women Dentists
American Dental Education Association (ADEA)
Asian Dental Student Organization
American Student Dental Association BU Chapter
Hispanic Student Dental Association
Muslim Student Association
Predoctoral Research Group
Student National Dental Association
Uniformed Services Student Dental Association

INTERNATIONAL DENTISTS

Graduates of international dental schools considered for traditional predoctoral program: No
Advanced standing program offered for graduates of international dental schools: Yes
Advanced standing program description: Program awarding a dental degree

COMBINED AND ALTERNATE DEGREES

Ph.D.	M.S.	M.P.H.	M.D.	B.A./B.S.	Other
—	—	—	—	✓	✓

Other Degrees: CAGS, M.S., M.S.D., D.Sc., D.Sc.D., Ph.D., and Internship; B.A./D.M.D. 7-year program offered to Boston University undergraduates; Advanced dental education programs offered in Advanced Education in General Dentistry (AEGD), Dental Public Health, Endodontics, Operative Dentistry, Oral Biology, Oral and Maxillofacial Pathology, Oral and Maxillofacial Surgery, Orthodontics, Pediatric Dentistry, Periodontics, and Prosthodontics

COSTS: 2012-13 SCHOOL YEAR

	FIRST YEAR	SECOND YEAR	THIRD YEAR	FOURTH YEAR
Tuition, resident	$62,000	$62,000	$62,000	$62,000
Tuition, nonresident	$62,000	$62,000	$62,000	$62,000
Tuition, other	$62,000	$62,000	$62,000	$62,000
Fees	$1,314	$1,314	$1,864	$1,314
Instruments, books, and supplies	$10,966	$8,576	$1,794	0
Estimated living expenses	$16,529	$16,529	$13,783	$16,529
Total, resident	$90,809	$88,419	$79,441	$79,843
Total, nonresident	$90,809	$88,419	$79,441	$79,843
Total, other	$90,809	$88,419	$79,441	$79,843

FINANCIAL AID

Student Financial Services (SFS) provides information about available resources that can help make dental education affordable while also assisting students to become proactive about financing their education. The role of SFS includes:

- Counseling for pre-admissions
- Delivering orientation, debt-management, and financial-awareness programs
- Administering institutional and federal aid programs
- Certifying credit-based private loan applications
- Providing student financial need documentation to outside scholarship agencies
- Conducting entrance and exit counseling sessions
- Revising and reevaluating student financial aid packages
- Making provisions for eligible students to receive advances for living expenses
- Ensuring that all aspects of the financial aid process are completed or remedied thoroughly and accurately as determined by office, institutional, and federal policies
- Maintaining a comprehensive website (www.bumc.bu.edu/osfs/sdm) that includes aid applications, links to the U.S. Department of Education, and much more

Staff members are available to assist students Monday through Thursday, from 8:30 a.m. to 6:00 p.m., and Friday, from 8:30 a.m. to 5:00 p.m., and can be reached at 617-638-5130, or by email at osfs-sdm@bu.edu.

HARVARD SCHOOL OF DENTAL MEDICINE

Dr. R. Bruce Donoff, Dean

GENERAL INFORMATION

The Harvard School of Dental Medicine (HSDM) was established in 1867 as the first university-based dental school in the United States. This relationship with a great university and its associated world-renowned medical center and teaching hospitals shapes the education of dental students. The Harvard School of Dental Medicine has achieved success in its mission of producing leaders in the field of dental medicine in clinical care, teaching, and research by being educationally innovative and by providing a professional school education that presents multiple opportunities for enrichment. The education of a Harvard dental student prepares women and men for a career of lifelong learning whether that be in clinical practice, teaching, research, oral health care delivery, or a combination of these. The school is proud of its tradition of producing graduates who have excelled in each of these career paths.

MISSION STATEMENT:

The Harvard School of Dental Medicine's mission is to develop and foster a community of global leaders advancing oral and systemic health.

Type of institution: Private
Year opened: 1867
Term type: Semester
Time to degree in months: 41
Start month: August

Doctoral dental degree offered: D.M.D.
Total predoctoral enrollment: 145
Estimated entering class size: 35
Campus setting: Urban
Campus housing available: Yes

PREPARATION

Formal minimum preparation in semester/quarter hours: Semester: 90 credit hours
Baccalaureate degree preferred: Yes
Number of first-year, first-time enrollees whose highest degree is:
- Baccalaureate: 35
- Master's: 0
- Ph.D. or other doctorate: 0

Of first-year, first-time enrollees without baccalaureates, the number with:
- Equivalent of 60 undergraduate credit hours or less: 0
- Equivalent of 61-90 undergraduate credit hours: 0
- Equivalent of 91 or more undergraduate credit hours: 0

PREREQUISITE COURSE	REQUIRED	RECOMMENDED	LAB REQUIRED	CREDITS (SEMESTER/QUARTER)
BCP (biology-chemistry-physics) sciences				
Biology	✓		✓	8/12
Chemistry, general/inorganic	✓		✓	8/12
Chemistry, organic	✓		✓	8/12
Physics	✓		✓	8/12
Additional biological sciences				
Anatomy				
Biochemistry	✓			3/5
Cell biology		✓		
Histology				
Immunology				
Microbiology		✓		
Molecular biology/genetics				
Physiology		✓		

(Prerequisite Courses continued)

CONTACT INFORMATION

www.hsdm.harvard.edu
188 Longwood Avenue
Cambridge, MA 02115

OFFICE OF ADMISSIONS
188 Longwood Avenue
Boston, MA 02115
Phone: 617-432-1443
Email: hsdm_dmd_admissions@hsdm.harvard.edu

FINANCIAL AID
188 Longwood Avenue
Boston, MA 02115
Phone: 617-432-1527

OFFICE OF DENTAL EDUCATION
Anne Berg
Director of Admissions and Student Affairs
188 Longwood Avenue
Boston, MA 02115
Phone: 617-432-1447

MINORITY AFFAIRS
Phone: 617-432-4247

HOUSING
Vanderbilt Hall
107 Louis Pasteur Avenue
Boston, MA 02115
Email: vanderbilt_hall@hms.harvard.edu

INTERNATIONAL STUDENTS
Office of Admissions
188 Longwood Avenue
Boston, MA 02115
Phone: 617-432-0569
Email: hsdm_dmd_admissions@hsdm.harvard.edu

PREPARATION (CONTINUED)

PREREQUISITE COURSE	REQUIRED	RECOMMENDED	LAB REQUIRED	CREDITS (SEMESTER/QUARTER)
Zoology				
Other				
Calculus	✓			6/9
English	✓			6/9

Community college coursework accepted for prerequisites: Yes, but prefer courses be taken at four-year institution
Community college coursework accepted for electives: Yes
Limits on community college credit hours: Yes, but prefer science courses at four-year institutions
Maximum number of community college credit hours: 60
Advanced placement (AP) credit accepted for prerequisites: Yes
Advanced placement (AP) credit accepted for electives: Yes
Comments regarding AP credit: Accepted for calculus and one English course
Prefer all science prerequisite courses be taken at a four-year institution
Job shadowing: Recommended

DAT

Mandatory: Yes
Latest DAT for consideration of application: 12/01/2013
Oldest DAT considered: 01/01/2011
When more than one DAT score is reported: Highest score is considered
Canadian DAT accepted: Yes
Application considered before DAT scores are submitted: No

DAT: 2012 ENTERING CLASS

ENROLLEE DAT SCORES	RANGE	MEAN
Academic Average	20-27	23.2
Perceptual Ability	19-29	22.2
Total Science	19-30	23.4

GPA: 2012 ENTERING CLASS

ENROLLEE GPA SCORES	RANGE	MEAN
Science GPA	3.47-4.06	3.85
Total GPA	3.60-4.11	3.85

APPLICATION AND SELECTION

TIMETABLE

Earliest filing date: 06/01/2013
Latest filing date: 12/15/2013
Earliest date for acceptance offers: 12/01/2013
Maximum time in days for applicant's response to acceptance offer:
30 days if accepted between December 1 and January 31
15 days if accepted on or after February 1
Response period may be lifted after April 15
Requests for deferred entrance considered: No
Fee for application: Yes, submit to school when Associated American Dental Schools Application Service (AADSAS) application is submitted.
Amount of fee for application:
In state: $75 Out of state: $75 International: $75
Fee waiver available: Yes, if AADSAS fee has been waived: Provide a copy of AADSAS fee waiver.

	FIRST DEPOSIT	SECOND DEPOSIT	THIRD DEPOSIT
Required to hold place	No	No	No

APPLICATION PROCESS

Participates in AADSAS: Yes
Accepts direct applicants: No
Secondary or supplemental application required: Yes, only when selected for interview
Interview is mandatory: Yes
Interview is by invitation: Yes

RESIDENCY

Admissions process distinguishes between in-state/in-province and out-of-state/out-of-province applicants: No
Applications are accepted from non-U.S. citizens/non-U.S. permanent residents: Yes

APPLICATION AND ENROLLMENT	NUMBER OF APPLICANTS	ESTIMATED NUMBER INTERVIEWED	ESTIMATED NUMBER ENROLLED
In-state or province applicants	60	6	2
Out-of-state or province applicants	1,015	95	33

Generally and over time, percentage of your first-year enrollment is in-state: 6-10%

Origin of out-of-state enrollees (U.S.): California- 7, Connecticut-1, Delaware-1, Florida-5, Hawaii-1, Kentucky-1, New Jersey-3, New York-5, Oregon-1, Pennsylvania-3, Texas-1, Washington-1, Wisconsin-1

Origin of international enrollees: No international enrollees in 2012

DEMOGRAPHIC DESCRIPTIONS OF APPLICANTS: 2012 ENTERING CLASS

	APPLICANTS		ENROLLEES	
	M	W	M	W
Hispanic/Latino of any race	24	39	1	2
American Indian or Alaska Native	0	1	0	0
Asian	161	173	4	9
Black or African American	15	17	0	0
Native Hawaiian or Other Pacific Islander	0	1	0	0
White	242	164	10	6
Two or more races	13	17	0	1
Race and ethnicity unknown	17	18	1	1
International	87	73	0	0

Note: 13 applicants did not report gender

	MINIMUM	MAXIMUM	MEAN
2012 entering class enrollees by age	21	28	23

Number of first-time enrollees over age 30: 0

CURRICULUM

The philosophy of education at HSDM is that dentistry is a specialty of medicine. In keeping with this belief, medical and dental students study together in the New Pathway curriculum at Harvard Medical School during the first two years. Dental clinical instruction occurs in treatment teams that utilize a comprehensive approach to patient care. Both didactic and clinical courses are taught by problem-based method of study and discussion in small tutorial groups. In this approach, cases based on actual clinical records or investigative problems are utilized to set the learning objectives. Students learn critical thinking and problem-solving techniques that will equip them for lifelong learning in the field of dental medicine. Students also take courses in research and complete a research project, thesis, and formal presentation over the course of the four-year training period.

Student research opportunities: Yes

SPECIAL PROGRAMS AND SERVICES

DURING DENTAL SCHOOL

Academic counseling and tutoring
Significant community service opportunities:
Internships, externships, or extramural programs
Mentoring
Opportunity to study for credit at institution abroad (available only during elective periods)
Personal counseling

ACTIVE STUDENT ORGANIZATIONS

American Association of Dental Research Student Research Group
American Association of Pediatric Dentistry
American Association of Women Dentists
American Dental Education Association (ADEA)
Alpha Omega Dental Fraternity, Delta Chapter
American Student Dental Association
Hispanic Dental Association
Student National Dental Association

INTERNATIONAL DENTISTS

Graduates of international dental schools considered for traditional predoctoral program: Yes; if prerequisite courses are taken at a U.S. college/university

Advanced standing program offered for graduates of international dental schools: No

COMBINED AND ALTERNATE DEGREES

Ph.D.	M.S.	M.P.H.	M.D.	B.A./B.S.	Other
✓	✓	✓	—	—	✓

Other Degrees: M.B.A.

COSTS: 2012-13 SCHOOL YEAR

	FIRST YEAR	SECOND YEAR	THIRD YEAR	FOURTH YEAR
Tuition, resident	$49,875	$49,875	$49,875	$49,875
Tuition, nonresident	$49,875	$49,875	$49,875	$49,875
Tuition, other	NA	NA	NA	NA
Fees	$1,482	$13,509	$14,706	$13,144
Instruments, books, and supplies	$1,950	$4,890	$4,599	$150
Estimated living expenses	$16,703	$18,640	$20,040	$16,703
Total, resident	$70,010	$86,941	$89,220	$79,872
Total, nonresident	$70,010	$86,941	$89,220	$79,872
Total, other	NA	NA	NA	NA

FINANCIAL AID

Visit the Harvard School of Dental Medicine website at www.hsdm.harvard.edu for information regarding financial aid.

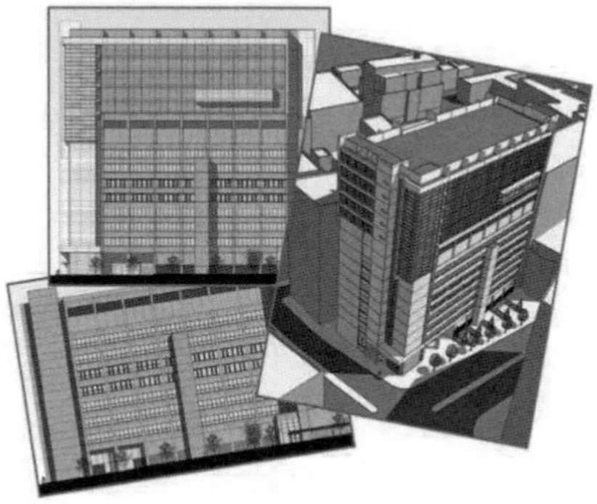

TUFTS UNIVERSITY
SCHOOL OF DENTAL MEDICINE

Dr. Huw F. Thomas, Dean

GENERAL INFORMATION

Tufts University School of Dental Medicine, a private institution, originated in 1868 as the Boston Dental College. It was incorporated in 1899 as a component of Tufts College. The School of Dental Medicine is located in downtown Boston adjacent to the Tufts Medical Center. In addition to the School of Dental Medicine, the Boston Health Sciences Campus is home to the School of Medicine, the Sackler School of Graduate Biomedical Sciences, the Gerald J. and Dorothy R. Friedman School of Nutrition Science and Policy, the Jaharis Family Center for Graduate Biomedical and Nutrition Research, the Jean Mayer Human Nutrition Research Center on Aging, and five hospitals. The School of Dental Medicine offers the D.M.D. program, an Advanced Standing Program for International Students, as well as accredited advanced education programs in six dental specialties that lead to a certificate or Master of Science Degree, and nonaccredited advanced education programs in four dental specialties.

MISSION STATEMENT:

Tufts University School of Dental Medicine is an accredited private dental school that provides education to diverse predoctoral and postgraduate students to prepare them to practice dentistry in the 21st century with knowledge of many different patient populations, all dental specialties, and varied practice settings. This education occurs in an ethical and professional environment in which high-quality dental care is provided to our patients. We strive to achieve a dynamic curriculum that provides excellent clinical training, integrates the health sciences with clinical experience, and utilizes modern technology. Our success is based on maintaining a strong faculty and staff, supported in their commitment to teaching and administration, ongoing development, scholarship, research, student services, and community service.

Type of institution: Private
Year opened: 1868
Term type: Semester
Time to degree in months: 42
Start month: September

Doctoral dental degree offered: D.M.D.
Total predoctoral enrollment: 703
Estimated entering class size: 185
Campus setting: Urban
Campus housing available: No

PREPARATION

Formal minimum preparation in semester/quarter hours: Semester: 31 Quarter: 46
Baccalaureate degree preferred: Yes, bachelor's degree required prior to matriculation
Number of first-year, first-time enrollees whose highest degree is:
- Baccalaureate: 164
- Master's: 20
- Ph.D. or other doctorate: 0

Of first-year, first-time enrollees without baccalaureates, the number with:
- Equivalent of 60 undergraduate credit hours or less: 0
- Equivalent of 61-90 undergraduate credit hours: 0
- Equivalent of 91 or more undergraduate credit hours: 0

PREREQUISITE COURSE	REQUIRED	RECOMMENDED	LAB REQUIRED	CREDITS (SEMESTER/QUARTER)
BCP (biology-chemistry-physics) sciences				
Biology	✓		✓	8
Chemistry, general/inorganic	✓		✓	8
Chemistry, organic	✓		✓	4
Physics	✓		✓	8
Additional biological sciences*				
Anatomy		✓		
Biochemistry	✓			3/5
Cell biology		✓		

(Prerequisite Courses continued)

CONTACT INFORMATION

http://dental.tufts.edu
One Kneeland Street
Boston, MA 02111

ADMISSIONS

Melissa L. Friedman
Director of Admissions
One Kneeland Street
Boston, MA 02111
Phone: 617-636-6639

FINANCIAL AID

Sandra Pearson
Director of Financial Aid
One Kneeland Street
Boston, MA 02111
Phone: 617-636-6640

STUDENT AFFAIRS

Katherine Vosker
Associate Director of Student Affairs
One Kneeland Street
Boston, MA 02111
Phone: 617-636-0887

HOUSING

Carrie Garinger
Assistant Director of Student Affairs
One Kneeland Street, DHS-7
Boston, MA 02111
Phone: 617-636-0882

INTERNATIONAL STUDENTS

Melissa L. Friedman
Director of Admissions
One Kneeland Street
Boston, MA 02111
Phone: 617-636-6639

PREPARATION (CONTINUED)

PREREQUISITE COURSE	REQUIRED	RECOMMENDED	LAB REQUIRED	CREDITS (SEMESTER/QUARTER)
Histology		✓		
Immunology		✓		
Microbiology		✓		
Molecular biology/genetics		✓		
Physiology		✓		
Zoology		✓		
*In addition to biochemistry, we require one additional upper-level biology course.				
Other				
Statistics				
Writing intensive courses	✓			4/6

Community college coursework accepted for prerequisites: No
Community college coursework accepted for electives: No
Limits on community college credit hours: No
Advanced placement (AP) credit accepted for prerequisites: No
Advanced placement (AP) credit accepted for electives: Yes
Comments regarding AP credit: The Admissions Committee will not recognize prerequisites completed by earning AP credits. Applicants who have received college credit and/or placed out of prerequisite courses because of AP credits must either retake those courses at a four-year institution or take an equal number of credits in upper-level coursework in the same discipline at a four-year institution.
Job shadowing: Required
Number of hours of job shadowing required or recommended: 75; 40 hours with General Dentist

DAT

Mandatory: Yes
Latest DAT for consideration of application: 02/01/2014
Oldest DAT considered: 06/01/2011
When more than one DAT score is reported: Highest score is considered
Canadian DAT accepted: Yes
Application considered before DAT scores are submitted: No

DAT: 2012 ENTERING CLASS

ENROLLEE DAT SCORES	RANGE	MEAN
Academic Average	16-25	20
Perceptual Ability	17-26	21
Total Science	16-28	20

GPA: 2012 ENTERING CLASS

ENROLLEE GPA SCORES	RANGE	MEAN
Science GPA	NR	3.31
Total GPA	NR	3.41

APPLICATION AND SELECTION

TIMETABLE

Earliest filing date: 06/04/2013
Latest filing date: 02/01/2014
Earliest date for acceptance offers: 12/01/2013
Maximum time in days for applicant's response to acceptance offer:
30 days if accepted on or after December 1
15 days if accepted on or after February 1
Requests for deferred entrance considered: In exceptional circumstances only
Fee for application: Yes, submitted only when requested
Amount of fee for application:
In state: $75 Out of state: $75 International: NA
Fee waiver available: No

	FIRST DEPOSIT	SECOND DEPOSIT	THIRD DEPOSIT
Required to hold place	Yes	Yes	No
Resident amount	$1,500	$500	
Nonresident amount	$1,500	$500	
Deposit due	NR	04/15/2014	
Applied to tuition	Yes	Yes	
Refundable	No	No	

APPLICATION PROCESS

Participates in Associated American Dental Schools Application Service (AADSAS): Yes
Accepts direct applicants: No
Secondary or supplemental application required: Yes, sent to interviewed candidates only
Secondary or supplemental application website: No
Interview is mandatory: Yes
Interview is by invitation: Yes

RESIDENCY

Admissions process distinguishes between in-state/in-province and out-of-state/out-of-province applicants: No
Applications are accepted from non-U.S. citizens/non-U.S. permanent residents: No

APPLICATION AND ENROLLMENT	NUMBER OF APPLICANTS	ESTIMATED NUMBER INTERVIEWED	ESTIMATED NUMBER ENROLLED
In-state or province applicants	172	65	34
Out-of-state or province applicants	4,463	476	156

Generally and over time, percentage of your first-year enrollment is in-state: NA (private school)

Origin of out-of-state enrollees (U.S.): California, Colorado, Connecticut, Florida, Georgia, Idaho, Illinois, Indiana, Kansas, Kentucky, Louisiana, Maine, Michigan, Minnesota, Missouri, North Carolina, Nebraska, New Hampshire, New Jersey, New Mexico, Nevada, New York, Ohio, Oregon, Pennsylvania, Rhode Island, Tennessee, Texas, Virginia, Vermont, Washington, Wisconsin

Origin of international enrollees: NA

DEMOGRAPHIC DESCRIPTIONS OF APPLICANTS: 2012 ENTERING CLASS

	APPLICANTS		ENROLLEES	
	M	W	M	W
Hispanic/Latino of any race	133	160	9	5
American Indian or Alaska Native	1	5	0	0
Asian	772	806	25	40
Black or African American	43	88	5	4
Native Hawaiian or Other Pacific Islander	3	1	0	0
White	1,132	826	47	44
Two or more races	60	64	3	8
Race and ethnicity unknown	67	60	0	0
International	189	169	0	0

Notes: 56 applicants of unknown gender

	MINIMUM	MAXIMUM	MEAN
2012 entering class enrollees by age	20	40	24

Number of first-time enrollees over age 30: 9

CURRICULUM

The curriculum of the School of Dental Medicine has been designed and modified over the years to reflect the changing needs of the dental profession and the public. The school's primary goal is to develop dental practitioners who are able to utilize their knowledge of the basic principles of human biology and human behavior in conjunction with their technical skills in diagnosing, treating, and preventing oral disease. The D.M.D. program, which extends over a four-year period, consists of a series of didactic, laboratory, and clinical experiences, resulting in the logical development of concepts and skills. Upon completion of the curriculum, the graduate will be both intellectually and technically prepared to practice the profession of dentistry as it exists today, to adapt to future changes, and to initiate and contribute to those changes, all of which will enhance the delivery of dental care. Please visit http://dental.tufts.edu for more information regarding our curriculum.

Student research opportunities: Yes

SPECIAL PROGRAMS AND SERVICES

PREDENTAL

Postbaccalaureate programs
Special affiliations with colleges and universities: Tufts University School of Arts and Sciences, 7-Year Joint Degree Program, 8-Year Early Assurance Program and Postbaccalaureate Joint Degree program; Marist College-Early Assurance Program; Tougaloo College-Early Assurance Program

DURING DENTAL SCHOOL

Academic counseling and tutoring
Community service opportunities
Internships, externships, or extramural programs
Mentoring
Personal counseling
Professional- and career-development programming
Training for those interested in academic careers
Transfer applicants considered if space is available

ACTIVE STUDENT ORGANIZATIONS

American Association of Dental Research Student Research Group
American Association of Women Dentists
American Dental Education Association (ADEA)
American Student Dental Association
Hispanic Dental Association
Student National Dental Association
Uniformed Services Dental Student Association

INTERNATIONAL DENTISTS

Graduates of international dental schools considered for traditional predoctoral program: No
Advanced standing program offered for graduates of international dental schools: Yes
Advanced standing program description: Program awarding a dental degree

COMBINED AND ALTERNATE DEGREES

Ph.D.	M.S.	M.P.H.	M.D.	B.A./B.S.	Other
—	✓	✓	—	✓	—

COSTS: 2012-13 SCHOOL YEAR

	FIRST YEAR	SECOND YEAR	THIRD YEAR	FOURTH YEAR
Tuition, resident	$61,920	$61,920	$61,920	$61,920
Tuition, nonresident	$61,920	$61,920	$61,920	$61,920
Tuition, other	NA	NA	NA	NA
Fees	$7571	$7857	$8141	$8141
Instruments, books, and supplies	$6800	$7385	$3930	$300
Estimated living expenses	$21,000	$25,200	$25,200	$18,900
Total, resident	$97,291	$102,362	$99,191	$89,261
Total, nonresident	$97,291	$102,362	$99,191	$89,261
Total, other	NA	NA	NA	NA

FINANCIAL AID

Students enrolled in the D.M.D., the Advanced Standing Program for International Students, and accredited postgraduate programs at Tufts University School of Dental Medicine can access a wide variety of both federal and institutional financial aid. Both merit and need-based grants are available to those students who qualify. The majority of funding available for students consists of student loans. These include both federal and institutional loans. International students can apply for private education loans provided they have a qualified cosigner for the loan. Financial aid application information for the 2014-15 academic year will be released in February 2014. The deadline for submitting a financial aid application for the 2014-15 academic year is May 2014. Award notices are released in mid-June. Application materials and further information are available on the website for the Financial Aid Office of Tufts University School of Dental Medicine: http://dental.tufts.edu/financial_aid.

UNIVERSITY OF DETROIT MERCY

UNIVERSITY OF DETROIT MERCY
SCHOOL OF DENTISTRY

Dr. Mert N. Aksu, Dean

GENERAL INFORMATION

The University of Detroit Mercy (UDM) School of Dentistry, an independent Catholic institution, is an urban-based school located in metropolitan Detroit. Located in southwest Detroit (January 2008), the school provides an opportunity to deliver oral health care to an extensive patient population, as well as continue its history of community outreach activities. The location provides classrooms, preclinical laboratories, clinics, cafeteria, and library—an improved environment for learning, research, and patient care. A new clinical simulation laboratory containing patient simulator mannequins and clinical workstations is carefully designed to enhance learning. A 42-chair hospital-based satellite clinic, with additional patient-care opportunities, is located nearby at the University Health Center of Detroit Receiving Hospital. The School of Dentistry is dedicated to educating dentists who are patient-care oriented and skilled in the art of self-evaluation and lifelong learning.

MISSION STATEMENT:

The University of Detroit Mercy, a Catholic university in the Jesuit and Mercy traditions, exists to provide excellent, student-centered, undergraduate and graduate education in an urban context. A UDM education seeks to integrate the intellectual, spiritual, ethical, and social development of students.

Through excellence in teaching, scholarship, and service, the University of Detroit Mercy School of Dentistry, in the Jesuit and Mercy traditions, strives to develop scientifically based, socially and ethically sensitive oral health professionals.

VISION:

The University of Detroit Mercy School of Dentistry will be an indispensable resource for meeting oral health care and educational needs of southeast Michigan. We will serve as a benchmark for effective community and professional collaborations that promote innovations in curriculum, evidence-based clinical education, technology, and research.

VALUES:

The faculty and staff of the School of Dentistry have identified five core values as intrinsic to our academic community. These values are evidenced in our daily activities and guide planning for the future.

Excellence **Service** **Respect** **Lifelong Learning** **Integrity**

Type of institution: Private and state-related
Year opened: 1932
Term type: Semester
Time to degree in months: 44
Start month: August

Doctoral dental degree offered: D.D.S.
Total predoctoral enrollment: 395
Estimated entering class size: 120
Campus setting: Urban
Campus housing available: No

PREPARATION

Formal minimum preparation in semester/quarter hours: Semester: 60 Quarter: 90
Baccalaureate degree preferred: Yes, 95% of entering students in 2011 received B.A./B.S. (includes 10 who will receive B.S. in 2012 as part of UDM's 7 Year B.S./D.D.S. Program)
Number of first-year, first-time enrollees whose highest degree is:
- Baccalaureate: 76
- Master's: 4
- Ph.D. or other doctorate: 1

Of first-year, first-time enrollees without baccalaureates, the number with:
- Equivalent of 60 undergraduate credit hours or less: 0
- Equivalent of 61-90 undergraduate credit hours: 1
- Equivalent of 91 or more undergraduate credit hours: 14

CONTACT INFORMATION

www.dental.udmercy.edu
Office of the Dean
2700 Martin Luther King Jr. Boulevard
Detroit, MI 48208-2576

OFFICE OF DENTAL ADMISSIONS
Dr. Gary E. Jeffers
Interim Director of Dental Admissions
Office of Dental Admissions
University of Detroit Mercy School of Dentistry
2700 Martin Luther King Jr. Boulevard
Detroit, MI 48208-2576
Phone: 313-494-6650
Email: jefferge@udmercy.edu
www.dental.udmercy.edu

OFFICE OF FINANCIAL AID
Camellia Taylor
Coordinator, Financial Aid
Office of Financial Aid
University of Detroit Mercy School of Dentistry
2700 Martin Luther King Jr. Boulevard
Detroit, MI 48208-2576
Phone: 313-494-6617
Email: taylorca2@udmercy.edu
www.dental.udmercy.edu

OFFICE OF STUDENT AFFAIRS
Juliette Niemi
Director of Student Affairs
Office of Student Affairs
University of Detroit Mercy School of Dentistry
2700 Martin Luther King Jr. Boulevard
Detroit, MI 48208-2576
Phone: 313-494-6850
Email: niemijc@udmercy.edu
www.dental.udmercy.edu

OFFICE OF MULTICULTURAL AFFAIRS
Dr. Deirdre D. Young
Director of Multicultural Affairs
University of Detroit Mercy School of Dentistry
2700 Martin Luther King Jr. Boulevard
Detroit, MI 48208-2576
Phone: 313-494-6653
Email: youngdd@udmercy.edu
www.dental.udmercy.edu

HOUSING OFFICE OF DENTAL
Carol J. Blackburn
Administrative Assistant, Dental Admissions
Office of Dental Admissions
University of Detroit School of Dentistry
2700 Martin Luther King Jr. Boulevard
Detroit, MI 48208-2576
Phone: 313-494-6650
Email: blackbcj@udmercy.edu
www.dental.udmercy.edu

PREPARATION (CONTINUED)

PREREQUISITE COURSE	REQUIRED	RECOMMENDED	LAB REQUIRED	CREDITS (SEMESTER/QUARTER)
BCP (biology-chemistry-physics) sciences				
Biology	✓		✓	8/12
Chemistry, general/inorganic	✓		✓	8/12
Chemistry, organic	✓		✓	8/12
Physics	✓		✓	8/12
Additional biological sciences				
Anatomy		✓		4/6
Biochemistry	✓			4/6
Cell biology		✓		4/6
Histology		✓		4/6
Immunology		✓		4/6
Microbiology	✓			3-5
Molecular biology/genetics		✓		4/6
Physiology		✓		8/12
Zoology		✓		4/6
Other				
Statistics		✓		3/5
Psychology		✓		
Sociology		✓		
Business courses		✓		
Communications courses		✓		

Community college coursework accepted for prerequisites: Yes; four-year college/university preferred
Community college coursework accepted for electives: Yes
Limits on community college credit hours: Yes; 60 semester hours/90 quarter hours.
Maximum number of community college credit hours: 60
Advanced placement (AP) credit accepted for prerequisites: Yes
Advanced placement (AP) credit accepted for electives: Yes
Comments regarding AP credit: If the prospective candidate has received AP credits in a prerequisite discipline(s) from his or her "home" college/university, he or she is strongly encouraged to pursue additional upper-division coursework within the discipline for which credit was received—equal to the number of recognized AP credits.
Job shadowing: Required
Number of hours of job shadowing required or recommended: Minimally, 60 hours within a general practice setting. A letter of recommendation also attests to activities and time in office.
Other factors considered in admission: Difficulty of a curriculum and achievement, letters of recommendation, personal statement, experience/exposure to the profession, research experience, motivation, community service, time management, and intrinsic values

DAT

Mandatory: Yes; recommended minimum of 20 on each section (20+ competitive)
Latest DAT for consideration of application: 01/15/2014
Oldest DAT considered: 02/01/2011
When more than one DAT score is reported: Most recent score only is considered
Canadian DAT accepted: Yes
Application considered before DAT scores are submitted: No

DAT: 2012 ENTERING CLASS

ENROLLEE DAT SCORES	RANGE	MEAN
Academic Average	17-30	20
Perceptual Ability	15-30	20
Total Science	17-25	20

GPA: 2012 ENTERING CLASS

ENROLLEE GPA SCORES	RANGE	MEAN
Science GPA	2.67-4.16	3.50
Total GPA	2.64-4.11	3.57

APPLICATION AND SELECTION

TIMETABLE

Earliest filing date: 05/15/2013
Latest filing date: 02/01/2014
Earliest date for acceptance offers: 12/01/2013
Maximum time in days for applicant's response to acceptance offer:
30 days if accepted on or after December 1
14 days if accepted on or after February 1
7 days if accepted on or after March 1
Requests for deferred entrance considered: Yes, in exceptional circumstances only
Fee for application: Yes, submitted at same time as Associated American Dental Schools Application Service (AADSAS) application.
Amount of fee for application:
In state: $75 Out of state: $75 International: $75
Fee waiver available: Yes, in exceptional circumstances only

	FIRST DEPOSIT	SECOND DEPOSIT	THIRD DEPOSIT
Required to hold place	Yes	No	No
Resident amount	$1,500		
Nonresident amount	$1,500		
Deposit due	As indicated in admission offer		
Applied to tuition	Yes		
Refundable	No		

APPLICATION PROCESS

Participates in AADSAS: Yes
Accepts direct applicants: No
Secondary or supplemental application required: No; only requirement is submission of $75 application fee and photo. Interview is mandatory: Yes
Interview is by invitation: Yes

RESIDENCY

Admissions process distinguishes between in-state/in-province and out-of-state/out-of-province applicants: No
Applications are accepted from non-U.S. citizens/non-U.S. permanent residents: Yes

APPLICATION AND ENROLLMENT	NUMBER OF APPLICANTS	ESTIMATED NUMBER INTERVIEWED	ESTIMATED NUMBER ENROLLED
In-state or province applicants	369	159	90
Out-of-state or province applicants	1,271	188	54

Generally and over time, percentage of your first-year enrollment is in-state: 60%
Origin of out-of-state enrollees (U.S.): California-9, Florida-4, Georgia-2, Illinois-4, Indiana-2, Minnesota-1, Mississippi-2, Ohio-2, Tennessee-3, Texas-2, Utah-1, Virginia-1
Origin of international enrollees: Canada-20 (Alberta-3, British Columbia-4, Ontario-13); Korea-1

DEMOGRAPHIC DESCRIPTIONS OF APPLICANTS: 2012 ENTERING CLASS

	APPLICANTS		ENROLLEES	
	M	W	M	W
Hispanic/Latino of any race	31	31	8	1
American Indian or Alaska Native	1	0	0	1
Asian	310	294	17	21
Black or African American	31	63	2	4
Native Hawaiian or Other Pacific Islander	2	2	0	0
White	439	313	57	27
Two or more races	17	21	0	2
Race and ethnicity unknown	24	33	2	1
International	24	23	1	0

Notes: Above enrollee data includes 20 Canadians (Asian: 7 male, 4 female; Caucasian: 5 male, 3 female; Race Unknown: 1 male); 1 International is from Korea. Total data for Hispanic applicants was adjusted to account for 7 applicants listed in more than one subcategory. One Hispanic applicant had no specific sex indicated and was omitted from above data. Female Asian enrollee data includes 1 female student repeating first year, not included among total applicant statistics. Above enrollee total actually included 3 in the ADEA/AADSAS Minority Report who reported two or more races, but 1 of those is listed as a female American Indian/Alaska Native as a result of official documentation provided to us. Minority Report indicates we have 2, or 1 each male and female Native Hawaiian or Other Pacific Islander applicants; but the subgroup total lists 4 such applicants, two each male and female for this subcategory, as one male and 1 female from this group are also listed among those reported to be of 2 or more races.

	MINIMUM	MAXIMUM	MEAN
2012 entering class enrollees by age	20	40	23

Number of first-time enrollees over age 30: 4

CURRICULUM

The majority of biomedical, behavioral, and preclinical sciences are concentrated in the first two years. The freshman curriculum is divided between biomedical and dental sciences, while the sophomore year is devoted primarily to dental sciences taught in a simulation environment. Limited patient care experiences occur in the first and second years. More than 75% of the curricular time during the third and fourth years is devoted to clinical practice. Patient care experiences are based on an evidence-based, comprehensive care model utilizing the expertise of generalists and specialists. Individual students are assigned a patient family and are responsible for addressing all the patient's dental needs. Outreach clinical rotations occurring during the fourth year expose the students to alternative practice settings in a community-based environment. Ethics, patient management, and current issues are addressed throughout the curriculum.

Student research opportunities: Yes

SPECIAL PROGRAMS AND SERVICES

PREDENTAL

Association of American Medical Colleges/ADEA Summer Medical and Dental Education Program (AAMC/ADEA SMDEP)
DAT workshops
Postbaccalaureate programs
Special affiliations with colleges and universities: The University of Detroit Mercy (UDM) has an academic program that enables students to earn a Doctorate of Dental Surgery (D.D.S.) and a baccalaureate degree in seven calendar years, rather than the traditional eight. Students enrolled in the program spend the first three years on the UDM McNichols Campus in the College of Engineering and Science. The last four years of the program occur in the School of Dentistry. This program is available only to high school students initiating their undergraduate education with strong academic credentials. Selective admission occurs at the undergraduate level.
Summer enrichment programs

DURING DENTAL SCHOOL

Academic counseling and tutoring
Community service opportunities
Mentoring
Personal counseling
Professional- and career-development programming
Training for those interested in academic careers
Transfer applicants considered if space is available—Considered rarely and only in exceptional circumstances; must be enrolled in another American Dental Association (ADA) accredited school, be in good standing, and be making satisfactory progress at the dental school in which they are enrolled; compatible curriculum required

ACTIVE STUDENT ORGANIZATIONS

Alpha Omega international professional dental fraternity
American Association of Dental Research Student Research Group
American Dental Education Association (ADEA)
American Student Dental Association
Christian Dental Association
Delta Sigma Delta international professional dental fraternity
Muslim Dental Students' Association
Psi Omega international professional dental fraternity
Student American Dental Hygiene Association
Student National Dental Association

INTERNATIONAL DENTISTS

Graduates of international dental schools considered for traditional predoctoral program: Yes
Advanced standing program offered for graduates of international dental schools: No

COMBINED AND ALTERNATE DEGREES

Ph.D.	M.S.	M.P.H.	M.D.	B.A./B.S.	Other
—	—	—	—	—	✓

Other Degree: B.S./D.D.S. for highly qualified high school applicants enrolled In UDM 7-year combined undergraduate/dental program

COSTS: 2012-13 SCHOOL YEAR

	FIRST YEAR	SECOND YEAR	THIRD YEAR	FOURTH YEAR
Tuition, resident	$60,090	$60,090	$60,090	$60,090
Tuition, nonresident	$60,090	$60,090	$60,090	$60,090
Tuition, other	NA	NA	NA	NA
Fees	$8,737	$6,693	$6,482	$8,843
Instruments, books, and supplies	$3,395	$4,673	$1,046	$260
Estimated living expenses	$10,758	$10,758	$10,758	$10,758
Total, resident	$82,980	$82,214	$78,376	$79,951
Total, nonresident	$82,980	$82,214	$78,376	$79,951
Total, other	NA	NA	NA	NA

**Note:* If student does not live w/parents, estimated annual living expenses are $17,864, and in such cases the total costs per year would have to be adjusted accordingly.

FINANCIAL AID

FINANCIAL AID APPLICATION PROCEDURES:

It is important for dental school applicants to apply for financial aid early (January–March 1, 2013). Funding is limited and processing takes time.

1. Free Application for Federal Student Aid (FAFSA)—electronically submit this form online at www.fafsa.ed.gov. All students interested in financial aid will need to complete this application.

- The University of Detroit Mercy (UDM) School of Dentistry federal code: E01403
- Read and follow the directions carefully. Failure to do so may cost you time in processing and could delay your financial aid award.
- If you don't understand the instructions, call the Financial Aid Office at 313-494-6617 or 313-993-3350 and ask for assistance.

2. AWARDING—Following admission and after all necessary information has been received, your completed file is reviewed, and an award is calculated. You will receive an electronic award letter in your university-assigned email account. If you agree to accept the assistance, as offered, electronically sign/accept the award letter and maintain a copy for your personal file. The school will electronically certify your Stafford loan upon receipt of notification of your accepted award.

There were 28 recipients of scholarships and grants in the 2012 entering class. Awards were between $7,500 and $70,022 with an average award of $22,220. Student loan recipients for 2012 received amounts between $21,122 and $91,682 with an average amount of $79,757. There were 106 student loan recipients.

The average 2012 graduate indebtedness was $177,387.

UNIVERSITY OF MICHIGAN
SCHOOL OF DENTISTRY

Dr. Peter J. Polverini, Dean

CONTACT INFORMATION

www.dent.umich.edu
1011 North University Avenue
Ann Arbor, MI 48109-1078
Phone: 734-763-3311

ADMISSIONS
Patricia Katcher
Admissions Associate Director
1011 North University Avenue, Room G226
Ann Arbor, MI 48109-1078
Phone: 734-763-3316
www.dent.umich.edu

FINANCIAL AID
Mary Gaynor
Assistant Director
1011 North University Avenue, Room G226
Ann Arbor, MI 48109-1078
Phone: 734-763-4119

STUDENT SERVICES
Dr. Marilyn Woolfolk
Assistant Dean for Student Services
1011 North University Avenue, Room 1208
Ann Arbor, MI 48109-1078
Phone: 734-763-3313

OFFICE OF MULTICULTURAL AFFAIRS AND RECRUITMENT INITIATIVES
Dr. Kenneth B. May
Director
1011 North University Avenue
Ann Arbor, MI 48109-1078
Phone: 734-763-3342
www.dent.umich.edu/mca

INTERNATIONALLY TRAINED DENTIST PROGRAM
Patricia Katcher
Admissions Associate Director
1011 North University Avenue
Ann Arbor, MI 48109-1078
Phone: 734-763-1068
Email: internationaldent@umich.edu
www.dent.umich.edu

GENERAL INFORMATION

The University of Michigan School of Dentistry, organized in 1875, was the first dental school established as an integral part of a state university and the second to become a part of any university. The University of Michigan is located in Ann Arbor, a city of 110,000 about 40 miles west of Detroit. Approximately 500 students are enrolled annually in various programs offered by the School of Dentistry (SOD): 1) the D.D.S. degree program; 2) advanced education programs leading to an M.S.; 3) a B.S. dental hygiene program; 4) a Ph.D. in Oral Health Sciences; and 5) a dual D.D.S./Ph.D. program. The School of Dentistry also offers comprehensive program offerings in continuing dental education.

MISSION STATEMENT:

Our mission is to promote optimal oral health in a culturally sensitive manner within the state, national, and international communities through education, research, and service.

The SOD will:

1. Educate oral health professionals and researchers in a model health care facility where students and clinicians:
   - emulate the highest standards of patient-centered care and
   - acquire the most advanced knowledge and skills to meet the changing needs of a diverse patient population.
2. Conduct research in the sciences and encourage collaborative efforts for the discovery and application of new knowledge with awareness of multiple environmental and social conditions; and
3. Serve the university, the community, and the profession through the sharing of knowledge, participation in professional activities, and the establishment of linkages:
   - to promote innovation and
   - to encourage and address diversity in research, education, patient care, and health policy.

Inherent in the mission is a dedication to stimulate the development of the faculty and staff and to inspire students to develop attitudes and skills necessary for continued professional growth. To pursue its mission, the SOD will foster and exemplify equity, diversity, and multicultural values.

Type of institution: Public
Year opened: 1875
Term type: Semester
Time to degree in months: 46
Start month: June

Doctoral dental degree offered: D.D.S.
Total predoctoral enrollment: 439
Estimated entering class size: 108
Campus setting: Suburban
Campus housing available: Yes

PREPARATION

Formal minimum preparation in semester/quarter hours: Semester: 90 Quarter: 135
Baccalaureate degree preferred: Yes
Number of first-year, first-time enrollees whose highest degree is:
  Baccalaureate: 93
  Master's: 9
  Ph.D. or other doctorate: 1
Of first-year, first-time enrollees without baccalaureates, the number with:
  Equivalent of 60 undergraduate credit hours or less: 0
  Equivalent of 61-90 undergraduate credit hours: 0
  Equivalent of 91 or more undergraduate credit hours: 5

PREREQUISITE COURSE	REQUIRED	RECOMMENDED	LAB REQUIRED	CREDITS (SEMESTER/QUARTER)
BCP (biology-chemistry-physics) sciences				
Biology	✓		✓	8/12
Chemistry, general/inorganic	✓		✓	8/12
Chemistry, organic	✓		✓	8/12
Physics	✓		✓	8/12

(Prerequisite Courses continued)

PREPARATION (CONTINUED)

PREREQUISITE COURSE	REQUIRED	RECOMMENDED	LAB REQUIRED	CREDITS (SEMESTER/QUARTER)
Additional biological sciences				
Anatomy		✓		
Biochemistry	✓			3/5
Cell biology				
Histology		✓		
Immunology				
Microbiology	✓			3/5
Molecular biology/genetics				
Physiology		✓		
Zoology				
Other				
Psychology	✓			3/5
Sociology	✓			3/5
English composition	✓			6/9

Community college coursework accepted for prerequisites: Yes
Community college coursework accepted for electives: Yes
Limits on community college credit hours: Yes
Maximum number of community college credit hours: 60
Advanced placement (AP) credit accepted for prerequisites: Yes
Advanced placement (AP) credit accepted for electives: Yes
Comments regarding AP credit: Applicants must receive credit for AP classes on their undergraduate transcripts.
Job shadowing: Required
Number of hours of job shadowing required: 100 hours
Other factors considered in admission: All prerequisite courses must have a grade of C or better; candidates must present strong letters of recommendation, strong examples of extracurricular/volunteer/work/research experiences, an original essay, and evidence of leadership capacity.

DAT

Mandatory: Yes
Latest DAT for consideration of application: 08/31/2013
Oldest DAT considered: 01/01/2010
When more than one DAT score is reported: Most recent score only is considered
Canadian DAT accepted: Yes
Application considered before DAT scores are submitted: No

DAT: 2012 ENTERING CLASS

ENROLLEE DAT SCORES	RANGE	MEAN
Academic Average	16-24	20
Perceptual Ability	16-26	21
Total Science	16-25	21

GPA: 2012 ENTERING CLASS

ENROLLEE GPA SCORES	RANGE	MEAN
Science GPA	2.72-4.12	3.49
Total GPA	2.64-4.00	3.57

APPLICATION AND SELECTION

TIMETABLE

Earliest filing date: 06/01/2013
Latest filing date: 10/15/2013
Earliest date for acceptance offers: 12/01/2013
Maximum time in days for applicant's response to acceptance offer:
30 days if accepted on or after December 1
15 days if accepted on or after February 1
Requests for deferred entrance considered: No
Fee for application: Yes, submitted at same time as Associated American Dental Schools Application Service (AADSAS) application
Amount of fee for application:
In state: $65 Out of state: $65 International: $65
Fee waiver available: Yes

	FIRST DEPOSIT	SECOND DEPOSIT	THIRD DEPOSIT
Required to hold place	Yes	No	No
Resident amount	$1,500		
Nonresident amount	$1,500		
Deposit due	As indicated in admission offer		
Applied to tuition	Yes		
Refundable	No		

APPLICATION PROCESS

Participates in AADSAS: Yes
Accepts direct applicants: No
Secondary or supplemental application required: No
Secondary or supplemental application website: NA
Interview is mandatory: Yes
Interview is by invitation: Yes

RESIDENCY

Admissions process distinguishes between in-state/in-province and out-of-state/out-of-province applicants: Yes
Preference given to residents of: Michigan
Reciprocity Admissions Agreement available for legal residents of: None
Applications are accepted from non-U.S. citizens/non-U.S. permanent residents: Yes

APPLICATION AND ENROLLMENT	NUMBER OF APPLICANTS	ESTIMATED NUMBER INTERVIEWED	ESTIMATED NUMBER ENROLLED
In-state or province applicants	325	113	65
Out-of-state or province applicants	1,843	183	43

Generally and over time, percentage of your first-year enrollment is in-state: 40%

Origin of out-of-state enrollees (U.S.): Alabama-1, Alaska-1, California-16, Florida-3, Georgia-2, Illinois-6, Indiana-1, Minnesota-1, Nevada-1, New Jersey-1, New Mexico-1, New York-1, Pennsylvania-1, Utah-1, Washington-3, Wisconsin-1

Origin of international enrollees: Canada-1, China-1

DEMOGRAPHIC DESCRIPTIONS OF APPLICANTS: 2012 ENTERING CLASS

	APPLICANTS		ENROLLEES	
	M	W	M	W
Hispanic/Latino of any race	52	45	1	1
American Indian or Alaska Native	1	0	0	0
Asian	344	345	14	8
Black or African American	21	49	0	0
Native Hawaiian or Other Pacific Islander	1	0	0	0
White	575	449	44	34
Two or more races	23	28	2	0
Race and ethnicity unknown	23	29	1	1
International	99	70	1	1

Notes: FOR APPLICANTS: 5-Unknown Race, Gender and Ethnicity/ 5-Asian-Unknown Gender/1-White Gender Unknown/1-Hispanic Gender Unknown/2-International Gender Unknown = Total of 14

	MINIMUM	MAXIMUM	MEAN
2012 entering class enrollees by age	21	38	23

Number of first-time enrollees over age 30: 1

CURRICULUM

The general objectives of dental education are to accomplish the following:

1) provide opportunities within a stimulating academic environment for students to develop an appreciation for and understanding of philosophical, social, and intellectual problems;
2) strongly orient the student to study the physical and biological sciences on which the practice of contemporary dentistry is based;
3) offer opportunities and experiences enabling the student to develop the essential clinical skills and critical thinking needed to provide the highest quality oral health service to patients;
4) foster the student's appreciation for the value, design, and methodology of dental research;
5) attain students' conformity—in letter and spirit—to the principles of ethics as an unquestioned part of professional life;
6) encourage students to consider career possibilities in dental research, dental education, dental leadership, and alternative health care delivery pathways, including dental public health; and
7) develop the potential of the dental graduate.

Student research opportunities: Yes

SPECIAL PROGRAMS AND SERVICES

PREDENTAL

Special affiliations with colleges and universities
Summer enrichment programs for 3rd-4th year undergraduates

DURING DENTAL SCHOOL

Academic counseling and tutoring
Community service opportunities
Internships, externships, or extramural programs
Mentoring
Personal counseling
Training for those interested in academic careers

ACTIVE STUDENT ORGANIZATIONS

American Association of Dental Research Student Research Group
American Association of Endodontists
American Association of Pediatric Dentists
American Association of Public Health Dentists
American Association of Women Dentists
American Dental Education Association (ADEA)
American Student Dental Association
Asian Dental Student Association
Christian Medical Dental Society
Dental Lesbian Gay Bisexual Transgender Alliance
Hispanic Dental Association
Student National Dental Association
Taft Honorary Society

INTERNATIONAL DENTISTS

Graduates of international dental schools considered for traditional predoctoral program: Yes

Advanced standing program offered for graduates of international dental schools: Yes

Advanced standing program description: D.D.S. awarded after successful completion of a 2 1/2 year program that includes preclinical, didactic, and clinical courses, as well as clinical rotations.

COMBINED AND ALTERNATE DEGREES

Ph.D.	M.S.	M.P.H.	M.D.	B.A./B.S.	Other
✓	✓	✓	—	—	—

COSTS: 2012-13 SCHOOL YEAR

	FIRST YEAR	SECOND YEAR	THIRD YEAR	FOURTH YEAR
Tuition, resident	$28,295	$28,295	$28,295	$28,295
Tuition, nonresident	$44,289	$44,289	$44,289	$44,289
Tuition, other	NA	NA	NA	NA
Fees	$245	$245	$245	$245
Instruments, books, and supplies	$7,088	$7,057	$5,584	$8,176
Estimated living expenses	$24,708	$24,708	$24,708	$24,708
Total, resident	$60,336	$60,305	$58,832	$61,424
Total, nonresident	$76,330	$76,299	$74,826	$77,418
Total, other	NA	NA	NA	NA

FINANCIAL AID

Financial aid application packets will be mailed to admitted students in February 2014 and are due on or before April 6, 2014. Students admitted after February 10, 2014, will receive the financial aid application packet shortly after notification of admission to the School of Dentistry and will have four weeks to apply for financial aid. Equal consideration for financial aid will be given to students admitted after February 10, 2014.

Notification of financial aid eligibility will begin in mid-April 2014.

A comprehensive publication, *A Guide to Financial Aid for Prospective Students*, can be located at www.dent.umich.edu/financialaid.

Mary Gaynor, Assistant Director of Financial Aid-D.D.S. Program, can be contacted at mgaynor@umich.edu or 734-763-4119.

UNIVERSITY OF MINNESOTA
SCHOOL OF DENTISTRY

Dr. Leon A. Assael, Dean

CONTACT INFORMATION

www.dentistry.umn.edu
15-163 Malcolm Moos Health Sciences Tower
515 Delaware Street SE
Minneapolis, MN 55455

OFFICE OF ADMISSIONS AND DIVERSITY

Dr. Naty Lopez
Assistant Dean, Admissions and Diversity
15-163 Malcolm Moos Health Sciences Tower
515 Delaware Street SE
Minneapolis, MN 55455
Phone: 612-625-7477
www.dentistry.umn.edu

OFFICE OF FINANCIAL AID

Elizabeth Holm
Financial Aid Advisor
210 Fraser Hall
Minneapolis, MN 55455
Phone: 612-624-0024
Email: holmx029@umn.edu

STUDENT AFFAIRS

Sara Johnson
Director, Student Affairs
15-106 Malcolm Moos Health Sciences Tower
515 Delaware Street SE
Minneapolis, MN 55455
Phone: 612-625-0927
www.dentistry.umn.edu

MINORITY AFFAIRS/DIVERSITY

Dr. Naty Lopez
Assistant Dean, Admissions and Diversity
15-163 Malcolm Moos Health Sciences Tower
515 Delaware Street SE
Minneapolis, MN 55455
Phone: 612-625-7477
www.dentistry.umn.edu

HOUSING AND RESIDENTIAL LIFE

Comstock Hall East
210 Delaware Street SE
Minneapolis, MN 55455
Phone: 612-624-2994
Email: housing@umn.edu
www.housing.umn.edu

INTERNATIONAL STUDENT AND SCHOLAR SERVICES

190 Hubert H. Humphrey Center
301 19th Avenue South
Minneapolis, MN 55455
Phone: 612-626-7100
www.isss.umn.edu

GENERAL INFORMATION

The School of Dentistry, established in 1888, is a state institution and part of a great university health center. Since the center is located on the Minneapolis campus of the university, students in dentistry enjoy a variety of academic, cultural, and recreational opportunities. The Minneapolis campus is located in the center of the Minneapolis-St. Paul area, a metropolitan area with a population of more than 2.7 million. The school's teaching and research facilities are in a health sciences building, completed in 1975, which holds shared basic science laboratories and lecture rooms for the health sciences. The School of Dentistry conducts a wide range of programs, including dentistry, dental hygiene, dental therapy, dental specialties, oral biology, and other advanced dental education and clinical training programs, as well as a comprehensive research program. A combined D.D.S./Ph.D. program, a D.D.S/Master's of Public Health program, and the Program for Advanced Standing Students (UMN PASS) for graduates of foreign dental schools are also available.

MISSION STATEMENT:

The University of Minnesota School of Dentistry improves oral and craniofacial health by educating clinicians and scientists who translate knowledge and experience into clinical practice. The school is committed to graduating professionals who provide the highest quality care and service to the people of the state of Minnesota and the world; discovering new knowledge through research, which will inspire innovation in the biomedical, behavioral, and clinical sciences; and providing oral health care to a diverse patient population in a variety of settings.

Type of institution: Public
Year opened: 1888
Term type: Semester
Time to degree in months: 45
Start month: August

Doctoral dental degree offered: D.D.S.
Total predoctoral enrollment: 413
Estimated entering class size: 98
Campus setting: Urban
Campus housing available: Yes

PREPARATION

Formal minimum preparation in semester/quarter hours: Semester: 87 Quarter: 130
Baccalaureate degree preferred: Yes
Number of first-year, first-time enrollees whose highest degree is:
- Baccalaureate: 95
- Master's: 1
- Ph.D. or other doctorate: 1

Of first-year, first-time enrollees without baccalaureates, the number with:
- Equivalent of 60 undergraduate credit hours or less: 0
- Equivalent of 61-90 undergraduate credit hours: 0
- Equivalent of 91 or more undergraduate credit hours: 0

PREREQUISITE COURSE	REQUIRED	RECOMMENDED	LAB REQUIRED	CREDITS (SEMESTER/QUARTER)
BCP (biology-chemistry-physics) sciences				
Biology	✓		✓	8/12
Chemistry, general/inorganic	✓		✓	8/12
Chemistry, organic	✓		✓	8/12
Physics	✓		✓	8/12
Additional biological sciences				
Anatomy		✓		3/5
Biochemistry	✓			3/5
Cell biology		✓		3/5
Histology		✓		3/5

(Prerequisite Courses continued)

PREPARATION (CONTINUED)

PREREQUISITE COURSE	REQUIRED	RECOMMENDED	LAB REQUIRED	CREDITS (SEMESTER/QUARTER)
Immunology		✓		3/5
Microbiology		✓		3/5
Molecular biology/genetics		✓		3/5
Physiology		✓		3/5
Zoology		✓		

Community college coursework accepted for prerequisites: Yes
Community college coursework accepted for electives: Yes
Limits on community college credit hours: Yes
Maximum number of community college credit hours: 64
Advanced placement (AP) credit accepted for prerequisites: Yes
Advanced placement (AP) credit accepted for electives: No
Job shadowing: Required
Number of hours of job shadowing required or recommended: Minimum 30
Other factors considered in admission: DAT scores, GPA, and non-academic factors

DAT

Mandatory: Yes
Latest DAT for consideration of application: 12/01/2013
Oldest DAT considered: 06/01/2010
When more than one DAT score is reported: Most recent score only is considered
Canadian DAT accepted: Yes
Application considered before DAT scores are submitted: No

DAT: 2012 ENTERING CLASS

ENROLLEE DAT SCORES	RANGE	MEAN
Academic Average	17-24	19.9
Perceptual Ability	17-27	20.9
Total Science	17-24	19.5

GPA: 2012 ENTERING CLASS

ENROLLEE GPA SCORES	RANGE	MEAN
Science GPA	2.65-4.06	3.52
Total GPA	2.78-4.08	3.60

APPLICATION AND SELECTION

TIMETABLE

Earliest filing date: 06/01/2013
Latest filing date: 12/01/2013
Earliest date for acceptance offers: 12/01/2013
Maximum time in days for applicant's response to acceptance offer: Varies
Requests for deferred entrance considered: For special circumstances
Fee for application: Yes, submitted at same time as AADSAS application.
Amount of fee for application:
In state: $75 Out of state: $75 International: $75
Fee waiver available: No

	FIRST DEPOSIT	SECOND DEPOSIT	THIRD DEPOSIT
Required to hold place	Yes	No	No
Resident amount	$1,000		
Nonresident amount	$1,000		
Deposit due	Varies		
Applied to tuition	Yes		
Refundable	No		

APPLICATION PROCESS

Participates in Associated American Dental Schools Application Service (AADSAS): Yes
Accepts direct applicants: No
Secondary or supplemental application required: Yes
Secondary or supplemental application website: www.dentistry.umn.edu
Interview is mandatory: Yes
Interview is by invitation: Yes

RESIDENCY

Admissions process distinguishes between in-state/in-province and out-of-state/out-of-province applicants: Yes
Applications are accepted from non-U.S. citizens/non-U.S. permanent residents: Yes

APPLICATION AND ENROLLMENT	NUMBER OF APPLICANTS	ESTIMATED NUMBER INTERVIEWED	ESTIMATED NUMBER ENROLLED
In-state or province applicants	225	80	65
Out-of-state or province applicants	941	138	32

Generally and over time, percentage of your first-year enrollment is in-state: 65%
Origin of out-of-state enrollees (U.S.): Colorado, Georgia, Illinois, Maryland, Michigan, North Dakota, New Jersey, Oregon, South Dakota, Virginia, Washington, Wisconsin
Origin of international enrollees: Canada, South Korea

DEMOGRAPHIC DESCRIPTIONS OF APPLICANTS: 2012 ENTERING CLASS

	APPLICANTS		ENROLLEES	
	M	W	M	W
Hispanic/Latino of any race	12	3	1	0
American Indian or Alaska Native	3	1	0	0
Asian	102	144	8	7
Black or African American	6	18	0	0
Native Hawaiian or Other Pacific Islander	1	1	0	0
White	381	332	35	40
Two or more races	20	31	0	3
Race and ethnicity unknown	13	6	0	0
International	53	39	0	3

Note: Our 98th enrollee is a DDS/PhD Dual degree student who applied in a previous application cycle.

	MINIMUM	MAXIMUM	MEAN
2012 entering class enrollees by age	21	46	24

Number of first-time enrollees over age 30: 6

CURRICULUM

The dental school has a strong reputation for educating fine clinicians and diagnosticians through a curriculum that involves progressive introduction to clinical training, integration of basic and applied clinical skills, and group and problem-based learning situations. During the students' final year, the school offers experiences in outreach clinical practice sites and a comprehensive-care clinic setting within the school. The school also encourages students to take elective courses in dental and other disciplines to enhance their clinical, didactic, and research knowledge base. The goal of the dental curriculum is to educate dental professionals whose scholarly capabilities, scientific acumen, cultural competency, and interpersonal skills are commensurate with their clinical mastery. This goal will provide graduates with the flexibility to adapt to continuing changes in health care and to developments in the practice of dentistry.

Student research opportunities: The summer research fellowship program provides a great opportunity for qualified students to conduct research with faculty mentors and contribute to the progress of dental and craniofacial research.

SPECIAL PROGRAMS AND SERVICES

PREDENTAL

American Student Dental Association Drill and Fill Experience
Dental School Preparation Course
Health Resources and Services Administration Health Careers Opportunity Programs
Summer enrichment programs: Summer Dental School Experience

DURING DENTAL SCHOOL

Academic counseling and tutoring
Community service opportunities
Internships, externships, or extramural programs
Mentoring
Opportunity to study for credit at institution abroad
Personal counseling
Professional- and career-development programming
Training for those interested in academic careers
Transfer applicants considered if space is available

ACTIVE STUDENT ORGANIZATIONS

American Association of Public Health Dentistry
American Dental Education Association (ADEA)
American Student Dental Association
Hispanic Student Dental Association
Student Council

INTERNATIONAL DENTISTS

Graduates of international dental schools considered for traditional predoctoral program: Yes
Advanced standing program offered for graduates of international dental schools: Yes
Advanced standing program description: The program awards a dental degree.

COMBINED AND ALTERNATE DEGREES					
Ph.D.	M.S.	M.P.H.	M.D.	B.A./B.S.	Other
✓	✓	✓	—	✓	—

COSTS: 2012-13 SCHOOL YEAR

	FIRST YEAR	SECOND YEAR	THIRD YEAR	FOURTH YEAR
Tuition, resident	$30,540	$39,036	$38,177	$38,177
Tuition, nonresident	$55,242	$70,342	$69,404	$69,404
Tuition, other	$55,242	$70,342	$69,404	$69,404
Fees	$5,288	$6,074	$5,465	$4,807
Instruments, books, and supplies	$5,530	$6,730	$6,291	$5,522
Estimated living expenses	$12,938	$17,251	$17,251	$17,251
Total, resident	$54,296	$69,091	$67,184	$65,757
Total, nonresident	$78,998	$100,397	$98,411	$96,984
Total, other	$79,312	$100,868	$98,881	$97,455

FINANCIAL AID

There were 76 recipients of student loans in the 2012 entering class. Amounts were between $33,000 and $106,022. Residents received an average amount of $64,398 and nonresidents received an average amount of $90,019. Scholarship and grant awards were between $0 and $96,156.

UNIVERSITY OF MISSISSIPPI
SCHOOL OF DENTISTRY

Dr. Gary W. Reeves, Dean

GENERAL INFORMATION

MISSION STATEMENT:

The University of Mississippi School of Dentistry's diverse student body, faculty, and staff exemplify qualities of leadership and dedication to preparing competent, ethical dentists and to furthering the health of Mississippi citizens. The school's environment fosters lifelong learning, collaborative teaching, service, and research through partnerships within the Medical Center and with community organizations and dental health practitioners throughout the state of Mississippi.

Type of institution: Public
Year opened: 1975
Term type: Semester
Time to degree in months: 48
Start month: August

Doctoral dental degree offered: D.M.D.
Total predoctoral enrollment: 141
Estimated entering class size: 35
Campus setting: Urban
Campus housing available: No

PREPARATION

Formal minimum preparation in semester/quarter hours: Semester: 90 Quarter: 120
Baccalaureate degree preferred: Yes
Number of first-year, first-time enrollees whose highest degree is:
- Baccalaureate: 35
- Master's: 13
- Ph.D. or other doctorate: 0

Of first-year, first-time enrollees without baccalaureates, the number with:
- Equivalent of 60 undergraduate credit hours or less: 0
- Equivalent of 61-90 undergraduate credit hours: 0
- Equivalent of 91 or more undergraduate credit hours: 0

PREREQUISITE COURSE	REQUIRED	RECOMMENDED	LAB REQUIRED	CREDITS (SEMESTER/QUARTER)
BCP (biology-chemistry-physics) sciences				
Biology	✓		✓	
Chemistry, general/inorganic	✓		✓	
Chemistry, organic	✓		✓	
Physics	✓		✓	
Additional biological sciences				
Anatomy*	✓			
Biochemistry*	✓			
Cell biology		✓		
Histology		✓		
Immunology		✓		
Microbiology*	✓			
Molecular biology/genetics		✓		
Physiology		✓		
Zoology				

*Note: One course in either anatomy, biochemistry, or microbiology is required.

Community college coursework accepted for prerequisites: Yes
Community college coursework accepted for electives: Yes
Limits on community college credit hours: Yes
Maximum number of community college credit hours: 65
Advanced placement (AP) credit accepted for prerequisites: Yes

CONTACT INFORMATION

http://dentistry.umc.edu
School of Dentistry
2500 North State Street
Jackson, MS 39216
Phone: 601-984-6000
Fax: 601-984-6014

ADMISSIONS AND STUDENT AFFAIRS

Dr. Wilhelmina O'Reilly
Assistant Dean
School of Dentistry
2500 North State Street
Jackson, MS 39216
Phone: 601-984-6009
http://dentistry.umc.edu

OFFICE OF STUDENT FINANCIAL AID

Carrie Cooper
Director of Financial Aid
Office of Financial Aid
2500 North State Street
Jackson, MS 39216
Phone: 601-984-1117
Email: cecooper@umc.edu

Advanced placement (AP) credit accepted for electives: Yes
Job shadowing: Recommended
Number of hours of job shadowing required or recommended: 40

DAT

Mandatory: Yes
Latest DAT for consideration of application: 10/31/2013
Oldest DAT considered: 10/31/2010
When more than one DAT score is reported: Highest score is considered
Canadian DAT accepted: No
Application considered before DAT scores are submitted: No

DAT: 2012 ENTERING CLASS

ENROLLEE DAT SCORES	RANGE	MEAN
Academic Average	17–22	18
Perceptual Ability	15–27	19.4
Total Science	16–22	18

GPA: 2012 ENTERING CLASS

ENROLLEE GPA SCORES	RANGE	MEAN
Science GPA	2.91–4.00	3.45
Total GPA	3.18–4.00	3.53

APPLICATION AND SELECTION

TIMETABLE

Earliest filing date: 07/01/2013
Latest filing date: 11/01/2013
Earliest date for acceptance offers: 08/31/2013
Maximum time in days for applicant's response to acceptance offer: 15 days from receipt of offer letter
Requests for deferred entrance considered: In exceptional circumstances only
Fee for application: Yes
Amount of fee for application:
In state: $50 Out of state: NR International: NA
Fee waiver available: No

	FIRST DEPOSIT	SECOND DEPOSIT	THIRD DEPOSIT
Required to hold place	No	No	No

APPLICATION PROCESS

Participates in Associated American Dental Schools Application Service (AADSAS): No
Accepts direct applicants: Yes
Secondary or supplemental application required: No
Interview is mandatory: Yes
Interview is by invitation: Yes

RESIDENCY

Admissions process distinguishes between in-state/in-province and out-of-state/out-of-province applicants: Yes
Preference given to residents of: Mississippi
Reciprocity Admissions Agreement available for legal residents of: None
Applications are accepted from non-U.S. citizens/non-U.S. permanent residents: No

APPLICATION AND ENROLLMENT	NUMBER OF APPLICANTS	ESTIMATED NUMBER INTERVIEWED	ESTIMATED NUMBER ENROLLED
In-state or province applicants	110	64	35
Out-of-state or province applicants	7	0	0

Generally and over time, percentage of your first-year enrollment is in-state: 100%
Origin of out-of-state enrollees (U.S.): NA
Origin of international enrollees: NA

DEMOGRAPHIC DESCRIPTIONS OF APPLICANTS: 2012 ENTERING CLASS

	APPLICANTS		ENROLLEES	
	M	W	M	W
Hispanic/Latino of any race	2	0	0	0
American Indian or Alaska Native	0	0	0	0
Asian	1	5	0	1
Black or African American	6	16	1	2
Native Hawaiian or Other Pacific Islander	0	0	0	0
White	47	32	20	11
Two or more races	0	1	0	0
Race and ethnicity unknown	5	2	0	0
International	NA	NA	NA	NA

	MINIMUM	MAXIMUM	MEAN
2012 entering class enrollees by age	22	37	23

Number of first-time enrollees over age 30: 2

CURRICULUM

The major emphasis of the dental curriculum is to train practitioners of general dentistry to provide total health care. This training is accomplished by employing a systems approach to a problem-oriented curriculum. Clinical experience begins in the second year, and a team approach to patient care is used on a limited basis through all four years. A team comprises one student from each class. Basic science and clinical science courses are integrated. Off-campus clinical experiences begin in the first year with a one-week community project somewhere in the state. These continue throughout the four years. A written evaluation of all courses and instructors is completed by each student at the end of each quarter. Audiovisual facilities and student learning laboratories are provided where applicable.

Student research opportunities: Yes

SPECIAL PROGRAMS AND SERVICES

PREDENTAL

DAT workshops
Postbaccalaureate programs
Summer enrichment programs
Impressions Program (Student National Dental Association)

DURING DENTAL SCHOOL

Academic counseling and tutoring
Community service opportunities
Internships, externships, or extramural programs
Mentoring
Personal counseling
Professional- and career development programming
Training for those interested in academic careers

ACTIVE STUDENT ORGANIZATIONS

American Association of Dental Research Student Research Group
American Association of Pediatric Dentistry
American Association of Women Dentists
American Dental Education Association (ADEA)
American Student Dental Association
Hispanic Dental Association
Student National Dental Association

INTERNATIONAL DENTISTS

Graduates of international dental schools considered for traditional predoctoral program: No
Advanced standing program offered for graduates of international dental schools: No

COMBINED AND ALTERNATE DEGREES

Ph.D.	M.S.	M.P.H.	M.D.	B.A./B.S.	Other
—	—	—	—	—	—

COSTS: 2012-13 SCHOOL YEAR

	FIRST YEAR	SECOND YEAR	THIRD YEAR	FOURTH YEAR
Tuition, resident	$20,530	$20,530	$20,530	$20,530
Tuition, nonresident				
Tuition, other				
Fees		$345	$2,335	$2,157
Instruments, books, and supplies	$6,839	$2,446	$1,885	$1,140
Estimated living expenses	$13,455	$13,455	$17,940	$17,940
Total, resident	$40,824	$36,776	$42,690	$41,767
Total, nonresident				
Total, other				

FINANCIAL AID

Recipients of scholarships and grants in the 2012 entering class received awards between $500 and $25,000.

A.T. STILL UNIVERSITY
MISSOURI SCHOOL OF DENTISTRY & ORAL HEALTH

Dr. Christopher G. Halliday, Dean

GENERAL INFORMATION

The Missouri School of Dentistry & Oral Health prepares caring, technologically adept dentists to become community and educational leaders. The school offers students an experience-rich learning environment where health professionals approach patient health as part of a team. The Missouri School of Dentistry & Oral Health is part of A.T. Still University, which also includes the Kirksville College of Osteopathic Medicine, Arizona School of Health Sciences, School of Health Management, Arizona School of Dentistry & Oral Health, and School of Osteopathic Medicine in Arizona.

MISSION STATEMENT:

The mission of the Missouri School of Dentistry & Oral Health is to educate caring, technologically adept dentists who become community and educational leaders serving those in need and to be the leader in the lifelong education of community responsive general dentists; to prepare graduates with a strong foundation of critical inquiry, evidence-based practice, research, cultural competency, an orientation to prevention, and interdisciplinary health care experiences; and to promote the delivery of optimal patient care and for the transfer of newly acquired knowledge, skills, and technology to the profession and to the community.

Type of institution: Private
Year opened: Anticipated in 2013
Term type: Semester
Time to degree in months: 48
Start month: July 2013

Doctoral dental degree offered: D.M.D.
Total predoctoral enrollment: Will be 40
Estimated entering class size: 40
Campus setting: Rural
Campus housing available: Yes

CONTACT INFORMATION

www.atsu.edu/mosdoh
800 West Jefferson Street
Kirksville, MO 63501
Phone: 660-626-2121

OFFICE OF ADMISSIONS
800 West Jefferson Street
Kirksville, MO 63501
Phone: 660-626-2237
www.atsu.edu

OFFICE OF FINANCIAL AID
800 West Jefferson Street
Kirksville, MO 63501
Phone: 660-626-2529
www.atsu.edu

OFFICE OF STUDENT SERVICES
800 West Jefferson Street
Kirksville, MO 63501
Phone: 660-626-2237
www.atsu.edu

PREPARATION

Formal minimum preparation in semester/quarter hours: Semester: 90 Quarter: 135
Baccalaureate degree preferred: Yes
Number of first-year, first-time enrollees whose highest degree is:
- Baccalaureate: --
- Master's: -
- Ph.D. or other doctorate: -

Of first-year, first-time enrollees without baccalaureates, the number with:
- Equivalent of 60 undergraduate credit hours or less: -
- Equivalent of 61-90 undergraduate credit hours: -
- Equivalent of 91 or more undergraduate credit hours: -

PREREQUISITE COURSE	REQUIRED	RECOMMENDED	LAB REQUIRED	CREDITS (SEMESTER/QUARTER)
BCP (biology-chemistry-physics) sciences				
Biology	✓		✓	8/12
Chemistry, general/inorganic	✓		✓	8/12
Chemistry, organic	✓		✓	8/12
Physics	✓		✓	8/12
Additional biological sciences				
Anatomy		✓		3/4
Biochemistry	✓			3/4
Cell biology				
Histology				
Immunology				
Microbiology		✓		3/4
Molecular biology/genetics				
Physiology	✓			3/4

(Prerequisite Courses continued)

PREPARATION (CONTINUED)

PREREQUISITE COURSE	REQUIRED	RECOMMENDED	LAB REQUIRED	CREDITS (SEMESTER/QUARTER)
Zoology				

Community college coursework accepted for prerequisites: Yes
Community college coursework accepted for electives: Yes
Limits on community college credit hours: No
Advanced placement (AP) credit accepted for prerequisites: Yes
Advanced placement (AP) credit accepted for electives: Yes
Job shadowing: Recommended
Number of hours of job shadowing required or recommended: 20
Other factors considered in admission: Community service experience is expected.

DAT

Mandatory: Yes
Latest DAT for consideration of application: 12/01/2013
Oldest DAT considered: 01/01/2010
When more than one DAT score is reported: Highest academic average score is considered.
Canadian DAT accepted: No
Application considered before DAT scores are submitted: No

DAT: 2012 ENTERING CLASS

ENROLLEE DAT SCORES	RANGE	MEAN
Academic Average	NA	NA
Perceptual Ability	NA	NA
Total Science	NA	NA

GPA: 2012 ENTERING CLASS

ENROLLEE GPA SCORES	RANGE	MEAN
Science GPA	NA	NA
Total GPA	NA	NA

APPLICATION AND SELECTION

TIMETABLE

Earliest filing date: 06/01/2013
Latest filing date: 12/01/2013
Earliest date for acceptance offers: Winter 2013
Maximum time in days for applicant's response to acceptance offer:
- 30 days if accepted on or after December 1 through January 31
- 15 days if accepted on or after February 1
- 48 hours after May 1

Requests for deferred entrance considered: In exceptional circumstances only
Fee for application: Yes, submitted only when requested
Amount of fee for application:
In state: $70 Out of state: $70 International: $70
Fee waiver available: Yes

	FIRST DEPOSIT	SECOND DEPOSIT	THIRD DEPOSIT
Required to hold place	Yes	Yes	No
Resident amount	$1,000	$1,000	
Nonresident amount	$1,000	$1,000	
Deposit due	As indicated in admission offer	05/01/2014	
Applied to tuition	Yes	Yes	
Refundable	No	No	

APPLICATION PROCESS

Participates in Associated American Dental Schools Application Service (AADSAS): Yes
Accepts direct applicants: No
Secondary or supplemental application required: Yes
Secondary or supplemental application website: Invitation will be sent by email.
Interview is mandatory: Yes
Interview is by invitation: Yes

RESIDENCY

Admissions process distinguishes between in-state/in-province and out-of-state/out-of-province applicants: No
Applications are accepted from non-U.S. citizens/non-U.S. permanent residents: No

APPLICATION AND ENROLLMENT	NUMBER OF APPLICANTS	ESTIMATED NUMBER INTERVIEWED	ESTIMATED NUMBER ENROLLED
All applicants	NA	NA	NA

DEMOGRAPHIC DESCRIPTIONS OF APPLICANTS: 2012 ENTERING CLASS

	APPLICANTS		ENROLLEES	
	M	W	M	W
Hispanic/Latino of any race	NA	NA	NA	NA
American Indian or Alaska Native	NA	NA	NA	NA
Asian	NA	NA	NA	NA
Black or African American	NA	NA	NA	NA
Native Hawaiian or Other Pacific Islander	NA	NA	NA	NA

White	NA	NA	NA	NA
Two or more races	NA	NA	NA	NA
Race and ethnicity unknown	NA	NA	NA	NA
International	NA	NA	NA	NA

	MINIMUM	MAXIMUM	MEAN
Previous year enrollees by age	NA	NA	NA

Number of first-time enrollees over age 30: NA

CURRICULUM

The curriculum at the Missouri School of Dentistry & Oral Health is designed to produce graduates who are technologically adept, professionally competent, patient-centered, and compassionate. The curriculum emphasizes patient care experiences through simulation, integration of biomedical and clinical sciences, and problem-solving scenarios to achieve clinical excellence. The curriculum includes a strong component of public health, leadership, and practice through weekly learning modules.

Student research opportunities: Yes

SPECIAL PROGRAMS AND SERVICES

DURING DENTAL SCHOOL

Academic counseling and tutoring
Community service opportunities
Internships, externships, or extramural programs
Mentoring
Personal counseling

INTERNATIONAL DENTISTS

Graduates of international dental schools considered for traditional predoctoral program: No
Advanced standing program offered for graduates of international dental schools: No

COMBINED AND ALTERNATE DEGREES

Ph.D.	M.S.	M.P.H.	M.D.	B.A./B.S.	Other
—	—	✓	—	—	—

COSTS: 2012-13 SCHOOL YEAR

	FIRST YEAR	SECOND YEAR	THIRD YEAR	FOURTH YEAR
Tuition, resident	NA	NA	NA	NA
Tuition, nonresident	NA	NA	NA	NA
Tuition, other	NA	NA	NA	NA
Fees	NA	NA	NA	NA
Instruments, books, and supplies	NA	NA	NA	NA
Estimated living expenses	NA	NA	NA	NA
Total, resident	NA	NA	NA	NA
Total, nonresident	NA	NA	NA	NA
Total, other	NA	NA	NA	NA

FINANCIAL AID

A.T. Still University (ATSU) Missouri School of Dentistry & Oral Health participates in the Direct Lending Program. Student loans are available for tuition, fees, and living expenses. The Missouri School of Dentistry & Oral Health is also involved in a number of scholarship programs such as the Health Professions Scholarship Program (HPSP)—military, the National Health Service Corps (NHSC), the Indian Health Service (IHS), and the Western Interstate Commission for Higher Education (WICHE). Federal loans are the most common form of financial assistance with 95% of the student body utilizing these loans.

UNIVERSITY OF MISSOURI - KANSAS CITY
SCHOOL OF DENTISTRY

Dr. Marsha A. Pyle, Dean

CONTACT INFORMATION

www.umkc.edu/dentistry
650 East 25th Street
Kansas City, MO 64108

ADMISSIONS

Richie Bigham
Assistant Dean for Student Programs
650 East 25th Street
Kansas City, MO 64108
Phone: 816-235-2082

STUDENT FINANCIAL AID OFFICE

Scott Sponholtz
Assistant Director – Hospital Hill
5115 Oak Street
Kansas City, MO 64110
Phone: 816-235-1154

STUDENT AFFAIRS

Richie Bigham
Assistant Dean for Student Programs
650 East 25th Street
Kansas City, MO 64108
Phone: 816-235-2080

MINORITY AFFAIRS/DIVERSITY

John Cottrell
Director Minority and Special Programs
650 East 25th Street
Kansas City, MO 64108
Phone: 816-235-2085

OFF-CAMPUS HOUSING ASSOCIATION

4825 Troost Avenue
Kansas City, MO 64110
Phone: 816-235-1428

GENERAL INFORMATION

The University of Missouri – Kansas City (UMKC) School of Dentistry originated in 1881 as the Kansas City Dental College. The name has changed and the school has grown and evolved into a multi-faceted institution, but it has maintained a tradition of excellence in education for over a century. The School offers a varied and complete range of educational experiences for students of dentistry and dental hygiene and for graduate and continuing education students, serving 109 predoctoral, 30 dental hygiene, and 25 graduate students each year. The first-rate faculty comprises scholars, scientists, and specialists, all dedicated to providing a quality and comprehensive education, individualized to each student's needs and goals. The School is also a model for technologically advanced administrative offices, instructional settings, and clinical facilities. It has a paperless clinic with 279 dental operatories and delivers clinical care to more than 60,000 patients annually. The School of Dentistry is situated a few miles north of the UMKC campus, atop Hospital Hill—a historic area of Kansas City, so-named because it is a nexus of health care and educational institutions. The School is surrounded by prestigious neighbors, including the UMKC schools of Medicine and Nursing, Children's Mercy Hospital, Truman Medical Center, and several other private and public medical facilities. Students profit from the opportunity of learning, working, and interacting with scholars, researchers, and professionals in many related areas of health care.

MISSION STATEMENT:

UMKC School of Dentistry serves as a leader in the advancement of oral health care through exceptional educational programs, scientific inquiry, patient care, and service to society. The goals of the school are to enhance the school's culture and organizational structure; provide educational programs that develop competent, compassionate, engaged learners; be nationally and internationally recognized for excellence in research; improve services to the community; and educate and train competent, caring, and community-involved clinicians.

Type of institution: Public
Year opened: 1881
Term type: Semester
Time to degree in months: 40
Start month: August
Doctoral dental degree offered: D.D.S.

Total predoctoral enrollment: 407
Estimated entering class size: 109
Campus setting: Urban
Campus housing available: Yes, on the Volker Campus.

PREPARATION

Formal minimum preparation in semester/quarter hours: Semester: 120 Quarter: 180
Baccalaureate degree preferred: Yes
Number of first-year, first-time enrollees whose highest degree is:
- Baccalaureate: 101
- Master's: 7
- Ph.D. or other doctorate: 0

Of first-year, first-time enrollees without baccalaureates, the number with:
- Equivalent of 60 undergraduate credit hours or less: 0
- Equivalent of 61-90 undergraduate credit hours: 0
- Equivalent of 91 or more undergraduate credit hours: 1

PREREQUISITE COURSE	REQUIRED	RECOMMENDED	LAB REQUIRED	CREDITS (SEMESTER/QUARTER)
BCP (biology-chemistry-physics) sciences				
Biology	✓		✓	16/24
Chemistry, general/inorganic	✓		✓	8/12
Chemistry, organic	✓		✓	8/12
Physics	✓		✓	8/12
Additional biological sciences				
Anatomy	✓			4/6

(Prerequisite Courses continued)

PREPARATION (CONTINUED)

PREREQUISITE COURSE	REQUIRED	RECOMMENDED	LAB REQUIRED	CREDITS (SEMESTER/QUARTER)
Biochemistry	✓			4/6
Cell biology	✓			4/6
Histology		✓		
Immunology				
Microbiology		✓		3
Molecular biology/genetics		✓		
Physiology	✓		✓	4/6
Zoology				

Community college coursework accepted for prerequisites: Yes, contact Director of Admissions for guidance.
Community college coursework accepted for electives: Yes
Limits on community college credit hours: Yes
Maximum number of community college credit hours: 60
Advanced placement (AP) credit accepted for prerequisites: No
Advanced placement (AP) credit accepted for electives: May be applied to undergraduate degree
Comments regarding AP credit: (1) May be applied to the undergraduate degree prior to entry into the D.D.S. program; (2) Do not meet prerequisite requirements unless have additional advanced courses in subject
Job shadowing: Required
Number of hours of job shadowing required or recommended: Minimum of five office settings, 100-120 hours
Other factors considered in admission: Investigation of dentistry, commitment to community, personal character, critical thinking/problem solving skills, interpersonal communication skills, and time management skills

DAT

Mandatory: Yes
Latest DAT for consideration of application: 10/01/2013
Oldest DAT for consideration of application: 10/01/2009
When more than one DAT score is reported: Most recent score only is considered
Canadian DAT accepted: Yes
Application considered before DAT scores are submitted: Applications are reviewed after the DAT scores arrive.

DAT: 2012 ENTERING CLASS

ENROLLEE DAT SCORES	RANGE	MEAN
Academic Average	17-23	19.0
Perceptual Ability	11-25	18.8
Total Science	15-25	18.6

GPA: 2012 ENTERING CLASS

ENROLLEE GPA SCORES	RANGE	MEAN
Science GPA	3.0-4.0	3.62
Total GPA	2.8-4.0	3.63

APPLICATION AND SELECTION

TIMETABLE

Earliest filing date: 06/01/2013
Latest filing date: 09/01/2013 preference for receipt of application materials
Earliest date for acceptance offers: 12/01/2013
Maximum time in days for applicant's response to acceptance offer:
30 days if accepted on or after December 1
15 days if accepted on or after February 1
Requests for deferred entrance considered: In exceptional circumstances only
Fee for application: Yes, submitted only when requested
Amount of fee for application:
In state: $35 Out of state: $35 International: NA
Fee waiver available: No

	FIRST DEPOSIT	SECOND DEPOSIT	THIRD DEPOSIT
Required to hold place	Yes	No	No
Resident amount	$200		
Nonresident amount	$200		
Deposit due	As indicated in admission offer		
Applied to tuition	Yes		
Refundable	No		

APPLICATION PROCESS

Participates in Associated American Dental Schools Application Service (AADSAS): Yes
Accepts direct applicants: Yes
Secondary or supplemental application required: Yes, with interview invitation
Secondary or supplemental application website: The UMKC School of Dentistry Survey is only available from our office.
Interview is mandatory: Yes
Interview is by invitation: Yes

RESIDENCY

Admissions process distinguishes between in-state/in-province and out-of-state/out-of-province applicants: Yes

Preference given to residents of: Arkansas, Hawaii, Kansas, Missouri, and New Mexico. Highly qualified applicants outside these states are welcome to apply.
Reciprocity Admissions Agreement available for legal residents of: Arkansas, Kansas, New Mexico
Applications are accepted from non-U.S. citizens/non-U.S. permanent residents: No

APPLICATION AND ENROLLMENT	NUMBER OF APPLICANTS	ESTIMATED NUMBER INTERVIEWED	ESTIMATED NUMBER ENROLLED
In-state or province applicants	163	80	77
Out-of-state or province applicants	598	96	32

Generally and over time, percentage of your first-year enrollment is in-state: 70%

Origin of out-of-state enrollees (U.S.): Hawaii-3, Iowa-1, Kansas-21, Maryland-1, New Mexico-5, Oklahoma-1

Origin of international enrollees: NA

DEMOGRAPHIC DESCRIPTIONS OF APPLICANTS: 2012 ENTERING CLASS

	APPLICANTS		ENROLLEES	
	M	W	M	W
Hispanic/Latino of any race	9	6	1	1
American Indian or Alaska Native	1	1	1	0
Asian	77	79	6	6
Black or African American	9	13	1	2
Native Hawaiian or Other Pacific Islander	1	0	0	0
White	261	215	47	34
Two or more races	29	33	3	5
Race and ethnicity unknown	16	11	1	1
International			0	0

	MINIMUM	MAXIMUM	MEAN
2012 entering year enrollees by age	21	44	24

Number of first-time enrollees over age 30: 11

CURRICULUM

The curriculum (eight semesters, two summer terms) offers an education leading to an effective and enriching career of public service, professional growth, and contribution. The program provides a sound background in the biomedical, behavioral, and clinical sciences with an emphasis on comprehensive oral health care delivered through a generalist-based team system of clinical education. Practice management courses are also built into the curriculum. The early exposure to clinical dentistry and the multidisciplinary, integrated preclinical curriculum is a hallmark of the program. Degrees Offered: Dental Degree—D.D.S. Additional Degrees: B.S. in Dental Hygiene; M.S. in Dental Hygiene Education; M.S. in Oral Biology; interdisciplinary Ph.D. program; graduate professional certificates in advanced dental education in general dentistry, oral and maxillofacial surgery, orthodontics and dentofacial orthopedics, pediatric dentistry, periodontics, and endodontics; and a variety of continuing education courses.

Student research opportunities: Yes: Summer Scholars Research Program following the first year of the D.D.S. program

SPECIAL PROGRAMS AND SERVICES

PREDENTAL

Online DAT Preparatory course available at www.cewebinar.com
Admissions Enhancement Program

DURING DENTAL SCHOOL

Academic counseling and tutoring
Community service opportunities
Internships, externships, or extramural programs
Mentoring
Online National Board Dental Examination Part II preparatory course
Personal counseling
Professional- and career-development programming
Senior Departmental Advanced Studies Program
Training for those interested in academic careers
Transfer applicants considered if space is available

ACTIVE STUDENT ORGANIZATIONS

Academy of LDS Dentists
American Association of Dental Research Student Research Group
American Association of Pediatric Dentistry
American Association of Women Dentists
American Dental Education Association (ADEA)
American Society of Dentistry for Children
American Student Dental Association
Hispanic Dental Association
Interfraternity Council, Delta Sigma Delta, Psi Omega, and Xi Psi Phi Fraternities
Student Council
Students Take Action
Student National Dental Association

INTERNATIONAL DENTISTS

Graduates of international dental schools considered for traditional predoctoral program: Yes, they are considered only if space is available in the second year. They must be permanent residents or U.S. citizens. Additionally, their legal state of residence must be Missouri or Kansas.
Advanced standing program offered for graduates of international dental schools: No

COMBINED AND ALTERNATE DEGREES

Ph.D.	M.S.	M.P.H.	M.D.	B.A./B.S.	Other
✓	✓	—	—	—	—

COSTS: 2012-13 SCHOOL YEAR

	FIRST YEAR	SECOND YEAR	THIRD YEAR	FOURTH YEAR
Tuition, resident	$27,779	$27,818	$34,583	$34,491
Tuition, nonresident	$53,857	$53,896	$67,182	$67,089
Tuition, other				
Fees				
Instruments, books, and supplies	$9,455	$8,850	$7,940	$7,665
Estimated living expenses	$17,230	$17,230	$17,230	$17,230
Total, resident	$54,464	$53,898	$59,753	$59,386
Total, nonresident	$80,542	$79,976	$92,352	$91,984
Total, other				

FINANCIAL AID

The UMKC Cashiers Office makes public current tuition rates, other costs, and payment information. For more information visit www.umkc.edu.

The Financial Aid and Scholarship Office web page contains information on the cost of attendance, estimated financial aid packages, and available aid programs. See the UMKC School of Dentistry page at www.umkc.edu/finaid under the Health Professionals heading.

The average 2012 graduate indebtedness in 2012 was $161,346.

CREIGHTON UNIVERSITY
SCHOOL OF DENTISTRY

Dr. Mark A. Latta, Dean

GENERAL INFORMATION

Creighton University, a private Jesuit school with a total enrollment of approximately 7,000 students, is one of the most diverse educational institutions of its size in the nation. The School of Dentistry was established in 1905. The major effort of the School of Dentistry is directed toward its education program leading to the D.D.S. degree. Creighton does, however, offer continuing education courses and cooperates with several local junior colleges in the training of dental auxiliaries. In addition, Creighton conducts research, provides dental health and dental health education services to the local community, and participates in an outreach program to the Dominican Republic. Creighton's School of Dentistry is a regional resource. Creighton students come from all parts of the United States, its territories, and some foreign countries.

MISSION STATEMENT:

The basic goal of the School of Dentistry is to provide primary care practitioners to address the oral health needs of society, particularly the segment of society that experiences inadequate dental health perpetuated by isolation and the absence or unavailability of dental health education facilities. In the fulfillment of this basic goal, the institution addresses its efforts to the following primary objective: to educate dental practitioners who are biologically oriented, clinically competent, socially sensitive, and ethically and morally responsible. As part of a Jesuit institution, adhering to the fundamental principles set forth by the Society of Jesus during its almost five centuries of existence, the school promotes a value orientation that is Judeo-Christian in philosophy. Incidental to the education program, the school attempts to provide an environment complementary to the development of the whole person.

Type of institution: Private
Year opened: 1905
Term type: Semester
Time to degree in months: 44
Start month: August

Doctoral dental degree offered: D.D.S.
Total predoctoral enrollment: 344
Estimated entering class size: 85
Campus setting: Urban
Campus housing available: Yes

CONTACT INFORMATION

www.creighton.edu/dentalschool
2500 California Plaza
Omaha, NE 68178
Phone: 402-280-5061
Fax: 402-280-5094

ADMISSIONS
2500 California Plaza
Omaha, NE 68178
Phone: 402-280-2695
www.creighton.edu/dentalschool

FINANCIAL AID
2500 California Plaza
Omaha, NE 68178
Phone: 800-282-5835
www.creighton.edu

MINORITY AFFAIRS/DIVERSITY
2500 California Plaza
Omaha, NE 68178
Phone: 402-280-2981
www.creighton.edu

HOUSING
2500 California Plaza
Omaha, NE 68178
Phone: 402-280-3016
www.creighton.edu

INTERNATIONAL STUDENTS
2500 California Plaza
Omaha, NE 68178
Phone: 402-280-2592

PREPARATION

Formal minimum preparation in semester/quarter hours: Semester: 64 Quarter: 96
Baccalaureate degree preferred: Yes
Number of first-year, first-time enrollees whose highest degree is:
- Baccalaureate: 81
- Master's: 2
- Ph.D. or other doctorate: 0

Of first-year, first-time enrollees without baccalaureates, the number with:
- Equivalent of 60 undergraduate credit hours or less: 0
- Equivalent of 61-90 undergraduate credit hours: 0
- Equivalent of 91 or more undergraduate credit hours: 2

PREREQUISITE COURSE	REQUIRED	RECOMMENDED	LAB REQUIRED	CREDITS (SEMESTER/QUARTER)
BCP (biology-chemistry-physics) sciences				
Biology	✓		✓	6/10
Chemistry, general/inorganic	✓		✓	8/12
Chemistry, organic	✓		✓	6/10
Physics	✓		✓	6/10
Additional biological sciences				
Anatomy		✓		3/5
Biochemistry		✓		3/5
Cell biology				

(Prerequisite Courses continued)

PREPARATION (CONTINUED)

PREREQUISITE COURSE	REQUIRED	RECOMMENDED	LAB REQUIRED	CREDITS (SEMESTER/QUARTER)
Histology				
Immunology				
Microbiology		✓		3/5
Molecular biology/genetics				
Physiology		✓		3
Zoology				
Other				
English	✓			6

Community college coursework accepted for prerequisites: No
Community college coursework accepted for electives: Yes
Limits on community college credit hours: Yes
Maximum number of community college credit hours: 64
Advanced placement (AP) credit accepted for prerequisites: No
Advanced placement (AP) credit accepted for electives: No
Job shadowing: Recommended
Number of hours of job shadowing required or recommended: 40

DAT

Mandatory: Yes
Latest DAT for consideration of application: 02/28/2014
Oldest DAT considered: 01/01/2009
When more than one DAT score is reported: Most recent score only is considered
Canadian DAT accepted: Yes
Application considered before DAT scores are submitted: No

DAT: 2012 ENTERING CLASS

ENROLLEE DAT SCORES	RANGE	MEAN
Academic Average	17.0-25.0	19.4
Perceptual Ability	17.0-26.0	20.5
Total Science	17.0-25.0	19.0

GPA: 2012 ENTERING CLASS

ENROLLEE GPA SCORES	RANGE	MEAN
Science GPA	2.94-4.05	3.45
Total GPA	3.18-4.03	3.58

APPLICATION AND SELECTION

TIMETABLE

Earliest filing date: 06/04/2013
Latest filing date: 02/01/2014
Earliest date for acceptance offers: 12/01/2013
Maximum time in days for applicant's response to acceptance offer:
30 days if accepted on or after December 1
15 days if accepted on or after February 1
Requests for deferred entrance considered: In exceptional circumstances only.
Fee for application: Yes, submitted at same time as Associated American Dental Schools Application Service (AADSAS) application
Amount of fee for application:
In state: $60 Out of state: $60 International: $60
Fee waiver available: No

	FIRST DEPOSIT	SECOND DEPOSIT	THIRD DEPOSIT
Required to hold place	Yes	Yes	No
Resident amount	$500	$300	
Nonresident amount	$500	$300	
Deposit due	As indicated in admission offer	As indicated in admission offer	
Applied to tuition	Yes	Yes	
Refundable	No	No	

APPLICATION PROCESS

Participates in AADSAS: Yes
Accepts direct applicants: No
Secondary or supplemental application required: Yes
Secondary or supplemental application website: www.creighton.edu/dentalschool/admissions/prospectivestudents/index.php
Interview is mandatory: No
Interview is by invitation: Yes

RESIDENCY

Admissions process distinguishes between in-state/in-province and out-of-state/out-of-province applicants: No
Applications are accepted from non-U.S. citizens/non-U.S. permanent residents: Yes

APPLICATION AND ENROLLMENT	NUMBER OF APPLICANTS	ESTIMATED NUMBER INTERVIEWED	ESTIMATED NUMBER ENROLLED
In-state or province applicants	71	NR	9
Out-of-state or province applicants	2,656	NR	76

Generally and over time, percentage of your first-year enrollment is in-state: 12%
Origin of out-of-state enrollees (U.S.): California-3, Colorado-3, Florida-2, Georgia-2, Hawaii-2, Idaho-8, Illinois-3, Iowa-4, Kansas-6, Minnesota-6, Missouri-5, New Mexico-5, North Dakota-4, Oklahoma-1, Tennessee-1, Texas-2, Utah-10, Washington-4, Wyoming-4
Origin of international enrollees: Vietnam-1

DEMOGRAPHIC DESCRIPTIONS OF APPLICANTS: 2012 ENTERING CLASS

	APPLICANTS		ENROLLEES	
	M	W	M	W
Hispanic/Latino of any race	94	69	4	0
American Indian or Alaska Native	3	5	1	0
Asian	350	306	5	3
Black or African American	26	46	1	4
Native Hawaiian or Other Pacific Islander	2	0	0	0
White	978	531	42	20
Two or more races	40	43	4	1
Race and ethnicity unknown	60	28	0	0
International	79	67	0	0

	MINIMUM	MAXIMUM	MEAN
2012 entering class enrollees by age	21	35	24

Number of first-time enrollees over age 30: 4

CURRICULUM

The four-year program is designed to provide maximum opportunity for clinical application of basic concepts. Essentially, the curriculum is a progression of experiences from basic and preclinical sciences to mastery of clinical skills. Basic sciences are cooperatively taught by both dental and medical school faculty under the aegis of the Department of Oral Biology. Clinical sciences are taught by full-time clinical faculty with the assistance of part-time faculty. The full-time faculty, representing both basic and clinical science disciplines by training and experience, ensure integration of basic and clinical sciences. The part-time faculty brings extensive and varied experience, based on their own private practices, to add another dimension to the program and to reinforce the concepts being taught.

Student research opportunities: Yes

SPECIAL PROGRAMS AND SERVICES

PREDENTAL

Postbaccalaureate programs: Please see website.
Summer enrichment programs: Please see website.

DURING DENTAL SCHOOL

Academic counseling and tutoring
Community service opportunities
Internships, externships, or extramural programs
Mentoring
Opportunity to study for credit at institution abroad
Personal counseling
Professional- and career-development programming
Training for those interested in academic careers
Transfer applicants considered if space is available

ACTIVE STUDENT ORGANIZATIONS

American Association of Dental Research Student Research Group
American Student Dental Association

INTERNATIONAL DENTISTS

Graduates of international dental schools considered for traditional predoctoral program: No
Advanced standing program offered for graduates of international dental schools: Yes
Advanced standing program description: Program awarding a dental degree

COMBINED AND ALTERNATE DEGREES					
Ph.D.	M.S.	M.P.H.	M.D.	B.A./B.S.	Other
—	—	—	—	—	—

COSTS: 2012-13 SCHOOL YEAR

	FIRST YEAR	SECOND YEAR	THIRD YEAR	FOURTH YEAR
Tuition, resident	$51,098	$51,098	$51,098	$51,098
Tuition, nonresident	$51,098	$51,098	$51,098	$51,098
Tuition, other	NA	NA	NA	NA
Fees	$1,032	$1,032	$1,032	$1,032
Instruments, books, and supplies	$6,986	$7,650	$7,050	$10,350
Estimated living expenses	$17,600	$17,600	$17,600	$14,400
Total, resident	$76,716	$77,380	$76,780	$76,880
Total, nonresident	$76,716	$77,380	$76,780	$76,880
Total, other	NA	NA	NA	NA

FINANCIAL AID

1. Apply for admission to Creighton's School of Dentistry. No financial aid commitment can be made until a student is accepted for admission.
2. Complete the Free Application for Federal Student Aid (FAFSA). It should be completed online at www.fafsa.ed.gov after January 1. All parental information must be completed for consideration for the Health Professions Student Loan Program.
3. New students are notified of their financial aid by an award letter that contains instructions for acceptance of aid.

It is recommended that application for financial aid be made between January 1 and April 1 preceding the fall semester in which one plans to enroll. Early application is desirable in order to ensure the availability of funds. However, no student will be considered for or granted financial aid until that student is accepted by the university for admission and/or is in good standing with the university.

All financial aid advanced by Creighton University must be used to pay tuition, fees, and university board and room charges before any other direct or indirect educational costs. The specific amount awarded will be governed by the eligibility of the student and by the funds available at the time of application. One half of the total annual award will be available at registration each semester.

In 2012, there were 153 recipients of scholarships and grants between $1,000 and $25,549. The average amount was $4,098.

UNIVERSITY OF Nebraska Medical Center

College of Dentistry

UNIVERSITY OF NEBRASKA MEDICAL CENTER
COLLEGE OF DENTISTRY

Dr. John W. Reinhardt, Dean

CONTACT INFORMATION

www.unmc.edu/dentistry
40th & Holdrege streets
Lincoln, NE 68583-0740
Phone: 402-472-1344
Fax: 402-472-6681

ADMISSIONS

Glenda M. Cunning
Enrollment Manager
40th & Holdrege streets
Lincoln, NE 68583-0740
Phone: 402-472-1363
Email: gcunning@unmc.edu

OFFICE OF FINANCIAL AID

Judith D. Walker
Executive Director, Student Services, Financial Aid
984265 Nebraska Medical Center
Omaha, NE 68198-4265
Phone: 402-559-4199
Email: jdwalker@unmc.edu

STUDENT AFFAIRS

Dr. Merlyn W. Vogt
Assistant Dean for Student Affairs
40th & Holdrege streets
Lincoln, NE 68583-0740
Phone: 402-472-1479
Email: mvogt@unmc.edu

GENERAL INFORMATION

The College of Dentistry, University of Nebraska Medical Center (UNMC), is a public institution. The Lincoln Dental College was founded in 1899 and was operated as a private school until 1917, when it became affiliated with the University of Nebraska. The college became part of the university's Medical Center on July 1, 1979. The college is located in Lincoln, Nebraska (population 258,000). The total number of students enrolled is 270, including 48 students enrolled in a two-year dental hygiene program and 50 advanced dental education and graduate students. Advanced dental programs are offered in endodontics, general practice residency, orthodontics, pediatric dentistry, and periodontics. A graduate program in dentistry leads to a clinically oriented M.S. degree. A graduate program in the oral biology department leads to a more traditional M.S. or Ph.D. degree.

MISSION STATEMENT:

The vision of the University of Nebraska Medical Center is to be a world-renowned health sciences center that delivers state-of-the-art health care through academic and private practice; prepares the best-educated health professionals and scientists; ranks among the leading research centers; advances our historic community to community health; and embraces the richness of diversity.

Type of institution: Public
Year opened: 1899
Term type: Semester
Time to degree in months: 45
Start month: August

Doctoral dental degree offered: D.D.S.
Total predoctoral enrollment: 180
Estimated entering class size: 45
Campus setting: Suburban
Campus housing available: Yes

PREPARATION

Formal minimum preparation in semester/quarter hours: Semester: 90 Quarter: 120
Baccalaureate degree preferred: Yes
Number of first-year, first-time enrollees whose highest degree is:
- Baccalaureate: 38
- Master's: 1
- Ph.D. or other doctorate: 0

Of first-year, first-time enrollees without baccalaureates, the number with:
- Equivalent of 60 undergraduate credit hours or less: 0
- Equivalent of 61-90 undergraduate credit hours: 0
- Equivalent of 91 or more undergraduate credit hours: 7

PREREQUISITE COURSE	REQUIRED	RECOMMENDED	LAB REQUIRED	CREDITS (SEMESTER/QUARTER)
BCP (biology-chemistry-physics) sciences				
Biology	✓		✓	8/12
Chemistry, general/inorganic	✓		✓	8/12
Chemistry, organic	✓		✓	8/12
Physics	✓		✓	8/12
Additional biological sciences				
Anatomy		✓		4/6
Biochemistry		✓		4/6
Cell biology		✓		4/6
Histology		✓		4/6
Immunology				
Microbiology		✓		4/6
Molecular biology/genetics		✓		4/6

(Prerequisite Courses continued)

PREPARATION (CONTINUED)

PREREQUISITE COURSE	REQUIRED	RECOMMENDED	LAB REQUIRED	CREDITS (SEMESTER/QUARTER)
Physiology		✓		4/6
Zoology				

Community college coursework accepted for prerequisites: No
Community college coursework accepted for electives: No
Limits on community college credit hours: Yes
Maximum number of community college credit hours: 30
Advanced placement (AP) credit accepted for prerequisites: No
Advanced placement (AP) credit accepted for electives: Yes
Comments regarding AP credit: Contact school for information.
Job shadowing: Required
Number of hours of job shadowing required or recommended: 35

DAT

Mandatory: Yes
Latest DAT for consideration of application: 11/15/2013
Oldest DAT considered: 08/01/2009
When more than one DAT score is reported: Most recent score only is considered.
Canadian DAT accepted: Yes
Application considered before DAT scores are submitted: Yes

DAT: 2012 ENTERING CLASS

ENROLLEE DAT SCORES	RANGE	MEAN
Academic Average	17-25	20
Perceptual Ability	16-26	21
Total Science	17-25	19

GPA: 2012 ENTERING CLASS

ENROLLEE GPA SCORES	RANGE	MEAN
Science GPA	3.27-4.0	3.73
Total GPA	3.43-4.0	3.80

APPLICATION AND SELECTION

TIMETABLE

Earliest filing date: 06/01/2013
Latest filing date: 02/01/2014
Earliest date for acceptance offers: 12/01/2013
Maximum time in days for applicant's response to acceptance offer:
30 days if accepted on or after December 1
15 days if accepted on or after February 1
Requests for deferred entrance considered: Yes
Fee for application: Yes, submitted only when requested.
Amount of fee for application:
In state: $50 Out of state: $50 International: $50
Fee waiver available: Yes

	FIRST DEPOSIT	SECOND DEPOSIT	THIRD DEPOSIT
Required to hold place	Yes	No	No
Resident amount	$200		
Nonresident amount	$200		
Deposit due	As indicated in admission offer		
Applied to tuition	Yes		
Refundable	No		

APPLICATION PROCESS

Participates in Associated American Dental Schools Application Service (AADSAS): Yes
Accepts direct applicants: No
Secondary or supplemental application required: Yes
Secondary or supplemental application website: Supplemental application not on website. It is mailed after application is received.
Interview is mandatory: Yes
Interview is by invitation: Yes

RESIDENCY

Admissions process distinguishes between in-state/in-province and out-of-state/out-of-province applicants: Yes
Preference given to residents of: Nebraska
Reciprocity Admissions Agreement available for legal residents of: Wyoming
Applications are accepted from non-U.S. citizens/non-U.S. permanent residents: Yes

APPLICATION AND ENROLLMENT	NUMBER OF APPLICANTS	ESTIMATED NUMBER INTERVIEWED	ESTIMATED NUMBER ENROLLED
In-state or province applicants	78	42	29
Out-of-state or province applicants	757	74	19

Generally and over time, percentage of your first-year enrollment is in-state: 66%
Origin of out-of-state enrollees (U.S.): Arizona-1, Colorado-1, Kansas-4, Minnesota-1, Missouri-1, South Dakota-5; Utah-1, Washington- 1, Wyoming-4
Origin of international enrollees: NA

DEMOGRAPHIC DESCRIPTIONS OF APPLICANTS: 2012 ENTERING CLASS

	APPLICANTS		ENROLLEES	
	M	W	M	W
Hispanic/Latino of any race	10	11	1	1
American Indian or Alaska Native	1	9	0	0
Asian	75	83	1	0
Black or African American	8	17	0	0
Native Hawaiian or Other Pacific Islander		1	0	1
White	323	233	21	19
Two or more races	15	21	2	2
Race and ethnicity unknown	13	8		
International				

	MINIMUM	MAXIMUM	MEAN
2012 entering class enrollees by age	21	34	24

Number of first-time enrollees over age 30: 2

CURRICULUM

The dental program is 44.5 months in duration with 36.5 months in actual attendance. There are eight semesters of 16 weeks each. In addition, attendance is required at three summer sessions (eight weeks each), one between each academic year until graduation. Objectives of the college are to:

1. Select applicants who have the personal and moral qualifications, technical potential, and scholastic ability for a professional career in dentistry;
2. Provide, within a flexible curriculum, a solid foundation of fundamental scientific knowledge and the basic technical skills necessary for using this education;
3. Motivate students to recognize and fulfill their social and moral responsibilities to their patients, their civic responsibility to the community, and their ethical obligation to the profession of dentistry; and
4. Inspire students to see the need for continuing education and for personal and professional evaluation throughout their dental careers.

Student research opportunities: Yes

SPECIAL PROGRAMS AND SERVICES

PREDENTAL

Association of American Medical Colleges/ADEA Summer Medical and Dental Education Program (AAMC/ADEA SMDEP)
Special affiliations with colleges and universities: Dillard University; Fort Lewis College
Other summer enrichment programs

DURING DENTAL SCHOOL

Academic counseling and tutoring
Community service opportunities
Internships, externships, or extramural programs
Mentoring
Personal counseling
Professional- and career-development programming
Training for those interested in academic careers

ACTIVE STUDENT ORGANIZATIONS

American Association of Dental Research Student Research Group
American Association of Women Dentists
American Dental Education Association (ADEA)
American Student Dental Association

INTERNATIONAL DENTISTS

Graduates of international dental schools considered for traditional predoctoral program: Yes
Advanced standing program offered for graduates of international dental schools: Yes
Advanced standing program description: Program awarding a dental degree.

COMBINED AND ALTERNATE DEGREES					
Ph.D.	M.S.	M.P.H.	M.D.	B.A./B.S.	Other
✓	—	—	—	—	—

COSTS: 2012-13 SCHOOL YEAR

	FIRST YEAR	SECOND YEAR	THIRD YEAR	FOURTH YEAR
Tuition, resident	$28,692	$28,692	$28,692	$22,954
Tuition, nonresident	$66,393	$66,363	$66,363	$53,090
Tuition, other				
Fees	$1,804	$1,820	$1,812	$1,548
Instruments, books, and supplies	$9,684*	$9,684*	$9,684*	$9,984*
Estimated living expenses	$20,400	$20,400	$20,400	$20,400
Total, resident	$60,580	$60,596	$60,588	$54,822
Total, nonresident	$98,251	$98,267	$98,259	$85,022
Total, other				

*Includes $2,000 equipment replacement fee

FINANCIAL AID

Students are provided financial aid application information at the time they are accepted. With the formal letter of acceptance, the UNMC College of Dentistry includes financial aid application processing information, as well as requests for credit score/consumer information and loan-debt information.

Filing of the Free Application for Federal Student Aid (FAFSA) is required for all need-based loans/grants/scholarships. FAFSA information must be received in the Financial Aid Office by April 1 to be considered for need-based scholarships and low-interest loans. Parent information is required on the FAFSA for Health Professional Student Loans (U.S. Department of Health and Human Services requirement).

Scholarships are awarded by the College of Dentistry, not the Financial Aid Office. Financial aid loan awards are not packaged until after the College of Dentistry finalizes its scholarship selections. Scholarship awards are made in late June/early July. Financial aid awards are finalized and delivered to students in early July.

UNIVERSITY OF NEVADA, LAS VEGAS
SCHOOL OF DENTAL MEDICINE

Dr. Karen P. West, Dean

CONTACT INFORMATION

http://dentalschool.unlv.edu
1001 Shadow Lane MS7410
Las Vegas, NV 89106
Phone: 702-774-2500

ADMISSIONS AND STUDENT AFFAIRS & MINORITY AFFAIRS/DIVERSITY

Dr. Christine C. Ancajas
Assistant Dean for Admissions and Student Affairs
1001 Shadow Lane MS 7411
Las Vegas, NV 89106
Phone: 702-774-2520
Email: christine.ancajas@unlv.edu

OFFICE OF FINANCIAL AID

Dr. Christopher A. Kypuros
Director of Financial Aid, Scholarships and Academic Endeavors
1001 Shadow Lane MS7411
Las Vegas, NV 89106
Phone: 702-774-2526
Email: christopher.kypuros@unlv.edu

GENERAL INFORMATION

The fully accredited University of Nevada, Las Vegas (UNLV) School of Dental Medicine (SDM) is located on the new UNLV Shadow Lane Campus. The dental school occupies 154,000 square feet in three buildings of this 18.2-acre campus. This area includes an 84-seat, state-of-the-art simulation laboratory; smart classrooms; and 231 ultramodern operatories in which more than 43,000 patients receive treatment annually in a fully electronic environment. Current advanced dental education programs include General Practice, Orthodontics and Dentofacial Orthopedics and Pediatric Dentistry, with other programs in the planning stages. UNLV SDM is dedicated to serving the Las Vegas community and has touched the lives of over 175,000 citizens. The faculty of UNLV SDM is one of the most diverse in dental education. Since its founding in 1957, UNLV has seen dramatic growth in its student population and its academic programs. UNLV consists of 14 colleges offering over 28,000 students more than 220 undergraduate, master's, and doctoral degree programs. Las Vegas is one of the country's fastest growing metropolitan areas.

MISSION STATEMENT:

The UNLV SDM will be a driving force toward improving the health of the citizens of Nevada through unique programs of oral health care services to the community, integrated biomedical, professional, and clinical curricula, and biomedical discovery.

Type of institution: Public
Year opened: 2002
Term type: Trimester
Time to degree in months: 45
Start month: September

Doctoral dental degree offered: D.M.D.
Total predoctoral enrollment: 315
Estimated entering class size: 80
Campus setting: Urban
Campus housing available: No

PREPARATION

Formal minimum preparation in semester/quarter hours: Semester: 90 Quarter: 120
Baccalaureate degree preferred: Yes; not required but highly recommended
Number of first-year, first-time enrollees whose highest degree is:
- Baccalaureate: 60
- Master's: 5
- Ph.D. or other doctorate: 0

Of first-year, first-time enrollees without baccalaureates, the number with:
- Equivalent of 60 undergraduate credit hours or less: 0
- Equivalent of 61-90 undergraduate credit hours: 0
- Equivalent of 91 or more undergraduate credit hours: 16

PREREQUISITE COURSE	REQUIRED	RECOMMENDED	LAB REQUIRED	CREDITS (SEMESTER/QUARTER)
BCP (biology-chemistry-physics) sciences				
Biology	✓		✓	8/12
Chemistry, general/inorganic	✓		✓	8/12
Chemistry, organic	✓		✓	8/12
Physics	✓		✓	8/12
Additional biological sciences				
Anatomy	✓			4/6
Biochemistry	✓			3/5
Cell biology		✓		3/5
Histology		✓		3/5
Immunology		✓		3/5
Microbiology		✓		4/6

(Prerequisite Courses continued)

PREPARATION (CONTINUED)

PREREQUISITE COURSE	REQUIRED	RECOMMENDED	LAB REQUIRED	CREDITS (SEMESTER/QUARTER)
Molecular biology/genetics		✓		4/6
Physiology		✓		
Zoology		✓		
Additional prerequisite				
Dental Shadowing	✓			Consistency over a long period of time preferred

Other factors considered in admission: Dental experience, extracurricular activities, community service, and letters of recommendation (4 total: 2 science, 1 dental professional, 1 personal)

Community college coursework accepted for prerequisites: Yes
Community college coursework accepted for electives: Yes
Limits on community college credit hours: Yes; maximum of 60 semester credits
Maximum number of community college credit hours: 60
Advanced placement (AP) credit accepted for prerequisites: No
Advanced placement (AP) credit accepted for electives: Yes

DAT

Mandatory: Yes, scores are good for 3 years.
Latest DAT for consideration of application: 02/01/2014
Oldest DAT considered: 01/01/2010
When more than one DAT score is reported: Highest score is considered
Canadian DAT accepted: No
Application considered before DAT scores are submitted: No

DAT: 2012 ENTERING CLASS

ENROLLEE DAT SCORES	RANGE	MEAN
Academic Average	16-25	19.7
Perceptual Ability	14-26	20.0
Total Science	16-26	19.6

GPA: 2012 ENTERING CLASS

ENROLLEE GPA SCORES	RANGE	MEAN
Science GPA	2.61-3.97	3.31
Total GPA	2.69-3.97	3.43

APPLICATION AND SELECTION

TIMETABLE

Earliest filing date: 06/01/2013
Latest filing date: 01/01/2014
Earliest date for acceptance offers: 12/01/2013
Maximum time in days for applicant's response to acceptance offer:
30 days if accepted on or after December 1
15 days if accepted on or after February 1
Requests for deferred entrance considered: In exceptional circumstances only
Fee for application: Yes, submitted at same time as AADSAS application
Amount of fee for application:
In state: $50 Out of state: $50 International: $50
Fee waiver available: No

	FIRST DEPOSIT	SECOND DEPOSIT	THIRD DEPOSIT
Required to hold place	Yes	Yes	No
Resident amount	$750	$1,000	
Nonresident amount	$750	$1,000	
Deposit due	As indicated in admission offer	05/01/2014	
Applied to tuition	Yes	Yes	
Refundable	No	No	

APPLICATION PROCESS

Participates in Associated American Dental Schools Application Service (AADSAS): Yes
Accepts direct applicants: No
Secondary or supplemental application required: Yes
Secondary or supplemental application website: http://dentalschool.unlv.edu
Interview is mandatory: Yes
Interview is by invitation: Yes

RESIDENCY

Admissions process distinguishes between in-state/in-province and out-of-state/out-of-province applicants: Yes
Preference given to residents of: Nevada
Reciprocity Admissions Agreement available for legal residents of: None
Applications are accepted from non-U.S. citizens/non-U.S. permanent residents: Yes

APPLICATION AND ENROLLMENT FOR 2011-2012 CYCLE	NUMBER OF APPLICANTS	ESTIMATED NUMBER INTERVIEWED	ESTIMATED NUMBER ENROLLED
In-state or province applicants	73	59	44
Out-of-state or province applicants	2,109	318	37
Total	2,182	377	81

Generally and over time, percentage of your first-year enrollment is in-state: 64%
Origin of out-of-state enrollees (U.S.): Arizona-3, Arkansas-1, California-15, Florida-1, Georgia-1, New Jersey-1, North Carolina-1, North Dakota-1, Utah-10, Virginia-1, Washington-1
Origin of international enrollees: Canada-1

DEMOGRAPHIC DESCRIPTIONS OF APPLICANTS: 2012 ENTERING CLASS

	APPLICANTS		ENROLLEES	
	M	W	M	W
Hispanic/Latino of any race	29	31	3	3
American Indian or Alaska Native	1	2	0	0
Asian	427	393	12	13
Black or African American	16	30	0	1
Native Hawaiian or Other Pacific Islander	0	1	0	0
White	670	326	38	11
Two or more races	103	72	0	0
Race and ethnicity unknown	56	25	0	0
International	0	0	1	0

Notes: The 2012 entering class contains one Canadian student who is described above as both "white" and "international." Total number of enrollees is 81.

	MINIMUM	MAXIMUM	MEAN
2012 entering class enrollees by age	22	40	26

Number of first-time enrollees over age 30: 12

CURRICULUM

The UNLV SDM is a driving force toward improving the health of the citizens of Nevada, through unique programs of oral health care services to the community. A highly integrated and timed approach toward discovery in the biomedical, professional, and clinical sciences encourages a continuous learning professional. Patient-centered clinical care, patient education, and community outreach reinforces the horizontally and vertically integrated curriculum. Scholarship provides an environment to produce collaborative research and scholarly activities. With faculty cultivated toward excellence, professionalism, and the medical model of total patient care, the school's mission is a constant goal: Toward perfect health through oral health.

Student research opportunities: Yes

SPECIAL PROGRAMS AND SERVICES

PREDENTAL

Special affiliations with colleges and universities
Summer enrichment programs: We provide a two-day UNLV Dental Simulation Course that involves a hands-on experience for predental students.

DURING DENTAL SCHOOL

Academic counseling and tutoring
Community service opportunities
Internships, externships, or extramural programs
Mentoring
Personal counseling
Professional- and career-development programming

ACTIVE STUDENT ORGANIZATIONS

American Association of Women Dentists
American Dental Education Association (ADEA)
American Student Dental Association
Hispanic Dental Association
Student National Dental Association

INTERNATIONAL DENTISTS

Graduates of international dental schools considered for traditional predoctoral program: Yes
Advanced standing program offered for graduates of international dental schools: No

COMBINED AND ALTERNATE DEGREES

Ph.D.	M.S.	M.P.H.	M.D.	B.A./B.S.	Other
—	—	—	—	—	✓

Other Degree: M.B.A.

COSTS: 2012-13 SCHOOL YEAR

	FIRST YEAR	SECOND YEAR	THIRD YEAR	FOURTH YEAR
Tuition and Fees, resident	$54,440	$54,440	$54,440	$36,294
Health Insurance (included in tuition)	$89,750	$89,750	$89,750	$59,834
Tuition and Fees, non-resident	$2,214	$2,214	$2,214	$2,214
Loan Fees	$450	$450	$450	$300
Books, and supplies	$6,924	$6,924	$6,924	$4,616
Room/Board	$20,706	$20,706	$20,706	$13,804
Personal	$4,650	$4,650	$4,650	$3,100
Transportation	$3,513	$3,513	$3,513	$2,342
Total, resident	$90,683	$90,683	$90,683	$60,456
Total, nonresident	$125,993	$125,993	$125,993	$83,996

Comments: Students may opt to waive health insurance if they have their own policy.

FINANCIAL AID

There were 74 recipients of student loans in the 2012 entering class. Loan amounts were between $2,200 and $69,538. Residents received an average loan amount of $53,638. Nonresidents received an average loan amount of $77,753.

The average 2012 graduate indebtedness was $225,936.

UNIVERSITY OF MEDICINE AND DENTISTRY OF NEW JERSEY
NEW JERSEY DENTAL SCHOOL

Dr. Cecile A. Feldman, Dean

CONTACT INFORMATION

http://dentalschool.umdnj.edu
110 Bergen Street
P.O. Box 1709
Newark, NJ 07101-1709
Phone: 973-972-5362
Fax: 973-972-0309

OFFICE OF ADMISSIONS

Dr. Rosa Chaviano-Moran
Assistant Dean of Admissions and Student Recruitment
110 Bergen Street
Room B-829
Newark, NJ 07101-1709
Phone: 973-972-5362

OFFICE OF STUDENT FINANCIAL AID

Cheryl White
Associate Director
30 Bergen Street
ADMC #1208
Newark, NJ 07103-2400
Phone: 973-972-4376

STUDENT AFFAIRS

Dr. Kim Fenesy
Associate Dean for Student Affairs
Interim Associate Dean for Academic Affairs
110 Bergen Street
Room B-825
Phone: 973-972-1699

OFFICE OF MULTICULTURAL AFFAIRS

Dr. Rosa Chaviano-Moran
Director of Multicultural Affairs
110 Bergen Street
Room B-829
Phone: 973-972-5362

HOUSING

180 West Market Street
Newark, NJ 07103-2400
Phone: 973-972-8796

GENERAL INFORMATION

Created by the state legislature in 1970, the University of Medicine and Dentistry of New Jersey (UMDNJ) is now a statewide network of academic health centers that includes eight schools on five campuses, enrolling more than 4,500 students. The school was established as part of the Seton Hall College of Medicine and Dentistry, admitting its first students in 1956. The school has since grown into the state's major resource for dental education, research, and community service. The dental school offers graduate dental educational specialty training in six areas: Endodontics, Oral Surgery, Orthodontics, Pediatric Dentistry, Periodontics and Prosthodontics. Hospital residencies are offered in General Practice and in Oral and Maxillofacial Surgery (which leads to a Doctor of Medicine degree). A fellowship in Oral Medicine is also available.

MISSION STATEMENT:

The mission of the New Jersey Dental School is the scientific exploration of factors that contribute to oral health and the dissemination and application of that knowledge toward the health and well-being of the community. This mission is accomplished through four interrelated activities: education, patient care, research, and community service, in a collegial environment.

Type of institution: Public
Year opened: 1956
Term type: Trimester
Time to degree in months: 48
Start month: August

Doctoral dental degree offered: D.M.D.
Total predoctoral enrollment: 410
Estimated entering class size: 90
Campus setting: Urban
Campus housing available: Yes

PREPARATION

Formal minimum preparation in semester/quarter hours: Semester: 90
Baccalaureate degree preferred: Yes
Number of first-year, first-time enrollees whose highest degree is:
- Baccalaureate: 67
- Master's: 17
- Ph.D. or other doctorate: 0

Of first-year, first-time enrollees without baccalaureates, the number with:
- Equivalent of 60 undergraduate credit hours or less: 0
- Equivalent of 61-90 undergraduate credit hours: 6
- Equivalent of 91 or more undergraduate credit hours: 0

PREREQUISITE COURSE	REQUIRED	RECOMMENDED	LAB REQUIRED	CREDITS (SEMESTER/QUARTER)
BCP (biology-chemistry-physics) sciences				
Biology	✓		✓	8/12
Chemistry, general/inorganic	✓		✓	8/12
Chemistry, organic	✓		✓	8/12
Physics	✓		✓	8/12
Additional biological sciences				
Anatomy		✓		
Biochemistry		✓		
Cell biology		✓		
Histology		✓		
Immunology		✓		
Microbiology		✓		
Molecular biology/genetics		✓		

(Prerequisite Courses continued)

PREPARATION (CONTINUED)

PREREQUISITE COURSE	REQUIRED	RECOMMENDED	LAB REQUIRED	CREDITS (SEMESTER/QUARTER)
Physiology		✓		
Zoology				
Other				
Sculpture/art		✓		
English	✓			6/12
Writing intensive courses		✓		

Community college coursework accepted for prerequisites: Yes
Community college coursework accepted for electives: Yes
Limits on community college credit hours: Yes
Maximum number of community college credit hours: 60
Advanced placement (AP) credit accepted for prerequisites: No
Advanced placement (AP) credit accepted for electives: Yes; AP credit must appear on undergraduate transcript
Comments regarding AP credit: Check school website for details.
Job shadowing: Required
Number of hours of job shadowing required or recommended: A minimum of 50 hours is recommended.

DAT

Mandatory: Yes
Latest DAT for consideration of application: 12/01/2013
Oldest DAT considered: 01/01/2011
When more than one DAT score is reported: Most recent score only is considered
Canadian DAT accepted: Yes
Application considered before DAT scores are submitted: No

DAT: 2012 ENTERING CLASS

ENROLLEE DAT SCORES	RANGE	MEAN
Academic Average	16.0-27.0	20.1
Perceptual Ability	14.0-29.0	20.9
Total Science	15.0-30.0	20.0

GPA: 2012 ENTERING CLASS

ENROLLEE GPA SCORES	RANGE	MEAN
Science GPA	2.43-4.13	3.53
Total GPA	1.87-4.22	3.59

APPLICATION AND SELECTION

TIMETABLE

Earliest filing date: 06/01/2013
Latest filing date: 12/01/2013
Earliest date for acceptance offers: 12/01/2013
Maximum time in days for applicant's response to acceptance offer:
30 days if accepted on or after December 1
21 days if accepted on or after January 1
15 days if accepted on or after February 1
Requests for deferred entrance considered: Yes
Fee for application: Yes, submitted at the request of Admissions Office
Amount of fee for application:
In state: $85 Out of state: $85
Fee waiver available: No

	FIRST DEPOSIT	SECOND DEPOSIT	THIRD DEPOSIT
Required to hold place	Yes	Yes	No
Resident amount	$1,500	$1,000	
Nonresident amount	$1,500	$1,000	
Deposit due	As indicated in admission offer	As indicated in admission offer	
Applied to tuition	Yes	Yes	
Refundable	No	No	

APPLICATION PROCESS

Participates in Associated American Dental Schools Application Service (AADSAS): Yes
Accepts direct applicants: No
Secondary or supplemental application required: No
Interview is mandatory: Yes
Interview is by invitation: Yes

RESIDENCY

Admissions process distinguishes between in-state/in-province and out-of-state/out-of-province applicants: Yes
Applicants are accepted from non-U.S. citizens/non-U.S. permanent residents: Yes

APPLICATION AND ENROLLMENT	NUMBER OF APPLICANTS	ESTIMATED NUMBER INTERVIEWED	ESTIMATED NUMBER ENROLLED
In-state or province applicants	349	154	63
Out-of-state or province applicants	1,516	153	26

Generally and over time, percentage of your first-year enrollment is in-state: 67%
Origin of out-of-state enrollees (U.S.): Florida-6, Illinois-1, New York-16, Pennsylvania-2
Origin of international enrollees: South Korea-1

DEMOGRAPHIC DESCRIPTIONS OF APPLICANTS: 2012 ENTERING CLASS

	APPLICANTS		ENROLLEES	
	M	W	M	W
Hispanic/Latino of any race	19	40	2	4
American Indian or Alaska Native	0	0	0	0
Asian	262	378	6	12
Black or African American	32	70	2	6
Native Hawaiian or Other Pacific Islander	0	1	0	0
White	396	369	26	16
Two or more races	62	73	6	3
Race and ethnicity unknown	36	30	3	2
International	44	34	0	1

	MINIMUM	MAXIMUM	MEAN
2012 entering class enrollees by age	20	33	23

Number of first-time enrollees over age 30: 2

CURRICULUM

UMDNJ-New Jersey Dental School is a publicly supported institution. Its mission is to promote professional standards of excellence among its students, faculty, and staff, while meeting the health needs of New Jersey citizens through the coordination of education, research, and service. The goal of the dental curriculum is to prepare competent general practitioners, who are able to manage the oral health care of the public. The curriculum also provides a foundation for graduates who seek advanced training in the dental specialties, biomedical research, and/or dental education. To accomplish this, graduates must understand the interrelationship of the biological, physical, clinical, and behavioral sciences to effectively practice three overlapping areas of professional responsibility: 1) comprehensive patient care; 2) participation in community dental-health programs; and 3) continuation of professional development.

Student research opportunities: Yes

SPECIAL PROGRAMS AND SERVICES

PREDENTAL

College Level Pipeline Programs: Gateway to Dentistry and Association of American Medical Colleges/ADEA Summer Medical and Dental Education Program (AAMC/ADEA SMDEP)

Other enrichment programs: High School Level: Decision for Dentistry. Elementary School Level: Dental Express and Dental Exploration

Special affiliations with colleges and universities: Caldwell College - B.S./D.M.D.; Fairleigh Dickinson University - B.S./D.M.D.; New Jersey City University - B.S./D.M.D.; Montclair State University - B.S./D.M.D.; New Jersey Institute of Technology - B.S./D.M.D.; North Carolina Central University - B.S./D.M.D.; Ramapo College - B.S./D.M.D.; Rowan University - B.S./D.M.D.; Rutgers University - B.S./D.M.D.; St. Peters College - B.S./D.M.D.; Stevens Institute of Technology - B.S./D.M.D.; The Richard Stockton College of New Jersey - B.S./D.M.D.

DURING DENTAL SCHOOL

Academic counseling and tutoring
Community service opportunities
Internships, externships, or extramural programs
Mentoring
Personal counseling
Professional- and career-development programming
Training for those interested in academic careers

ACTIVE STUDENT ORGANIZATIONS

American Association of Women Dentists
American Dental Education Association (ADEA)
American Student Dental Association
Hispanic Dental Association
Indian Student Dental association
Student National Dental Association

INTERNATIONAL DENTISTS

Graduates of international dental schools considered for traditional predoctoral program: No

Advanced standing program offered for graduates of international dental schools: Yes

Advanced standing program description: Program awarding a dental degree (D.M.D.) following a 27-month didactic and clinical program.

COMBINED AND ALTERNATE DEGREES

Ph.D.	M.S.	M.P.H.	M.D.	B.A./B.S.	Other
✓	✓	✓	—	—	—

COSTS: 2012-13 SCHOOL YEAR (SUBJECT TO INCREASE)

	FIRST YEAR	SECOND YEAR	THIRD YEAR	FOURTH YEAR
Tuition, resident	$34,445	$34,445	$34,445	$34,445
Tuition, nonresident	$55,268	$55,268	$55,268	$55,268
Tuition, other	NA	NA	NA	NA
Fees	$4,103	$4,308	$4,608	$5,048
Instruments, books, and supplies	$12,069	$6,669	$6,293	$2,950
Estimated living expenses	$4,010	$3,609	$4,812	$4,411
Room and Board (Maintaining own residence)	$13,860	$12,474	$16,632	$15,246
Room and Board (Living at home)	$3,540	$3,186	$4,248	$3,894
Total, resident (Maintaining own residence)	$71,717	$65,312	$71,866	$66,753
Total, resident (Living at home)	$62,397	$56,024	$59,482	$55,401
Total, nonresident	$93,540	$86,135	$92,689	$87,576
Total, other	NA	NA	NA	NA

FINANCIAL AID

There were no scholarships and/or grants awarded in the 2012 entering class.

COLUMBIA UNIVERSITY
COLLEGE OF DENTAL MEDICINE

Dr. Ronnie Myers, Interim Dean

GENERAL INFORMATION

The College of Dental Medicine of Columbia University is a private dental school in the city of New York. The college is an integral part of the Columbia University Medical Center. It traces its origin to the year 1852, when the New York State legislature chartered the college. The college became the School of Dental and Oral Surgery of Columbia University in 1916, when dentistry was recognized as an integral part of the health sciences. It is now the College of Dental Medicine. Many departments of the university contribute to, and collaborate in, the education of dental and advanced dental education students, and students are thus assured a broad foundation for sound professional development. Columbia remains one of the few dental colleges whose students share the biomedical courses of the first year and a half with the medical students, in this instance, of the College of Physicians and Surgeons.

MISSION STATEMENT:

The college's mission is tripartite: education, patient care, and research. The mission of the College of Dental Medicine is to train general dentists and dental specialists in a setting that emphasizes the biomedical basis of comprehensive dental care and stimulates professional growth. Additionally, a core mission is to inspire, support, and promote faculty, predoctoral and advanced dental education students, and hospital resident participation in research to advance the professional knowledge base. Comprehensive dental care including all specialties is provided for the underserved community of northern Manhattan.

Type of institution: Private
Year opened: 1852
Term type: Semester
Time to degree in months: 45
Start month: August

Doctoral dental degree offered: D.D.S.
Total predoctoral enrollment: 300
Estimated entering class size: 80
Campus setting: Urban
Campus housing available: Yes

PREPARATION

Formal minimum preparation in semester/quarter hours: Semester: 90 Quarter: 120
Baccalaureate degree preferred: Yes
Number of first-year, first-time enrollees whose highest degree is:
- Baccalaureate: 75
- Master's: 5
- Ph.D. or other doctorate: 0

Of first-year, first-time enrollees without baccalaureates, the number with:
- Equivalent of 60 undergraduate credit hours or less: 0
- Equivalent of 61-90 undergraduate credit hours: 0
- Equivalent of 91 or more undergraduate credit hours: 0

PREREQUISITE COURSE	REQUIRED	RECOMMENDED	LAB REQUIRED	CREDITS (SEMESTER/QUARTER)
BCP (biology-chemistry-physics) sciences				
Biology	✓		✓	8/12
Chemistry, general/inorganic	✓		✓	8/12
Chemistry, organic	✓		✓	8/12
Physics	✓		✓	8/12
Additional biological sciences				
Anatomy		✓		4/6
Biochemistry		✓		4/6
Cell biology		✓		4/6
Histology				
Immunology				

(Prerequisite Courses continued)

CONTACT INFORMATION

www.dental.columbia.edu
630 West 168th Street
New York, NY 10032
Phone: 212-305-3478
Fax: 212-305-1034

ADMISSIONS AND STUDENT AFFAIRS

Dr. Laureen Zubiaurre-Bitzer
Associate Dean
Phone: 212-305-3478
email: laz1@columbia.edu

Sandi Garcia
Assistant Dean of Admissions and Student Affairs
Phone: 212-342-1697
email: sb64@columbia.edu

FINANCIAL AID

Ellen Spilker
Executive Director
Phone: 212-305-4100
email: cpmc-sfp@columbia.edu

OFFICE OF DIVERSITY AFFAIRS

Dr. Dennis Mitchell
Senior Associate Dean
Phone: 212-342-3716
http://www.dental.columbia.edu/page/office-diversity-affairs

HOUSING

50 Haven Avenue
Bard Hall, 1st floor
New York, NY 10032
Phone: 212-304-7000
http://housing.hs.columbia.edu

INTERNATIONAL STUDENTS

Bonnie Garner
Assistant Manager
650 West 168th Street
New York, NY 10032
Phone: 212-305-5455
Email: bLg12@columbia.edu

PREPARATION (CONTINUED)

PREREQUISITE COURSE	REQUIRED	RECOMMENDED	LAB REQUIRED	CREDITS (SEMESTER/QUARTER)
Microbiology				
Molecular biology/genetics				
Physiology		✓		
Zoology				
Other				
English	✓			6/9
Mathematics	✓			6/9

Community college coursework accepted for prerequisites: Yes
Community college coursework accepted for electives: Yes
Limits on community college credit hours: No
Maximum number of community college credit hours: NA
Advanced placement (AP) credit accepted for prerequisites: Yes
Advanced placement (AP) credit accepted for electives: Yes
Comments regarding AP credit: None
Job shadowing: Recommended
Number of hours of job shadowing required or recommended: Not specified
Other factors considered in admission: Noncognitive factors including community service/volunteerism and other extracurricular activities

DAT

Mandatory: Yes
Latest DAT for consideration of application: 12/01/2013
Oldest DAT considered: 01/01/2011
When more than one DAT score is reported: Highest score is considered.
Canadian DAT accepted: Yes
Application considered before DAT scores are submitted: No

DAT: 2012 ENTERING CLASS

ENROLLEE DAT SCORES	RANGE	MEAN
Academic Average	19-27	23.0
Perceptual Ability	14-30	21.5
Total Science	19-30	23.0

GPA: 2012 ENTERING CLASS

ENROLLEE GPA SCORES	RANGE	MEAN
Science GPA	2.6-4.17	3.60
Total GPA	2.7-4.17	3.60

APPLICATION AND SELECTION

TIMETABLE

Earliest filing date: 06/01/2013
Latest filing date: 12/30/2013
Earliest date for acceptance offers: 12/01/2013
Maximum time in days for applicant's response to acceptance offer:
30 days if accepted on or after December 1
15 days if accepted on or after February 1
Requests for deferred entrance considered: No
Fee for application: Yes, submitted at same time as Associated American Dental Schools Application Service (AADSAS) application
Amount of fee for application:
In state: $75 Out of state: $75 International: $75
Fee waiver available: Yes, upon documentation by college of high financial need

	FIRST DEPOSIT	SECOND DEPOSIT	THIRD DEPOSIT
Required to hold place	Yes	Yes	No
Resident amount	$2,000	$1,000	
Nonresident amount	$2,000	$1,000	
Deposit due	Immediate	As indicated in Acceptance Letter	
Applied to tuition	Yes	Yes	
Refundable	No	No	

APPLICATION PROCESS

Participates in Associate American Dental Schools Application Service (AADSAS): Yes
Accepts direct applicants: No
Secondary or supplemental application required: Yes, a fee of $75
Secondary or supplemental application website: None
Interview is mandatory: Yes
Interview is by invitation: Yes, by invitation only

RESIDENCY

Admissions process distinguishes between in-state/in-province and out-of-state/out-of-province applicants: No
Applications are accepted from non-U.S. citizens/non-U.S. permanent residents: Yes

APPLICATION AND ENROLLMENT	NUMBER OF APPLICANTS	ESTIMATED NUMBER INTERVIEWED	ESTIMATED NUMBER ENROLLED
In-state or province applicants	412	86	27
Out-of-state or province applicants	2,042	240	53

Generally and over time, percentage of your first-year enrollment is in-state: 20%
Origin of out-of-state enrollees (U.S.): California-9, Connecticut-2, Florida-9, Georgia-1, Illinois-3, Maryland-1, Massachusetts-5, Minnesota-1, New Jersey-7, North Carolina-3, Pennsylvania-4, Texas-4, Utah-1, Virginia-2
Origin of international enrollees: Canada-1

DEMOGRAPHIC DESCRIPTIONS OF APPLICANTS: 2012 ENTERING CLASS

	APPLICANTS		ENROLLEES	
	M	W	M	W
Hispanic/Latino of any race	57	83	4	4
American Indian or Alaska Native	0	0	0	0
Asian	388	441	16	8
Black or African American	34	71	1	3
Native Hawaiian or Other Pacific Islander	0	1	0	0
White	463	411	19	17
Two or more races	26	34	1	2
Race and ethnicity unknown	55	37	2	2
International	179	174	0	1

	MINIMUM	MAXIMUM	MEAN
2012 entering class enrollees by age	20	37	23

Number of first-time enrollees over age 30: 2

CURRICULUM

The curriculum at the College of Dental Medicine is unique in both content and approach, and is strongly medically oriented. Interdisciplinary integration characterizes all phases of the curriculum: biomedical, preclinical and clinical. Students begin with 1.5 years of study in four challenging biomedical foundation courses which are shared with the College of Physicians and Surgeons: Molecular Mechanisms in Health and Disease, Clinical Human Anatomy, and The Body in Health and Disease, parts I and II. Dental correlations are provided throughout this period by the dental faculty using small group sessions and case-based and team-based-learning approaches. Clinical clerkships are scheduled in the second and third semester to enable the students to apply what they are learning in the biomedical courses: medical history, physical diagnosis, and in the behavioral science courses: patient interviewing, wellness counseling, nutritional assessment, counseling in cases of addictive behavior. These experiences help students acquire the knowledge and skills necessary to become competent health care providers. Semester 4 is devoted to basic dental science courses as well as an intensive, case-based preclinical dental simulation course. In this course interdisciplinary faculty work with the students to develop the skills needed to provide comprehensive dental care. The clinical phase of the curriculum follows the comprehensive dental care model, in which students under the guidance of their faculty mentors provide complete general dental care to a panel of patients. Throughout these two years demonstration of clinical skills and the ability to bring to completion the care of the assigned patients are stressed. In year 3 all students have a total of 4 rotations to affiliated hospitals: 2 two-week rotations in physical diagnosis in the fall semester and 2 three-week rotations in general dentistry in the spring semester. Primary medicine grand rounds provide opportunities to integrate previously learned biomedical information into the dental care of the students' own patients. An honors program in an area of individual interest is available for a select group of students during the final semester.

Student research opportunities: Yes, extensive opportunities are available.

SPECIAL PROGRAMS AND SERVICES

PREDENTAL

Association of American Medical Colleges/ADEA Summer Medical and Dental Education Program (AAMC/ADEA SMDEP)
Postbaccalaureate programs
Special affiliations with colleges and universities: Columbia College, Barnard College, Columbia University School of Engineering
Other summer enrichment programs

DURING DENTAL SCHOOL

Academic counseling and tutoring: shared with medical school
Community service opportunities
Internships, externships, or extramural programs: extensive, supported Global Health Externship Program
Mentoring
Personal and career counseling
Professional- and career-development programming
Training for those interested in academic and research careers

ACTIVE STUDENT ORGANIZATIONS

American Association of Dental Research Student Research Group
American Association of Pediatric Dentistry
American Association of Women Dentists
American Student Dental Association
Hispanic Dental Association
Student National Dental Association
For more information on student organizations, visit http://dental.columbia.edu/sga/organizations.html

INTERNATIONAL DENTISTS

Graduates of international dental schools considered for traditional predoctoral program: No
Advanced standing program offered for graduates of international dental schools: Yes
Advanced standing description: Entry in mid-year 2 of regular four-year D.D.S. curriculum

COMBINED AND ALTERNATE DEGREES

Ph.D.	M.S.	M.P.H.	M.D.	B.A./B.S.	Other
—	✓	✓	—	—	✓

Other Degree: M.B.A., M.A. in Education, M.A. in Dental Informatics

COSTS: 2012-13 SCHOOL YEAR

	FIRST YEAR	SECOND YEAR	THIRD YEAR	FOURTH YEAR
Tuition, resident	$52,504	$52,504	$52,504	$52,504
Tuition, nonresident	$52,504	$52,504	$52,504	$52,504
Tuition, other				
Fees	$14,792	$14,687	$14,687	$14,687
Instruments, books, and supplies	$1,550	$1,545	$645	$3,140
Estimated living expenses	$19,632	$21,006	$25,211	$22,533
Total, resident	$88,478	$89,742	$93,047	$92,864
Total, nonresident	$88,478	$89,742	$93,047	$92,864
Total, other				

FINANCIAL AID

There were 40 recipients of scholarships and grants and 75 recipients of student loans in the 2012 entering class. Scholarship and grant awards were between $1,000 and $9,850 with an average award of $6,360. Student loan amounts were between $7,500 and $87,675.

The average 2012 graduate indebtedness was $243,967.

NEW YORK UNIVERSITY
COLLEGE OF DENTISTRY

Dr. Charles N. Bertolami, Herman Robert Fox Dean

GENERAL INFORMATION

New York University College of Dentistry (NYUCD) is a private institution that offers students the advantage of a metropolitan setting. Founded in 1865, the college is the largest and the third oldest dental school in the United States. The college offers professional training leading to the D.D.S. degree, as well as advanced dental education and specialty training. The College of Dentistry is administered by the David B. Kriser Dental Center, New York University, which is composed of two buildings located on First Avenue from East 24th Street to East 25th Street in New York City. Additional programs offered include a bachelor's degree and associate degree in dental hygiene, continuing dental education programs, Program for Advanced Study in Dentistry for International Graduates, M.S. program in Oral Biology in collaboration with the New York University Graduate School of Arts and Sciences, an M.S. in Clinical Research, and an M.S. in Biomaterials.

MISSION STATEMENT:

The College of Dentistry will partner with students in achieving academic excellence; providing the best oral health care; and engaging in research, scholarship, and creative endeavors to improve the health of the highly diverse populations in New York City and around the world.

Type of institution: Private
Year opened: 1865
Term type: Semester
Time to degree in months: 48
Start month: August
Doctoral dental degree offered: D.D.S.

Total predoctoral enrollment: 1,295
Estimated entering class size: 360
Campus setting: Urban
Campus housing available: No, the majority of students live in off-campus apartments.

CONTACT INFORMATION

www.nyu.edu/dental
345 East 24th Street, 10th Floor
New York, NY 10010
Phone: 212-998-9818
Fax: 212-995-4240
Email: dental.admissions@nyu.edu

OFFICE OF ADMISSIONS

Dr. Eugenia E. Mejia
Senior Director of Admissions
Phone: 212-998-9818
Email: dental.admissions@nyu.edu

OFFICE OF FINANCIAL AID

dental.financial.aid@nyu.edu

OFFICE OF STUDENT AFFAIRS

Madiha Bhatti
Director for Student Affairs
madiha.bhatti@nyu.edu

OFFICE FOR INTERNATIONAL STUDENTS AND SCHOLARS

www.nyu.edu/oiss

DIVERSITY INITIATIVES

Madiha Bhatti
madiha.bhatti@nyu.edu

PREPARATION

Formal minimum preparation in semester/quarter hours: Semester: 90 Quarter: 120
Baccalaureate degree preferred: Yes
Number of first-year, first-time enrollees whose highest degree is:
- Baccalaureate: 206
- Master's: 29
- Ph.D. or other doctorate: 0

Of first-year, first-time enrollees without baccalaureates, the number with:
- Equivalent of 60 undergraduate credit hours or less: 0
- Equivalent of 61-90 undergraduate credit hours: 0
- Equivalent of 91 or more undergraduate credit hours: 9

PREREQUISITE COURSE	REQUIRED	RECOMMENDED	LAB REQUIRED	CREDITS (SEMESTER/QUARTER)
BCP (biology-chemistry-physics) sciences				
Biology	✓		✓	8/12
Chemistry, general/inorganic	✓		✓	8/12
Chemistry, organic	✓		✓	8/12
Physics	✓		✓	8/12
Additional biological sciences				
Anatomy		✓		4/6
Biochemistry		✓		4/6
Cell biology		✓		4/6
Histology		✓		4/6
Immunology		✓		4/6
Microbiology		✓		4/6

(Prerequisite Courses continued)

PREPARATION (CONTINUED)

PREREQUISITE COURSE	REQUIRED	RECOMMENDED	LAB REQUIRED	CREDITS (SEMESTER/QUARTER)
Molecular biology/genetics				4/6
Physiology				
Zoology				
Other				
English	✓			6/9

Community college coursework accepted for prerequisites: Yes; prefer courses be taken at four-year college
Community college coursework accepted for electives: Yes
Limits on community college credit hours: Yes, 60 credit hours
Maximum number of community college credit hours: 60
Advanced placement (AP) credit accepted for prerequisites: No
Advanced placement (AP) credit accepted for electives: Yes
Comments regarding AP credit: Students with AP credits in the sciences are expected to take a higher-level science course in that discipline.
Job shadowing: Required
Number of hours of job shadowing required or recommended: 100
Other factors considered in admissions: Yes

DAT

Mandatory: Yes
Latest DAT for consideration of application: 02/01/2014
Oldest DAT considered: 01/01/2011
When more than one DAT score is reported: Highest score is considered
Canadian DAT accepted: Yes
Application considered before DAT scores are submitted: No

DAT: 2012 ENTERING CLASS

ENROLLEE DAT SCORES	RANGE	MEAN
Academic Average	—	21
Perceptual Ability	—	20
Total Science	—	21

GPA: 2012 ENTERING CLASS

ENROLLEE GPA SCORES	RANGE	MEAN
Science GPA	—	3.44
Total GPA	—	3.53

APPLICATION AND SELECTION

TIMETABLE

Earliest filing date: 06/01/2013
Latest filing date: 02/01/2014
Earliest date for acceptance offers: 12/01/2013
Maximum time in days for applicant's response to acceptance offer:
30 days if accepted on or after December 1
15 days if accepted on or after February 1
Requests for deferred entrance considered: In exceptional circumstances only
Fee for application: Yes, submitted at same time as Associated American Dental Schools Application Service (AADSAS) application
Amount of fee for application:
In state: $80 Out of state: $80 International: $80
Fee waiver available: Yes

	FIRST DEPOSIT	SECOND DEPOSIT	THIRD DEPOSIT
Required to hold place	Yes	Yes	No
Resident amount	$1,500	$3,500	
Nonresident amount	$1,500	$3,500	
Deposit due	As indicated in admission offer	As indicated in admission offer	
Applied to tuition	Yes	Yes	
Refundable	No	No	

APPLICATION PROCESS

Participates in Associated American Dental Schools Application Service (AADSAS): Yes
Accepts direct applicants: No
Secondary or supplemental application required: Yes, at time of interview
Secondary or supplemental application website: None
Interview is mandatory: Yes
Interview is by invitation: Yes

RESIDENCY

Admissions process distinguishes between in-state/in-province and out-of-state/out-of-province applicants: No
Applications are accepted from non-U.S. citizens/non-U.S. permanent residents: Yes

APPLICATION AND ENROLLMENT	NUMBER OF APPLICANTS	ESTIMATED NUMBER INTERVIEWED	ESTIMATED NUMBER ENROLLED
In-state or province applicants	576	—	83
Out-of-state or province applicants	4,551	—	164

Generally and over time, percentage of your first-year enrollment is in-state: 35%

Origin of out-of-state enrollees (U.S.): Alabama-2, Arizona-1, California-27, Colorado-2, Connecticut-1, Florida-17, Illinois-2, Kentucky-1, Louisiana-1, Maine-2, Maryland-2, Massachusetts-3, Michigan-2, Minnesota-2, Mississippi-1, Missouri-2, New Jersey-36, North Carolina-5, Ohio-3, Pennsylvania-3, South Carolina-1, Texas-3, Utah-1, Virginia-1, Washington-2, Wisconsin-2

Origin of international enrollees: Afghanistan-1, Belarus-1, Canada-16, China-2, Columbia-1, India-2, Iran-5, Israel-1, Jordan-1, Libya-1, Mexico-1, Poland-1, South Korea-22, Spain-1, Taiwan-1, Thailand-1, Venezuela-1

DEMOGRAPHIC DESCRIPTIONS OF APPLICANTS: 2012 ENTERING CLASS

	APPLICANTS		ENROLLEES	
	M	W	M	W
Hispanic/Latino of any race	149	196	7	12
American Indian or Alaska Native	1	2	0	1
Asian	905	972	26	46
Black or African American	68	119	2	5
Native Hawaiian or Other Pacific Islander	3	1	0	0
White	1,075	807	62	40
Two or more races	65	69	1	0
Race and ethnicity unknown	90	72	2	4
International	244	224	20	19

Note: There were 51 applicants who did not report a gender.

	MINIMUM	MAXIMUM	MEAN
2012 entering class enrollees by age	20	40	24

Number of first-time enrollees over age 30: 15

CURRICULUM

NYUCD's educational philosophy is based upon the conviction that real life is not the rote repetition of information; rather, it is the application of knowledge to solve problems associated with disease. Thus, NYUCD has initiated a hands-on approach early in the learning process in combination with a rigorous program that requires critical thinking and problem-solving. NYUCD's four-year curriculum is fully integrated and does not teach along traditional departmental structure. The biomedical sciences are taught in three segments over the first three years. The clinical sciences emphasize general dentistry and are also fully integrated. Education is broad in scope, yet focused and applied to real-world problems and issues. Patient contact begins in the first year, and students earn patient care privileges through achievement.

Student research opportunities: NYUCD has a vital program of dental student research. Dental students may be introduced to research at an early stage in their careers—inspiring them and helping them see that research can be an exciting and fulfilling career trajectory. Their first opportunity to participate in the research program at NYUCD is for eight weeks during the summer before they begin their studies. Participants in the summer program work with faculty mentors on their research studies full time and attend seminars three times a week. At the end of the eight weeks, the students present posters describing the studies on which they worked. The Honors in Research Program is designed to provide dental students with the opportunity to participate in a research project from their D1 to D4 years. Thus, D.D.S. students have an opportunity to gain research experience at NYUCD.

SPECIAL PROGRAMS AND SERVICES

PREDENTAL

Special affiliations with colleges and universities: New York University College of Arts and Science - B.A./D.D.S. 7-year combined degree program; Adelphi University - B.A./D.D.S. 7-year combined degree program

Summer enrichment programs: Research program available for high school and undergraduate students

DURING DENTAL SCHOOL

Academic counseling and tutoring
Community service opportunities: national and international outreach programs
Mentoring
Personal counseling
Professional- and career-development programming
Training for those interested in academic careers
Transfer applicants considered if space is available

ACTIVE STUDENT ORGANIZATIONS

American Association of Dental Research Student Research Group
American Dental Education Association (ADEA)
American Student Dental Association
Asian dental clubs
Community Service Club
Hispanic Dental Association
Student National Dental Association
Women in Dentistry
Women of Color in Dentistry

INTERNATIONAL DENTISTS

Graduates of international dental schools considered for traditional predoctoral program: Yes
Advanced standing program offered for graduates of international dental schools: No
Advanced standing program description: None

COMBINED AND ALTERNATE DEGREES

Ph.D.	M.S.	M.P.H.	M.D.	B.A./B.S.	Other
—	—	✓	—	✓	—

Comment: A seven-year combined B.A./D.D.S. degree program is available through collaboration with the New York University College of Arts and Science and Adelphi University.

COSTS: 2012-13 SCHOOL YEAR

	FIRST YEAR	SECOND YEAR	THIRD YEAR	FOURTH YEAR
Tuition, resident	$59,921	$59,921	$59,921	$59,921
Tuition, nonresident	$59,921	$59,921	$59,921	$59,921
Tuition, other				
Fees	$3,611	$3,611	$3,611	$3,611
Instruments, books, and supplies	$7,365	$5,066	$7,035	$4,985
Estimated living expenses	$33,764	$36,815	$36,815	$30,713
Total, resident	$104,661	$105,413	$107,382	$99,230
Total, nonresident	$104,661	$105,413	$107,382	$99,230
Total, other				

FINANCIAL AID

NYUCD requires applicants to submit the Free Application for Federal Student Aid (FAFSA). New York State residents may also submit the New York State Tuition Assistance Program (TAP) application. It is recommended that students file the FAFSA before March of the year admission is sought. The online FAFSA form opens on January 1. Applicants should take care to complete all required sections, including parents' financial data, even if the student is financially independent. Once the form is completed, it should be submitted to the central processor (rather than NYUCD), who will forward the data to NYUCD electronically. Each year the school awards a limited number of scholarships to admitted applicants. Eligibility for a Dean's Award is based on the overall GPA, DAT scores, and the overall competitiveness of the application with regard to the applicant pool.

STONY BROOK UNIVERSITY
SCHOOL OF DENTAL MEDICINE

Dr. Ray C. Williams, Dean

GENERAL INFORMATION

The School of Dental Medicine (SDM) was established in 1973 and is a major component of the Health Sciences Center of Stony Brook University, a leading public university of the state of New York located on the north shore of Long Island. The school is internationally recognized for excellence in education, clinical rigor, and innovative "personalized" curricula via its small size relative to peer institutions. Predoctoral dental students routinely participate in providing early and comprehensive clinical care, interprofessional training, global and community outreach programs, as well as research experiences as part of their Doctor of Dental Surgery (D.D.S.) curriculum. Opportunities to pursue concurrent masters' degrees as well as a combined D.D.S./Ph.D. degree provide additional educational enrichment. The Stony Brook University School of Dental Medicine's comprehensive educational programs and supportive learning environment graduates professionals who are competent to enter clinical general practice, committed to lifelong learning, and who become leaders in the fields of patient care, academia, research, and service/engagement.

MISSION STATEMENT:

The mission of Stony Brook University School of Dental Medicine is to advance the oral and general health of the local and global community through our continuous pursuit of excellence in education, patient care, discovery, and leadership.

Type of institution: Public
Year opened: 1973
Term type: Semester
Time to degree in months: 44
Start month: August

Doctoral dental degree offered: D.D.S.
Total predoctoral enrollment: 158
Estimated entering class size: 42
Campus setting: Suburban
Campus housing available: Yes

PREPARATION

Formal minimum preparation in semester/quarter hours: Semester: 60 Quarter: 90
Baccalaureate degree preferred: Yes
Number of first-year, first-time enrollees whose highest degree is:
- Baccalaureate: 38
- Master's: 1
- Ph.D. or other doctorate: 2

Of first-year, first-time enrollees without baccalaureates, the number with:
- Equivalent of 60 undergraduate credit hours or less: 0
- Equivalent of 61-90 undergraduate credit hours: 0
- Equivalent of 91 or more undergraduate credit hours: 0

PREREQUISITE COURSE	REQUIRED	RECOMMENDED	LAB REQUIRED	CREDITS (SEMESTER/QUARTER)
BCP (biology-chemistry-physics) sciences				
Biology	✓		✓	8/12
Chemistry, general/inorganic	✓		✓	8/12
Chemistry, organic	✓		✓	8/12
Physics	✓		✓	8/12
Additional biological sciences				
Anatomy		✓		4/6
Biochemistry		✓		4/6
Cell biology		✓		4/6
Histology		✓		4/6
Immunology		✓		4/6
Microbiology		✓		4/6

(Prerequisite Courses continued)

CONTACT INFORMATION

www.stonybrookmedicalcenter.org/dental
Phone: 631-632-8950
Fax: 631-632-7130

OFFICE OF EDUCATION
Dr. Hugh Finch
Director, Admissions and Student Affairs
Rockland Hall, Room 115
Stony Brook, NY 11794
Phone: 631-632-3745
http://dentistry.stonybrookmedicine.edu/dental/student/admissions

OFFICE OF FINANCIAL AID
Deborah Schade
Student Services
Rockland Hall, Room 148
Stony Brook, NY 11794-8709
Phone: 631-632-3027
Email: Deborah.Schade@stonybrook.edu

MINORITY AFFAIRS/DIVERSITY
Dr. Fred Ferguson
Rockland Hall, Room 126
Stony Brook, NY 11794
Phone: 631-632-8902
www.hsc.stonybrook.edu/dental/minoritydental

THE DIVISON OF CAMPUS RESIDENCE
Stony Brook University
Stony Brook, NY 11794
Phone: 631-632-6966
Email: reside@notes.cc.sunysb.edu
www.studentaffairs.stonybrook.edu/res

PREPARATION (CONTINUED)

PREREQUISITE COURSE	REQUIRED	RECOMMENDED	LAB REQUIRED	CREDITS (SEMESTER/QUARTER)
Molecular biology/genetics		✓		4/6
Physiology		✓		4/6
Zoology		✓		4/6
Other				
Calculus 1	✓			4/6
Calculus 2 or Statistics	✓			4/6
Writing Intensive Course	✓			6/9

Community college coursework accepted for prerequisites: Yes, but prerequisites from four-year college preferred
Community college coursework accepted for electives: Yes
Limits on community college credit hours: Yes
Maximum number of community college credit hours: 60
Advanced placement (AP) credit accepted for prerequisites: Must score 4 or above for credit
Advanced placement (AP) credit accepted for electives: Must score 4 or above for credit
Comments regarding AP credit: For prerequisite courses, additional course(s) should be taken within that discipline to demonstrate scholastic ability at the college level.
Job shadowing: Required
Number of hours of job shadowing required or recommended: 60 hours or more preferred.
Other factors considered in admission: Academic experience and performance, DAT, letters of evaluation, exposure to and comprehension of the dental profession, communication skills, life experiences, prior research, service and/or leadership, and interview performance

DAT

Mandatory: Yes
Oldest DAT considered: Current score obtained after 06/04/2009
When more than one DAT score is reported: All scores are reviewed.
Canadian DAT accepted: No
Application considered before DAT scores are submitted: No

DAT: 2012 ENTERING CLASS

ENROLLEE DAT SCORES	RANGE	MEAN
Academic Average	NA	21
Perceptual Ability	NA	21
Total Science	NA	21

GPA: 2012 ENTERING CLASS

ENROLLEE GPA SCORES	RANGE	MEAN
Science GPA	NA	3.60
Total GPA	NA	3.67

APPLICATION AND SELECTION

TIMETABLE

Earliest filing date: 06/15/2013
Latest filing date: 12/01/2013
Earliest date for acceptance offers: 12/01/2013
Maximum time in days for applicant's response to acceptance offer:
- 30 days if accepted on or after December 1
- 20 days if accepted after January 1
- 10 days if accepted after February 1
- Applicants accepted after May 1 may be required to respond within seven days or sooner depending on proximity to the start of the academic year
- Response period may be lifted after May 15

Requests for deferred entrance considered: No
Fee for application: Yes, submitted at same time as Associated American Dental Schools Application Service (AADSAS) application.
Amount of fee for application:
In state: $100 Out of state: $100 International: $100
Fee waiver available: No

	FIRST DEPOSIT	SECOND DEPOSIT	THIRD DEPOSIT
Required to hold place	Yes	No	No
Resident amount	$350		
Nonresident amount	$350		
Deposit due	As indicated in admission offer		
Applied to tuition	Yes		
Refundable	Yes		
Refundable by	As indicated in admission offer		

APPLICATION PROCESS

Participates in AADSAS: Yes
Accepts direct applicants: No
Secondary or supplemental application required: No
Interview is mandatory: Yes
Interview is by invitation: Yes

RESIDENCY

Admissions process distinguishes between in-state/in-province and out-of-state/out-of-province applicants: Yes
Preference given to residents of: New York State
Reciprocity Admissions Agreement available for legal residents of: None
Applications are accepted from non-U.S. citizens/non-U.S. permanent residents: Yes

APPLICATION AND ENROLLMENT	NUMBER OF APPLICANTS	ESTIMATED NUMBER INTERVIEWED	ESTIMATED NUMBER ENROLLED
In-state or province applicants	451	111	37
Out-of-state or province applicants	646	46	4

Generally and over time, percentage of your first-year enrollment is in-state: 90%
Origin of out-of-state enrollees (U.S.): Colorado-1, New Jersey-2, Utah-1,
Origin of international enrollees: NA

DEMOGRAPHIC DESCRIPTIONS OF APPLICANTS: 2012 ENTERING CLASS

	APPLICANTS		ENROLLEES	
	M	W	M	W
Hispanic/Latino of any race	26	34	1	0
American Indian or Alaska Native	0	0	0	0
Asian	158	194	1	5
Black or African American	16	28	0	0
Native Hawaiian or Other Pacific Islander	0	0	0	0
White	248	244	16	14
Two or more races	6	11	0	0
Race and ethnicity unknown	26	21	2	1
International	38	32	0	0

Notes: Fifteen applicants did not report gender.

	MINIMUM	MAXIMUM	MEAN
2012 entering class enrollees by age	21	31	23

Number of first-time enrollees over age 30: 2

CURRICULUM

The Stony Brook University School of Dental Medicine predoctoral curriculum provides a comprehensive learning model, which includes an integrated biomedical education, early entry to clinical patient care, research opportunities, and community service learning. Education in the basic, behavioral, and clinical sciences emphasizes development of critical thinking skills leading to excellence in the practice of dentistry. Predoctoral dental students are integrated with medical school colleagues in the basic science curriculum of years 1 and 2. In addition, preclinical training begins in year 1, leading to early patient care delivery at the end of that year followed by extensive, patient-centered experiences in years 2, 3, and 4. Students engage in local, regional, and global community outreach programs (e.g., U.S. Indian Health Service, Chile, Madagascar, and Kenya). Research experience is encouraged and provided as early as the summer prior to matriculation.

Student research opportunities: Yes, newly accepted students may begin research opportunities during the summer prior to matriculation.

SPECIAL PROGRAMS AND SERVICES

PREDENTAL

Summer enrichment programs: Research opportunities

DURING DENTAL SCHOOL

Academic counseling and tutoring
Community service opportunities (local, national, and international)
Internships, externships, or extramural programs
Interprofessional training and adjunctive degree program
Mentoring
Personal counseling
Professional- and career-development programming
Research/translational research

ACTIVE STUDENT ORGANIZATIONS

American Association of Pediatric Dentistry Student Chapter
American Dental Education Association (ADEA)
American Student Dental Association
Dental Fraternities: Alpha Omega, Xi Psi Phi
Dental Student Organization
Minority Student Dental Association
Stony Brook Dental Student Research Society

INTERNATIONAL DENTISTS

Graduates of international dental schools considered for traditional predoctoral program: Yes
Advanced standing program offered for graduates of international dental schools: No
Advanced standing program description: NA

COMBINED AND ALTERNATE DEGREES

Ph.D.	M.S.	M.P.H.	M.D.	B.A./B.S.	Other
✓	✓	✓	—	—	✓

Other: M.B.A.

COSTS: 2012-13 SCHOOL YEAR

	FIRST YEAR	SECOND YEAR	THIRD YEAR	FOURTH YEAR
Tuition, resident	$25,450	$25,450	$25,450	$25,450
Tuition, nonresident	$57,230	$57,230	$57,230	$57,230
Tuition, other	NA	NA	NA	NA
Fees	$10,147	$13,463	$10,325	$10,195
Instruments, books, and supplies	$11,525	$6,913	$2,205	$476
Estimated living expenses	$20,130	$20,130	$22,143	$22,143
Optional laptop (cost not included in total resident or total non-resident)	$2,500*			
Total, resident	$67,252	$68,456	$62,623	$60,744
Total, nonresident	$99,032	$100,236	$94,403	$92,524
Total, other	NA	NA	NA	NA

*Cost for laptop can be included in financial aid package.

FINANCIAL AID

In order to be considered for financial aid from the federal Title IV programs, students must meet basic eligibility requirements. Please review the U.S. Department of Education's Funding Education Beyond High School: The Guide to Federal Student Aid for specific eligibility details at http://studentaid.ed.gov/students/publications/student_guide/index.html. The federal financial aid application process begins with the completion of the Free Application for Federal Student Aid (FAFSA). In order for us to receive a copy of students' FAFSA results, they must include the Stony Brook University federal school code 002838 when completing their FAFSA. Students are strongly encouraged to file their FAFSA before April 1, 2014. In order to be awarded any financial aid, they must first be admitted into a degree-granting program at Stony Brook University.

A student's financial aid budget or cost of attendance is made up of two parts, direct costs and indirect costs. Direct costs are paid to the university and include tuition, fees, and room and board (if living on campus) or only tuition and fees if the student does not live on campus. Indirect costs are not paid directly to the university and include items such as books and supplies, transportation, and personal expenses. These items are more individually variable than direct costs. To view the 2012-13 D.D.S. cost of attendance please visit the Stony Brook University School of Dental Medicine website at http://sbumc.informatics.sunysb.edu/dentalfinancial/cost..

Student loan recipients received amounts ranging between $8,500 and $63,963, with an average amount of $40,500.

UNIVERSITY AT BUFFALO
SCHOOL OF DENTAL MEDICINE

Dr. Michael Glick, Dean

CONTACT INFORMATION

http://dental.buffalo.edu/

DEAN'S OFFICE
325 Squire Hall
Buffalo, NY 14214
Phone: 716-829-2836
Fax: 716-833-3517

OFFICE OF STUDENT ADMISSIONS
Dr. David H. Brown
Director of Student Admissions
315 Squire Hall
Buffalo, NY 14214
Phone: 716-829-2839
http://dental.buffalo.edu/

OFFICE OF FINANCIAL AID
104 Harriman Hall
Buffalo, NY 14214
http://financialaid.buffalo.edu/graduate/dentalschool.php

STUDENT AFFAIRS
315 Squire Hall
Buffalo, NY 14214
Phone: 716-829-2839
http://dental.buffalo.edu/

MINORITY AFFAIRS/DIVERSITY
315 Squire Hall
Buffalo, NY 14214
Phone: 716-829-2839

UNIVERSITY RESIDENCE HALLS AND APARTMENTS
106 Spaulding Quad Ellicott Complex
Buffalo, NY 14261
Phone: 866-285-8806
http://housing.buffalo.edu/

INTERNATIONAL STUDENTS
Student Admissions
315 Squire Hall
Buffalo, NY 14214
Phone: 716-829-2839

GENERAL INFORMATION

The University at Buffalo School of Dental Medicine (UB SDM) was founded in 1892 as the fourth unit of the private University of Buffalo, which became a part of the State University of New York system in 1962. Today, the School of Dental Medicine serves the dental health care needs of New York State as a part of the University at Buffalo's South Campus Health Sciences Center. The primary mission of the UB SDM is to lead innovation in oral health education, research, and service, and to improve quality of life. The school improves the oral and general health of the people of the state of New York through its teaching, research, and service commitments. The school maintains its tradition of educating general practitioners and dental specialists to provide the highest quality of patient-centered care to the communities they serve. This education is based on a dynamic curriculum employing the latest information technologies and emphasizing the interactions among basic biomedical and behavioral sciences, clinical sciences, and clinical practice. In addition, the school continues to prepare individuals for leadership roles in the basic and oral health sciences and in dental education.

Type of institution: Public
Year opened: 1892
Term type: Semester
Time to degree in months: 43
Start month: August

Doctoral dental degree offered: D.D.S.
Total predoctoral enrollment: 401
Estimated entering class size: 90
Campus setting: Urban
Campus housing available: Yes

PREPARATION

Formal minimum preparation in semester/quarter hours: Semester: 90 Quarter: 120
Baccalaureate degree preferred: Yes
Number of first-year, first-time enrollees whose highest degree is:
- Baccalaureate: 76
- Master's: 12
- Ph.D. or other doctorate: 0

Of first-year, first-time enrollees without baccalaureates, the number with:
- Equivalent of 60 undergraduate credit hours or less: 0
- Equivalent of 61-90 undergraduate credit hours: 0
- Equivalent of 91 or more undergraduate credit hours: 2

PREREQUISITE COURSE	REQUIRED	RECOMMENDED	LAB REQUIRED	CREDITS (SEMESTER/QUARTER)
BCP (biology-chemistry-physics) sciences				
Biology	✓		✓	8/12
Chemistry, general/inorganic	✓		✓	8/12
Chemistry, organic	✓		✓	8/12
Physics	✓		✓	8/12
Additional biological sciences				
Anatomy		✓		
Biochemistry		✓		
Cell biology		✓		
Histology		✓		
Immunology		✓		
Microbiology		✓		
Molecular biology/genetics		✓		
Physiology		✓		
Zoology				

(Prerequisite Courses continued)

PREPARATION (CONTINUED)

PREREQUISITE COURSE	REQUIRED	RECOMMENDED	LAB REQUIRED	CREDITS (SEMESTER/QUARTER)
Other				
English	✓			8/12

Comment: English prerequisite must include composition.

Community college coursework accepted for prerequisites: Yes, strongly preferred from four-year college
Community college coursework accepted for electives: Yes, preferred from four-year college
Limits on community college credit hours: No, courses preferred from four-year college
Maximum number of community college credit hours: None; courses preferred from four-year college
Advanced placement (AP) credit accepted for prerequisites: Yes
Advanced placement (AP) credit accepted for electives: Yes
Comments regarding AP credit: AP credit will be accepted by UB SDM if your undergraduate institution accepted your AP credit, with the exception of biology. The biology prerequisite must be taken at an undergraduate institution.
Job shadowing: Required
Number of hours of job shadowing required or recommended: 100
Other factors considered in admission: Prior to application, candidates are strongly encouraged to acquire a minimum of 100 hours experience in the field of clinical dentistry in a variety of settings (general practice, specialty, hospital).

DAT

Mandatory: Yes
Latest DAT for consideration of application: 11/01/2013 (official scores must be received by Associated American Dental Schools Application Service (AADSAS) prior to 12/01/2013)
Oldest DAT considered: 01/01/2010
When more than one DAT score is reported: Highest score is considered
Canadian DAT accepted: Yes
Application considered before DAT scores are submitted: No

DAT: 2012 ENTERING CLASS

ENROLLEE DAT SCORES	RANGE	MEAN
Academic Average	16.0-25.0	19.9
Perceptual Ability	16.0-27.0	20.7
Total Science	16.0-25.0	19.6

GPA: 2012 ENTERING CLASS

ENROLLEE GPA SCORES	RANGE	MEAN
Science GPA	2.33-4.16	3.11
Total GPA	2.68-4.15	3.28

APPLICATION AND SELECTION

TIMETABLE

Earliest filing date: 06/04/2013
Latest filing date: 12/01/2013
Earliest date for acceptance offers: 12/01/2013
Maximum time in days for applicant's response to acceptance offer:
30 days if accepted on or after December 1
15 days if accepted on or after February 1
Requests for deferred entrance considered: In exceptional circumstances only
Fee for application: Yes, submitted at same time as Associated American Dental Schools Application Service (AADSAS) application
Amount of fee for application:
In state: $75 Out of state: $75 International: $75
Fee waiver available: Yes

	FIRST DEPOSIT	SECOND DEPOSIT	THIRD DEPOSIT
Required to hold place	Yes	No	No
Resident amount	$350		
Nonresident amount	$350		
Deposit due	As indicated in admission offer		
Applied to tuition	Yes		
Refundable	Yes		
Refundable by	03/01/2014		

APPLICATION PROCESS

Participates in AADSAS: Yes
Accepts direct applicants: No
Secondary or supplemental application required: No
Interview is mandatory: Yes
Interview is by invitation: Yes

RESIDENCY

Admissions process distinguishes between in-state/in-province and out-of-state/out-of-province applicants: Yes
Preference given to residents of: New York State
Reciprocity Admissions Agreement available for legal residents of: None
Applications are accepted from non-U.S. citizens/non-U.S. permanent residents: Yes

APPLICATION AND ENROLLMENT	NUMBER OF APPLICANTS	ESTIMATED NUMBER INTERVIEWED	ESTIMATED NUMBER ENROLLED
In-state or province applicants	450	152	69
Out-of-state or province applicants	1,357	104	21

Generally and over time, percentage of your first-year enrollment is in-state: 76%
Origin of out-of-state enrollees (U.S.): Arizona-2, California-1, Connecticut-1, Georgia-1, Illinois-1, New Jersey-3, Pennsylvania-3, Rhode Island-1, Utah-1, Washington-2
Origin of international enrollees: Canada-3, Haiti-1, Tanzania-1

DEMOGRAPHIC DESCRIPTIONS OF APPLICANTS: 2012 ENTERING CLASS

	APPLICANTS		ENROLLEES	
	M	W	M	W
Hispanic/Latino of any race	47	42	1	0
American Indian or Alaska Native	1	1	0	0
Asian	291	301	10	11
Black or African American	27	30	2	0
Native Hawaiian or Other Pacific Islander	0	0	0	0
White	447	328	35	31
Two or more races	19	18	0	0
Race and ethnicity unknown	36	34	0	0
International	107	78	0	0

	MINIMUM	MAXIMUM	MEAN
2012 entering class enrollees by age	20	37	24

Number of first-time enrollees over age 30: 2

CURRICULUM

The D.D.S. program provides students with the basic science training, clinical expertise, and analytical skills necessary to attain the highest level of proficiency as practitioners. Our graduates practice across the country, in many different settings, in all areas of dental medicine as general practitioners and specialists in private practice, as dental researchers, health care administrators, faculty in dental schools, and managers in the private sector.

Student research opportunities: Yes

SPECIAL PROGRAMS AND SERVICES

DURING DENTAL SCHOOL

Academic counseling and tutoring
Community service opportunities: Buffalo Outreach and Community Assistance (BOCA)
Internships, externships, or extramural programs
Mentoring
Personal counseling
Professional- and career-development programming
Training for those interested in academic careers

ACTIVE STUDENT ORGANIZATIONS

Alpha Omega
American Association for Dental Research Student Research Group
American Student Dental Association
BOCA
Delta Sigma Delta
Financial Literacy Club
Hispanic Dental Association
Student Professionalism and Ethics Club

INTERNATIONAL DENTISTS

Graduates of international dental schools considered for traditional predoctoral program: Yes
Advanced standing program offered for graduates of international dental schools: Yes
Advanced standing program description: Available at http://dental.buffalo.edu/Education/DDSProgram/InternationalDentistProgramDDS.aspx

COMBINED AND ALTERNATE DEGREES

Ph.D.	M.S.	M.P.H.	M.D.	B.A./B.S.	Other
✓	✓	—	—	✓	✓

Other degree: M.B.A.

COSTS: 2012-13 SCHOOL YEAR

	FIRST YEAR	SECOND YEAR	THIRD YEAR	FOURTH YEAR
Tuition, resident	$25,450	$25,450	$25,450	$25,450
Tuition, nonresident	$57,230	$57,230	$57,230	$57,230
Tuition, other	NA	NA	NA	NA
Fees	$8,649	$8,387	$8,237	$8,237
Instruments, books, and supplies	$6,750	$5,152	$2,114	$1,818
Estimated living expenses	$17,564	$17,564	$17,564	$17,564
Total, resident	$58,413	$56,553	$53,365	$53,069
Total, nonresident	$90,193	$88,333	$85,145	$84,849
Total, other	NA	NA	NA	NA

FINANCIAL AID

If you need help financing your education, U.S. citizen or eligible noncitizens should apply for federal financial aid by filling out a Free Application for Federal Student Aid (FAFSA) online at www.fafsa.ed.gov. The FAFSA application is required for any student wishing to apply for federal aid, including all federal loans. Students interested in applying for Federal Direct Stafford loans must file a FAFSA at www.fafsa.ed.gov every year in attendance. The FAFSA collects students' household financial information to determine their eligibility for all of the federal financial aid programs. The FAFSA is available online as of January 1. The university's priority date for filing the FAFSA is March 1. You may receive more detailed information by visiting the Student Response Center website at http://financialaid.buffalo.edu/graduate/dentalschool.php.

EAST CAROLINA UNIVERSITY
SCHOOL OF DENTAL MEDICINE

Dr. D. Gregory Chadwick, Dean

GENERAL INFORMATION

The School of Dental Medicine at East Carolina University is part of a major health sciences center that includes the Brody School of Medicine and colleges of Nursing and Allied Health Sciences. The School of Dental Medicine, which is part of East Carolina University—with a total enrollment of more than 25,000 students—is a member institution of the University of North Carolina System. The dental school opened for its first students in August 2011. Students spend the first three years of the predoctoral program in Ledyard E. Ross Hall, the school's new 188,000-square-foot, state-of-the-art building. Training in the fourth year will be provided in university-owned, community-based service learning centers located across the state of North Carolina. Residency programs will be provided in Advanced Education in General Dentistry and Pediatric Dentistry, and through the affiliated General Practice Residency program at Vidant Medical Center. All programs will focus on preparing outstanding, community-minded primary care clinicians ready to serve all segments of society, with an emphasis on serving in rural areas and within communities of need.

CONTACT INFORMATION

www.ecu.edu/dentistry
1851 MacGregor Downs Road, MS 701
Greenville, NC 27834-4300

OFFICE OF STUDENT AFFAIRS

B. Lamont Lowery
Director of Admissions

Dr. Margaret B. Wilson
Associate Dean for Student Affairs
Phone: 252-737-7043
Fax: 252-744-7049

MISSION STATEMENT:

The mission of the dental school at East Carolina University is to:

1. Prepare leaders with outstanding clinical skills, an ethical bearing, sound judgment, and a passion to serve.
2. Provide educational opportunities for individuals from historically underrepresented groups, disadvantaged backgrounds, and underserved areas.
3. Provide and enhance oral health services for underserved North Carolinians through implementation of community-oriented service learning and interprofessional collaborations.
4. Foster an environment where creativity, collaboration, and diversity are embraced.
5. Guide future clinical practice and dental education through innovation and discovery.

Type of institution: Public
Year opened: 2011
Term type: Trimester
Time to degree in months: 44
Start month: August

Doctoral dental degree offered: D.M.D.
Total predoctoral enrollment: 200 planned
Estimated entering class size: 50
Campus setting: Health Sciences Center
Campus housing available: No

PREPARATION

Formal minimum preparation in semester/quarter hours: Bachelor's degree
Baccalaureate degree preferred: Bachelor's degree is required.
Number of first-year, first-time enrollees whose highest degree is:
- Baccalaureate: 46
- Master's: 6
- Ph.D. or other doctorate: 0

Of first-year, first-time enrollees without baccalaureates, the number with:
- Equivalent of 60 undergraduate credit hours or less: 0
- Equivalent of 61-90 undergraduate credit hours: 0
- Equivalent of 91 or more undergraduate credit hours: 0

PREREQUISITE COURSE	REQUIRED	RECOMMENDED	LAB REQUIRED	CREDITS (SEMESTER/QUARTER)
BCP (biology-chemistry-physics) sciences				
Biology	✓		✓	1 year
Chemistry, general/inorganic	✓		✓	1 year
Chemistry, organic	✓		✓	1 year
Physics	✓		✓	1 year
Additional biological sciences				
Anatomy		✓		

(Prerequisite Courses continued)

PREPARATION (CONTINUED)

PREREQUISITE COURSE	REQUIRED	RECOMMENDED	LAB REQUIRED	CREDITS (SEMESTER/QUARTER)
Biochemistry		✓		
Cell biology		✓		
Histology		✓		
Immunology		✓		
Microbiology		✓		
Molecular biology/genetics		✓		
Physiology		✓		
Zoology		✓		
Other				
English	✓			1 year
College mathematics	✓			1 year

Community college coursework accepted for prerequisites: In some instances
Community college coursework accepted for electives: Yes
Limits on community college credit hours: Yes
Maximum number of community college credit hours: 60
Advanced placement (AP) credit accepted for prerequisites: In some instances
Advanced placement (AP) credit accepted for electives: Yes
Comments regarding AP credit: We strongly recommend applicants who receive AP credit to then avail themselves of the opportunity to take additional higher-level courses.
Job shadowing: Strongly recommended
Number of hours of job shadowing required or recommended: No specific requirement
Other factors considered in admission: Demonstrated commitment to, and leadership in, community service, particularly related to promoting health

DAT

Mandatory: Yes
Latest DAT for consideration of application: December 2013
Oldest DAT considered: 07/01/2011
When more than one DAT score is reported: All scores will be reviewed, with emphasis on the most recent set of scores.
Canadian DAT accepted: No
Application considered before DAT scores are submitted: Yes, but decision regarding interview cannot occur until DAT scores are received and favorably reviewed.

DAT: 2012 ENTERING CLASS

ENROLLEE DAT SCORES	RANGE	MEAN
Academic Average	17 - 22	19.2
Perceptual Ability	15 - 25	19.0
Total Science	17 - 23	18.8

GPA: 2012 ENTERING CLASS

ENROLLEE GPA SCORES	RANGE	MEAN
Science GPA	2.30 – 4.0	3.28
Total GPA	2.56 – 4.0	3.39

APPLICATION AND SELECTION

TIMETABLE

Earliest filing date: June 2013
Latest filing date: 12/01/2013
Earliest date for acceptance offers: 12/01/2013
Maximum time in days for applicant's response to acceptance offer:
30 days if accepted on or after December 1
15 days if accepted on or after February 1
Requests for deferred entrance considered: In exceptional circumstances only
Fee for application: Yes, nonrefundable
Amount of fee for application:
In state: $80 Out of state: NA International: NA
Fee waiver available: No

	FIRST DEPOSIT	SECOND DEPOSIT	THIRD DEPOSIT
Required to hold place	Yes	No	No
Resident amount	$300	No	No
Nonresident amount	N/A	No	No
Deposit due	As indicated in admissions offer	No	No
Applied to tuition	Yes	No	No
Refundable	No	No	No

APPLICATION PROCESS

Participates in Associated American Dental Schools Application Service (AADSAS): Yes
Accepts direct applicants: No
Secondary or supplemental application required: Yes
Secondary or supplemental application website: Provided to applicants at time AADSAS is received
Interview is mandatory: Yes
Interview is by invitation: Yes

RESIDENCY

Admissions process distinguishes between in-state/in-province and out-of-state/out-of-province applicants: Yes

Preference given to residents of: Only residents of North Carolina are eligible for admission.
Reciprocity Admissions Agreement available for legal residents of: None
Applications are accepted from non-U.S. citizens/non-U.S. permanent residents: Only if determined to be residents of North Carolina

APPLICATION AND ENROLLMENT	NUMBER OF APPLICANTS	ESTIMATED NUMBER INTERVIEWED	ESTIMATED NUMBER ENROLLED
In-state or province applicants	399	224	52
Out-of-state or province applicants	34	0	0

Generally and over time, percentage of your first-year enrollment is in-state: 100%
Origin of out-of-state enrollees (U.S.): NA
Origin of international enrollees: NA

DEMOGRAPHIC DESCRIPTIONS OF APPLICANTS: 2012 ENTERING CLASS

	APPLICANTS		ENROLLEES	
	M	W	M	W
Hispanic/Latino of any race	4	2	1	0
American Indian or Alaska Native	1	1	0	1
Asian	37	39	0	1
Black or African American	13	36	0	2
Native Hawaiian or Other Pacific Islander	0	0	0	
White	136	96	25	20
Two or more races	10	12	2	0
Race and ethnicity unknown	8	1	0	0
International	0	0	0	0

	MINIMUM	MAXIMUM	MEAN
2012 entering class enrollees by age	23	34	25

Number of first-time enrollees over age 30: 5

CURRICULUM

The goal of the curriculum is to interlace problem solving into all aspects of didactic and clinical experiences. Every basic science and preclinical course has a seminar component that will involve group collaboration on increasingly difficult cases and topical problems intended to make problem assessment, solution research, and self-reflection equal components to knowledge acquisition. This philosophy continues throughout the four years of clinical training. Unique to ECU are the clinical experiences in the Community Service Learning Centers. Utilizing the best practices in health science informatics, the curriculum is designed to provide the highest level of educational experiences in a collaborative and challenging environment. The students are required to play an active role in their success as young professionals.

SPECIAL PROGRAMS AND SERVICES

DURING DENTAL SCHOOL

Academic counseling and tutoring
Community service opportunities
Internships, externships, or extramural programs
Mentoring
Personal counseling
Professional- and career-development programming
Training for those interested in academic careers

ACTIVE STUDENT ORGANIZATIONS

American Association for Dental Research Student Research Group
American Association of Pediatric Dentistry
American Association of Women Dentists
American Dental Education Association (ADEA)
American Student Dental Association
Hispanic Dental Association
Student National Dental Association
Student Professional Ethics Association

INTERNATIONAL DENTISTS

Graduates of international dental schools considered for traditional predoctoral program: Only if they are North Carolina residents
Advanced standing program offered for graduates of international dental schools: We do not offer an advanced program for internationally trained dentists.

COMBINED AND ALTERNATE DEGREES					
Ph.D.	M.S.	M.P.H.	M.D.	B.A./B.S.	Other
—	—	—	—	—	—

COSTS: 2012-13 SCHOOL YEAR

	FIRST YEAR	SECOND YEAR	THIRD YEAR	FOURTH YEAR
Tuition, resident	$22,817	$22,817	NR	NR
Tuition, nonresident				
Tuition, other				
Fees	$2,111	$2,111	NR	NR
Instruments, books, and supplies	$8,374	$3,940	NR	NR
Estimated living expenses	$20,841	$20,841	NR	NR
Total, resident	$54,143	$49,709	NR	NR
Total, nonresident				
Total, other				

Comments: The School of Dental Medicine at East Carolina University only admits residents of North Carolina.

FINANCIAL AID

Once finalized and approved, the School of Dental Medicine's schedule of tuition and fees is posted on the school's website. On the day of the admissions interview, a financial aid counselor will meet with the applicants and provide them with a summary of the projected cost of education. Available financial aid options will be described, and applicants will be directed to the Federal Financial Aid Loan Information website, which describes all federal loans available to graduate and professional school students. Applicants will be advised that they will need to complete a Free Application for Federal Student Aid (FAFSA) soon after January 1, but no later than February 14, of the matriculation year.

Based on the information provided by the student, the U.S. Department of Education will prepare a need analysis for each student and send it electronically to the ECU Office of Student Financial Aid. For admitted students, once the FAFSA is received in the Office of Student Financial Aid, the student's level of financial need will be determined and funds will be awarded accordingly. This information will be conveyed to the student in the form of an award letter including instructions for accepting awards.

UNIVERSITY OF NORTH CAROLINA AT CHAPEL HILL
SCHOOL OF DENTISTRY

Dr. Jane A. Weintraub, Dean

GENERAL INFORMATION

The University of North Carolina at Chapel Hill has the distinction of being the first state university in the United States. Chapel Hill is a college community of 57,000 located near the center of the state and in close proximity to the Research Triangle Park. UNC School of Dentistry accepted its first D.D.S. class in 1950. The school currently occupies four buildings—its original building (Old Dental Building), a five-story, 110,000-square-foot building providing teaching and clinical facilities (Brauer Hall), a six-story patient care facility (Tarrson Hall), and a new 216,000-square-foot facility for teaching and research (Koury Oral Health Sciences Building). The new building, which opened in March 2012, replaces the former dental research and dental office buildings. The dental school offers graduate education in 13 areas including nine dental specialties, Advanced Education in General Dentistry (AEGD) and General Practice Residency (GPR) programs, Oral Biology, and Clinical Research. Also available are academic programs for dental hygienists and dental assistants, as well as a master's level course of study that prepares dental hygienists for teaching careers.

MISSION STATEMENT:

The mission of the School of Dentistry is to promote the health of the people of North Carolina, the nation, and the world through excellence in teaching, patient care, research, and service.

Type of institution: Public
Year opened: 1950
Term type: Semester
Time to degree in months: 46
Start month: August

Doctoral dental degree offered: D.D.S.
Total predoctoral enrollment: 318
Estimated entering class size: 81
Campus setting: Suburban
Campus housing available: Yes

CONTACT INFORMATION

www.dentistry.unc.edu
University of North Carolina at Chapel Hill
School of Dentistry
Manning Drive and Columbia Street
Chapel Hill, NC 27599-7450
Phone: 919-966-1161
Fax: 919-966-4049

ADMISSIONS
1611 Koury Oral Health Sciences Building
Campus Box 7450
Chapel Hill, NC 27599-7450
Phone: 919-537-3348
Fax: 919-966-5795
www.dentistry.unc.edu

FINANCIAL AID
University of North Carolina at Chapel Hill
111 Pettigrew Hall
Chapel Hill, NC 27599-2300
Phone: 919-962-3620
www.studentaid.unc.edu

ACADEMIC AFFAIRS
1611 Koury Oral Health Sciences Bldg
Campus Box 7450
Chapel Hill, NC 27599-7450
Phone: 919-537-3347
Fax: 919-966-5795
www.dentistry.unc.edu

PREPARATION

Formal minimum preparation in semester/quarter hours: Semester: 96 Quarter: 144
Baccalaureate degree preferred: Yes
Number of first-year, first-time enrollees whose highest degree is:
- Baccalaureate: 75
- Master's: 6
- Ph.D. or other doctorate: 0

Of first-year first-time enrollees without baccalaureates, the number with:
- Equivalent of 60 undergraduate credit hours or less: 0
- Equivalent of 61-90 undergraduate credit hours: 0
- Equivalent of 91 or more undergraduate credit hours: 0

PREREQUISITE COURSE	REQUIRED	RECOMMENDED	LAB REQUIRED	CREDITS (SEMESTER/QUARTER)
BCP (biology-chemistry-physics) sciences				
Biology, general	✓		✓	4/6
Biology, anatomy	✓		✓	4/6
Chemistry, general/inorganic	✓		✓	8/12
Chemistry, organic	✓			6/10
Physics	✓			6/10
Additional biological sciences				
Biochemistry	✓			3/5
Cell biology				
Histology				
Immunology				
Microbiology				

(Prerequisite Courses continued)

PREPARATION (CONTINUED)

Molecular biology/genetics
Physiology
Zoology

Community college coursework accepted for prerequisites: Yes, but prerequisite courses preferred from four-year college/university
Community college coursework accepted for electives: Yes
Limits on community college credit hours: Yes
Maximum number of community college credit hours: 64
Advanced placement (AP) credit accepted for prerequisites: Yes
Advanced placement (AP) credit accepted for electives: Yes
Job shadowing: Required
Number of hours of job shadowing required or recommended: Not specified
Other factors considered in admission: Academic abilities, psychomotor skills, service commitment, self-directed learner, and knowledge of the dental profession

DAT

Mandatory: Yes
Latest DAT for consideration of application: 11/01/2013
Oldest DAT considered: 01/01/2010
When more than one DAT score is reported: Highest score is considered
Canadian DAT accepted: Yes
Application considered before DAT scores are submitted: No

DAT: 2012 ENTERING CLASS

ENROLLEE DAT SCORES	RANGE	MEAN
Academic Average	17-28	20
Perceptual Ability	15-26	20
Total Science	16-28	20

GPA: 2012 ENTERING CLASS

ENROLLEE GPA SCORES	RANGE	MEAN
Science GPA	2.17-4	3.52
Total GPA	2.39-4	3.57

APPLICATION AND SELECTION

TIMETABLE

Earliest filing date: 06/03/2013
Latest filing date: 12/02/2013
Earliest date for acceptance offers: 12/02/2013
Maximum time in days for applicant's response to acceptance offer:
30 days if accepted on or after December 1 (after first selection meeting)
21 days if accepted on or after February 1 (after second selection meeting)
Requests for deferred entrance considered: No
Fee for application: Yes, submitted at same time as Associated American Dental Schools Application Service (AADSAS) application.
Amount of fee for application:
In-state: $82 Out-of-state: $82 International: $82
Fee waiver available: No

	FIRST DEPOSIT	SECOND DEPOSIT	THIRD DEPOSIT
Required to hold place	Yes	No	No
Resident amount	$500		
Non-resident amount	$500		
Deposit due	As indicated in admission offer		
Applied to tuition	Yes		
Refundable	No		

APPLICATION PROCESS

Participates in AADSAS: Yes
Accepts direct applicants: No
Secondary or supplemental application required: Yes
Secondary or supplemental application website: https://www.dentistry.unc.edu/secure/academic/dds/supplementalapplication/index.cfm
Interview is by invitation: Yes
Interview is mandatory: Yes

RESIDENCY

Admissions process distinguishes between in-state/in-province and out-of-state/out-of-province applicants: Yes
Preference given to residents of: North Carolina
Reciprocity Admissions Agreement available for legal residents of: None
Applications are accepted from non-U.S. citizens/non-U.S. permanent residents: Yes

APPLICATION AND ENROLLMENT	NUMBER OF APPLICANTS	ESTIMATED NUMBER INTERVIEWED	ESTIMATED NUMBER ENROLLED
In-state or province applicants	313	174	68
Out-of-state or province applicants	1,014	83	13

Generally and over time, percentage of your first-year enrollment is in-state: 80-85%
Origin of out-of-state or -province enrollees: Alabama-1, Florida-1, Georgia-2, Illinois-1, Indiana-1, Kansas-1, Michigan-1, New York-1, Pennsylvania-1, Ohio-1, Texas-1
Origin of international enrollees: Jamaica-1

DEMOGRAPHIC DESCRIPTIONS OF APPLICANTS: 2012 ENTERING CLASS

	APPLICANTS		ENROLLEES	
	M	W	M	W
Hispanic/Latino of any race	61	77	2	4
American Indian or Alaska Native	1	1	0	0
Asian	164	205	5	3
Black or African American	27	81	5	8
Native Hawaiian or Other Pacific Islander	0	0	0	0
White	556	450	25	24
Two or more races	3	2	0	1
Race and ethnicity unknown	22	24	2	1
International	1	0	1	0

Note: The figures on this table represent men and women who applied through AADSAS but did not necessarily complete the UNC School of Dentistry supplemental application. Nineteen (19) applicants did not report gender.

	MINIMUM	MAXIMUM	MEAN
2012 entering year enrollees by age	21	40	24

Number of first-time enrollees over age 30: 7

CURRICULUM

The program consists of eight semesters of 16 weeks each, plus three required 10-week summer semesters. Although the majority of students require four years to meet the degree requirements, circumstances may necessitate an extended period of study. The first year includes courses in the core basic sciences, introductory dental sciences, and introduction to patient management, which focuses on the relationship between the health care provider and the patient. Students begin patient care in the summer of the first year. During the second year, students continue taking biological science courses, and the next series of dental science and health care delivery systems courses. During the first part of the second year, students assume full patient care privileges, begin delivering comprehensive care services, and are responsible for providing both therapeutic and preventive treatment for their patients. In the third year, students spend a significant amount of time providing comprehensive care for their patients. A series of intermediate dental science courses are offered. During the summer of their third year, students complete two required externships (community setting and hospital setting) at extramural sites located throughout the state and beyond. Fourth-year students assume responsibility for patients who require more advanced dental care in a mentored, general dentistry group practice. Advanced dental science courses, updates, and practice-related material are offered during the fourth year.

Student research opportunities: Yes

SPECIAL PROGRAMS AND SERVICES

PREDENTAL

Summer enrichment programs: the Medical Education Program (MED) and the Science Enrichment Preparation Program (SEP)

DURING DENTAL SCHOOL

Academic counseling and tutoring
Community service opportunities
Internships, externships and extramural programs
Mentoring
Personal counseling
Training for those interested in academic careers
Transfer applicants considered if space is available

ACTIVE STUDENT ORGANIZATIONS

American Association of Dental Research Student Research Group
American Association of Women Dentists
American Dental Education Association (ADEA)
American Student Dental Association
Hispanic Dental Association
Student National Dental Association

INTERNATIONAL DENTISTS

Graduates of international dental schools considered for traditional predoctoral program: Yes
Advanced standing program offered for graduates of international dental schools: No

COMBINED AND ALTERNATE DEGREES

Ph.D.	M.S.	M.P.H.	M.D.	B.A./B.S.	Other
✓	✓	✓	—	—	—

COSTS: 2012-13 SCHOOL YEAR

	FIRST YEAR	SECOND YEAR	THIRD YEAR	FOURTH YEAR
Tuition, resident	$29,167	$30,879	$30,139	$25,764
Tuition, nonresident	$54,455	$60,800	$58,081	$41,766
Tuition, other	NA	NA	NA	NA
Fees (Lease Fee)	$2,500	$2,500	$2,500	$2,500
Instruments, books, and supplies	$4,964	$5,519	$2,333	$1,670
Estimated living expenses	NR	NR	NR	NR
Total, resident	$36,631	$38,898	$34,972	$29,934
Total, nonresident	$61,919	$68,819	$62,914	$45,936
Total, other	NA	NA	NA	NA

FINANCIAL AID

There were approximately 20 grant/scholarship recipients in the 2012 entering class. Awards ranged from $5,000 to $25,000. Seventy-eight students received student loans ranging from $40,500 to $74,360. The average loan for North Carolina residents was $40,835, and $50,408 for nonresidents. The average debt for the graduating class of 2012 was $172,912.

CASE WESTERN RESERVE UNIVERSITY
SCHOOL OF DENTAL MEDICINE

Dr. Jerold S. Goldberg, Dean

GENERAL INFORMATION

The School of Dental Medicine was organized in 1892 as the Dental Department of Western Reserve University. Since 1969 the facilities of the school of dentistry have been located in Case Western Reserve University's Health Science Center adjacent to the schools of medicine and nursing and to the University Hospitals of Cleveland, Ohio. The School of Dental Medicine has conferred degrees on more than 5,500 graduates. Education in the basic sciences and technique, as well as preclinical laboratory work, is carried out by each student in an individually assigned area in the multidisciplinary laboratories. The 50,000-square-foot dental clinic floor consists of two major clinics and five specialty clinics. The major clinics are made up of cubicles fully equipped as private operatories. Drawing from a population of more than one million people, the clinics provide a broad spectrum of care to the population, affording the student substantial clinical experience.

MISSION STATEMENT:

The mission of the Case Western Reserve University School of Dental Medicine is to provide outstanding programs in oral health education, patient care, focused research and scholarship, and service that are of value to our constituents. We will accomplish this in an environment that fosters collegiality and professionalism and enables a diverse group of students to become competent practitioners of dentistry and contribute to the health and well-being of individuals and populations.

Type of institution: Private
Year opened: 1892
Term type: Semester
Time to degree in months: 48
Start month: August

Doctoral dental degree offered: D.M.D.
Total predoctoral enrollment: 282
Estimated entering class size: 75
Campus setting: Urban
Campus housing available: No

PREPARATION

Formal minimum preparation in semester/quarter hours: Semester: 60 Quarter: 90
Baccalaureate degree preferred: Yes, strongly recommended
Number of first-year, first-time enrollees whose highest degree is:
- Baccalaureate: 61
- Master's: 5
- Ph.D. or other doctorate: 1

Of first-year, first-time enrollees without baccalaureates, the number with:
- Equivalent of 60 undergraduate credit hours or less: 0
- Equivalent of 61-90 undergraduate credit hours: 3
- Equivalent of 91 or more undergraduate credit hours: 5

PREREQUISITE COURSE	REQUIRED	RECOMMENDED	LAB REQUIRED	CREDITS (SEMESTER/QUARTER)
BCP (biology-chemistry-physics) sciences				
Biology	✓		✓	6/10
Chemistry, general/inorganic	✓		✓	6/10
Chemistry, organic	✓		✓	6/10
Physics	✓		✓	6/10
Additional biological sciences				
Anatomy		✓		3/5
Biochemistry		✓		3/5
Cell biology		✓		3/5
Histology		✓		3/5
Immunology		✓		3/5
Microbiology		✓		3/5

(Prerequisite Courses continued)

CONTACT INFORMATION

http://dental.case.edu
10900 Euclid Avenue
Cleveland, OH 44106-4905
Phone: 216-368-3266
Fax: 216-368-3204

ADMISSIONS

Dr. Emil Chuck
Director of Admissions
10900 Euclid Avenue
Cleveland, OH 44106-4905
Phone: 216-368-2460
http://dental.case.edu

FINANCIAL AID

Barbara A. Sciulli
Financial Aid Officer
10900 Euclid Avenue
Cleveland, OH 44106-4905
Phone: 216-368-3256
http://dental.case.edu

STUDENT SERVICES OFFICE

Philip C. Aftoora
Director of Student Services
10900 Euclid Avenue
Cleveland, OH 44106-4905
Phone: 216-368-3201
http://dental.case.edu

MINORITY AFFAIRS/DIVERSITY

Dr. Kristin Williams
Minority Coordinator
10900 Euclid Avenue
Cleveland, OH 44106-4905
Phone: 216-368-2392
http://dental.case.edu

INTERNATIONAL STUDENTS

Director of International Student Services
10900 Euclid Avenue
Cleveland, OH 44106-7038
Phone: 216-368-2517
http://studentaffairs.case.edu/international

PREPARATION (CONTINUED)

PREREQUISITE COURSE	REQUIRED	RECOMMENDED	LAB REQUIRED	CREDITS (SEMESTER/QUARTER)
Molecular biology/genetics		✓		3/5
Physiology		✓		3/5

Community college coursework accepted for prerequisites: Yes, majority of prerequisites taken at a four-year college
Community college coursework accepted for electives: Yes
Limits on community college credit hours: Yes
Maximum number of community college credit hours: 60
Advanced placement (AP) credit accepted for prerequisites: Yes
Advanced placement (AP) credit accepted for electives: Yes
Comments regarding AP credit: Provided they appear on official transcript—additional upper level coursework in the subject is strongly recommended.
Job shadowing: Recommended
Number of hours of job shadowing required or recommended: 20—Shadowing of multiple dentists recommended
Other factors considered in admission: Academic performance, DAT scores, personal essay, and faculty letters of recommendation

DAT

Mandatory: Yes
Latest DAT for consideration of application: 01/31/2014
Oldest DAT considered: 01/01/2011
When more than one DAT score is reported: Highest score is considered
Canadian DAT accepted: Yes
Application considered before DAT scores are submitted: No

DAT: 2012 ENTERING CLASS

ENROLLEE DAT SCORES	RANGE	MEAN
Academic Average	16.0-25.0	19.7
Perceptual Ability	15.0-26.0	19.7
Total Science	16.0-24.0	19.6

GPA: 2012 ENTERING CLASS

ENROLLEE GPA SCORES	RANGE	MEAN
Science GPA	2.64-4.00	3.46
Total GPA	2.75-4.00	3.53

APPLICATION AND SELECTION

TIMETABLE

Earliest filing date: 06/01/2013
Latest filing date: 01/01/2014
Earliest date for acceptance offers: 12/01/2013
Maximum time in days for applicant's response to acceptance offer:
30 days if accepted on or after December 1
15 days if accepted on or after February 1
Requests for deferred entrance considered: In exceptional circumstances only

Fee for application: Yes, submitted at same time as Associated American Dental Schools Application Service (AADSAS) application.
Amount of fee for application:
In state: $55 Out of state: $55 International: $55
Fee waiver available: Yes, the undergraduate financial aid office must show need.

	FIRST DEPOSIT	SECOND DEPOSIT	THIRD DEPOSIT
Required to hold place	Yes	No	No
Resident amount	$1,000		
Nonresident amount	$1,000		
Deposit due	30 or 15 days from date of acceptance		
Applied to tuition	Yes		
Refundable	No		

APPLICATION PROCESS

Participates in AADSAS: Yes
Accepts direct applicants: Yes
Secondary or supplemental application required: No, only AADSAS application required
Interview is mandatory: Yes
Interview is by invitation: Yes

RESIDENCY

Admissions process distinguishes between in-state/in-province and out-of-state/out-of-province applicants: No
Applications are accepted from non-U.S. citizens/non-U.S. permanent residents: Yes

APPLICATION AND ENROLLMENT	NUMBER OF APPLICANTS	ESTIMATED NUMBER INTERVIEWED	ESTIMATED NUMBER ENROLLED
In-state or province applicants	200	61	24
Out-of-state or province applicants	2,799	326	50

Generally and over time, percentage of your first-year enrollment is in-state: 20%

Origin of out-of-state enrollees (U.S.): Arizona-1, California-6, Connecticut-1, Florida-2, Georgia-1, Illinois-1, Indiana-3, Maryland-1, Massachusetts-3, New Jersey-2, New York-2, Oregon-1, Pennsylvania-5, Puerto Rico-1, Texas-2, Virginia-1

Origin of international enrollees: Canada-10, China-1, Kenya-1, Nigeria-1, South Korea-3, United Kingdom-1

DEMOGRAPHIC DESCRIPTIONS OF APPLICANTS: 2012 ENTERING CLASS

	APPLICANTS		ENROLLEES	
	M	W	M	W
Hispanic/Latino of any race	70	60	1	3
American Indian or Alaska Native	0	2	0	0
Asian	466	456	2	14
Black or African American	32	58	0	2
Native Hawaiian or Other Pacific Islander	1	1	0	0
White	860	531	16	14
Two or more races	35	35	2	0
Race and ethnicity unknown	40	28	1	1
International	159	135	6	11

Note: 1 Asian Enrollee did not report a gender. 30 Applicants did not report a gender.

	MINIMUM	MAXIMUM	MEAN
2012 entering class enrollees by age	19	37	24

Number of first-time enrollees over age 30: 8

CURRICULUM

The Case Western Reserve University School of Dental Medicine has created the new model for dental education. The new curriculum is grounded in principles that exemplify educational formats embracing experiential learning. Key features of our curriculum are small group learning environment where students retain responsibility for learning; time allocated for independent study, integration of concepts, and reflection; and cornerstone experiences that integrate multiple content areas in powerful learning scenarios within the school and the larger community.

Student research opportunities: Yes

SPECIAL PROGRAMS AND SERVICES

PREDENTAL

Association of American Medical Colleges/ADEA Summer Medical and Dental Education Program (AAMC/ADEA SMDEP)

Special affiliations with colleges and universities:

- Denison University: 3+4 Program
- University of Toledo: 3+4 Program
- Walsh University: 3+4 Program
- Westminster College: 3+4 Program
- Wooster College: 3+4 Program

DURING DENTAL SCHOOL

Academic counseling and tutoring
Community service opportunities: Healthy Smiles dental sealant program in first year
Internships, externships, or extramural programs
Mentoring
Personal counseling
Professional- and career-development programming
Training for those interested in academic careers

ACTIVE STUDENT ORGANIZATIONS

American Dental Education Association (ADEA)
American Student Dental Association

INTERNATIONAL DENTISTS

Graduates of international dental schools considered for traditional predoctoral program: Yes

Advanced standing program offered for graduates of international dental schools: Yes

Advanced standing program description: Program awarding a dental degree

COMBINED AND ALTERNATE DEGREES

Ph.D.	M.S.	M.P.H.	M.D.	B.A./B.S.	Other
—	✓	✓	—	✓	✓

Other degree: M.C.R.T. (Master's in clinical research training)

COSTS: 2012-13 SCHOOL YEAR

	FIRST YEAR	SECOND YEAR	THIRD YEAR	FOURTH YEAR
Tuition resident, non-resident, and other	$56,400	$56,400	$56,400	$56,400
Fees	$2,828	$3,777	$5,378	$5,394
Instruments, books, and supplies	$14,956	$9,129	$4,712	$1,488
Estimated living expenses	$17,530	$17,530	$21,425	$21,425
Total resident, non-resident, and other	$91,714	$86,836	$87,915	$84,707

Comments: Supplies include required tablet computer.

FINANCIAL AID

Case Western Reserve University School of Dental Medicine participates in the federal student loan programs: Stafford, Perkins, Health Professions, and federal Graduate PLUS loans. We therefore require that the Free Application for Federal Student Aid (FAFSA), which can be found on www.fafsa.ed.gov, as well as our own online application form, be completed before May 15 of the year you matriculate. Please note that these programs are available for U.S. citizens and eligible noncitizens.

For the 2012 academic year, 7% of our students are recipients of the Health Professions Scholarship Program (HPSP) offered by the United States Air Force, Army, or Navy.

The median 2012 graduate indebtedness, including undergraduate indebtedness, was $261,707.

THE OHIO STATE UNIVERSITY
COLLEGE OF DENTISTRY

Dr. Patrick M. Lloyd, Dean

CONTACT INFORMATION

www.dent.osu.edu
305 West 12th Avenue
Columbus, OH 43210
Phone: 614-292-3361

RECRUITMENT AND ADMISSIONS

Annette McMurry, J.D.
Director of Admissions
305 West 12th Avenue
Columbus, OH 43210
Phone: 614-292-3361
Email: mcmurry.7@osu.edu
www.dent.osu.edu/admissions

Ken Sigler, M.Ed.
Associate Director of Admissions
305 West 12th Avenue
Columbus, OH 43210
Phone: 614-292-3361
Email: sigler.62@osu.edu

REGISTRAR AND FINANCIAL AID

Office of Financial Aid
305 West 12th Avenue
Columbus, OH 43210
Phone: 614-292-7768

Michael Murray
Registrar
305 West 12th Avenue
Columbus, OH 43210
Phone: 614-292-4404
Email: murray.287@osu.edu
www.dent.osu.edu/oaa

OFFICE OF ACADEMIC AFFAIRS AND STUDENT SERVICES

Susannah Turner
Director of Student Affairs
0116 Postle Hall
305 West 12th Avenue
Columbus, OH 43210
Phone: 614-688-1103
Email: turner.647@osu.edu
www.dent.osu.edu/studentaffairs

MINORITY AFFAIRS/DIVERSITY

www.osu.edu/diversity

GRADUATE & PROFESSIONAL HOUSING

http://housing.osu.edu/gradpro.asp

GENERAL INFORMATION

Since 1890, The Ohio State University College of Dentistry has had a long-standing history of academic excellence and research innovation. As the third-largest public dental school in the country and one of only two dental schools in Ohio, the College of Dentistry offers a dynamic environment in which to work and learn. It is located within a medical center complex at a top national research university in a thriving metropolitan community. The college draws upon a unique combination of strengths. A full range of dental specialty programs is offered at a single site, and extensive clinical training includes service work at a variety of outreach sites around the state. A high-profile research program draws extensive support from two top funding institutions—the National Institutes of Health (NIH) and the National Science Foundation (NSF). Here you will meet top practitioners and researchers who are shaping the future of dentistry and the health care field. Please visit our website at www.dent.osu.edu/admission for detailed information.

MISSION STATEMENT:

The mission of The Ohio State University College of Dentistry is to produce dental professionals who are prepared for entry into practice, advanced dental education, or specialized practice. Graduates are prepared to meet the oral health care needs of the citizens of Ohio and the nation, to conduct research that will expand the scientific base upon which dentistry is practiced, and to provide service to the profession.

Type of institution: Public
Year opened: 1890
Term type: Semester
Time to degree in months: 45
Start month: August

Doctoral dental degree offered: D.D.S.
Total predoctoral enrollment: 430
Estimated entering class size: 110
Campus setting: Urban
Campus housing available: Yes

PREPARATION

Formal minimum preparation in semester/quarter hours: Semester: 60 Quarter: 90
Baccalaureate degree preferred: Yes
Number of first-year, first-time enrollees whose highest degree is:
- Baccalaureate: 99
- Master's: 10
- Ph.D. or other doctorate: 0

Of first-year, first-time enrollees without baccalaureates, the number with:
- Equivalent of 60 undergraduate credit hours or less: 0
- Equivalent of 61-90 undergraduate credit hours: 0
- Equivalent of 91 or more undergraduate credit hours: 0

PREREQUISITE COURSE	REQUIRED	RECOMMENDED	LAB REQUIRED	CREDITS (SEMESTER/QUARTER)
BCP (biology-chemistry-physics) sciences				
Biology	✓		✓	6/10
Chemistry, general/inorganic	✓		✓	9/15
Chemistry, organic	✓		✓	6/10
Physics	✓		✓	3/5
Additional biological sciences				
Anatomy	✓		✓	3/5
Biochemistry	✓			3/5
Cell biology		✓		
Histology		✓		
Immunology		✓		
Microbiology	✓			3/5

(Prerequisite Courses continued)

PREPARATION (CONTINUED)

PREREQUISITE COURSE	REQUIRED	RECOMMENDED	LAB REQUIRED	CREDITS (SEMESTER/QUARTER)
Molecular biology/genetics		✓		
Physiology	✓			3/5
Zoology				
Other				
Freshman English	✓			3/3
English composition	✓			3/3

Community college coursework accepted for prerequisites: Not recommended
Community college coursework accepted for electives: Yes
Limits on community college credit hours: No
Maximum number of community college credit hours: None
Advanced placement (AP) credit accepted for prerequisites: Yes
Advanced placement (AP) credit accepted for electives: Yes
Job shadowing: Required
Number of hours of job shadowing required or recommended: 20
Other factors considered in admission: Nonacademic experiences are considered and include volunteer hours, research, leadership, military service, athletic participation, employment, and other noncognitive factors.

DAT

Mandatory: Yes
Latest DAT for consideration of application: NA
Oldest DAT considered: Scores good for 2 years prior to submitting application
When more than one DAT score is reported: Most recent score only is considered
Canadian DAT accepted: Yes
Application considered before DAT scores are submitted: No

DAT: 2012 ENTERING CLASS

ENROLLEE DAT SCORES	RANGE	MEAN
Academic Average	15.0-26.0	20.0
Perceptual Ability	15.0-27.0	20.6
Total Science	14.0-26.0	19.7

GPA: 2012 ENTERING CLASS

ENROLLEE GPA SCORES	RANGE	MEAN
Science GPA	2.21-4.00	3.40
Total GPA	2.92-4.00	3.65

APPLICATION AND SELECTION

TIMETABLE

Earliest filing date: 06/04/2013
Latest filing date: 09/15/2013 (in-state applicants), 09/01/2013 (out-of-state applicants)
Earliest date for acceptance offers: 12/01/2013
Maximum time in days for applicant's response to acceptance offer:
30 days if accepted between December 1 and January 1
15 days if accepted on or after January 1
Requests for deferred entrance considered: In exceptional circumstances only
Fee for application: Yes, submitted only when requested
Amount of fee for application:
In state: $60 Out of state: $60 International: $70

Fee waiver available: No
Transfer: $80

	FIRST DEPOSIT	SECOND DEPOSIT	THIRD DEPOSIT
Required to hold place	Yes	Yes	No
Resident amount	$200	$500	
Nonresident amount	$200	$500	
Deposit due	At time of acceptance	At time of acceptance	
Applied to tuition	No	Yes	
Refundable	No	No	

APPLICATION PROCESS

Participates in Associated American Dental Schools Application Service (AADSAS): Yes
Accepts direct applicants: No
Secondary or supplemental application required: Yes
Secondary or supplemental application website: Link sent to applicants via email
Interview is mandatory: Yes
Interview is by invitation: Yes

RESIDENCY

Admissions process distinguishes between in-state/in-province and out-of-state/out-of-province applicants: Yes
Preference given to residents of: Ohio
Reciprocity Admissions Agreement available for legal residents of: None
Applications are accepted from non-U.S. citizens/non-U.S. permanent residents: Yes

APPLICATION AND ENROLLMENT	NUMBER OF APPLICANTS	ESTIMATED NUMBER INTERVIEWED	ESTIMATED NUMBER ENROLLED
In-state or province applicants	235	109	88
Out-of-state or province applicants	649	71	22

Generally and over time, percentage of your first-year enrollment is in-state: 75-85%
Origin of out-of-state enrollees (U.S.): California-2, Georgia-1, Indiana-1, Iowa-2, Michigan-3, Minnesota-1, Missouri-2, New York-1, Oklahoma-1, Pennsylvania-3, South Carolina-1, Tennessee-1
Origin of international enrollees: China-1, Hong Kong-1, Korea-1

DEMOGRAPHIC DESCRIPTIONS OF APPLICANTS: 2012 ENTERING CLASS

	APPLICANTS		ENROLLEES	
	M	W	M	W
Hispanic/Latino of any race	9	16	2/1*	1
American Indian or Alaska Native	0	1	0	0
Asian	79	91	4	6
Black or African American	5	19	1*	2*
Native Hawaiian or Other Pacific Islander	0	0	0	0
White	359	214	49**	34
Two or more races	8	16	1	3
Race and ethnicity unknown	16	13	1	2
International	17	11	1	2

Notes:
* DentPath Admit: Applicant applied the year before and was admitted for this year after completion of the DentPath Program.
** Includes one deferred applicant.

	MINIMUM	MAXIMUM	MEAN
2012 entering class enrollees by age	21	37	24

Number of first-time enrollees over age 30: 9

CURRICULUM

The D.D.S. curriculum includes 11 semesters of instruction. During the first and second years, students study the basic sciences, preclinical dentistry, and early clinic courses through lecture, computer-assisted self-instruction, laboratory experience, and clinical activities. Classrooms and labs have multimedia audio-visual capabilities. Interactive learning technology (TurningPoint®) is utilized. Using written, oral, and lab examinations/skill tests, faculty members evaluate student performance in basic science and preclinical courses. Some didactic and lab courses continue into the third and fourth years. During the third and fourth years, there is a significant emphasis on clinical experiences and patient treatment. Students acquire clinical experience under faculty supervision in the college clinic and are evaluated on their daily performance. Clinical experience is self-paced and includes requirements. Programs in general practice, care for home-bound patients, and training at off-site clinics are included and required.

Student research opportunities: Yes

SPECIAL PROGRAMS AND SERVICES

PREDENTAL

DAT workshops
Postbaccalaureate programs

DURING DENTAL SCHOOL

Academic counseling and tutoring
Community service opportunities
Internships, externships, or extramural programs
Mentoring
Personal counseling
Professional- and career-development programming
Training for those interested in academic careers
Transfer applicants considered if space is available

ACTIVE STUDENT ORGANIZATIONS

Alpha Omega International Dental Fraternity
American Association of Women Dentists
American Student Dental Association
Christian Medical Dental Association
Delta Sigma Delta (international dental fraternity)
Dental Entrepreneurs Society
Hispanic Student Dental Association
Psi Omega Fraternity
Smiles for Schools
Student Government Association
Student National Dental Association
Student Research Group

INTERNATIONAL DENTISTS

Graduates of international dental schools considered for traditional predoctoral program: Yes
Advanced standing program offered for graduates of international dental schools: No

COMBINED AND ALTERNATE DEGREES

Ph.D.	M.S.	M.P.H.	M.D.	B.A./B.S.	Other
✓	✓	In progress	—	—	✓

Other Degree: D.D.S./Ph.D.

COSTS: 2012-13 SCHOOL YEAR

	FIRST YEAR 2 SEMESTERS	SECOND YEAR 3 SEMESTERS	THIRD YEAR 3 SEMESTERS	FOURTH YEAR 3 SEMESTERS
Tuition, resident	$31,448	$41,917	$41,917	$41,172
Tuition, nonresident	$66,632	$88,705	$88,705	$87,960
Tuition, other	NA	NA	NA	NA
Fees	$497	$746	$746	$746
Instruments, books, and supplies	$5,778	$7,587	$5,178	$7,342
Estimated living expenses	$15,876	$19,845	$19,845	$19,845
Total, resident	$53,102	$69,349	$66,940	$69,104
Total, nonresident	$88,286	$116,137	$113,728	$115,892
Total, other	NA	NA	NA	NA

Comments: Nonresident students are eligible to apply for residency after their first year.

FINANCIAL AID

Financial aid consists of loans (which must be repaid) and scholarships.

SCHOLARSHIPS

Through the generosity of alumni, friends, and supporters of the College of Dentistry, various scholarships are awarded to students each year. The awarding philosophy of the college is to provide aid to students who are in need and to those students who have a record of academic excellence and accomplishment. Additionally, a select number of awards are given to students based on community service and leadership. Students who are admitted to the college by February 15 and submit the Free Application for Federal Student Aid (FAFSA) form with parent information by February 15 will be considered for all College of Dentistry scholarships.

LOANS

Loan assistance is readily available to students who attend The Ohio State University. Loan programs commonly used by dental students include the federal Stafford Loan program, federal Graduate PLUS or private loans, and university loans.

FAFSA

Students interested in receiving financial aid (university loans, federal loans, and scholarships) must complete the FAFSA form online (www.fafsa.ed.gov). These applications are available after January 1 and must be completed and submitted by February 15.

MORE INFORMATION

The average 2012 graduate indebtedness was $196,000 (this number includes all students with or without debt).

UNIVERSITY OF OKLAHOMA
COLLEGE OF DENTISTRY

Dr. Stephen K. Young, Dean

CONTACT INFORMATION

www.dentistry.ouhsc.edu
Phone: 405-271-5444
Fax: 405-271-3423

OFFICE OF ADMISSIONS

Sally Davenport
Admissions Coordinator
1201 North Stonewall Avenue
Room 512
Oklahoma City, OK 73117
Phone: 405-271-3530
Email: sally-davenport@ouhsc.edu

OFFICE OF FINANCIAL AID

Pamela Jordan
Director of Student Financial Aid
Student Union, Room 301
P.O. Box 26901
Oklahoma City, OK 73126-0901
Phone: 405-271-2118
Email: financial_aid@ouhsc.edu

HSC STUDENT AFFAIRS

Kate Stanton
Executive Director, Student Affairs
Student Union, Room 300
P.O. Box 26901
Oklahoma City, OK 73126-0901
Phone: 405-271-2416
Email: kate-stanton@ouhsc.edu

MINORITY AFFAIRS/DIVERSITY

Brian Corpening
Assistant Provost for Diversity and Community
Robert M. Bird Health Science Library
Room 164
Oklahoma City, OK 73117
Phone: 405-271-2390
Email: brian-corpening@ouhsc.edu

HOUSING

Maryann Henderson
900 North Stonewall Avenue
Oklahoma City, OK 73117
Phone: 405-271-0500
Email: maryann@ou.edu

GENERAL INFORMATION

The University of Oklahoma College of Dentistry emphasizes high standards in clinical and practical preparation. Having significant opportunities for treating patients is a hallmark of the student's educational experience and promotes the formation of strong clinical skills and development of excellent practitioners. Facilities are well-appointed and students are afforded the best equipment on which to learn, including the latest in electronic patient records and digital imaging capability. A capable and experienced teaching faculty approaches its responsibilities with a high level of concern and oversees the student's professional progression through a well-designed curriculum and rigorous training program. The College of Dentistry is part of the Health Sciences Center in Oklahoma City, a 15-block campus near city center that includes several major teaching hospitals, research facilities, and Colleges of Allied Health, Medicine, Nursing, Pharmacy, and Public Health.

MISSION STATEMENT:

The mission of the University of Oklahoma College of Dentistry is to improve the health of Oklahomans and shape the future of dentistry by developing highly qualified dental practitioners and scientists through excellence in education, patient care, research, community service, and facilities.

Type of institution: Public
Year opened: 1972
Term type: Semester
Time to degree in months: 48
Start month: June

Doctoral dental degree offered: D.D.S.
Total predoctoral enrollment: 232
Estimated entering class size: 56
Campus setting: Urban
Campus housing available: Yes

PREPARATION

Formal minimum preparation in semester/quarter hours: Semester: 90 Quarter: 135
Baccalaureate degree preferred: Yes
Number of first-year, first-time enrollees whose highest degree is:
- Baccalaureate: 46
- Master's: 6
- Ph.D. or other doctorate: 2

Of first-year, first-time enrollees without baccalaureates, the number with:
- Equivalent of 60 undergraduate credit hours or less: 0
- Equivalent of 61-90 undergraduate credit hours: 0
- Equivalent of 91 or more undergraduate credit hours: 2

PREREQUISITE COURSE	REQUIRED	RECOMMENDED	LAB REQUIRED	CREDITS (SEMESTER/QUARTER)
BCP (biology-chemistry-physics) sciences				
Biology	✓		✓	16/24
Chemistry, general/inorganic	✓		✓	8/12
Chemistry, organic	✓		✓	8/12
Physics	✓		✓	8/12
Additional biological sciences				
Anatomy		✓		
Biochemistry	✓			3/5
Cell biology		✓		
Histology				
Immunology				
Microbiology		✓		
Molecular biology/genetics		✓		

(Prerequisite Courses continued)

PREPARATION (CONTINUED)

PREREQUISITE COURSE	REQUIRED	RECOMMENDED	LAB REQUIRED	CREDITS (SEMESTER/QUARTER)
Physiology		✓		
Zoology		✓		

Community college coursework accepted for prerequisites: Yes
Community college coursework accepted for electives: Yes
Limits on community college credit hours: No
Maximum number of community college credit hours: No maximum number.
Advanced placement (AP) credit accepted for prerequisites: Yes
Advanced placement (AP) credit accepted for electives: Yes
Comments regarding AP credit: We will accept AP credit for prerequisites in English and psychology. Prerequisites in science may also be met by AP, but often students will take additional upper-division science coursework.
Job shadowing: Required
Number of hours of job shadowing required or recommended: 100
Other factors considered in admission: Strength of schedule, term course load, GPA for last 60 credits, and record of course withdrawals

DAT

Mandatory: Yes
Latest DAT for consideration of application: 11/01/2013
Oldest DAT considered: 05/2008
When more than one DAT score is reported: Highest score is considered
Canadian DAT accepted: Yes
Application considered before DAT scores are submitted: No

DAT: 2012 ENTERING CLASS

ENROLLEE DAT SCORES	RANGE	MEAN
Academic Average	17-26	20.2
Perceptual Ability	15-24	20.1
Total Science	16-26	19.9

GPA: 2012 ENTERING CLASS

ENROLLEE GPA SCORES	RANGE	MEAN
Science GPA	2.58-4.00	3.58
Total GPA	2.48-4.00	3.61

APPLICATION AND SELECTION

TIMETABLE

Earliest filing date: 06/01/2013
Latest filing date: 10/01/2013
Earliest date for acceptance offers: 12/01/2013
Maximum time in days for applicant's response to acceptance offer:
30 days if accepted on or after December 1
15 days if accepted on or after February 1
Requests for deferred entrance considered: In exceptional circumstances only
Fee for application: Yes, Associated American Dental Schools Application Service (AADSAS) application fee and Supplemental application fee.
Amount of fee for application:
In state: $79 Out of state: $79 International: $79
Fee waiver available: No

	FIRST DEPOSIT	SECOND DEPOSIT	THIRD DEPOSIT
Required to hold place	Yes	No	No
Resident amount	$800		
Nonresident amount	$800		
Deposit due	As indicated in admission offer		
Applied to tuition	Yes		
Refundable	No		

APPLICATION PROCESS

Participates in AADSAS: Yes
Accepts direct applicants: No
Secondary or supplemental application required: Yes, $79 application fee
Secondary or supplemental application website: https://app.applyyourself.com/?id=uok-dent
Interview is mandatory: Yes
Interview is by invitation: Yes

RESIDENCY

Admissions process distinguishes between in-state/in-province and out-of-state/out-of-province applicants: Yes
Preference given to residents of: Oklahoma
Reciprocity Admissions Agreement available for legal residents of: None
Applications are accepted from non-U.S. citizens/non-U.S. permanent residents: Yes

APPLICATION AND ENROLLMENT	NUMBER OF APPLICANTS	ESTIMATED NUMBER INTERVIEWED	ESTIMATED NUMBER ENROLLED
In-state or province applicants	146	107	45
Out-of-state or province applicants	545	84	11

Generally and over time, percentage of your first-year enrollment is in-state: 25%
Origin of out-of-state enrollees (U.S.): AR-1, GA-1, MN-1, TX-2, UT-4, VA-1, WA-1
Origin of international enrollees: 0

DEMOGRAPHIC DESCRIPTIONS OF APPLICANTS: 2012 ENTERING CLASS

	APPLICANTS		ENROLLEES	
	M	W	M	W
Hispanic/Latino of any race	22	24	0	0
American Indian or Alaska Native	4	4	1	1
Asian	72	78	3	5
Black or African American	2	9	0	1
Native Hawaiian or Other Pacific Islander	0	0	0	0
White	247	144	31	13
Two or more races	32	24	1	0
Race and ethnicity unknown	5	4	0	0
International	6	9	0	0

	MINIMUM	MAXIMUM	MEAN
2012 entering class enrollees by age	20	41	25

Number of first-time enrollees over age 30: 7

CURRICULUM

The curriculum integrates theoretical knowledge, applied technique training, and clinical experience. The early curriculum focuses on developing a solid foundation in the biomedical sciences and commences preparation in the clinical sciences with introduction to the various disciplines in dentistry. As the student rises through the curriculum, the instruction shifts more and more to hands-on, preclinical exercises, in which students learn how to perform procedures in a laboratory or simulated patient environment. By the third year, the student is schooled in more sophisticated aspects of dental care and spends substantially more time treating patients under the supervision of a licensed dentist. In the fourth year, the emphasis is on comprehensive management and treatment of patients. While the student gradually acquires more expertise and assumes a growing responsibility for delivery of patient care as he/she advances through training, it should be noted that the opportunity to interact with patients and provide appropriate limited care is presented within the first year. This is a hallmark of the educational experience at the University of Oklahoma College of Dentistry and is consistent with our reputation for providing an excellent clinical education with a strong patient contact component. The curriculum utilizes both competency assessments and overall clinical requirements to ensure the attainment of appropriate skill levels and a sufficient number of practice opportunities needed to develop clinical proficiency. Knowledge and development are addressed in other key areas necessary to prepare graduates for their roles as responsible health care professionals, including direct experiences in service outreach, research and scholarly activity, and courses designed in practice management.

Student research opportunities: Yes

SPECIAL PROGRAMS AND SERVICES

PREDENTAL

Summer enrichment programs

DURING DENTAL SCHOOL

Academic counseling and tutoring
Community service opportunities
Internships, externships, or extramural programs
Mentoring
Personal counseling
Professional- and career-development programming
Training for those interested in academic careers

ACTIVE STUDENT ORGANIZATIONS

Albert Staples Society
American Association of Dental Research Student Research Group
American Association of Women Dentists
American Student Dental Association
Christian Medical Dental Association
Good Shepherd Mission
Rural Interest Group
Student Professional & Ethics Association

INTERNATIONAL DENTISTS

Graduates of international dental schools considered for traditional predoctoral program: Yes
Advanced standing program offered for graduates of international dental schools: Yes

COMBINED AND ALTERNATE DEGREES

Ph.D.	M.S.	M.P.H.	M.D.	B.A./B.S.	Other
—	—	—	—	—	—

COSTS: 2012-13 SCHOOL YEAR

	FIRST YEAR	SECOND YEAR	THIRD YEAR	FOURTH YEAR
Tuition, resident	$19,147	$19,147	$19,147	$19,147
Tuition, nonresident	$45,448	$45,448	$45,448	$45,448
Tuition, other	NA	NA	NA	NA
Fees	$5,973	$6,147	$5,815	$5,627
Instruments, books, and supplies	$14,096	$12,953	$1,916	$2,833
Estimated living expenses	$27,900	$27,900	$27,900	$27,900
Total, resident	$67,116	$66,147	$54,778	$55,507
Total, nonresident	$93,417	$92,448	$81,079	$81,808
Total, other	NA	NA	NA	NA

Comments: Costs are subject to change without notice. Figures (except tuition) represent an approximate breakdown of education expenses.

FINANCIAL AID

In the 2012 entering class, there were 12 recipients of scholarships and grants. Award amounts were between $800 and $8,450. There were 55 recipients of student loans. Loan amounts were between $315 and $90,000. The average loan amount for nonresidents was $59,452 and $40,945 for residents.

The average 2012 graduate indebtedness was $158,265.

OREGON HEALTH & SCIENCE UNIVERSITY
SCHOOL OF DENTISTRY

Dr. Gary T. Chiodo, Interim Dean

CONTACT INFORMATION

www.ohsu.edu/sod
611 SW Campus Drive
Room 610
Portland, OR 97239-3097
Phone: 503-494-8801
Fax: 503-494-8351

OFFICE OF ADMISSIONS AND STUDENT AFFAIRS
611 SW Campus Drive
Room 601
Portland, OR 97239-3097
Phone: 503-494-5274
www.ohsu.edu/sod

FINANCIAL AID OFFICE
3181 SW Sam Jackson Park Road, L109
Portland, OR 97239-3098
Phone: 503-494-7800
www.ohsu.edu/finaid

GENERAL INFORMATION

Located in Portland, a city of 583,776 residents in a greater metropolitan area of approximately 2.3 million, the Oregon Health & Science University (OHSU) School of Dentistry is a nonprofit public corporation with a public mission. The School of Dentistry is located in the wooded hills of southwest Portland on a 116-acre campus. Paths for joggers, bicyclists, and pedestrians connect the university with the heart of the city just two miles away. The dental school was established in 1898. The objectives of the dental program are to impart the scientific knowledge and clinical skills needed in the practice of dentistry, to instill standards of professional conduct as a way of life, and to promote a dedication to continuous, lifelong professional study and self-improvement.

MISSION STATEMENT:

The School of Dentistry shares the mission of the Oregon Health & Science University to provide educational programs, basic and clinical research, and high-quality care and community programs. We strive to foster an environment of mutual respect where the free exchange of ideas can flourish. The dental school prepares graduates in general dentistry and the dental specialties to deliver compassionate and ethical orofacial health care.

Type of institution: Public
Year opened: 1898
Term type: Quarter
Time to degree in months: 47
Start month: August

Doctoral dental degree offered: D.M.D.
Total predoctoral enrollment: 300
Estimated entering class size: 75
Campus setting: Urban
Campus housing available: No

PREPARATION

Formal minimum preparation in semester/quarter hours: Semester: 90 Quarter: 135 (completed at the time of application). Coursework must be completed at an accredited U.S. or Canadian college or university. Other than Canadian, no international coursework is accepted.
Baccalaureate degree preferred: Yes
Number of first-year, first-time enrollees whose highest degree is:
- Baccalaureate: 75
- Master's: 0
- Ph.D. or other doctorate: 0

Of first-year, first-time enrollees without baccalaureates, the number with:
- Equivalent of 60 undergraduate credit hours or less: 0
- Equivalent of 61-90 undergraduate credit hours: 0
- Equivalent of 91 or more undergraduate credit hours: 0

PREREQUISITE COURSE	REQUIRED	RECOMMENDED	LAB REQUIRED	CREDITS (SEMESTER/QUARTER)
BCP (biology-chemistry-physics) sciences				
Biology	✓		✓	8/12
Chemistry, general/inorganic	✓		✓	8/12
Chemistry, organic	✓		✓	8/12
Physics	✓		✓	8/12
Additional biological sciences				
Anatomy	✓		✓	4/6
Biochemistry	✓			4/6
Cell biology		✓		4/6
Histology		✓		4/6
Immunology		✓		4/6
Microbiology		✓		4/6

(Prerequisite Courses continued)

PREPARATION (CONTINUED)

PREREQUISITE COURSE	REQUIRED	RECOMMENDED	LAB REQUIRED	CREDITS (SEMESTER/QUARTER)
Molecular biology/genetics		✓		4/6
Physiology	✓		✓	4/6
Zoology		✓		4/6
Other				
English composition	✓			8/12

Community college coursework accepted for prerequisites: Yes
Community college coursework accepted for electives: Yes
Limits on community college credit hours: Yes
Maximum number of community college credit hours: 32 preferred
Advanced placement (AP) credit accepted for prerequisites: Yes
Advanced placement (AP) credit accepted for electives: Yes
Comments regarding AP credit: AP/International Baccalaureate (IB) credit is only accepted if academic credit for specific courses is recorded on an official transcript.
Job shadowing: Required
Number of hours of job shadowing required or recommended: A required minimum of 50 documented hours completed prior to application is required in a clinical setting of which 25 hours must occur in one or more general practices..
Other factors considered in admission: Community service, work experience, research experience, extracurricular activities, and demonstrated passion for dentistry.

DAT

Mandatory: Yes. No less than 15 in all scored areas will be considered.
Latest DAT for consideration of application: 11/01/2013
Oldest DAT considered: 01/01/2010
When more than one DAT score is reported: Most recent score only is considered
Canadian DAT accepted: No
Application considered before DAT scores are submitted: No

DAT: 2012 ENTERING CLASS

ENROLLEE DAT SCORES	RANGE	MEAN
Academic Average	17–23	19.1
Perceptual Ability	15–28	20.1
Total Science	15–23	19.0

GPA: 2012 ENTERING CLASS

ENROLLEE GPA SCORES	RANGE	MEAN
Science GPA	2.67–4.00	3.59
Total GPA	2.98–4.00	3.65

APPLICATION AND SELECTION

TIMETABLE

Earliest filing date: 06/01/2013
Latest filing date: 11/01/2013
Earliest date for acceptance offers: 12/01/2013
Maximum time in days for applicant's response to acceptance offer:
30 days if accepted on or after December 1
15 days if accepted on or after February 1
5 days if accepted on or after May 15
Requests for deferred entrance considered: No
Fee for application: Yes, submitted at same time as Associated American Dental Schools Application Service (AADSAS) application

Amount of fee for application:
In state: $75 Out of state: $75 International: $75
Fee waiver available: Check school website for details.

	FIRST DEPOSIT	SECOND DEPOSIT	THIRD DEPOSIT
Required to hold place	Yes	No	No
Resident amount	$1,000		
Nonresident amount	$1,000		
Deposit due	As indicated in admission offer		
Applied to tuition	Yes		
Refundable	No		

APPLICATION PROCESS

Participates in AADSAS: Yes
Accepts direct applicants: No
Secondary or supplemental application required: Yes, only for those applicants invited to interview
Interview is mandatory: Yes
Interview is by invitation: Yes

RESIDENCY

Admissions process distinguishes between in-state/in-province and out-of-state/out-of-province applicants: Yes
Preference given to residents of: Oregon
Reciprocity Admissions Agreement available for legal residents of: Alaska, Arizona, Hawaii, Montana, New Mexico, North Dakota, Wyoming
Applications are accepted from non-U.S. citizens/non-U.S. permanent residents: Yes

APPLICATION AND ENROLLMENT	NUMBER OF APPLICANTS	ESTIMATED NUMBER INTERVIEWED	ESTIMATED NUMBER ENROLLED
In-state or province applicants	105	49	40
Out-of-state or province applicants	1,079	74	70

Generally and over time, percentage of your first-year enrollment is in-state: 55%

Origin of out-of-state enrollees (U.S.): Arizona-4, California-4, Hawaii-2, Idaho-3, Indiana-1, Louisiana-1, Montana-4, North Dakota-1, Pennsylvania-1, Utah-5, Virginia-1, Washington-6, Wyoming-1

Origin of international enrollees: Canada-2, Sweden-1

DEMOGRAPHIC DESCRIPTIONS OF APPLICANTS: 2012 ENTERING CLASS

	APPLICANTS		ENROLLEES	
	M	W	M	W
Hispanic/Latino of any race	31	32	1	2
American Indian or Alaska Native	1	3	0	0
Asian	144	151	10	8
Black or African American	7	6	0	0
Native Hawaiian or Other Pacific Islander	0	1	0	0
White	442	222	29	17
Two or more races	27	23	4	1
Race and ethnicity unknown	17	12	0	0
International	34	21	1	2

Notes: Ten applicants did not report gender of which one also did not report ethnicity.

	MINIMUM	MAXIMUM	MEAN
2012 entering class enrollees by age	21	30	24

Number of first-time enrollees over age 30: 2

CURRICULUM

The four-year predoctoral dental curriculum leads to the award of the doctor of dental medicine (D.M.D.) degree. The objectives of this curriculum are education of competent general practitioners of dentistry and preparation for lifelong learning and advanced training. The first year begins with an integrated approach in teaching the basic sciences. Students are introduced to the fundamentals of oral radiology, dental materials, prosthodontics, operative dentistry, periodontology, and prevention of dental disease. The second year emphasizes development of the skills needed for dental techniques. This development includes didactic and laboratory courses in facial growth, fixed and removable prosthodontics, operative dentistry, oral surgery, periodontology, and endodontology. Emphasis during the third and fourth years is on clinical practice, supported by lecture and seminar sessions dealing with diagnosis of oral disease, application of dental materials, treatment planning, and clinical treatment procedures. Also, opportunities exist for dental students to participate in supervised programs that afford educational experiences off campus. Health care is more than a collection of knowledge and skills; dental professionals need certain personal qualities to meet the needs of their patients and the standards of their peers. The school fosters each student's commitment to support high ethical and moral values, a liking for people and for unselfish service, an understanding of human relations, the ability to communicate, and a broad understanding of the community's and nation's health goals.

Student research opportunities: Yes

SPECIAL PROGRAMS AND SERVICES

PREDENTAL

The School of Dentistry offers two enrichment programs for students interested in a dental career. Both programs are offered during the academic year. Dental Explorers is a seven-month program for those currently enrolled in high school or college. Students may also register for a one-quarter course—referred to as Aspects of Dentistry (CHEM 199)— through Portland State University. Both programs are administered by the School of Dentistry and have lecture and laboratory components with an emphasis on providing the students with a "hands-on" experience.

DURING DENTAL SCHOOL

Academic counseling and tutoring
Community service opportunities
Internships, externships, or extramural programs
Mentoring
Personal counseling

ACTIVE STUDENT ORGANIZATIONS

Academy of LDS Dentists
American Dental Education Association (ADEA)
American Student Dental Association
Christian Medical and Dental Association
Cycling Interest Group
Delta Sigma Delta Dental Fraternity
Dental Student Government
Dental Student Research Group
Global Health Center Student Interest Group
Hispanic Dental Association
OHSU Pride
OHSU Student Council (All Hill Council)
Omicron Kappa Upsilon Honor Society
Queers & Allies in Healthcare
Student Professionalism and Ethics Club
Xi Psi Phi Dental Fraternity

INTERNATIONAL DENTISTS

Graduates of international dental schools considered for traditional predoctoral program: No

Advanced standing program offered for graduates of international dental schools: No

COMBINED AND ALTERNATE DEGREES

Ph.D.	M.S.	M.P.H.	M.D.	B.A./B.S.	Other
—	—	—	—	—	—

COSTS: 2012-13 SCHOOL YEAR

	FIRST YEAR	SECOND YEAR	THIRD YEAR	FOURTH YEAR
Tuition, resident	$36,258	$37,812	$37,402	$36,379
Tuition, nonresident	$58,702	$61,255	$60,916	$60,247
Tuition, other	NA	NA	NA	NA
Fees	$6,192	$6,430	$6,430	$6,480
Instruments, books, and supplies	$16,428	$9,254	$4,860	$2,897
Estimated living expenses	$18,524	$18,524	$18,524	$18,524
Total, resident	$77,402	$72,020	$67,216	$64,280
Total, nonresident	$99,846	$95,463	$90,730	$88,148
Total, other	NA	NA	NA	NA

Comments: During the 2011-2012 academic year, 84% of all enrolled OHSU dental students received financial aid totaling $19.2 million

FINANCIAL AID

There were 68 student loan recipients in the 2012 entering class. Loan amounts were between $20,000 and $102,961. The average loan amount came to $73,358 for resident, and to $90,526 for nonresidents. This year, each student who was awarded financial aid received it in the form of a scholarship or a grant.

THE MAURICE H. KORNBERG SCHOOL OF DENTISTRY, TEMPLE UNIVERSITY

Dr. Amid I. Ismail, Dean

GENERAL INFORMATION

The Maurice H. Kornberg School of Dentistry at Temple University is the second oldest dental school in continuous existence. As a major urban institution in the heart of a federally designated health professional shortage area, the dental school has a diverse patient population from a variety of socioeconomic and cultural backgrounds. The large size and diversity of this patient pool contribute immeasurably to a student's dental education. The student body is among the most diverse in the country. Most states and several countries are represented by Temple students. The relaxed and friendly team-oriented atmosphere generates strong relationships among students, staff, and faculty.

MISSION STATEMENT:

The Maurice H. Kornberg School of Dentistry promotes oral health through the education of diverse general and specialty dentists with advanced skills who provide comprehensive, patient-centered, evidence-based care and engage in research, scholarly activities, and community service.

VISION:

The Maurice H. Kornberg School of Dentistry is a center for excellence in clinical dental education, patient care, research, and community-based service.

Type of institution: Private and state-related
Year opened: 1863
Term type: Semester
Time to degree in months: 48
Start month: August

Doctoral dental degree offered: D.M.D.
Total predoctoral enrollment: 535
Estimated entering class size: 128
Campus setting: Urban
Campus housing available: No

PREPARATION

Formal minimum preparation in semester/quarter hours: Semester: 90 Quarter: 120
Baccalaureate degree preferred: Yes
Number of first-year, first-time enrollees whose highest degree is:
- Baccalaureate: 109
- Master's: 12
- Ph.D. or other doctorate: 1

Of first-year, first-time enrollees without baccalaureates, the number with:
- Equivalent of 60 undergraduate credit hours or less: 0
- Equivalent of 61-90 undergraduate credit hours: 0
- Equivalent of 91 or more undergraduate credit hours: 6

PREREQUISITE COURSE	REQUIRED	RECOMMENDED	LAB REQUIRED	CREDITS (SEMESTER/QUARTER)
BCP (biology-chemistry-physics) sciences				
Biology	✓		✓	8/12
Chemistry, general/inorganic	✓		✓	8/12
Chemistry, organic	✓		✓	8/12
Physics	✓		✓	8/12
Additional biological sciences				
Anatomy		✓		4/6
Biochemistry		✓		4/6
Cell biology		✓		4/6
Histology		✓		4/6
Immunology		✓		4/6
Microbiology		✓		4/6

(Prerequisite Courses continued)

CONTACT INFORMATION

www.temple.edu/dentistry
3223 North Broad Street
Philadelphia, PA 19140

ADMISSIONS

Dr. Lisa P. Deem
Associate Dean for Admissions, Diversity and Student Services
3223 North Broad Street
Philadelphia, PA 19140
Phone: 215-707-2801
www.temple.edu/dentistry

STUDENT FINANCIAL SERVICES

Thomas Maiorano
Assistant Director
3340 North Broad Street
Philadelphia, PA 19140
Phone: 215-707-2667
Email: thomas.maiorano@temple.edu

RECRUITMENT

Brian Hahn
Recruitment Coordinator
3223 North Broad Street
Philadelphia, PA 19140
Phone: 215-707-7663
Email: brian.hahn@temple.edu

HOUSING & FINANCIAL AID SUPPORT SERVICES

C. Terry Griffin
Student Services Coordinator
3223 North Broad Street
Philadelphia, PA 19140
Phone: 215-707-2952
Email: terry.griffin@temple.edu

INTERNATIONAL STUDENTS

C. Terry Griffin
Student Services Coordinator
3223 North Broad Street
Philadelphia, PA 19140
Phone: 215-707-2952
Email: terry.griffin@temple.edu

PREPARATION (CONTINUED)

PREREQUISITE COURSE	REQUIRED	RECOMMENDED	LAB REQUIRED	CREDITS (SEMESTER/QUARTER)
Molecular biology/genetics		✓		4/6
Physiology		✓		4/6
Zoology		✓		4/6

Community college coursework accepted for prerequisites: No
Community college coursework accepted for electives: Yes
Limits on community college credit hours: Yes
Maximum number of community college credit hours: 6
Advanced placement (AP) credit accepted for prerequisites: No
Advanced placement (AP) credit accepted for electives: Yes
Job shadowing: Recommended
Number of hours of job shadowing required or recommended: The applicant should demonstrate substantial exposure to the dental profession.
Other factors considered in admission: Number of schools attended and credit hours per semester

DAT

Mandatory: Yes
Latest DAT for consideration of application: 01/15/2014
Oldest DAT considered: 06/01/2011
When more than one DAT score is reported: Highest academic average scores are considered
Canadian DAT accepted: Yes
Application considered before DAT scores are submitted: No

DAT: 2012 ENTERING CLASS

ENROLLEE DAT SCORES	RANGE	MEAN
Academic Average	17.0-24.0	19.7
Perceptual Ability	16.0-27.0	20.0
Total Science	16.0-24.0	19.6

GPA: 2012 ENTERING CLASS

ENROLLEE GPA SCORES	RANGE	MEAN
Science GPA	2.81-4.00	3.41
Total GPA	2.99-3.96	3.51

APPLICATION AND SELECTION

TIMETABLE

Earliest filing date: 06/01/2013
Latest filing date: 01/15/2014
Earliest date for acceptance offers: 12/01/2013
Maximum time in days for applicant's response to acceptance offer:
30 days if accepted on or after December 1
15 days if accepted on or after February 1
Requests for deferred entrance considered: No
Fee for application: Yes, submitted only when requested
Amount of fee for application:
In state: $50 Out of state: $50 International: $50
Fee waiver available: No

	FIRST DEPOSIT	SECOND DEPOSIT	THIRD DEPOSIT
Required to hold place	Yes	Yes	No
Resident amount	$1,000	$500	
Nonresident amount	$1,000	$500	
Deposit due	As indicated in admission offer		
Applied to tuition	Yes	Yes	
Refundable	No	No	

APPLICATION PROCESS

Participates in Associated American Dental Schools Application Service (AADSAS): Yes
Accepts direct applicants: No
Secondary or supplemental application required: Yes
Secondary or supplemental application website: No
Interview is mandatory: Yes
Interview is by invitation: Yes

RESIDENCY

Admissions process distinguishes between in-state/in-province and out-of-state/out-of-province applicants: Yes
Preference given to residents of: Delaware, Pennsylvania
Reciprocity Admissions Agreement available for legal residents of: None
Applications are accepted from non-U.S. citizens/non-U.S. permanent residents: Yes

APPLICATION AND ENROLLMENT	NUMBER OF APPLICANTS	ESTIMATED NUMBER INTERVIEWED	ESTIMATED NUMBER ENROLLED
In-state or province applicants	329	136	58
Out-of-state or province applicants	3,722	345	70

Generally and over time, percentage of your first-year enrollment is in-state: 50%
Origin of out-of-state enrollees (U.S.): Alabama-1, Arizona-2, California-4, Delaware-3, Florida-8, Georgia-2, Hawaii-1, Illinois-1, Maryland-3, New Jersey-13, New York-11, North Carolina-1, Ohio-1, South Dakota-1, Texas-3, Utah-3, Virginia-6, Wisconsin-3
Origin of international enrollees: Canada-1 (British Columbia), Colombia-1, South Korea-1

DEMOGRAPHIC DESCRIPTIONS OF APPLICANTS: 2012 ENTERING CLASS

	APPLICANTS		ENROLLEES	
	M	W	M	W
Hispanic/Latino of any race	120	126	8	6
American Indian or Alaska Native	0	3	0	0
Asian	692	701	14	14
Black or African American	54	114	5	0
Native Hawaiian or Other Pacific Islander	0	1	0	0
White	1,029	658	43	30
Two or more races	54	60	0	2
Race and ethnicity unknown	78	58	2	1
International	170	133	1	2

	MINIMUM	MAXIMUM	MEAN
2012 entering class enrollees by age	21	30	24

Number of first-time enrollees over age 30: 0

CURRICULUM

The primary emphasis of the predoctoral program is to prepare graduates for the general practice of dentistry. The curriculum provides students with significant experience in all phases of dental practice and instills the basic science and patient management skills they will rely on as dental practitioners. The curriculum also lays a solid foundation for careers in the specialties of dentistry, dental education, and research.

Student research opportunities: Yes

SPECIAL PROGRAMS AND SERVICES

PREDENTAL

Special affiliations with colleges and universities: Alvernia College, Cabrini College, Caldwell University, Coppin State University, Edinboro University of Pennsylvania, Elizabethtown College, Indiana University of Pennsylvania, Juniata College, King's College, Mansfield University, Moravian College, Philadelphia University, Rowan University, Saint Francis College, Shippensburg University, Susquehanna University, Temple University, University of Pittsburgh at Titusville, West Chester University, Widener University, Wilkes University, William Paterson University

DURING DENTAL SCHOOL

Academic counseling and tutoring
Internships, externships, or extramural programs
Transfer applicants considered if space is available

ACTIVE STUDENT ORGANIZATIONS

American Association of Women Dentists
American Student Dental Association
Hispanic Dental Association
Student National Dental Association

INTERNATIONAL DENTISTS

Graduates of international dental schools considered for traditional predoctoral program: Yes
Advanced standing program offered for graduates of international dental schools: Yes
Advanced standing program description: Program awarding a dental degree.

COMBINED AND ALTERNATE DEGREES

Ph.D.	M.S.	M.P.H.	M.D.	B.A./B.S.	Other
—	✓	✓	—	✓	✓

Other Degree: D.M.D./M.B.A., M.S. in Oral Biology

COSTS: 2012-13 SCHOOL YEAR

	FIRST YEAR	SECOND YEAR	THIRD YEAR	FOURTH YEAR
Tuition, resident	$44,286	$44,286	$44,286	$44,286
Tuition, nonresident	$54,228	$54,228	$54,228	$54,228
Tuition, other	NA	NA	NA	NA
Fees	$590	$590	$590	$590
Instruments, books, and supplies	$9,312	$7,628	$1,800	$1,300
Estimated living expenses	$13,180	$15,816	$15,816	$11,862
Other, Resident	$8,610	$10,677	$10,332	$8,140
Other, Non Resident	$9,320	$11,529	$11,184	$8,778
Total Resident	$75,978	$78,997	$72,824	$66,178
Total Non-Resident	$86,630	$89,791	$83,618	$76,758

FINANCIAL AID

Students who wish to be considered for any type of federal financial aid must complete the Free Application for Federal Student Aid (FAFSA) by March 1 of the award year for priority consideration. There are a limited number of scholarships and loans for students from disadvantaged backgrounds and students with extremely high need. In order to be considered for such scholarships and loans, students must provide complete parental information on the FAFSA form and provide complete copies of their and their parents' IRS tax return for the 2013 filing year (including W-2s). More information on the types of financial aid available can be found at www.temple.edu/sfs. The average 2012 graduate indebtedness was $219,073.

UNIVERSITY OF PENNSYLVANIA
SCHOOL OF DENTAL MEDICINE

Dr. Denis F. Kinane, Morton Amsterdam Dean

GENERAL INFORMATION

With a history deeply rooted in forging precedents in dental education, research, and clinical care, the University of Pennsylvania School of Dental Medicine (Penn Dental Medicine) is continuously evaluating and adapting its programs to remain at the forefront of dental medicine, preparing its graduates to do the same. Established in 1898, the School is among the oldest University-affiliated dental institutions in the country, attracting students from throughout the country and around the world. Annually, the School awards D.M.D. degrees to approximately 150 students. In addition to the four-year D.M.D. program, the School offers a two-year D.M.D program for internationally trained dentists; postgraduate programs in the clinical specialties of endodontics, oral medicine, oral and maxillofacial radiology, oral and maxillofacial surgery, orthodontics, pediatric dentistry, periodontics, periodontics/orthodontics, and periodontics prosthesis; a Master of Science in Oral Biology; and a Doctor of Science in Dentistry.

The close association with the other graduate and professional schools within the University of Pennsylvania facilitates interdisciplinary study and research. Penn Dental Medicine views scholarship as a central component of excellence in instruction and patient care and places a high priority on research. With its own basic science faculty (unusual among dental schools nationwide), the school's research enterprise is multidisciplinary, spanning both the basic and clinical sciences and offering many opportunities for student research. Because Penn Dental Medicine is a leading provider of dental care for the Philadelphia community, students are exposed to a large and diverse patient population and a depth of clinical experiences.

MISSION STATEMENT:

The mission of Penn Dental Medicine Is to educate predoctoral and graduate dental students in the highest quality clinical and research environment..

Type of institution: Private
Year opened: 1878
Term type: Semester
Time to degree in months: 45
Start month: August

Doctoral dental degree offered: D.M.D.
Total predoctoral enrollment: 523
Estimated entering class size: 120
Campus setting: Urban
Campus housing available: Yes

PREPARATION

Formal minimum preparation in semester/quarter hours: Semester: NR Quarter: NR
Baccalaureate degree preferred: Yes
Number of first-year, first-time enrollees whose highest degree is:
- Baccalaureate: 105
- Master's: 14
- Ph.D. or other doctorate: 0

Of first-year, first-time enrollees without baccalaureates, the number with:
- Equivalent of 60 undergraduate credit hours or less: 0
- Equivalent of 61-90 undergraduate credit hours: 2
- Equivalent of 91 or more undergraduate credit hours: 0

PREREQUISITE COURSE	REQUIRED	RECOMMENDED	LAB REQUIRED	CREDITS (SEMESTER/QUARTER)
BCP (biology-chemistry-physics) sciences				
Biology	✓		✓	8/12
Chemistry, general/inorganic	✓		✓	8/12
Chemistry, organic	✓		✓	8/12
Physics	✓		✓	8/12
Additional biological sciences				
Anatomy		✓		

(Prerequisite Courses continued)

CONTACT INFORMATION

www.dental.upenn.edu
University of Pennsylvania School of Dental Medicine
The Robert Schattner Center
240 South 40th Street
Philadelphia, PA 19104-6030

OFFICE OF ADMISSIONS
Dr. Olivia Sheridan
Assistant Dean for Admissions
The Robert Schattner Center
240 South 40th Street
Room 122
Philadelphia, PA 19104-6030
Phone: 215-898-8943
www.dental.upenn.edu

OFFICE OF ADMISSIONS
Corky Cacas
Director of Admissions
The Robert Schattner Center
240 South 40th Street
Room 122
Philadelphia, PA 19104-6030
Phone: 215-898-8943
www.dental.upenn.edu

FINANCIAL AID & OFFICE OF STUDENT AFFAIRS
Susan Schwartz
Assistant Dean for Student Affairs
The Robert Schattner Center
240 South 40th Street
Philadelphia, PA 19104-6030
Phone: 215-898-4550
www.dental.upenn.edu

MINORITY AFFAIRS/DIVERSITY
Dr. Beverley Crawford
Director of Diversity
The Robert Schattner Center
240 South 40th Street
Philadelphia, PA 19104-6030
Phone: 215-898-2840
Email: beverlyc@dental.upenn.edu

PREPARATION (CONTINUED)

PREREQUISITE COURSE	REQUIRED	RECOMMENDED	LAB REQUIRED	CREDITS (SEMESTER/QUARTER)
Biochemistry	✓			4/6
Cell biology		✓		
Histology		✓		
Immunology		✓		
Microbiology		✓		
Molecular biology/genetics		✓		
Physiology		✓		
Zoology		✓		
Other				
Math	✓			4/6
English or writing intensive course	✓			8/12

Community college coursework accepted for prerequisites: Yes
Community college coursework accepted for electives: Yes
Limits on community college credit hours: Yes
Maximum number of community college credit hours: 60
Advanced placement (AP) credit accepted for prerequisites: Yes
Advanced placement (AP) credit accepted for electives: Yes
Comments regarding AP credit: AP credit is allowed as long as it appears on the official college transcript from the applicant's undergraduate institution.
Job shadowing: Required
Other factors considered in admission: Yes

DAT

DAT Mandatory: Yes
Latest DAT for consideration of application: 12/01/2013
Oldest DAT considered: 01/01/2010
When more than one DAT score is reported: Highest score is considered.
Canadian DAT accepted: Yes
Application considered before DAT scores are submitted: Yes

DAT: 2012 ENTERING CLASS

ENROLLEE DAT SCORES	RANGE	MEAN
Academic Average	18-26	21
Perceptual Ability	16-28	21
Total Science	17-29	21

GPA: 2012 ENTERING CLASS

ENROLLEE GPA SCORES	RANGE	MEAN
Science GPA	2.88-4.16	3.57
Total GPA	2.93-4.08	3.62

APPLICATION AND SELECTION

TIMETABLE

Earliest filing date: 06/01/2013
Latest filing date: 12/01/2013
Earliest date for acceptance offers: 12/01/2013
Maximum time in days for applicant's response to acceptance offer:
40 days if accepted on or after December 1
15 days if accepted on or after February 1

Requests for deferred entrance considered: No
Fee for application: Yes, submitted at same time as Associated American Dental Schools Application Service (AADSAS) application
Amount of fee for application:
In state: $60 Out of state: $60 International: $60
Fee waiver available: No

	FIRST DEPOSIT	SECOND DEPOSIT	THIRD DEPOSIT
Required to hold place	Yes	Yes	No
Resident amount	$500	$500	
Nonresident amount	$500	$500	
Deposit due	As indicated in admission offer	As indicated in admission offer	
Applied to tuition	Yes	Yes	
Refundable	No	No	

APPLICATION PROCESS

Participates in AADSAS: Yes
Accepts direct applicants: No
Secondary or supplemental application required: Yes.
All applicants must complete supplemental application, available on website: www.dental.upenn.edu
Interview is mandatory: Yes
Interview is by invitation: Yes

RESIDENCY

Admissions process distinguishes between in-state/in-province and out-of-state/out-of-province applicants: No
Applications are accepted from non-U.S. citizens/non-U.S. permanent residents: Yes

APPLICATION AND ENROLLMENT	NUMBER OF APPLICANTS	ESTIMATED NUMBER INTERVIEWED	ESTIMATED NUMBER ENROLLED
In-state or province applicants	169	33	15
Out-of-state or province applicants	2,247	291	104

Generally and over time, percentage of your first-year enrollment is in-state: 15%
Origin of out-of-state enrollees (U.S.): Alabama-1, Arizona-2, California-19, Connecticut-5, District of Columbia-1, Florida-10, Georgia-2, Illinois-5, Kentucky-1, Maryland-4, Massachusetts-6, Michigan-3, New Hampshire-1, New Jersey-9, New York-8, North Carolina-1, South Carolina-2, Texas-3, Virginia-7, Washington-1, Wisconsin-1
Origin of international enrollees: Canada-4, Kenya-1, People's Republic of China-1, South Korea-5, Zambia-1

DEMOGRAPHIC DESCRIPTIONS OF APPLICANTS: 2012 ENTERING CLASS

	APPLICANTS		ENROLLEES	
	M	W	M	W
Hispanic/Latino of any race	49	70	4	5
American Indian or Alaska Native	0	1	0	0
Asian	378	447	17	30
Black or African American	31	49	1	2
Native Hawaiian or Other Pacific Islander	0	0	0	0
White	533	427	18	21
Two or more races	32	31	2	1
Race and ethnicity unknown	43	35	3	1
International	143	116	8	6

	MINIMUM	MAXIMUM	MEAN
2012 entering class enrollees by age	21	39	23

Number of first-time enrollees over age 30: 5

CURRICULUM

The program spans 45 months, with students in actual attendance 38 months. Four-week summer sessions between the second and third years and the third and fourth years are mandatory. The first year continues through the month of June. The basic science courses are taught in the first and second years through lectures, seminars, and laboratory experiences. Clinical training begins with dental health education in community settings and dental assisting in the Main Clinic in the first year continuing through the second year. The third and fourth years emphasize the general practice of dentistry and fourth-year students gain additional clinical skills in a hospital setting through a four-week externship. Much effort is made to integrate the basic and clinical sciences throughout the four-year program. Among the program highlights is an offering of more than 40 elective courses during the second, third, and fourth year, a community service component, interdisciplinary dual degree programs, the option of an international externship during the fourth year and an honors program in clinical, community dentistry, and research for eligible students.

Student research opportunities: Yes

SPECIAL PROGRAMS AND SERVICES

PREDENTAL

Special affiliations with colleges and universities: University of Pennsylvania; Hampton University; Lehigh University; Muhlenberg College; Villanova University

Summer enrichment programs: Introduction to dentistry and dental simulation lab

DURING DENTAL SCHOOL

Academic counseling and tutoring

Community service opportunities: Mandatory graduation requirement

Internships, externships, or extramural programs: Hospital-based externships in U.S. or abroad

Mentoring

Personal counseling

Professional- and career-development programming

Training for those interested in academic careers

ACTIVE STUDENT ORGANIZATIONS

Alpha Omega International Dental Fraternity

American Dental Education Association (ADEA)

American Student Dental Association

Christian Dental Society

Community Health and Service Organization

Delta Sigma Delta (international dental fraternity)

Hispanic Dental Association

Indian Student Dental Association

Psi Omega Fraternity (dental)

Student National Dental Association

Vernon J. Brightman Research Society

INTERNATIONAL DENTISTS

Graduates of international dental schools considered for traditional predoctoral program: Yes

Advanced standing program offered for graduates of international dental schools: Yes

Advanced standing program description: Program awarding a dental degree

COMBINED AND ALTERNATE DEGREES

Ph.D.	M.S.	M.P.H.	M.D.	B.A./B.S.	Other
✓	✓	✓	—	✓	✓

Other Degrees: M.S. in Bioethics, M.S.E. in Bioengineering, M.B.A. (Business Administration)

COSTS: 2012-13 SCHOOL YEAR

	FIRST YEAR	SECOND YEAR	THIRD YEAR	FOURTH YEAR
Tuition resident, non-resident, and other	$63,770	$63,770	$63,770	$63,770
Fees	$3,238	$3,238	$3,881	$3,803
Instruments, books, and supplies	$15,884	$13,725	$15,656	$14,312
Estimated living expenses	$16,309	$17,998	$17,998	$16,309
Total resident, non-resident, and other	$99,201	$98,731	$101,305	$98,194

FINANCIAL AID

The University of Pennsylvania School of Dental Medicine makes every effort to assist qualified students in pursuing their dental education. The university helps students locate financial aid resources according to their need and eligibility. Available resources include need-based aid (grants and loans), other loans, and merit scholarships. To be considered for need-based financial aid, applicants must be U.S. citizens or permanent residents. Need-based financial assistance is available in the form of grants and federal subsidized and unsubsidized loans. Aid is awarded, based on the level of need, after reviewing a student's entire financial situation, including parental information. Parental financial information must be submitted. A student may borrow the expected family contribution from other funding sources. International and advanced standing students will be considered for nonuniversity based funding (private educational loans).

Each year the school awards a limited number of Dean's Scholarships to highly competitive students in the applicant pool. These scholarships recognize outstanding students on their academic as well as nonacademic achievements. Included among the factors considered in selecting scholarship recipients are the following: academic record, DAT scores, extracurricular activities, predental experience, research experience, community service, and leadership qualities, as assessed by the application and interview with the Admissions Committee. Recipients are selected from those who are admitted through the School's admissions process. There is no separate application for the Dean's Scholarships. To remain eligible for a scholarship beyond the first year, a recipient must maintain a 3.0 GPA and remain in good standing.

UNIVERSITY OF PITTSBURGH
SCHOOL OF DENTAL MEDICINE

Dr. Thomas W. Braun, Dean

GENERAL INFORMATION

The University of Pittsburgh is a state-related institution located in the city's Oakland District. The School of Dental Medicine, founded in 1896, is one of the schools in the University Health Complex, which consists of the schools of Medicine, Nursing, Pharmacy, Health Related Professions, and Public Health, as well as affiliated university hospitals. With an emphasis on competency-based performance, our first professional students are educated to provide optimal dental care for the public. Furthermore, our dental residency programs and dental hygiene program provide predoctoral students the opportunity to work cooperatively with other members of the dental profession. Dental residency programs are offered in advanced dental education in general dentistry, endodontics, pediatric dentistry, periodontics, prosthodontics, maxillofacial prosthodontics, orthodontics, anesthesiology, dental informatics, and maxillofacial surgery.

MISSION STATEMENT:

Please visit www.dental.pitt.edu to read the complete mission statement for the University of Pittsburgh School of Dental Medicine.

Type of institution: Private and state-related
Year opened: 1896
Term type: Semester
Time to degree in months: 45
Start month: August

Doctoral dental degree offered: D.M.D.
Total predoctoral enrollment: 314
Estimated entering class size: 80
Campus setting: Urban
Campus housing available: No

PREPARATION

Formal minimum preparation in semester/quarter hours: Semester: 90 Quarter: 120
Baccalaureate degree preferred: Yes
Number of first-year, first-time enrollees whose highest degree is:
- Baccalaureate: 79
- Master's: 1
- Ph.D. or other doctorate: 0

Of first-year, first-time enrollees without baccalaureates, the number with:
- Equivalent of 60 undergraduate credit hours or less: 0
- Equivalent of 61-90 undergraduate credit hours: 0
- Equivalent of 91 or more undergraduate credit hours: 0

PREREQUISITE COURSE	REQUIRED	RECOMMENDED	LAB REQUIRED	CREDITS (SEMESTER/QUARTER)
BCP (biology-chemistry-physics) sciences				
Biology	✓		✓	8/12
Chemistry, general/inorganic	✓			8/12
Chemistry, organic	✓			6/10
Physics	✓			6/10
Additional biological sciences				
Anatomy		✓		3/4
Biochemistry	✓			3/4
Cell biology		✓		3/4
Histology		✓		3/4
Immunology				
Microbiology		✓		3/4
Molecular biology/genetics				
Physiology		✓		3/4

(Prerequisite Courses continued)

CONTACT INFORMATION

www.dental.pitt.edu
3501 Terrace Street
Dean's Suite, 4th Floor Salk Hall
Pittsburgh, PA 15261
Phone: 412-648-8880

ADMISSIONS

Dr. Kenneth Etzel
Rosemary Mangold
3501 Terrace Street
Suite 2114 Salk
Pittsburgh, PA 15261
Phone: 412-648-8437

FINANCIAL AID

3501 Terrace Street
Suite 2114 Salk
Pittsburgh, PA 15261
Phone: 412-648-9806

STUDENT AFFAIRS

Aileen Brasacchio
3501 Terrace Street
Suite 2114 Salk
Pittsburgh, PA 15261
Phone: 412-648-8422

MINORITY PROGRAMS

3501 Terrace Street
Suite 2114 Salk
Pittsburgh, PA 15261
Phone: 412-648-8840

ADVANCED STANDING PROGRAM FOR FOREIGN TRAINED DENTISTS

Dr. Anitha Potluri
3501 Terrace Street
Pittsburgh, PA 15261
Phone: 412-383-8633
Email: anp60@pitt.edu

PREPARATION (CONTINUED)

PREREQUISITE COURSE	REQUIRED	RECOMMENDED	LAB REQUIRED	CREDITS (SEMESTER/QUARTER)
Zoology				
Other				
English	✓			6/10

Community college coursework accepted for prerequisites: Yes, up to 30% of prerequisites
Community college coursework accepted for electives: Yes, up to 30% of coursework
Limits on community college credit hours: Yes
Maximum number of community college credit hours: 30%
Advanced placement (AP) credit accepted for prerequisites: No
Advanced placement (AP) credit accepted for electives: No
Comments regarding AP credit: AP courses are counted as credits earned but will not be considered as prerequisites.
Job shadowing: Required
Number of hours of job shadowing required or recommended: 50—Ongoing shadowing is required at various practices.

DAT

Mandatory: Yes
Latest DAT for consideration of application: 09/30/2013
Oldest DAT considered: 01/01/2010
When more than one DAT score is reported: Highest score is considered
Canadian DAT accepted: Yes
Application considered before DAT scores are submitted: No, scores must be submitted with application.

DAT: 2012 ENTERING CLASS

ENROLLEE DAT SCORES	RANGE	MEAN
Academic Average	17-30	20.8
Perceptual Ability	18-27	21.3
Total Science	18-26	20.8

GPA: 2012 ENTERING CLASS

ENROLLEE GPA SCORES	RANGE	MEAN
Science GPA	2.79-4.05	3.5
Total GPA	3.07-4.01	3.6

APPLICATION AND SELECTION

TIMETABLE

Earliest filing date: 06/04/2013
Latest filing date: 11/01/2013
Earliest date for acceptance offers: 12/01/2012
Maximum time in days for applicant's response to acceptance offer:
30 days if accepted on or after December 1
15 days if accepted on or after January 1
Requests for deferred entrance considered: No
Fee for application: Yes, submitted at same time as Associated American Dental Schools Application Service (AADSAS) application
Amount of fee for application:
In state: $35 Out of state: $35 International: $50 (U.S.)
Fee waiver available: No

	FIRST DEPOSIT	SECOND DEPOSIT	THIRD DEPOSIT
Required to hold place	Yes	Yes	No
Resident amount	$750	$750	
Nonresident amount	$750	$750	
Deposit due	As indicated in admission offer	04/01/2014	
Applied to tuition	Yes	Yes	
Refundable	No	No	

APPLICATION PROCESS

Participates in AADSAS: Yes
Accepts direct applicants: No
Secondary or supplemental application required: No; application fee and a recent 2x2 head shot photo only
Interview is mandatory: Yes
Interview is by invitation: Yes

RESIDENCY

Admissions process distinguishes between in-state/in-province and out-of-state/out-of-province applicants: No
Applications are accepted from non-U.S. citizens/non-U.S. permanent residents: Yes

APPLICATION AND ENROLLMENT	NUMBER OF APPLICANTS	ESTIMATED NUMBER INTERVIEWED	ESTIMATED NUMBER ENROLLED
In-state or province applicants	250	60	28
Out-of-state or province applicants	2,015	238	51

Generally and over time, percentage of your first-year enrollment is in-state: 35%
Origin of out-of-state enrollees (U.S.): California-5, Florida-4, Georgia-3, Illinois-1, Indiana-1, Maryland-1, Massachusetts-2, Michigan-1, Minnesota-1, New Hampshire -1, New Jersey-3, New York-5, North Carolina-5, Ohio-2, Oregon-1, Texas-4, Virginia-1, Washington-3
Origin of international enrollees: Canada-2, China-2, Hong Kong-1, South Korea-7, Zimbabwe-1

DEMOGRAPHIC DESCRIPTIONS OF APPLICANTS: 2012 ENTERING CLASS

	APPLICANTS		ENROLLEES	
	M	W	M	W
Hispanic/Latino of any race	48	57	2	2
American Indian or Alaska Native	7	8	1	0
Asian	444	455	17	18
Black or African American	31	41	1	1
Native Hawaiian or Other Pacific Islander	0	0	0	0
White	699	499	23	14
Two or more races	—	—	—	—
Race and ethnicity unknown	—	—	—	—
International	207	173	7	6

Notes: Any discrepancies are due to international applicants also being counted based on race/ethnicity.

	MINIMUM	MAXIMUM	MEAN
2012 entering class enrollees by age	21	34	26

Number of first-time enrollees over age 30: 1

CURRICULUM

The School of Dental Medicine combines rigorous classroom instruction with innovative hands-on experience in a clinical setting. Students in the first and second years train in state-of-the-art simulation clinics, balanced with a mix of traditional classroom lectures and small group situations. Third- and fourth-year students simulate private practice in module clinics under close supervision of clinical faculty. Students are encouraged to individualize their programs through elective courses in their third and fourth years. Elective study may range from a minimum of two courses to any number the student feels he or she can schedule comfortably. Additionally, clinical practice and social perspectives are expanded through elective study; the program provides opportunities for enrichment through electives at off-campus sites.

Student research opportunities: Yes

SPECIAL PROGRAMS AND SERVICES

PREDENTAL

Postbaccalaureate programs

DURING DENTAL SCHOOL

Academic counseling and tutoring
Community service opportunities
Internships, externships, or extramural programs
Mentoring
Personal counseling
Professional- and career-development programming
Training for those interested in academic careers
Transfer applicants considered if space is available

ACTIVE STUDENT ORGANIZATIONS

American Association of Dental Research Student Research Group
American Association of Women Dentists
American Dental Education Association (ADEA)
American Student Dental Association
Asian Pacific American Student Dental Association
Christian Dental Association
Dental Muslim Students' Association
Dental Periodontology Club
Dentist Anesthesiologist Club for Students
Hispanic Dental Association
Sports Dentistry Club
Student Chapters of American Academy of Pediatric Dentistry
Student National Dental Association

INTERNATIONAL DENTISTS

Graduates of international dental schools considered for traditional predoctoral program: Yes

Advanced standing program offered for graduates of international dental schools: Yes

Advanced standing program description: Program awarding a dental degree, Other: two-year program

COMBINED AND ALTERNATE DEGREES

Ph.D.	M.S.	M.P.H.	M.D.	B.A./B.S.	Other
✓	✓	✓	—	—	—

COSTS: 2012-13 SCHOOL YEAR

	FIRST YEAR	SECOND YEAR	THIRD YEAR	FOURTH YEAR
Tuition, resident	$40,212	$40,212	$40,212	$40,212
Tuition, nonresident	$46,566	$46,566	$46,566	$46,566
Tuition, other				
Fees	$6,859	$6,727	$8,379	$6,569
Instruments, books, and supplies	$11,475	$9,639	$5,275	$4,513
Estimated living expenses	$21,000	$21,000	$21,000	$21,000
Total, resident	$79,546	$77,578	$74,866	$72,294
Total, nonresident	$85,900	$83,932	$81,220	$78,648
Total, other				

FINANCIAL AID

A commitment to a dental education is a significant investment of time and energy as well as a significant financial investment. At the University of Pittsburgh School of Dental Medicine, we want our students to make wise choices, especially about paying for dental school. We strive to help our students understand the financial resources available and how to obtain them. Scholarships are awarded through the School of Dental Medicine Student Services Office. Applicants are reviewed on the basis of academic status and financial need. The amount of each award ranges from $500 to $10,000 per academic year. Loan programs available include Stafford loans (subsidized and unsubsidized), Health Professions Student Loans, and alternative/private loans. In order to qualify for Stafford loans and/or Graduate PLUS loans, each student is required to complete the Free Application for Federal Student Aid (FAFSA) online at www.fafsa.ed.gov by April 30. A student may borrow up to the amount of his or her estimated budget for the academic year in which he or she is registered for classes.

There were 82 recipients of scholarships and grants in the 2012 entering class. Awards were between $1,000 and $10,000 with an average amount of $5,000. In 2012, there were 249 student loan recipients of amounts between $33,233 and $47,167. The average student loan was $47,167.

The average 2012 graduate indebtedness was $200,000.

UNIVERSITY OF PUERTO RICO
SCHOOL OF DENTAL MEDICINE

Dr. Humberto J. Villa Rivera, Dean

CONTACT INFORMATION

http://dental.rcm.upr.edu
P.O. Box 365067
San Juan, PR 00936-5067
Phone: 787-758-2525, ext. 1113
Fax: 787-751-0990

OFFICE OF ADMISSIONS

P.O. Box 365067
San Juan, PR 00936-5067
Phone: 787-758-2525

OFFICE OF FINANCIAL AID

Rafael Solis
Director
P.O. Box 365067
San Juan, PR 00936-5067
Phone: 787-758-2525
Email: rafael.solis@upr.edu
www.rcm.upr.edu

STUDENT AFFAIRS

Dr. Aileen M. Torres
Assistant Dean for Student Affairs
P.O. Box 365067
San Juan, PR 00936-5067
Phone: 787-758-2525, ext. 1113
Email: aileen.torres1@upr.edu

MINORITY AFFAIRS/DIVERSITY

Dr. Aileen M. Torres
Assistant Dean for Student Affairs
P.O. Box 365067
San Juan, PR 00936-5067
Phone: 787-758-2525, ext. 1113
Email: aileen.torres1@upr.edu

HOUSING OFFICE

P.O. Box 365067
San Juan, PR 00936-5067
Phone: 787-758-2525
Email: nitza.rivera@upr.edu

INTERNATIONAL STUDENTS

Dr. Jose R. Matos
International Program Director
P.O. Box 365067
San Juan, PR 00936-5067
Phone: 787-758-2525, ext. 1113
Email: jose.matos5@upr.edu

GENERAL INFORMATION

On June 21, 1956, the legislature of Puerto Rico, on the recommendation of the Superior Education Council of the University, approved legislation establishing the School of Dental Medicine. The first class started in August 1957. The School of Dental Medicine is one of the faculties forming the University of Puerto Rico and is located in the Medical Sciences Campus in Río Piedras, Puerto Rico. The School of Dental Medicine is fully accredited by the Council of Dental Education of the American Dental Association (ADA). It offers the following academic programs: 1) a four-year program leading to the D.M.D. degree; 2) advanced education programs in dental specialties of oral and maxillofacial surgery, general practice, prosthodontics, pediatric dentistry, endodontics (in conjunction with Lutheran Medical Center), and orthodontics; and 3) continuing education.

MISSION STATEMENT:

The University of Puerto Rico School of Dental Medicine (UPR-SDM) has, as its main mission, the training of dentists who will become an integral part of the multidisciplinary team of health professionals that will satisfy the needs of the people of Puerto Rico. In the fulfillment of this mission, the school is committed to three complementary activities: teaching, research, and service. Its teaching role is directed toward the development of a doctoral program in dental medicine that will form competent graduates in the practice of general dentistry with critical thinking skills and bioethical sensibility to respond to the needs of their patients. The school fosters the search for scientific knowledge and the improvement of the practice of the profession through research in dental sciences. Services are aimed at fostering the well-being of the patient and the community, strengthening academic programs, and supporting the institution's research efforts.

Type of institution: Public
Year opened: 1957
Term type: Semester
Time to degree in months: 41
Start month: August

Doctoral dental degree offered: D.M.D.
Total predoctoral enrollment: 196
Estimated entering class size: 40
Campus setting: Urban
Campus housing available: No

PREPARATION

Formal minimum preparation in semester/quarter hours: Semester: 90 Quarter: 135
Baccalaureate degree preferred: Yes
Number of first-year, first-time enrollees whose highest degree is:
- Baccalaureate: 35
- Master's: 2
- Ph.D. or other doctorate: 0

Of first-year, first-time enrollees without baccalaureates, the number with:
- Equivalent of 60 undergraduate credit hours or less: 0
- Equivalent of 61-90 undergraduate credit hours: 0
- Equivalent of 91 or more undergraduate credit hours: 5

PREREQUISITE COURSE	REQUIRED	RECOMMENDED	LAB REQUIRED	CREDITS (SEMESTER/QUARTER)
BCP (biology-chemistry-physics) sciences				
Biology	✓		✓	8/12
Chemistry, general/inorganic	✓		✓	8/12
Chemistry, organic	✓		✓	8/12
Physics	✓		✓	8/12
Additional biological sciences				
Anatomy		✓		
Biochemistry		✓		3/5
Cell biology		✓		

(Prerequisite Courses continued)

PREPARATION (CONTINUED)

PREREQUISITE COURSE	REQUIRED	RECOMMENDED	LAB REQUIRED	CREDITS (SEMESTER/QUARTER)
Histology		✓		
Immunology		✓		
Microbiology		✓		3/4
Molecular biology/genetics		✓		
Physiology		✓		3/5
Zoology				
Other				
English	✓			12/18
Spanish	✓			12/18
Social Sciences	✓			6/9

Community college coursework accepted for prerequisites: Yes
Community college coursework accepted for electives: Yes
Limits on community college credit hours: No
Maximum number of community college credit hours: 90
Advanced placement (AP) credit accepted for prerequisites: Yes
Advanced placement (AP) credit accepted for electives: Yes
Comments regarding AP credit: AP credits must appear on college transcript as accepted by college.
Job shadowing: Recommended
Number of hours of job shadowing required or recommended: No minimum
Other factors considered in admission: Extra science credits, research work done, and community service

DAT

Mandatory: Yes
Latest DAT for consideration of application: 11/30/2013
Oldest DAT considered: 01/01/2010
When more than one DAT score is reported: Highest score is considered.
Canadian DAT accepted: No
Application considered before DAT scores are submitted: No

DAT: 2012 ENTERING CLASS

ENROLLEE DAT SCORES	RANGE	MEAN
Academic Average	15-19	17
Perceptual Ability	15-22	18
Total Science	15-20	16

GPA: 2012 ENTERING CLASS

ENROLLEE GPA SCORES	RANGE	MEAN
Science GPA	2.89-4.00	3.40
Total GPA	2.99-4.00	3.51

APPLICATION AND SELECTION

TIMETABLE

Earliest filing date: 06/01/2013
Latest filing date: 12/01/2013
Earliest date for acceptance offers: 03/30/2014
Maximum time in days for applicant's response to acceptance offer:
15 days if accepted on or after December 1
15 days if accepted on or after February 1

Requests for deferred entrance considered: In exceptional circumstances only
Fee for application: Yes, submitted at same time as Associated American Dental Schools Application Service (AADSAS) application.
Amount of fee for application:
In state: $20 Out of state: $20 International: $25
Fee waiver available: No

	FIRST DEPOSIT	SECOND DEPOSIT	THIRD DEPOSIT
Required to hold place	Yes	No	No
Resident amount	$100		
Nonresident amount	$100		
Deposit due	As indicated in admission offer		
Applied to tuition	Yes		
Refundable	No		

APPLICATION PROCESS

Participates in AADSAS: Yes
Accepts direct applicants: No
Secondary or supplemental application required: Yes
Secondary or supplemental application website: www.rcm.upr.edu
Yes, applicant must contact the school
Interview is mandatory: Yes
Interview is by invitation: Yes

RESIDENCY

Admissions process distinguishes between in-state/in-province and out-of-state/out-of-province applicants: Yes
Preference given to residents of: Puerto Rico
Reciprocity Admissions Agreement available for legal residents of: Puerto Rico
Applications are accepted from non-U.S. citizens/non-U.S. permanent residents: Yes

APPLICATION AND ENROLLMENT	NUMBER OF APPLICANTS	ESTIMATED NUMBER INTERVIEWED	ESTIMATED NUMBER ENROLLED
In-state or province applicants	105	78	38
Out-of-state or province applicants	285	23	4

Generally and over time, percentage of your first-year enrollment is in-state: 95%

Origin of out-of-state enrollees (U.S.): Florida-2, Texas-1, Utah-1

Origin of international enrollees: Colombia-2, Cuba-2, Dominican Republic-3, Mexico-1

DEMOGRAPHIC DESCRIPTIONS OF APPLICANTS: 2011 ENTERING CLASS

	APPLICANTS		ENROLLEES	
	M	W	M	W
Hispanic/Latino of any race	NR	NR	16	25
American Indian or Alaska Native	NR	NR	0	0
Asian	NR	NR	0	0
Black or African American	NR	NR	0	0
Native Hawaiian or Other Pacific Islander	NR	NR	0	0
White	NR	NR	1	0
Two or more races	NR	NR	0	0
Race and ethnicity unknown	NR	NR	0	0
International	NR	NR	0	0

Note: A total of 202 Hispanic/Latino students applied and only 41 enrolled.

	MINIMUM	MAXIMUM	MEAN
Previous year enrollees by age	20	52	24

Number of first-time enrollees over age 30: 3

CURRICULUM

Year 1. Basic science with introduction to clinic situations.

Year 2. Continuation of basic science and technical courses.

Year 3. Clinic rotations through each of the different disciplines in dentistry.

Year 4. Delivery of comprehensive dental care under conditions that approximate private practice, with extramural community programs in locations nationwide. Dental Degree Offered: D.M.D.

Student research opportunities: Yes

SPECIAL PROGRAMS AND SERVICES

PREDENTAL

Special affiliations with colleges and universities: University of Rochester - Combined double D.M.D./Ph.D. degree; Lutheran Medical Center (advanced dental education programs in Endodontics and Advanced Education in General Dentistry)

Summer enrichment programs

DURING DENTAL SCHOOL

Academic counseling and tutoring

Community service opportunities

Internships, externships, or extramural programs

Mentoring

Opportunity to study for credit at institution abroad

Personal counseling

Training for those interested in academic careers

Transfer applicants considered if space is available

ACTIVE STUDENT ORGANIZATIONS

American Association of Women Dentists

American Dental Education Association (ADEA)

American Student Dental Association

Hispanic Dental Association

Student Council

INTERNATIONAL DENTISTS

Graduates of international dental schools considered for traditional predoctoral program: No

Advanced standing program offered for graduates of international dental schools: Yes

Advanced standing program description: Program awarding a dental degree

COMBINED AND ALTERNATE DEGREES

Ph.D.	M.S.	M.P.H.	M.D.	B.A./B.S.	Other
✓	—	—	—	—	—

COSTS: 2013-14 SCHOOL YEAR

	FIRST YEAR	SECOND YEAR	THIRD YEAR	FOURTH YEAR
Tuition, resident	$9,101	$8,751	$8,415	$8,091
Tuition, nonresident	$15,000	$15,000	$15,000	$15,000
Tuition, other (books)	$1,000	$950	$983	$935
Fees (Maintenance, Laboratories, Technology, Educational Resources Fund, Special Fees)	$1,775	$1,742	$1,973	$1,610
Instruments, books, and supplies	$10,046	$8,959	$2,000	$1,000
Estimated living expenses	$12,700	$12,968	$14,068	$12,968
Total, resident	$34,622	$33,370	$27,439	$24,604
Total, nonresident	$40,521	$39,619	$34,024	$31,513
Total, other				

FINANCIAL AID

Students apply to the customary federal loans and scholarships available based on the federal criteria for disadvantaged students. Financial aid funds are provided by the legislature of the commonwealth of Puerto Rico and the federal government. These resources are distributed through scholarships, student loans, and work-study programs. The Medical Sciences Campus (MSC) also offers teaching and research assistantships, which are funded by institutional budget allocations and distributed based primarily on academic merit rather than financial need. Decisions regarding assistantships are made by a committee chaired by the MSC Associate Dean for Academic Affairs. Fifty percent of the total School of Dental Medicine's student body receives some kind of financial aid (scholarship/federal loan). As a state-supported institution of higher education, the UPR-SDM offers island residents quality education at a low cost. Tuition fees shown above are among the lowest in the nation for a health sciences campus. Fifty-six percent of the graduating class finished with an amount of debt between $50,000 and $100,000 and only four students had higher debts in 2009. The amount of debt for our students is considerably lower than their private counterparts in Puerto Rico and the United States.

MEDICAL UNIVERSITY OF SOUTH CAROLINA
JAMES B. EDWARDS COLLEGE OF DENTAL MEDICINE

Dr. John J. Sanders, Dean

GENERAL INFORMATION

The James B. Edwards College of Dental Medicine (CDM) was founded in 1967 and graduated its first class in June 1971. It is a state-supported institution located in the Basic Science Building of the Medical University of South Carolina complex. The dental school has an enrollment of 257 degree-seeking students at this time. Residency programs currently include oral and maxillofacial surgery, pediatric dentistry, periodontics, and orthodontics. The Dental Medicine Scientist Training Program (DMSTP) enables selected students to earn D.M.D. and Ph.D. degrees simultaneously. Faculty members are from a wide variety of backgrounds and experiences. They have generated a scholarly and self-critical educational environment. Students are exposed to a broad range of research activities, and multiple opportunities are available in research participation. The focus of predoctoral education is state-of-the-art clinical instruction inclusive of clinical, radiology, and information technology to ensure each graduate's competency in clinical dentistry. CDM also offers residency/graduate programs in Advanced Education in General Dentistry (AEGD), Endodontics, Oral and Maxillofacial Surgery, Orthodontics, Pediatric Dentistry, and Periodontics.

MISSION STATEMENT:

The James B. Edwards College of Dental Medicine's mission is to develop principled, skilled, and compassionate practitioners and leaders in oral health care; to expand the body of knowledge about oral and related diseases; and to serve the citizens of the state of South Carolina and beyond by providing exemplary oral health care.

Type of institution: Public
Year opened: 1967
Term type: Semester
Time to degree in months: 48
Start month: June

Doctoral dental degree offered: D.M.D.
Total predoctoral enrollment: 257
Estimated entering class size: 72
Campus setting: Urban
Campus housing available: No

PREPARATION

Formal minimum preparation in semester/quarter hours: Semester: 120 Quarter: 180
Baccalaureate degree preferred: Yes
Number of first-year, first-time enrollees whose highest degree is:
- Baccalaureate: 68
- Master's: 4
- Ph.D. or other doctorate: 0

Of first-year, first-time enrollees without baccalaureates, the number with:
- Equivalent of 60 undergraduate credit hours or less: 0
- Equivalent of 61-90 undergraduate credit hours: 0
- Equivalent of 91 or more undergraduate credit hours: 0

PREREQUISITE COURSE	REQUIRED	RECOMMENDED	LAB REQUIRED	CREDITS (SEMESTER/QUARTER)
BCP (biology-chemistry-physics) sciences				
Biology	✓		✓	8/12
Chemistry, general/inorganic	✓		✓	8/12
Chemistry, organic	✓		✓	8/12
Physics	✓		✓	8/12
Additional biological sciences				
Anatomy		✓		8/12
Biochemistry		✓		4/6
Cell biology		✓		4/6
Histology		✓		4/6
Immunology		✓		4/6

(Prerequisite Courses continued)

CONTACT INFORMATION

www.musc.edu/dentistry

OFFICE OF ENROLLMENT MANAGEMENT
Bill Liner
Dental Medicine Admissions Specialist
41 Bee Street
MSC 203
Charleston, SC 29425
Phone: 843-792-4892
www.musc.edu/em

FINANCIAL AID
Ashley Stuckey
Dental Medicine Financial Aid Counselor
45 Courtenay Drive, SS-354
MSC 176
Charleston, SC 29425
Phone: 843-792-0205
www.musc.edu/financialmanagement

STUDENT AFFAIRS
Dr. Tariq Javed
Associate Dean for Academic and Student Affairs
173 Ashley Avenue, BSB-443
MSC 507
Charleston, SC 29425
Phone: 843-792-2345
www.musc.edu/dentistry

MINORITY AFFAIRS/DIVERSITY
Dr. Gwendolyn B. Brown
Director of Diversity
173 Ashley Avenue, BSB-123
MSC 507
Charleston, SC 29425
Phone: 843-792-4425
www.musc.edu/dentistry/diversity

MUSC OFF-CAMPUS HOUSING
Nadia Mariutto
Housing Coordinator
45 Courtenay Drive, SW-213
MSC 171
Charleston, SC 29425
Phone: 843-792-0394
www.musc.edu/housing

INTERNATIONAL SUPPORT SERVICES
Denise Fowler
Program Manager
45 Courtenay Drive
MSC 175
Charleston, SC 29425
Phone: 843-792-7083
www.musc.edu/internationalsupport

PREPARATION (CONTINUED)

PREREQUISITE COURSE	REQUIRED	RECOMMENDED	LAB REQUIRED	CREDITS (SEMESTER/QUARTER)
Microbiology		✓		4/6
Molecular biology/genetics		✓		4/6
Physiology		✓		4/6
Zoology		✓		8/12

Community college coursework accepted for prerequisites: Yes
Community college coursework accepted for electives: Yes
Limits on community college credit hours: Yes
Maximum number of community college credit hours: 8
Advanced placement (AP) credit accepted for prerequisites: Yes
Advanced placement (AP) credit accepted for electives: Yes
Job shadowing: Recommended
Number of hours of job shadowing required or recommended: 50

DAT

Mandatory: Yes
Latest DAT for consideration of application: 12/01/2013
Oldest DAT considered: 12/01/2009
When more than one DAT score is reported: Highest score is considered.
Canadian DAT accepted: No
Application considered before DAT scores are submitted: No

DAT: 2012 ENTERING CLASS

ENROLLEE DAT SCORES	RANGE	MEAN
Academic Average	17-23	19.0
Perceptual Ability	17-30	20.0
Total Science	NR	NR

GPA: 2012 ENTERING CLASS

ENROLLEE GPA SCORES	RANGE	MEAN
Science GPA	2.74-4.0	3.62
Total GPA	2.89-4.0	3.67

APPLICATION AND SELECTION

TIMETABLE

Earliest filing date: 06/04/2013
Latest filing date: 01/15/2014
Earliest date for acceptance offers: 12/01/2013
Maximum time in days for applicant's response to acceptance offer:
30 days if accepted on or after December 1
15 days if accepted on or after February 1
Requests for deferred entrance considered: No
Fee for application: Yes, submitted only when requested.
Amount of fee for application:
In state: $95 Out of state: $95 International: $95
Fee waiver available: No

	FIRST DEPOSIT	SECOND DEPOSIT	THIRD DEPOSIT
Required to hold place	Yes	No	No
Resident amount	$485		
Nonresident amount	$485		
Deposit due	As indicated in offer letter		
Applied to tuition	No		
Refundable	No		

APPLICATION PROCESS

Participates in Associated American Dental Schools Application Service (AADSAS): Yes
Accepts direct applicants: No
Secondary or supplemental application required: Yes
Secondary or supplemental application website: http://academicdepartments.musc.edu/em/admissions/apply.htm
Interview is mandatory: Yes
Interview is by invitation: Yes

RESIDENCY

Admissions process distinguishes between in-state/in-province and out-of-state/out-of-province applicants: Yes
Preference given to residents of: South Carolina
Reciprocity Admissions Agreement available for legal residents of: None
Applications are accepted from non-U.S. citizens/non-U.S. permanent residents: Yes

APPLICATION AND ENROLLMENT	NUMBER OF APPLICANTS	ESTIMATED NUMBER INTERVIEWED	ESTIMATED NUMBER ENROLLED
In-state or province applicants	173	105	53
Out-of-state or province applicants	749	69	19

Generally and over time, percentage of your first-year enrollment is in-state: 72%
Origin of out-of-state enrollees (U.S.): California-2, Florida-2, Georgia-3, Idaho-1, Maryland-1, Minnesota-1, New Jersey-1, New Mexico-1, New York-1, North Carolina-2, Ohio-1, Tennessee-1, Utah-1, Virginia-1
Origin of international enrollees: NA

DEMOGRAPHIC DESCRIPTIONS OF APPLICANTS: 2012 ENTERING CLASS

	APPLICANTS		ENROLLEES	
	M	W	M	W
Hispanic/Latino of any race	0	0	0	0
American Indian or Alaska Native	1	1	0	0
Asian	60	66	1	6
Black or African American	6	34	0	3
Native Hawaiian or Other Pacific Islander	0	1	0	0
White	351	307	28	31
Two or more races	16	25	2	0
Race and ethnicity unknown	16	16	0	1
International	15	7	0	0

	MINIMUM	MAXIMUM	MEAN
2012 entering class enrollees by age	21	39	24

Number of first-time enrollees over age 30: 5

CURRICULUM

Year 1: Basic sciences and preclinical dental courses

Year 2: Additional basic science courses and preclinical courses

Year 3: Clinical instruction and patient treatment in all disciplines

Year 4: Clinical instruction, patient treatment, and extramural rotations; senior seminars for treatment planning, implantology, and practice administration

Student research opportunities: Yes

SPECIAL PROGRAMS AND SERVICES

DURING DENTAL SCHOOL

Academic counseling and tutoring
Internships, externships, or extramural programs
Community service opportunities
Mentoring
Personal counseling
Professional- and career-development programming
Training for those interested in academic careers

ACTIVE STUDENT ORGANIZATIONS

American Association of Dental Research Student Research Group
American Association of Women Dentists
American Dental Education Association (ADEA)
American Student Dental Association
Student National Dental Association

INTERNATIONAL DENTISTS

Graduates of international dental schools considered for traditional predoctoral program: Yes

Advanced standing program offered for graduates of international dental schools: No

COMBINED AND ALTERNATE DEGREES

Ph.D.	M.S.	M.P.H.	M.D.	B.A./B.S.	Other
—	—	—	—	—	✓

Other Degree: D.M.D./Ph.D.

COSTS: 2012-13 SCHOOL YEAR

	FIRST YEAR	SECOND YEAR	THIRD YEAR	FOURTH YEAR
Tuition, resident	$41,914	$30,720	$41,914	$41,914
Tuition, nonresident	$73,603	$53,710	$73,603	$73,603
Tuition, other	NA	NA	NA	NA
Fees	$19,630	$18,480	$18,520	$18,520
Instruments, books, and supplies	$4,189	$2,100	$2,885	$5,645
Estimated living expenses	$23,352	$19,460	$23,352	$23,352
Total, resident	$89,085	$70,760	$86,671	$89,431
Total, nonresident	$120,774	$93,750	$118,360	$121,120
Total, other	NA	NA	NA	NA

Comments: All costs are subject to change without notice.

FINANCIAL AID

In the 2012 entering class, there were 60 recipients of student loans. The smallest loan amount was $1,500 and the largest loan amount was $125,259.

MEHARRY MEDICAL COLLEGE
SCHOOL OF DENTISTRY

Dr. Janet H. Southerland, Dean

GENERAL INFORMATION

The School of Dentistry of Meharry Medical College is a private, nonprofit school. The college was organized in 1876 to educate physicians. Ten years later, the dental department was established, and other health professional disciplines were added later. The institution is named in honor of the Meharry family, who gave and established early support for the college in response to help from a black farmer who aided one of the Meharry brothers in a time of need.

MISSION STATEMENT:

Meharry Medical College exists to improve the health and health care of minority and underserved communities by offering excellent education and training programs in the health sciences; placing special emphasis on providing opportunities to people of color and individuals from disadvantaged backgrounds, regardless of race or ethnicity; delivering high-quality health services; and conducting research that fosters the elimination of health disparities.

Type of institution: Private
Year opened: 1886
Term type: Semester
Time to degree in months: 48
Start month: June

Doctoral dental degree offered: D.D.S.
Total predoctoral enrollment: 209
Estimated entering class size: 60
Campus setting: Urban
Campus housing available: Yes

PREPARATION

Formal minimum preparation in semester/quarter hours: Semester: 90 Quarter: 135
Baccalaureate degree required: While not required, it is preferred that applicants have a bachelor's degree prior to matriculation
Number of first-year, first-time enrollees whose highest degree is:
- Baccalaureate: 51
- Master's: 9
- Ph.D. or other doctorate: 0

Of first-year, first-time enrollees without baccalaureates, the number with:
- Equivalent of 60 undergraduate credit hours or less: 0
- Equivalent of 61-90 undergraduate credit hours: 0
- Equivalent of 91 or more undergraduate credit hours: 5

PREREQUISITE COURSE	REQUIRED	RECOMMENDED	LAB REQUIRED	CREDITS (SEMESTER/QUARTER)
BCP (biology-chemistry-physics) sciences				
Biochemistry	✓			3/5
Biology	✓		✓	8/12
Chemistry, general/inorganic	✓		✓	8/12
Chemistry, organic	✓		✓	8/12
Physics	✓		✓	4/6
Additional biological sciences				
Anatomy		✓		3/5
Cell biology		✓		3/5
Histology		✓		3/5
Immunology		✓		3/5
Microbiology		✓		3/5
Molecular biology/genetics		✓		3/5
Physiology		✓		3/5
Zoology		✓		3/5

(Prerequisite Courses continued)

CONTACT INFORMATION

www.mmc.edu/education/sod
1005 Dr. D.B. Todd Jr. Boulevard
Nashville, TN 37208
Phone: 615-327-6207
Fax: 615-327-6213

OFFICE OF ADMISSIONS AND RECRUITMENT

Angelo Lee
Director of Admissions and Recruitment
1005 Dr. D.B. Todd Jr. Boulevard
Nashville, TN 37208
Phone: 615-327-6223
Email: admissions@mmc.edu
www.mmc.edu/prospectivestudents

OFFICE OF FINANCIAL AID

Barbara Tharpe
Director of Financial Aid
1005 Dr. D.B. Todd Jr. Boulevard
Nashville, TN 37208
Phone: 615-327-6826
Email: financial aid@mmc.edu
www.mmc.edu/prospectivestudents

STUDENT AFFAIRS

Dr. Cherae Farmer Dixon
Associate Dean of Academic and Student Affairs
1005 Dr. D.B. Todd Jr. Boulevard
Nashville, TN 37208
Phone: 615-327-6076
www.mmc.edu/education/sod

PREPARATION (CONTINUED)

PREREQUISITE COURSE	REQUIRED	RECOMMENDED	LAB REQUIRED	CREDITS (SEMESTER/QUARTER)
Other				
English composition	✓			6/9
English literature		✓		
Calculus/statistics	✓			3/5

Community college coursework accepted for prerequisites: Yes
Community college coursework accepted for electives: Yes
Limits on community college credit hours: No
Maximum number of community college credit hours: NA
Advanced placement (AP) credit accepted for prerequisites: No
Advanced placement (AP) credit accepted for electives: Yes
Comments regarding AP credit: AP credits are not accepted.
Job shadowing: Recommended
Number of hours of job shadowing required or recommended: 50
Other factors considered in admission: Yes

DAT

Mandatory: Yes
Latest DAT for consideration of application: 12/15/2013
Oldest DAT considered: 01/15/2011
When more than one DAT score is reported: Most recent score only is considered
Canadian DAT accepted: Yes
Application considered before DAT scores are submitted: No

DAT: 2012 ENTERING CLASS

ENROLLEE DAT SCORES	RANGE	MEAN
Academic Average	16.0-21.0	18.0
Perceptual Ability	14.0-22.0	18.0
Total Science	15.0-22.0	18.0

GPA: 2012 ENTERING CLASS

ENROLLEE GPA SCORES	RANGE	MEAN
Science GPA	2.06-3.93	3.08
Total GPA	2.30-3.88	3.20

APPLICATION AND SELECTION

TIMETABLE

Earliest filing date: 06/01/2013
Latest filing date: 12/15/2013
Earliest date for acceptance offers: 12/01/2013
Maximum time in days for applicant's response to acceptance offer:
30 days if accepted on or after December 1
15 days if accepted on or after February 1
Fee for application: Yes, supplemental application completed online
Amount of fee for application:
In state: $65 Out of state: $65 International: $65
Fee waiver available: No

	FIRST DEPOSIT	SECOND DEPOSIT	THIRD DEPOSIT
Required to hold place	Yes		
Resident amount	$800		
Nonresident amount	$800		
Deposit due	As indicated in admission offer		
Applied to tuition	Yes		
Refundable	No		

APPLICATION PROCESS

Participates in Associated American Dental Schools Application Service (AADSAS): Yes
Accepts direct applicants: No
Secondary or supplemental application required: Yes
Secondary or supplemental application website: www.mmc.edu/prospectivestudents/admissions/sod
Interview is mandatory: Yes
Interview is by invitation: Yes

RESIDENCY

Admissions process distinguishes between in-state/in-province and out-of-state/out-of-province applicants: No
Applications are accepted from non-U.S. citizens/non-U.S. permanent residents: Yes

APPLICATION AND ENROLLMENT	NUMBER OF APPLICANTS	ESTIMATED NUMBER INTERVIEWED	ESTIMATED NUMBER ENROLLED
In-state or province applicants	85	144	7
Out-of-state or province applicants	1,884	76	53

Generally and over time, percentage of your first-year enrollment is in-state: 12%
Origin of out-of-state enrollees (U.S.): Alabama-3, Arkansas-1, California-4, Florida-4, Georgia-7, Illinois-3, Indiana-1, Kansas-1, Louisiana-7, Michigan-1, Mississippi-2, New Jersey-2, New York-3, North Carolina-5, Ohio-1, Oklahoma-1, South Carolina-1, Texas-3, Virginia-2
Origin of international enrollees: Jamaica-1

DEMOGRAPHIC DESCRIPTIONS OF APPLICANTS: 2012 ENTERING CLASS

	APPLICANTS		ENROLLEES	
	M	W	M	W
Hispanic/Latino of any race	32	35	1	1
American Indian or Alaska Native	3	6	0	0
Asian	307	312	2	2
Black or African American	170	305	18	33
Native Hawaiian or Other Pacific Islander	1	2	0	0
White	351	236	2	0
Two or more races	50	117	0	0
Race and ethnicity unknown	18	24	0	0
International	NR	NR	0	1

	MINIMUM	MAXIMUM	MEAN
2012 entering class enrollees by age	21	40	25

Number of first-time enrollees over age 30: 4

CURRICULUM

Meharry's School of Dentistry combines educational tradition and innovation in the curriculum. As a result, students are able to develop the appropriate foundation of knowledge and skills that allow them to become the best in their fields. The educational program of the School of Dentistry is composed of a multifaceted curriculum. The iterative instructional pattern ensures a sound knowledge base in general dentistry. Instructional efforts strike a balance between cognitive/intellective preparation, practical application, and the inculcation of professional ethical standards.

Year 1. Most academic effort is devoted to basic sciences.

Year 2. Preclinical courses are emphasized and prepare students for the clinical diagnosis and treatment of patients.

Years 3 and 4. The final two years are devoted to clinical instruction.

Student research opportunities: Yes

SPECIAL PROGRAMS AND SERVICES

PREDENTAL

Postbaccalaureate programs: By invitation only

DURING DENTAL SCHOOL

Academic counseling and tutoring
Community service opportunities
Internships, externships, or extramural programs
Mentoring
Personal counseling
Professional- and career-development programming
Training for those interested in academic careers
Transfer applicants considered if space is available and student is in good academic standing

ACTIVE STUDENT ORGANIZATIONS

American Association of Dental Research Student Research Group
American Association of Pediatric Dentistry
American Association of Women Dentists, Student Chapter
American Dental Education Association (ADEA) Council of Students, Residents, and Fellows (ADEA COSRF)
American Student Dental Association
Hispanic Student Dental Association
Student National Dental Association

INTERNATIONAL DENTISTS

Graduates of international dental schools considered for traditional predoctoral program: No

Advanced standing program offered for graduates of international dental schools: No

COMBINED AND ALTERNATE DEGREES

Ph.D.	M.S.	M.P.H.	M.D.	B.A./B.S.	Other
—	—	—	—	—	—

COSTS: 2012-13 SCHOOL YEAR

	FIRST YEAR	SECOND YEAR	THIRD YEAR	FOURTH YEAR
Tuition resident, non-resident, and other	$42,235	$42,235	$42,235	$42,235
Fees	$12,077	$20,377	$10,377	$6,917
Instruments, books, and supplies	$1,500	$2,000	$2,000	$1,600
Estimated living expenses	$32,627	$29,849	$29,849	$30,261
Total resident, nonresident, and other	$88,439	$94,461	$84,461	$81,013

FINANCIAL AID

There are 209 full-time dental students enrolled in Meharry Medical College's School of Dentistry for the 2012-13 award year. Cost of attendance ranges from $81,269 to $94,461 for the current academic year. Ninety-two percent (92%) of the student body relies on financial assistance to help finance their health professions education. Federal direct subsidized and unsubsidized loan amounts cannot exceed $40,500. Federal Graduate PLUS (GradPLUS) loans range up to $53,961. More than $500,000 in institutional scholarships will be awarded to the School of Dentistry enrollees. The average scholarship awards range from $500 to $35,000, depending on the scholarship fund.

UNIVERSITY OF TENNESSEE HEALTH SCIENCE CENTER
COLLEGE OF DENTISTRY

Dr. Timothy L. Hottel, Dean

GENERAL INFORMATION

The University of Tennessee Health Science Center College of Dentistry is a state-assisted institution, the oldest in the South, and located in Memphis (area population about one million). The college accepts 90 students per year into the program. The University of Tennessee Health Science Center is the state's health sciences campus and contains educational, research, and service programs in all health-related fields in an environment of integrated activities. Advanced dental education programs in General Practice Residencies (GPR), Orthodontics and Dentofacial Orthopedics, Oral and Maxillofacial Surgery, Pediatric Dentistry, Periodontics, Endodontics, and Prosthodontics are offered on the Memphis campus. Programs in Oral and Maxillofacial Surgery and GPR are also offered at the hospital-based unit of the college at Knoxville. The college participates in the Southern Regional Education Board, providing for enrollment of residents of Arkansas.

MISSION STATEMENT:

To improve human oral health through education, research, clinical care, and public service

Type of institution: Public
Year opened: 1878
Term type: Semester
Time to degree in months: 46
Start month: August

Doctoral dental degree offered: D.D.S.
Total predoctoral enrollment: 328
Estimated entering class size: 90
Campus setting: Urban
Campus housing available: No

PREPARATION

Formal minimum preparation in semester/quarter hours: Semester: 98 Quarter: 150
Baccalaureate degree preferred: Yes
Number of first-year, first-time enrollees whose highest degree is:
- Baccalaureate: 90
- Master's: 5
- Ph.D. or other doctorate: 0

Of first-year, first-time enrollees without baccalaureates, the number with:
- Equivalent of 60 undergraduate credit hours or less: 0
- Equivalent of 61-90 undergraduate credit hours: 0
- Equivalent of 91 or more undergraduate credit hours: 0

PREREQUISITE COURSE	REQUIRED	RECOMMENDED	LAB REQUIRED	CREDITS (SEMESTER/QUARTER)
BCP (biology-chemistry-physics) sciences				
Biology	✓		✓	2/8 (8 semester hours)
Chemistry, general/inorganic	✓		✓	2/8 (8 semester hours)
Chemistry, organic	✓		✓	2/8 (8 semester hours)
Physics	✓		✓	2/8 (8 semester hours)
Additional biological sciences				
Anatomy		✓		1/2 (4 semester hours)
Biochemistry	✓			1/2 (3 semester hours)
Cell biology		✓		
Histology	✓			1/2 (4 semester hours)
Immunology		✓		
Microbiology	✓			1/2 (4 semester hours)
Molecular biology/genetics		✓		
Physiology		✓		
Zoology		✓		

CONTACT INFORMATION

www.uthsc.edu/dentistry
University of Tennessee Health Science Center
875 Union Avenue
Memphis, TN 38163
Phone: 800-788-0040
Fax: 901-448-1625

OFFICE OF ADMISSIONS

Dr. J. Stansill Covington, III
Associate Dean
875 Union Avenue
Memphis, TN 38163
Phone: 901-448-6268

OFFICE OF FINANCIAL AID

910 Madison Avenue
Suite 525
Memphis, TN 38163
Phone: 901-448-5568

STUDENT AFFAIRS

Dr. J. Stansill Covington, III
Associate Dean
875 Union Avenue
Memphis, TN 38163
Phone: 901-448-6268

MINORITY AFFAIRS

Michael Alston, Director
920 Madison Avenue
Suite 420
Memphis, TN 38163
Phone: 901-448-2112

HOUSING OFFICE

(No on-campus housing is available.)

INTERNATIONAL STUDENTS

Dr. J. Stansill Covington, III
Associate Dean
875 Union Avenue
Memphis, TN 38163
Phone: 901-448-6268

PREPARATION (CONTINUED)

Community college coursework accepted for prerequisites: Yes, but not encouraged
Community college coursework accepted for electives: Yes
Limits on community college credit hours: No
Maximum number of community college credit hours: None
Advanced placement (AP) credit accepted for prerequisites: Yes
Advanced placement (AP) credit accepted for electives: Yes
Comments regarding AP credit:
Job shadowing: Required
Number of hours of job shadowing required or recommended: At least 50 under a General Dentist

DAT

Mandatory: Yes
Latest DAT for consideration of application: 09/30/2013
Oldest DAT considered: 01/01/2010
When more than one DAT score is reported: Most recent score only is considered
Canadian DAT accepted: No
Application considered before DAT scores are submitted: No

DAT: 2012 ENTERING CLASS

ENROLLEE DAT SCORES	RANGE	MEAN
Academic Average	16.0-24.0	19.0
Perceptual Ability	15.0-27.0	20.0
Total Science	15.0-24.0	19.0

GPA: 2012 ENTERING CLASS

ENROLLEE GPA SCORES	RANGE	MEAN
Science GPA	2.79-4.00	3.49
Total GPA	2.94-4.00	3.57

APPLICATION AND SELECTION

TIMETABLE

Earliest filing date: 06/01/2013
Latest filing date: 9/30/2013
Earliest date for acceptance offers: 12/01/2013
Maximum time in days for applicant's response to acceptance offer:
30 days if accepted on or after December 1
15 days if accepted on or after January 1
15 days if accepted on or after February 1
Requests for deferred entrance considered: Yes
Fee for application: Yes, submitted only when requested by the admissions committee
Amount of fee for application:
In state: $75 Out of state: $75 International: $75
Fee waiver available: No

	FIRST DEPOSIT	SECOND DEPOSIT	THIRD DEPOSIT
Required to hold place	Yes	Yes	No
Resident amount	$1,000	0	
Nonresident amount	$1,000	0	
Deposit due	As indicated in admission offer		
Applied to tuition	Yes	Yes	
Refundable	No	No	

APPLICATION PROCESS

Participates in Associated American Dental Schools Application Service (AADSAS): Yes
Accepts direct applicants: No
Secondary or supplemental application required: No
Interview is mandatory: Yes
Interview is by invitation: Yes

RESIDENCY

Admissions process distinguishes between in-state/in-province and out-of-state/out-of-province applicants: Yes
Preference given to residents of: Tennessee
Reciprocity Admissions Agreement available for legal residents of: Arkansas
Applications are accepted from non-U.S. citizens/non-U.S. permanent residents: No, an applicant must either be a U.S. citizen or U.S. resident alien at the time of application.

APPLICATION AND ENROLLMENT	NUMBER OF APPLICANTS	ESTIMATED NUMBER INTERVIEWED	ESTIMATED NUMBER ENROLLED
In-state or province applicants	167	71	47
Out-of-state or province applicants	1,057	105	43

Generally and over time, percentage of your first-year enrollment is in-state: NR
Origin of out-of-state enrollees (U.S.): Alabama-1, Arkansas-35, Florida-1, Georgia-2, Kansas-1, Louisianna-2, Mississippi-1
Origin of international enrollees: India-1

DEMOGRAPHIC DESCRIPTIONS OF APPLICANTS: 2012 ENTERING CLASS

	APPLICANTS		ENROLLEES	
	M	W	M	W
Hispanic/Latino of any race	33	27	2	1
American Indian or Alaska Native	1	2	0	0
Asian	117	118	5	5
Black or African American	21	47	1	3
Native Hawaiian or Other Pacific Islander	0	1	0	0
White	469	302	54	18
Two or more races	18	14	1	0
Race and ethnicity unknown	21	7	0	0
International	10	6		

	MINIMUM	MAXIMUM	MEAN
2012 entering class enrollees by age	20	45	24

Number of first-time enrollees over age 30: 5

CURRICULUM

The educational philosophy of the College of Dentistry is to provide opportunities for students to learn how to think in a problem-solving manner. The principal objective of the curriculum is to graduate a general practitioner who is professional, ethical, people-oriented, knowledgeable, and skillful in delivering comprehensive patient care. The basic sciences are presented in carefully planned lecture/laboratory procedures by each department. However, selected segments of material have been combined into interdepartmental team teaching programs. Students are oriented to clinical activities in the first year, and delivery of patient care begins in the second year. Comprehensive, total patient care is delivered in individual student cubicles. Basic science and clinical science faculty members use a team approach to teaching in some general areas, such as growth and development, oral diagnosis, and pain control.

Student research opportunities: Yes

SPECIAL PROGRAMS AND SERVICES

PREDENTAL

DAT workshops

DURING DENTAL SCHOOL

Academic counseling and tutoring
Community service opportunities
Internships, externships, or extramural programs
Mentoring
Personal counseling
Professional- and career-development programming

ACTIVE STUDENT ORGANIZATIONS

American Association of Dental Research Student Research Group
American Association of Pediatric Dentistry
American Association of Women Dentists
American Dental Education Association (ADEA)
American Student Dental Association
Student National Dental Association
Xi Psi Phi and Psi Omega professional dental fraternities

INTERNATIONAL DENTISTS

Graduates of international dental schools considered for traditional predoctoral program: Yes
Advanced standing program offered for graduates of international dental schools: Yes, but only if space is available
Advanced standing program description: Program awarding a dental degree

COMBINED AND ALTERNATE DEGREES

Ph.D.	M.S.	M.P.H.	M.D.	B.A./B.S.	Other
✓	—	—	—	—	—

COSTS: 2012-13 SCHOOL YEAR

	FIRST YEAR	SECOND YEAR	THIRD YEAR	FOURTH YEAR
Tuition, resident	$26,828	$26,828	$26,828	$26,828
Tuition, nonresident	$63,504	$63,504	$63,504	$63,504
Tuition, other	NA	NA	NA	NA
Fees	$5,305	$5,052	$5,025	$5,052
Instruments, books, and supplies	$12,410	$10,340	$4,490	$460
Estimated living expenses	$21,516	$23,472	$23,472	$21,516
Total, resident	$67,059	$65,692	$59,842	$53,856
Total, nonresident	$102,735	$102,368	$96,518	$90,532
Total, other	NA	NA	NA	NA

FINANCIAL AID

There were 11 recipients of scholarships and grants in the 2012 entering class, totaling $150,000. Awards ranged between $10,000 and $20,000. These funds are not guaranteed from year to year.

Eighty-three (83) students received loans. The average amount was $67,820.

TEXAS A&M UNIVERSITY
BAYLOR COLLEGE OF DENTISTRY

Dr. Lawrence E. Wolinsky, Dean

CONTACT INFORMATION

www.bcd.tamhsc.edu
3302 Gaston Avenue
Dallas, TX 75246
Phone: 214-828-8100

OFFICE OF RECRUITMENT AND ADMISSIONS

Dr. Barbara Miller
Executive Director
Phone: 214-828-8231
Email: admissions-bcd@bcd.tamhsc.edu

OFFICE OF FINANCIAL AID

Kay Egbert
Director
Phone: 214-828-8236
Email: kegbert@bcd.tamhsc.edu

STUDENT AFFAIRS

Dr. Jack Long
Associate Dean
Phone: 214-828-8240
Email: jlong@bcd.tamhsc.edu

CENTER OF EXCELLENCE IN DIVERSITY

Dr. Ernestine Lacy
Office of Student Development and Multicultural Affairs
Phone: 214-828-8374
Email: eslacy@bcd.tamhsc.edu

HOUSING

Moira Allen
Director
Phone: 214-828-8210
Email: mallen@bcd.tamhsc.edu

GENERAL INFORMATION

HISTORY:

Texas A&M University Baylor College of Dentistry (BCD) opened its doors in 1905 to its first 40 students as State Dental College. With a commitment to excellence, the college evolved in 1918 from its humble beginnings in 1905 to an affiliation—as Baylor University College of Dentistry—with Baylor University. The affiliation lasted until 1971. The college continued for an additional 25 years as an independent private institution; then, in 1996, Baylor College of Dentistry entered an entirely new era as a public institution and member of the Texas A&M University System. On January 1, 1999, the college became one of five founding components of the Texas A&M Health Science Center. The arrival of 2005 ushered in a celebration of 100 years of educating dentists to serve the citizens of the state of Texas and beyond.

LOCATION:

The BCD campus is conveniently located in the Dallas metropolitan area, about one mile from the downtown business district within the Baylor University Medical Center complex.

MISSION STATEMENT:

The mission of BCD is to improve the oral health of Texans and shape the future of dentistry by developing exemplary clinicians, educators, and scientists; caring for the needs of a diverse community; serving as a leader in health professions education; and seeking innovations in science, education, and health care delivery.

Type of institution: Public
Year opened: 1905
Term type: Semester
Time to degree in months: 48
Start month: August

Doctoral dental degree offered: D.D.S.
Total predoctoral enrollment: 402
Estimated entering class size: 104
Campus setting: Urban
Campus housing available: No

PREPARATION

Formal minimum preparation in semester/quarter hours: Semester: 90 Quarter: 120
Baccalaureate degree preferred: Yes
Number of first-year, first-time enrollees whose highest degree is:
- Baccalaureate: 100
- Master's: 4
- Ph.D. or other doctorate: 0

Of first-year, first-time enrollees without baccalaureates, the number with:
- Equivalent of 60 undergraduate credit hours or less: 0
- Equivalent of 61-90 undergraduate credit hours: 0
- Equivalent of 91 or more undergraduate credit hours: 0

PREREQUISITE COURSE	REQUIRED	RECOMMENDED	LAB REQUIRED	CREDITS (SEMESTER/QUARTER)
BCP (biology-chemistry-physics) sciences				
Biochemistry	✓			3/5
Biology	✓		✓	14/21
Chemistry, general/inorganic	✓		✓	8/12
Chemistry, organic	✓		✓	8/12
Physics	✓		✓	8/12
Additional biological sciences				
Anatomy		✓		4/6

(Prerequisite Courses continued)

PREPARATION (CONTINUED)

PREREQUISITE COURSE	REQUIRED	RECOMMENDED	LAB REQUIRED	CREDITS (SEMESTER/QUARTER)
Cell biology		✓		3/5
Histology		✓		3/5
Immunology		✓		3/5
Microbiology		✓		3/5
Molecular biology/genetics		✓		3/5
Physiology		✓		3/5
Zoology		✓		3/5
Other required courses				
English	✓			6/10
Statistics	✓			3/5

Community college coursework accepted for prerequisites: Yes
Community college coursework accepted for electives: Yes
Limits on community college credit hours: Yes
Maximum number of community college credit hours: 60
Advanced placement (AP) credit accepted for prerequisites: Yes
Advanced placement (AP) credit accepted for electives: Yes
Job shadowing: Required
Number of hours of job shadowing required or recommended: 75 minimum with a general dentist
Other factors considered in admission: Noncognitive factors are considered. Volunteer work and community service are also required.

DAT

Mandatory: Yes
Latest DAT for consideration of application: 12/01/2013
Oldest DAT considered: 01/01/2008
When more than one DAT score is reported: Most recent score is considered
Canadian DAT accepted: Yes
Application considered before DAT scores are submitted: No

DAT: 2012 ENTERING CLASS

ENROLLEE DAT SCORES	RANGE	MEAN
Academic Average	NA	20.0
Perceptual Ability	NA	20.0
Total Science	NA	19.9

GPA: 2012 ENTERING CLASS

ENROLLEE GPA SCORES	RANGE	MEAN
Science GPA	NA	3.47
Total GPA	NA	3.52

APPLICATION AND SELECTION

TIMETABLE

Earliest filing date: 05/01/2013
Latest filing date: 09/30/2013
Earliest date for acceptance offers: 12/01/2013
Maximum time in days for applicant's response to acceptance offer:
30 days if accepted on or after December 1
15 days if accepted on or after February 1

Requests for deferred entrance considered: Yes
Fee for application: Yes, submitted only when requested
Amount of fee for application:
In state: $0 Out of state: $50 International: $50
Fee waiver available: Check school website for details.

	FIRST DEPOSIT	SECOND DEPOSIT	THIRD DEPOSIT
Required to hold place	Yes	No	No
Resident amount	$200		
Nonresident amount	$200		
Deposit due	As indicated in admission offer		
Applied to tuition	Yes		
Refundable	No		

APPLICATION PROCESS

Participates in Associated American Dental Schools Application Service (AADSAS): Yes
Participates in Texas Medical and Dental Schools Application Service (TMDSAS) (Texas residents MUST apply through TMDSAS): Yes
Accepts direct applicants: Yes, for non-Texas residents only
Secondary or supplemental application required: Yes
Secondary or supplemental application website: www.bcd.tamhsc.edu
Interview is mandatory: Yes
Interview is by invitation: Yes

RESIDENCY

Admissions process distinguishes between in-state/in-province and out-of-state/out-of-province applicants: Yes
Preference given to residents of: Texas, New Mexico, Arkansas, Louisiana, Oklahoma, Utah
Reciprocity Admissions Agreement available for legal residents of: Arkansas, New Mexico
Applications are accepted from non-U.S. citizens/non-U.S. permanent residents: Yes

APPLICATION AND ENROLLMENT	NUMBER OF APPLICANTS	ESTIMATED NUMBER INTERVIEWED	ESTIMATED NUMBER ENROLLED
In-state or province applicants	961	217	98
Out-of-state or province applicants	679	21	6

Generally and over time, percentage of your first-year enrollment is in-state: 90%

Origin of out-of-state enrollees (U.S.): Arkansas-1, Louisiana-1, Michigan-1, New Mexico-1, South Carolina-1, Utah-1

Origin of international enrollees: NA

DEMOGRAPHIC DESCRIPTIONS OF APPLICANTS: 2012 ENTERING CLASS

	APPLICANTS		ENROLLEES	
	M	W	M	W
Hispanic/Latino of any race	77	106	13	10
American Indian or Alaska Native	7	6	0	0
Asian	224	291	7	10
Black or African American	36	57	9	6
Native Hawaiian or Other Pacific Islander	0	0	0	0
White	440	320	22	23
Two or more races	11	14	0	1
Race and ethnicity unknown	30	20	3	0
International	0	1	0	0

	MINIMUM	MAXIMUM	MEAN
2012 entering class enrollees by age	21	34	24

Number of first-time enrollees over age 30: 3

CURRICULUM

Our comprehensive clinical curriculum prepares our graduates for general practice and specialty programs, as well as academic, administrative, and public service dentistry.

Year D1: Emphasis on basic science courses; introduction to clinics with rotations for observation; preclinical technique courses. The summer break after the first year allows time for an optional research and/or clinical experience.

Year D2: Emphasis on preclinical technique instruction in a simulated clinic environment optimizes the transition to the clinics; introduction to practice management and clinic computer systems; beginnings of preliminary patient treatment.

Year D3: Continuation of clinical dentistry studies and direct patient treatment within a discipline-supervised comprehensive care clinic.

Year D4: General dentistry program encompassing comprehensive patient care with advanced procedures and approximating private practice; extramural rotations and selective courses allowing for experience in specialty areas.

Courses in Evidence-Based Dentistry, Professional Ethics, and Cultural Competency enhance the clinically focused curriculum.

Student research opportunities: Yes

SPECIAL PROGRAMS AND SERVICES

PREDENTAL

DAT workshops
Postbaccalaureate programs
Special affiliations with colleges and universities
Summer enrichment programs

DURING DENTAL SCHOOL

Academic counseling and tutoring
Community service opportunities
Internships, externships, or extramural programs
Personal counseling
Professional- and career-development programming
Training for those interested in academic careers
Transfer applicants considered if space is available

ACTIVE STUDENT ORGANIZATIONS

American Association of Dental Research Student Research Group
American Association of Pediatric Dentistry
American Dental Education Association (ADEA)
American Student Dental Association
Asian-American Dental Association
Dental Fraternities and Honor Societies
Hispanic Student Dental Association
Muslim Dental Association
Student National Dental Association
Texas Association of Women Dentists

INTERNATIONAL DENTISTS

Graduates of international dental schools considered for traditional predoctoral program: No, U.S. college coursework requirements must be met.

Advanced standing program offered for graduates of international dental schools: Not at the present time

COMBINED AND ALTERNATE DEGREES

Ph.D.	M.S.	M.P.H.	M.D.	B.A./B.S.	Other
✓	—	—	—	—	—

COSTS: 2012-13 SCHOOL YEAR

	FIRST YEAR	SECOND YEAR	THIRD YEAR	FOURTH YEAR
Tuition, resident	$13,315	$13,315	$13,315	$13,315
Tuition, nonresident	$24,115	$24,115	$24,115	$24,115
Tuition, other	NA	NA	NA	NA
Fees	$8,284	$8,284	$8,284	$8,284
Instruments, books, and supplies	$3,649	$2,466	$1,864	$703
Estimated living expenses	$22,353	$22,353	$26,824	$29,369*
Total, resident	$47,601	$46,418	$50,287	$51,671
Total, nonresident	$58,401	$57,218	$61,087	$62,471
Total, other	NA	NA	NA	NA

*This amount includes $2,545 in examination fees for the Western Regional Examination Board (WREB) and for National Board Dental Examinations (NBDEs).

FINANCIAL AID

There were 55 recipients of scholarships and grants in the 2012 entering class. Award amounts were between $1,000 and $19,000. Student loan recipients received loan amounts between $ 8,500 and $48,900. The average amount for residents was $ 38,150 and, for nonresidents, $46,601. There were 84 recipients of student loans. The average 2012 D.D.S. graduating class individual indebtedness for dental school was $140,798.

UNIVERSITY OF TEXAS HEALTH SCIENCE CENTER AT SAN ANTONIO
DENTAL SCHOOL

Dr. William W. Dodge, Dean *ad interim*

CONTACT INFORMATION

www.dental.uthscsa.edu
7703 Floyd Curl Drive
San Antonio, TX 78229
Phone: 210-567-3160
Fax: 210-567-6721

REGISTRAR'S OFFICE

7703 Floyd Curl Drive
San Antonio, TX 78229-3900
registrars@uthscsa.edu
210-567-2621

FINANCIAL AID OFFICE

Dental School Financial Aid Counselor
7703 Floyd Curl Drive
San Antonio, TX 78229
Phone: 210-567-2635
www.studentservices.uthscsa.edu/financialaid

DENTAL DEAN'S OFFICE

Dr. Adriana Segura
Associate Dean for Student Affairs
7703 Floyd Curl Drive
San Antonio, TX 78229
Phone: 210-567-3180

INTERNATIONAL EDUCATION

Dr. David Bohnenkamp
Director, International Dentist Education Program
7703 Floyd Curl Drive
San Antonio, TX 78229
Phone: 210-567-1411
www.dental.uthscsa.edu/admissions/idep

GENERAL INFORMATION

The Texas legislature created the University of Texas Health Science Center at San Antonio Dental School, a public institution, in 1969. Located in the heart of the South Texas Medical Center, it is one of five Health Science Center schools. A leader in research activities, the Dental School also has strong clinical and didactic programs. Numerous research opportunities are available to students, and the interdisciplinary aspect of many research programs is regarded as one of the institution's strengths. Clinical training occurs in the school's clinics and Hospital University, as well as at various extramural sites in San Antonio and southern Texas. The dental school also offers advanced education in all of the dental specialties and advanced training in general dentistry (GPR and AEGD). The school is situated in northwest San Antonio, the eighth largest city in the United States, and there is a large selection of excellent housing adjacent to the campus.

MISSION STATEMENT:

The Dental School mission is the acquisition, dissemination, and use of knowledge toward the enhancement of oral health. The mission is addressed through six interrelated action components: education, research, patient care, community, faculty and staff, and infrastructure.

Type of institution: Public
Year opened: 1970
Term type: Semester
Time to degree in months: 48
Start month: July

Doctoral dental degree offered: D.D.S.
Total predoctoral enrollment: 413
Estimated entering class size: 100
Campus setting: Suburban
Campus housing available: No

PREPARATION

Formal minimum preparation in semester/quarter hours: Semester: 90 Quarter: 120
Baccalaureate degree preferred: Yes
Number of first-year, first-time enrollees whose highest degree is:
- Baccalaureate: 61
- Master's: 1
- Ph.D. or other doctorate: 0

Of first-year, first-time enrollees without baccalaureates, the number with:
- Equivalent of 60 undergraduate credit hours or less: 0
- Equivalent of 61-90 undergraduate credit hours: 0
- Equivalent of 91 or more undergraduate credit hours: 38

PREREQUISITE COURSE	REQUIRED	RECOMMENDED	LAB REQUIRED	CREDITS (SEMESTER/QUARTER)
BCP (biology-chemistry-physics) sciences				
Biology	✓		✓	14/21
Chemistry, general/inorganic	✓		✓	8/12
Chemistry, organic	✓		✓	8/12
Physics	✓		✓	8/12
Additional biological sciences				
Anatomy		✓		
Biochemistry	✓			3/5
Cell biology		✓		
Histology		✓		
Immunology		✓		
Microbiology		✓		

(Prerequisite Courses continued)

PREPARATION (CONTINUED)

PREREQUISITE COURSE	REQUIRED	RECOMMENDED	LAB REQUIRED	CREDITS (SEMESTER/QUARTER)
Molecular biology/genetics		✓		
Physiology		✓		
Zoology		✓		
Other				
English	✓			6/10
Statistics	✓			3/5

Community college coursework accepted for prerequisites: Yes
Community college coursework accepted for electives: Yes
Limits on community college credit hours: No
Maximum number of community college credit hours: NA
Advanced placement (AP) credit accepted for prerequisites: No
Advanced placement (AP) credit accepted for electives: No
Comments regarding AP credit: AP credit is accepted only if the undergraduate student is awarded credit for a specific course, including department, catalog number, and title. Lump sum credit is not accepted.
Other factors considered in admission: Academic history, community service, research activities, leadership, interpersonal skills, communication skills, and knowledge of the profession

DAT

Mandatory: Yes
Latest DAT for consideration of application: 12/01/2013
Oldest DAT considered: 12/01/2008
When more than one DAT score is reported: Most recent score is considered
Canadian DAT accepted: Yes
Application considered before DAT scores are submitted: No

DAT: 2012 ENTERING CLASS

ENROLLEE DAT SCORES	RANGE	MEAN
Academic Average	17.0-26.0	20.0
Perceptual Ability	10.0-29.0	19.0
Total Science	NA	NA

GPA: 2012 ENTERING CLASS

ENROLLEE GPA SCORES	RANGE	MEAN
Science GPA	2.28-4.00	3.52
Total GPA	2.59-4.00	3.59

APPLICATION AND SELECTION

TIMETABLE

Earliest filing date: 05/01/2013
Latest filing date: 10/01/2013
Earliest date for acceptance offers: 12/01/2013
Maximum time in days for applicant's response to acceptance offer:
30 days if accepted on or after December 1
15 days if accepted on or after January 1
Requests for deferred entrance considered: In exceptional circumstances only.
Fee for application: Yes, submitted only when requested.
Amount of fee for application:
In state: $55 Out of state: $100 International: $100
Fee waiver available: No

	FIRST DEPOSIT	SECOND DEPOSIT	THIRD DEPOSIT
Required to hold place	Yes	No	No
Resident amount	$60		
Non-Resident amount	$60		
Deposit due	As indicated in admission offer		
Applied to tuition	No		
Refundable	No		

APPLICATION PROCESS

Participates in Associated American Dental Schools Application Service (AADSAS): Yes
Participates in Texas Medical and Dental Schools Application Service (for Texas applicants applying to Texas Dental Schools): Yes
Accepts direct applicants: No
Secondary or supplemental application required: No
Interview is mandatory: Yes
Interview is by invitation: Yes

RESIDENCY

Admissions process distinguishes between in-state/in-province and out-of-state/out-of-province applicants: Yes
Preference given to residents of: Texas
Reciprocity Admissions Agreement available for legal residents of: None
Applications are accepted from non-U.S. citizens/non-U.S. permanent residents: Yes

APPLICATION AND ENROLLMENT	NUMBER OF APPLICANTS	ESTIMATED NUMBER INTERVIEWED	ESTIMATED NUMBER ENROLLED
In-state or province applicants	957	280	94
Out-of-state or province applicants	489	21	6

Generally and over time, percentage of your first-year enrollment is in-state: 92%
Origin of out-of-state enrollees (U.S.): Colorado-1, Kansas-1, California-1, New Mexico-1, Utah-1, Oklahoma-1
Origin of international enrollees: South Korea

DEMOGRAPHIC DESCRIPTIONS OF APPLICANTS: 2012 ENTERING CLASS

	APPLICANTS		ENROLLEES	
	M	W	M	W
Hispanic/Latino of any race	75	105	11	8
American Indian or Alaska Native	0	3	0	0
Asian	185	247	9	17
Black or African American	23	38	1	2
Native Hawaiian or Other Pacific Islander	1	1	0	0
White	345	290	32	15
Two or more races	18	19	1	2
Race and ethnicity unknown	24	9	1	0
International	25	30	0	1

Notes: 8 applicants did not report their gender

	MINIMUM	MAXIMUM	MEAN
2012 entering class enrollees by age	20	43	23

Number of first-time enrollees over age 30: 7

CURRICULUM

The educational program embraces the philosophy of comprehensive care. Dental preclinical courses begin the freshman year so that a significant component of patient care may be incorporated into the sophomore year. Clinical patient care and research activities for students are emphasized in our program. An electronic curriculum support system uses a specifically configured laptop computer to access current information through integrated multimedia searches. The ability to access information in real time is an important feature of the curriculum and directly supports the school's mission of developing forward-thinking dentists capable of independent learning throughout their practicing careers.

Student research opportunities: Yes

SPECIAL PROGRAMS AND SERVICES

PREDENTAL

Special affiliations with colleges and universities in Texas: Dual Degree/Early Acceptance (3+4) Program

DURING DENTAL SCHOOL

Academic counseling and tutoring
Community service opportunities
Internships, externships, or extramural programs
Mentoring
Personal counseling
Professional- and career-development programming
Research opportunities
Training for those interested in academic careers
Transfer applicants considered if space is available

ACTIVE STUDENT ORGANIZATIONS

American Association of Dental Research Student Research Group
American Association of Pediatric Dentistry
American Association of Women Dentists
American Dental Education Association (ADEA)
American Student Dental Association
Hispanic Student Dental Association
Student Government Association
Uniformed Services Dental Student Association

INTERNATIONAL DENTISTS

Graduates of international dental schools considered for traditional predoctoral program: Yes
Advanced standing program offered for graduates of international dental schools: Yes
Advanced standing program description: Program awarding a dental degree to International Dentists

COMBINED AND ALTERNATE DEGREES

Ph.D.	M.S.	M.P.H.	M.D.	B.A./B.S.	Other
✓	✓	✓	—	—	—

COSTS: 2012-13 SCHOOL YEAR

	FIRST YEAR	SECOND YEAR	THIRD YEAR	FOURTH YEAR
Tuition, resident	$15,925	$15,925	$15,925	$15,925
Tuition, nonresident	$26,725	$26,725	$26,725	$26,725
Tuition, other	NA	NA	NA	NA
Fees	$7,314	$6,864	$3,284	$5,400
Instruments, books, and supplies	$7,142	$2,427	$1,352	$1,352
Estimated living expenses	$27,536	$27,536	$27,536	$27,536
Total, resident	$57,917	$52,752	$51,097	$50,213
Total, nonresident	$68,717	$63,552	$61,897	$61,013
Total, other	NA	NA	NA	NA

FINANCIAL AID

Students apply for financial aid by completing the online Free Application for Federal Student Aid (FAFSA). Students are then selected for awards on a first-come, first-served basis, provided all of the necessary documentation that is requested has been submitted. Applicants are always encouraged to apply early so that they can be included in the first round of awards. The Associate Dean of Student Affairs awards scholarships, with approval by the Scholarship Committee, based upon the criteria established for each award.

THE UNIVERSITY OF TEXAS
SCHOOL OF DENTISTRY AT HOUSTON

Dr. John A. Valenza, Dean

GENERAL INFORMATION

The University of Texas School of Dentistry at Houston, located in the world-renowned Texas Medical Center, is a public professional school with a unique heritage and unparalleled environmental advantages. The School of Dentistry was founded in 1905 as the first dental school in Texas; as such, it has a long and proud tradition of educating quality oral health care professionals. The school is one of the cornerstones of excellence that contributes to the strengths of The University of Texas Health Science Center at Houston by offering an excellent clinical education in an established research and service climate. The primary focus of the School of Dentistry is the education of highly competent oral health care professionals for the state of Texas. In pursuit of excellence, the school places major energies on its students as it teaches the basic and clinical sciences along with professional and ethical standards in an environment of collegiality. The School of Dentistry moved into its new state-of-the-art building in May 2012.

MISSION STATEMENT:

The central mission of The University of Texas School of Dentistry at Houston is to advance human health by providing high-quality education, patient care, and research in oral health for Texas, the nation, and the world. The mission is accomplished by attracting and retaining high-quality, culturally diverse faculty, staff, and students; developing and presenting comprehensive and contemporary dental education programs; generating and disseminating new knowledge through basic, translational, and clinical research; providing comprehensive, compassionate, and ethical oral health care; and improving the overall health of citizens of Texas and beyond in a professionally enriching and collegial educational environment. Professionalism and Culture at the School of Dentistry are based upon our commitment to the core values of excellence, integrity, respect, responsibility, innovation, collaboration, and leadership. Our strategic direction regarding culture and environment includes our commitment to foster a diverse, inclusive, and culturally sensitive setting that emphasizes ethics, professionalism, core values, and self-assessment.

Type of institution: Public
Year opened: 1905
Term type: Semester
Time to degree in months: 46
Start month: August

Doctoral dental degree offered: D.D.S.
Total predoctoral enrollment: 352
Estimated entering class size: 100
Campus setting: Urban
Campus housing available: Yes

PREPARATION

Formal minimum preparation in semester/quarter hours: Semester: 90 Quarter: 134
Baccalaureate degree preferred: Yes
Number of first-year, first-time enrollees whose highest degree is:
- Baccalaureate: 93
- Master's: 2
- Ph.D. or other doctorate: 3

Of first-year, first-time enrollees without baccalaureates, the number with:
- Equivalent of 60 undergraduate credit hours or less: 0
- Equivalent of 61-90 undergraduate credit hours: 0
- Equivalent of 91 or more undergraduate credit hours: 1

PREREQUISITE COURSE	REQUIRED	RECOMMENDED	LAB REQUIRED	CREDITS (SEMESTER/QUARTER)
BCP (biology-chemistry-physics) sciences				
Biology	✓		✓	14/21
Chemistry, general/inorganic	✓		✓	8/12
Chemistry, organic	✓		✓	8/12
Physics	✓		✓	8/12

(Prerequisite Courses continued)

CONTACT INFORMATION

www.db.uth.tmc.edu
7500 Cambridge
Suite 6350
Houston, TX 77054
Phone: 713-486-4021
Fax: 713-486-4425

ADMISSIONS
7500 Cambridge
Suite 4120
Houston, TX 77054
Phone: 713-486-4151
www.db.uth.tmc.edu

OFFICE OF STUDENT FINANCIAL AID
7000 Fannin Street
Suite 2220
Houston, TX 77030
Phone: 713-500-3860
www.uthouston.edu/sfs

OFFICE OF STUDENT AND ALUMNI AFFAIRS
7500 Cambridge
Suite 4120
Houston, TX 77054
Phone: 713-486-4151
www.db.uth.tmc.edu/administration/student-alumni-affairs

CULTURAL & INSTITUTIONAL DIVERSITY
Dr. Ronald Johnson
Chief Academic Diversity Officer
7000 Fannin Street
Suite 1690
Houston, TX 77030
Phone: 713-500-3455
Email: ronald.johnson@uth.tmc.edu

UNIVERSITY HOUSING
1885 El Paseo
Houston, TX 77054
Phone: 713-500-8444
http://ae.uth.tmc.edu/housing/index.html

INTERNATIONAL STUDENTS
Office of International Affairs
P. O. Box 20036
Houston, TX 77225-0036
Phone: 713-500-3176
http://www.uthouston.edu/international-affairs/

PREPARATION (CONTINUED)

PREREQUISITE COURSE	REQUIRED	RECOMMENDED	LAB REQUIRED	CREDITS (SEMESTER/QUARTER)
Additional biological sciences				
Anatomy		✓		
Biochemistry	✓			3/5
Cell biology		✓		
Histology		✓		
Immunology		✓		
Microbiology	✓			3/5
Molecular biology/genetics		✓		
Physiology		✓		
Zoology		✓		
Other				
English	✓			6/10
Statistics	✓			3/5

Community college coursework accepted for prerequisites: Yes
Community college coursework accepted for electives: Yes
Limits on community college credit hours: Yes
Maximum number of community college credit hours: No more than 60 credit hours recommended
Advanced placement (AP) credit accepted for prerequisites: Yes
Advanced placement (AP) credit accepted for electives: Yes
Job shadowing: Required
Other factors considered in admission: Academic history, leadership, service, communication and interpersonal skills, knowledge of profession, goals, potential for serving underrepresented or underserved populations, and integrity

DAT

Mandatory: Yes
Latest DAT for consideration of application: 12/01/2013
Oldest DAT considered: 2007
When more than one DAT score is reported: Most recent score only is considered
Canadian DAT accepted: Yes
Application considered before DAT scores are submitted: No

DAT: 2012 ENTERING CLASS

ENROLLEE DAT SCORES	RANGE	MEAN
Academic Average	15.0-24.0	19.7
Perceptual Ability	15.0-29.0	19.8
Total Science	15.0-26.0	19.5

GPA: 2012 ENTERING CLASS

ENROLLEE GPA SCORES	RANGE	MEAN
Science GPA	2.47-4.00	3.63
Total GPA	2.69-4.00	3.69

APPLICATION AND SELECTION

TIMETABLE

Earliest filing date: 05/01/2013
Latest filing date: 10/01/2013
Earliest date for acceptance offers: 12/01/2013
Maximum time in days for applicant's response to acceptance offer:
30 days if accepted on or after December 1
15 days if accepted on or after February 1

Requests for deferred entrance considered: In exceptional circumstances only
Fee for application: Yes, submitted at time of application
Amount of fee for application:
In state: $55 Out of state: $100 International: $100
Fee waiver available: No

	FIRST DEPOSIT	SECOND DEPOSIT	THIRD DEPOSIT
Required to hold place	No	No	No
Resident amount	NA		
Nonresident amount	NA		
Deposit due	NA		
Applied to tuition	NA		
Refundable	NA		
Refundable by	NA		

APPLICATION PROCESS

Participates in Associated American Dental Schools Application Service (AADSAS): Yes
Participates in Texas Medical and Dental Schools Application Service (for Texas applicants applying to Texas dental schools): Yes
Accepts direct applicants: No
Secondary or supplemental application required: No
Interview is mandatory: Yes
Interview is by invitation: Yes

RESIDENCY

Admissions process distinguishes between in-state/in-province and out-of-state/out-of-province applicants: Yes
Preference given to residents of: Texas
Reciprocity Admissions Agreement available for legal residents of: None
Applications are accepted from non-U.S. citizens/non-U.S. permanent residents: Yes

APPLICATION AND ENROLLMENT	NUMBER OF APPLICANTS	ESTIMATED NUMBER INTERVIEWED	ESTIMATED NUMBER ENROLLED
In-state or province applicants	980	275	99
Out-of-state or province applicants	472	6	0

Generally and over time, percentage of your first-year enrollment is in-state: 100%

Origin of out-of-state enrollees (U.S.): NA

Origin of international enrollees: NA

DEMOGRAPHIC DESCRIPTIONS OF APPLICANTS: 2012 ENTERING CLASS

	APPLICANTS		ENROLLEES	
	M	W	M	W
Hispanic/Latino of any race	74	111	11	9
American Indian or Alaska Native	3	5	1	1
Asian	187	242	9	14
Black or African American	31	57	2	4
Native Hawaiian or Other Pacific Islander	0	0	0	0
White	328	274	23	24
Two or more races	39	51	1	0
Race and ethnicity unknown	26	18	0	0
International	0	0	0	0

Note: 6 people did not report gender.

	MINIMUM	MAXIMUM	MEAN
2012 entering class enrollees by age	20	39	24

Number of first-time enrollees over age 30: 11

CURRICULUM

The curriculum utilizes a basic lecture system that is supplemented with seminars, discussion groups, laboratories/simulation, and online resources. There is intentional integration of basic science material into preclinical and clinical disciplines to ensure development of sound critical thinking and clinical skills. First exposure to clinic occurs in the first year, and responsibility for comprehensive patient care begins the second year.

Year 1: Basic sciences with introduction to clinical situations

Year 2: Continuation of basic sciences and clinical courses plus definitive clinical patient treatment

Year 3: Didactic clinical sciences and clinical care within vertically integrated practices

Year 4: Didactic clinical sciences and delivery of comprehensive dental care in a competency-based, vertically integrated group practice and community-based environment

Student research opportunities: Yes

SPECIAL PROGRAMS AND SERVICES

PREDENTAL

Association of American Medical Colleges/ADEA Summer Medical and Dental Education Program (AAMC/ADEA SMDEP)

Special affiliations with colleges and universities: The University of Texas at Brownsville - Pipeline Program; The University of Texas-Pan American - Pipeline Program; The University of Texas at El Paso - Pipeline Program; The University of Houston-Downtown - Pipeline Program; Prairie View A&M University - Pipeline Program; Texas A&M University-Corpus Christi - Pipeline Program; Texas A&M International University - Pipeline Program; Texas A&M University-Kingsville - Pipeline Program

DURING DENTAL SCHOOL

Academic counseling and tutoring
Community service opportunities
Internships, externships, or extramural programs
Mentoring
Personal counseling
Professional- and career-development programming
Training for those interested in academic careers
Transfer applicants considered if space is available

ACTIVE STUDENT ORGANIZATIONS

Academy of General Dentistry
Alpha Omega International Dental Fraternity
American Association of Dental Research Student Research Group
American Association of Women Dentists
American Dental Education Association (ADEA)
American Student Dental Association
Asian American Student Dental Association
Christian Dental Fellowship
Delta Sigma Delta
Hispanic Student Dental Association
Pediatric Education Dental Society
Psi Omega
Student National Dental Association

INTERNATIONAL DENTISTS

Graduates of international dental schools considered for traditional predoctoral program: No

Advanced standing program offered for graduates of international dental schools: Yes

Advanced standing program description: Program awarding a D.D.S. degree: Advanced standing may be awarded to international graduates allowing them to enter the D.D.S. program as a DS2. Offers are extended only if space is available in the DS2 class.

COMBINED AND ALTERNATE DEGREES

Ph.D.	M.S.	M.P.H.	M.D.	B.A./B.S.	Other
—	—	—	—	—	—

COSTS: 2012-13 SCHOOL YEAR

	FIRST YEAR	SECOND YEAR	THIRD YEAR	FOURTH YEAR
Tuition, resident	$16,988	$16,988	$16,988	$16,988
Tuition, nonresident	$28,177	$28,177	$28,177	$28,177
Tuition, other	NA	NA	NA	NA
Fees	$4,988	$4,638	$5,513	$5,588
Instruments, books, and supplies	$7,744	$6,915	$1,200	$580
Estimated living expenses	$23,784	$23,784	$23,784	$19,820
Total, resident	$53,504	$52,325	$47,485	$42,976
Total, nonresident	$64,693	$63,514	$58,674	$54,165
Total, other	NA	NA	NA	NA

Comments: Fees include health insurance premium of approximately $1,200. May be waived if student is covered by another policy. Tuition installment plan available.

FINANCIAL AID

Please refer to The University of Texas at Houston Student Financial Services website at www.uthouston.edu/sfs.

ROSEMAN UNIVERSITY OF HEALTH SCIENCES
COLLEGE OF DENTAL MEDICINE

Dr. Richard N. Buchanan, Dean

GENERAL INFORMATION

The Roseman University of Health Sciences, with campuses located in Henderson, Nevada, and South Jordan, Utah, was founded in 1999 as a private, nonprofit, independent educational institution to address the health care needs of the intermountain region through innovative educational programs, scholarship, and public service.

The university provides teaching and learning environments that prepare students and residents to become competent, caring, ethical professionals and lifelong learners dedicated to providing exceptional service in their chosen professions.

The Roseman University of Health Sciences College of Dental Medicine (CODM) Doctor of Dental Medicine program is located on the South Jordan, Utah, campus. The CODM's new, state-of-the-art, 125,000-square-foot building opened in fall 2011 and houses classroom complexes, labs, preclinical and clinical facilities, as well as faculty and staff offices. The clinic will have 189 operatories in which patient care will be provided. The CODM is adjacent to the existing 119,000-square-foot, two-story campus building housing Roseman's College of Pharmacy, College of Nursing, and M.B.A. program.

Roseman University of Health Sciences CODM will emphasize the development of lifelong colleagues at every level. This approach encourages all students, faculty, and staff to make each interaction reflect a sincere desire to develop one another as lifelong colleagues during the educational program and throughout their professional careers.

The Roseman University of Health Sciences is regionally accredited by the Northwest Commission on Colleges and Universities. The dental education program is accredited by the Commission on Dental Accreditation and has been granted the accreditation status of "initial accreditation." The Commission is a specialized accrediting body recognized by the U.S. Department of Education.

MISSION STATEMENT:

MISSION:

Roseman University of Health Sciences is a leader in transforming health care education with an uncompromising commitment to provide individuals the freedom to learn and grow in a collaborative and supportive environment that fosters success.

VISION:

Roseman University of Health Sciences aspires to be the first choice among "best-in-class" institutions of higher learning; universally recognized as an innovative, transforming force in health care education; and as a vibrant, stimulating place to work and learn.

CORE VALUES:

We ascribe to the foundational, cultural, and behavioral norms of all "best-in-class" institutions of higher learning, that is, professionalism, integrity, diversity, accountability, collegiality, social responsibility, and ethical behavior are all integral to the enduring relationships Roseman University of Health Sciences maintains with the constituencies it serves. In addition to these basic norms, Roseman University of Health Sciences espouses the following core values, which are inherent in its unique mission and vision:

- RISK-TAKING: We value responsible risk-taking that leads to the sustainable growth of the institution.
- INNOVATION: We value innovations in education, organizational structures, and physical surroundings that create a vibrant, stimulating environment in which to work, to learn, and to grow.
- INDIVIDUAL AND COLLECTIVE ACHIEVEMENT OF EXCELLENCE: We value a culture that fosters and celebrates excellence and achievement for one and all.
- PASSION AND COMMITMENT: We value passion and true commitment as the requisite components of transformational leadership in education and the health professions.
- EMPOWERMENT: We value the empowerment of individuals through the provision of a collaborative, supportive environment in which to learn and to work.

CONTACT INFORMATION

www.roseman.edu
10920 South River Front Parkway
South Jordan, UT 84095
Phone: 801-878-1400
Fax: 801-878-1308

OFFICE OF ADMISSIONS

Dr. William Harman
Associate Dean for Admissions and Student Affairs
Amanda Farr, Admissions
10920 South River Front Parkway
South Jordan, UT 84095
Phone: 801-878-1405
Fax: 801-878-1309
Email: wharman@roseman.edu
afarr@roseman.edu

FINANCIAL AID

Francisca Aquino
Assistant Director of Financial Aid
10920 South River Front Parkway
South Jordan, UT 84095
Phone: 801-878-1031
Fax: 801-254-7191
Email: faquino@roseman.edu

STUDENT AFFAIRS

Dr. William Harman
Associate Dean for Admissions and Student Affairs
10920 South River Front Parkway
South Jordan, UT 84095
Phone: 801-878-1403
Fax: 801-878-1307
Email: wharman@roseman.edu

MINORITY AFFAIRS/DIVERSITY

Dr. Victor A. Sandoval
Associate Dean for Academic Affairs
10920 South River Front Parkway
South Jordan, UT 84095
Phone: 801-878-1408
Fax: 801-878-1305
Email: vsandoval@roseman.edu

Type of institution: Private
Year D.M.D. program opened: 2011
Term type: Academic Year
Time to degree in months: 44
Start month: August

Doctoral dental degree offered: D.M.D.
2012 entering class size: 80
Estimated entering class size 2012 and after: 80
Campus setting: Suburban
Campus housing available: No

PREPARATION

Formal minimum preparation in semester/quarter hours: Semester: 60 Quarter: 90
Baccalaureate degree preferred: Yes
Number of first-year, first-time enrollees whose highest degree is:
- Baccalaureate: 56
- Master's: 6
- Ph.D. or other doctorate: 0

Of first-year, first-time enrollees without baccalaureates, the number with:
- Equivalent of 60 undergraduate credit hours or less: 0
- Equivalent of 61-90 undergraduate credit hours: 0
- Equivalent of 91 or more undergraduate credit hours: 18

PREREQUISITE COURSE	REQUIRED	RECOMMENDED	LAB REQUIRED	CREDITS (SEMESTER/QUARTER)
BCP (biology-chemistry-physics) sciences				
Biology	✓		✓	4 semester courses
Chemistry, general/inorganic	✓		✓	2 semester courses
Chemistry, organic	✓		✓	2 semester courses
Physics	✓		✓	2 semester courses
Additional biological sciences				
Anatomy		✓		
Biochemistry	✓			1 semester course
Cell biology		✓		
Histology				
Immunology				
Microbiology				
Molecular biology/genetics		✓		
Physiology		✓		
Zoology				
Other:				
Statistics		✓		

Refer to www.roseman.edu for complete information on prerequisites.

Community college coursework accepted for prerequisites: Yes
Community college coursework accepted for electives: Yes
Limits on community college credit hours: No
Advanced placement (AP) credit accepted for prerequisites: Yes
Advanced placement (AP) credit accepted for electives: Yes
Comments regarding AP credit: Credit must be shown on undergraduate transcript.
Job shadowing: Recommended
Number of hours of job shadowing recommended: Sufficient to make informed career decision
Other factors considered in admission: Refer to www.roseman.edu for specific information on admissions requirements.

DAT

Mandatory: Yes
Latest DAT for consideration of application: Preference for scores submitted by December 1 of the year prior to matriculation
Oldest DAT considered: 3 years prior to date of Associated American Dental Schools Application Service (AADSAS) application
When more than one DAT score is reported: Roseman will consider the most recent score submitted.
Canadian DAT accepted: Yes
Application considered before DAT scores are submitted: No

DAT: 2012 ENTERING CLASS

ENROLLEE DAT SCORES	RANGE	MEAN
Academic Average	23-17	20
Perceptual Ability	30-18	22
Total Science	24-17	20

GPA: 2012 ENTERING CLASS

ENROLLEE GPA SCORES	RANGE	MEAN
Science GPA		3.20
Total GPA		3.31

APPLICATION AND SELECTION

TIMETABLE

Earliest filing date: 06/01/2013
Latest filing date: 12/01/2013
Earliest date for acceptance offers: 12/01/2013
Maximum time in days for applicant's response to acceptance offer:
30 days for candidates admitted between December 1 and January 31
15 days for candidates admitted after February 1
Response period may be lifted after May 15
Requests for deferred entrance considered: Yes
Fee for application: Yes, see www.roseman.edu for information.
Fee waiver available: Considered on an individual basis with appropriate documentation from ADEA AADSAS Fee Assistance Program (FAP)

	FIRST DEPOSIT	SECOND DEPOSIT	THIRD DEPOSIT
Required to hold place	$1,000	NA	NA
Resident amount	0		
Nonresident amount	0		
Deposit due	By due date stated in letter of acceptance		
Applied to tuition	100%		
Refundable	No		
Refundable by	NA		

APPLICATION PROCESS

Participates in AADSAS: Yes
Accepts direct applicants: No
Secondary or supplemental application required: No
Interview is mandatory: Yes
Interview is by invitation: Yes

RESIDENCY

Admissions process distinguishes between in-state/in-province and out-of-state/out-of-province applicants: No
Applications are accepted from non-U.S. citizens/non-U.S. permanent residents: Yes

APPLICATION AND ENROLLMENT	NUMBER OF APPLICANTS	ESTIMATED NUMBER INTERVIEWED	ESTIMATED NUMBER ENROLLED
In-state or province applicants	142	56	29
Out-of-state or province applicants	1,277	172	51

Generally and over time, percentage of your first-year enrollment is in-state: 44%
Origin of out-of-state enrollees (U.S.): AZ-3, CA-16, FL-1, GA-1, IA-1, ID-4, IL-2, MD-3, MO-2, NH-1, NY-1, OR-4, SD-1, TX-4, VA-1, WA-3, WY-1
Origin of international enrollees: Canada-2, South Korea-1

DEMOGRAPHIC DESCRIPTIONS OF APPLICANTS: 2012 ENTERING CLASS

	APPLICANTS		ENROLLEES	
	M	W	M	W
Hispanic/Latino of any race	51	40	0	0
American Indian or Alaska Native	1	0	0	0
Asian	223	213	6	13
Black or African American	13	10	0	0
Native Hawaiian or Other Pacific Islander	0	1	0	0
White	506	167	51	8
Two or more races	21	18	0	0
Race and ethnicity unknown	33	17	2	0
International	115	74	2*	1*

Note: Our 3 international enrollees are counted twice—once in the the International section and also in the demographic breakdown.

	MINIMUM	MAXIMUM	MEAN
2012 entering class enrollees by age	21	42	26

Number of first-time enrollees over age 30: 8

CURRICULUM

Roseman University of Health Sciences is committed to the following educational strategies: mastery learning, unique classroom complex, block curriculum, outcomes-based education, active and collaborative learning, contemporary technology and clinics.

With an emphasis on student-centered, active learning, Roseman teaches using the "Block Curriculum System" rather than the traditional semester/quarter system. The system allows students to concentrate on one or two didactic subjects at a time, enabling them to master the content. This system also necessitates that faculty provide varied instructional activities for students that support active learning techniques and strategies, as well as accommodating different learning styles to promote high achievement.

The CODM's classroom complexes have been designed to emphasize active and collaborative learning as well as support the use of advanced technology in instructional activities. The design produces an inclusive atmosphere in the classroom—one that allows the instructor to engage students directly and one in which students can see and interact with their classmates, encouraging student involvement and participation.

Detailed information about the classroom complex design, mastery learning, and the block curriculum is available at www.roseman.edu under Educational Philosophy.

Student research opportunities: Yes

SPECIAL PROGRAMS AND SERVICES

DURING DENTAL SCHOOL

Academic counseling and support
Community Service opportunities
Externships, or extramural programs
Mentoring
Personal counseling
Professional- and career-development programming
Research opportunities
Training for those interested in academic careers

ACTIVE STUDENT ORGANIZATIONS

American Dental Education Association (ADEA)
American Student Dental Association
Student Professionalism and Ethics Club
Student Government

INTERNATIONAL DENTISTS

Graduates of international dental schools considered for traditional predoctoral program: Yes
Advanced standing program offered for graduates of international dental schools: No

COMBINED AND ALTERNATE DEGREES

Ph.D.	M.S.	M.P.H.	M.D.	B.A./B.S.	Other
—	—	—	—	—	—

COSTS: 2012-13 SCHOOL YEAR

	FIRST YEAR	SECOND YEAR	THIRD YEAR	FOURTH YEAR
Tuition, resident	$60,900	$60,900	NA	NA
Tuition, nonresident	$60,900	$60,900	NA	NA
Tuition, other	NA	NA	NA	NA
Fees	$4,476	$2,922	NA	NA
Instruments, books, and supplies	$10,180	$6,650	NA	NA
Estimated living expenses	NA	NA	NA	NA
Total, resident	$75,556	$70,472	NA	NA
Total, nonresident	$75,556	$70,472	NA	NA
Total, other				

FINANCIAL AID

Roseman University of Health Sciences is a Direct Lending institution. All Stafford and PLUS loans will be processed under the Federal Direct Loan Program.

- Complete the Roseman Loan Request Statement(s) and submit submit it (them) to the Financial Aid Office.
- If you have not previously completed a Direct Loan Master Promissory Note(s) (MPN) with the Department of Education, you must complete one. Carefully read and follow directions when completing the MPN. The MPN will cover all federal Stafford or PLUS loans you borrow with the Department of Education for up to 10 years.
- If you are offered a Parent PLUS or a Graduate PLUS loan, you must complete a PLUS Request application on www.studentloans.gov. The PLUS application will perform a credit check and notify you of the results.
- You also are required to complete Loan Entrance Counseling before you can receive your first disbursement of funds. You can complete Direct Loan Entrance Counseling at www.studentloans.gov.
- The Department of Education will disburse your loan(s) to the Bursar's Office in installments, one at the start of the loan period and one in the middle of the loan period (loan periods generally correspond to the academic year).

For answers to specific financial aid questions, please contact the Financial Aid Office directly.

UNIVERSITY OF UTAH
SCHOOL OF DENTISTRY

Dr. G. Lynn Powell, Founding Dean

CONTACT INFORMATION

www.dentistry.utah.edu
26 South 2000 East
Suite 5900
Salt Lake City, UT 84112-5750
Phone: 801-581-8951
Fax: 801-585-6485

ADMISSIONS

Dr. Gary W. Lowder
Director
26 South 2000 East
Suite 5900
Salt Lake City, UT 84112-5750
Phone: 801-581-8951
Fax: 801-585-6485
Email: dental.admissions@hsc.utah.edu

FINANCIAL AID

Julie Oyler
Manager
26 South 2000 East
Suite 5900
Salt Lake City, UT 84112-5750
Phone: 801-581-8951
Fax: 801-585-6485
Email: julie.oyler@hsc.utah.edu
www.dentistry.utah.edu

STUDENT AFFAIRS

Nancy Comarell
Director, Administration
26 South 2000 East
Suite 5900
Salt Lake City, UT 84112-5750
Phone: 801-581-8951
Fax: 801-585-6485
Email: nancy.comarell@hsc.utah.edu
www.dentistry.utah.edu

MINORITY AFFAIRS/DIVERSITY

Dr. Evelyn Gopez
Associate Vice President
Health Sciences
CNC 5th Floor
Salt Lake City, UT 84132
Phone: 801-585-0574
Fax: 801-585-3109

HOUSING

Housing and Residential Education
www.housing.utah.edu
Phone: 801-587-2002

GENERAL INFORMATION

The University of Utah School of Dentistry will grant its first D.D.S. degree in 2017. The School of Dentistry is part of the University of Utah's Health Sciences, the Intermountain West's only academic medical center. Our new School of Dentistry building is slated for completion in late 2014. The Health Sciences comprise the University of Utah Health Care, the School of Medicine, the School of Dentistry, and the colleges of Pharmacy, Nursing, and Health. Our classes are currently held in the Health Sciences Education Building, an award-winning facility in the heart of the education corridor of the Health Sciences. Opportunities for cross-professional education and collaboration in this rich environment are unlimited. The University of Utah ranks first in the country in spinoff companies resulting from university research and innovations, while University of Utah Health Care has been ranked among the top 10 academic medical centers in the country. In 2010, the University of Utah Health Care was ranked first in the country. The University of Utah Health Sciences serve people in six states—Utah, Idaho, Montana, Wyoming, and portions of Nevada and Colorado—nearly 10% of the continental United States.

The University of Utah School of Dentistry builds on Utah's Regional Dental Education Program (RDEP), launched in 1980. Since its inception 32 years ago, Utah's program has successfully recruited top students who are pursuing careers in dentistry. With the inauguration of the new School of Dentistry, the RDEP program will be retired when the last RDEP students complete their education in 2016.

Located on the Wasatch front, the University of Utah School of Dentistry overlooks a vibrant and growing city. Salt Lake City and its surrounding areas offer spectacular beauty and some of the world's best recreational opportunities. While Utah is renowned for its ski resorts, it may be less well known for its spectacular biking, hiking, fishing and other recreational activities. Utah is the home of 5 national parks with some of the most stunning geography in the world. Salt Lake City is also a hub for the visual and performing arts.

MISSION STATEMENT:

The mission of the University of Utah School of Dentistry is twofold:

1. To educate and train excellent, compassionate and ethical dentists to partner with other health care providers in order to serve our community and the world we live in
2. To further our understanding of the therapeutic management of oral structures and functions through research and its translation

Type of institution: State
Year opened: 2013
Term type: Semester
Time to degree in months: 46
Start month: August

Doctoral dental degree offered: D.D.S.
Total Predoctoral enrollment: 80 when fully enrolled
Estimated entering class size: 20
Campus setting: Urban
Campus housing available: Yes

PREPARATION

Formal minimum preparation in semester hours: Semester: 90
Baccalaureate degree preferred: Yes
Number of first-year, first-time enrollees whose highest degree is:
- Baccalaureate: NA
- Master's: NA
- Ph.D. or other doctorate: NA

Of first-year, first-time enrollees without baccalaureates, the number with:
- Equivalent of 60 undergraduate credit hours or less: NA
- Equivalent of 61-90 undergraduate credit hours: NA
- Equivalent of 91 or more undergraduate credit hours: NA

PREREQUISITE COURSE	REQUIRED	RECOMMENDED	LAB REQUIRED	CREDITS (SEMESTER/QUARTER)
BCP (biology-chemistry-physics) sciences				
Biology	✓			6
Chemistry, general/inorganic	✓		✓	6
Chemistry, organic	✓		✓	8
Physics	✓			6
Additional biological sciences				
Anatomy		✓		
Biochemistry	✓			3
Cell biology		✓		
Histology		✓		
Immunology				
Microbiology		✓		
Molecular biology/genetics		✓		
Physiology	✓			3
Zoology				
Other				
Additional biology, chemistry, and/or physics courses		✓		
English composition/technical writing	✓			6
Business		✓		
Computers		✓		
3-Dimensional art		✓		
Communications		✓		
Ethics		✓		

Community college coursework accepted for prerequisites: Yes, if the credits can be transferred to an accredited four-year institution
Community college coursework accepted for electives: Yes, if the credits can be transferred to an accredited four-year institution
Limits on community college credit hours: Yes
Maximum number of community college credit hours: 60
Advanced placement (AP) credit accepted for prerequisites: No
Advanced placement (AP) credit accepted for electives: Yes, if the credits can be applied toward a bachelor's degree
Comments regarding AP credit: It is recommended to take course work beyond introductory classes waived by AP
Job shadowing: Required
Number of hours of job shadowing required or recommended: 40
Other factors considered in admission: Demonstrated Community Service—Applicants must demonstrate community service through volunteerism or service-oriented employment.

DAT

Mandatory: Yes
Latest DAT for consideration of application: 11/01/2013
Oldest DAT considered: NA
When more than one DAT score is reported: Most recent score only is considered.
Canadian DAT accepted: No
Application considered before DAT scores are submitted: No

APPLICATION AND SELECTION

TIMETABLE (FOR STUDENTS ENTERING FALL 2014)

Earliest filing date: 06/03/2013
Latest filing date: 01/01/2014
Earliest date for acceptance offers: 12/01/2013
Maximum time in days for applicant's response to acceptance offer: 30
Requests for deferred entrance considered: No
Fee for application: Yes
Amount of fee for application:
In state: $75 Out of state: $75 International: N/A
Fee waiver available: No

	FIRST DEPOSIT	SECOND DEPOSIT	THIRD DEPOSIT
Required to hold place	$500	$500	No
Resident amount	$500	$500	
Nonresident amount	$500	$500	
Deposit due	30 days		
Applied to tuition	Yes	Yes	
Refundable	No	No	

APPLICATION PROCESS

Participates in Associated American Dental Schools Application Service (AADSAS): Yes
Accepts direct applicants: No
Secondary or supplemental application required: Yes
Secondary or supplemental application website: www.dentistry.utah.edu
Interview is mandatory: Yes
Interview is by invitation: Yes

RESIDENCY

Admissions process distinguishes between in-state and out-of-state applicants: Yes
Preference given to residents of: Utah
Reciprocity Admissions Agreement available for legal residents of: NA
Applications are accepted from non-U.S. citizens/non-U.S. permanent residents: No

CURRICULUM

The University of Utah School of Dentistry will utilize new innovations in dental education combined with time-tested methods. Professional qualities and ethical conduct will be the core elements in providing quality, comprehensive dental care to our patients. The D.D.S. program will provide students with an excellent clinical education in the School's dental clinics and the University of Utah's community clinics. The curriculum is based on a progressive presentation of oral health topics and subjects with increasing depth and complexity throughout the length of the program. This curriculum will support and maintain academic excellence in the oral health sciences through professional interaction with University Health Sciences disciplines such as medicine, pharmacy, etc. Students will be active participants along with faculty in their education process. The majority of student education will take place in our new Oral Health Sciences Education Building that includes lecture and seminar rooms, technique and simulation labs, and comprehensive and specialty care clinics. In addition to clinical experiences in the Oral Health Sciences Building, students will participate in community and mobile clinics reaching out to underserved populations in Utah. The school will promote research to enhance knowledge, advance oral health care, and transition findings to the practice of dentistry.

SPECIAL PROGRAMS AND SERVICES

PREDENTAL

Pre-Dental Advising Office: ppa@uc.utah.edu

DURING DENTAL SCHOOL

Academic counseling and tutoring
Community service opportunities
Internships, externships, or extramural programs
Mentoring
Personal counseling
Professional- and career-development programming
Research opportunities
Training for those interested in academic careers

ACTIVE STUDENT ORGANIZATIONS

To be determined

INTERNATIONAL DENTISTS

Graduates of international dental schools considered for traditional Predoctoral program: No
Advanced standing program offered for graduates of international dental schools: No

COMBINED AND ALTERNATE DEGREES

Ph.D.	M.S.	M.P.H.	M.D.	B.A./B.S.	Other
—	—	—	—	—	—

ESTIMATED COSTS: 2012-13 SCHOOL YEAR

	FIRST YEAR	SECOND YEAR	THIRD YEAR	FOURTH YEAR
Tuition, resident	TBD			
Tuition, nonresident	TBD			
Tuition, other	TBD			
Fees	TBD			
Instruments, books, and supplies	TBD			
Estimated living expenses	TBD			
Total, resident	TBD			
Total, nonresident	TBD			
Total, other	TBD			

FINANCIAL AID

Students need to complete the Free Application for Federal Student Aid (FAFSA) in order to apply for financial aid. The Financial Aid Office encourages all students to file the FAFSA via the Web at www.fafsa.ed.gov after January 1 of the admission year. Students may estimate their income for the previous year in order to complete the FAFSA. The school code for the University of Utah is 003675. Once the student has submitted the completed FAFSA application, the Financial Aid Office will be able to determine the student's eligibility for federal aid.

VIRGINIA COMMONWEALTH UNIVERSITY
SCHOOL OF DENTISTRY

Dr. David C. Sarrett, Dean

GENERAL INFORMATION

Virginia Commonwealth University (VCU) School of Dentistry is a state-supported school founded in 1893. The school is located in a historic district of Richmond, which has a population of 200,000, with approximately 1,000,000 residing in the metropolitan area. VCU has two major campuses that are less than three miles from each other: the Monroe Park Campus with an enrollment of more than 26,000 students and the VCU Medical Campus with 3,500 students. VCU's Medical campus is the site of nationally ranked comprehensive academic health center and is composed of the VCU Medical Center and the schools of Allied Health Professions, Dentistry, Medicine, Nursing, and Pharmacy.

MISSION STATEMENT:

The VCU School of Dentistry is a public, urban, research dental school, supported by the commonwealth of Virginia to serve the people of the state and the nation. The school's mission is to provide educational programs that prepare graduates who are qualified to provide dental care services; generate new knowledge through research and other scholarly activity; and provide quality oral health care to the public and service to the community. The school's overall higher purpose is enhancing the quality of life through improved oral health. In the pursuit of its higher purpose, the school is guided by a set of unchanging core values—commitment to the oral health needs of Virginia residents; excellence in teaching and promotion of learning; advancement of science and scholarship; ethical, compassionate, evidence-based patient care; a culture of lifelong learning; professional and social responsibility; and respect in interaction with all people.

Type of institution: Public
Year opened: 1893
Term type: Semester
Time to degree in months: 42
Start month: July

Doctoral dental degree offered: D.D.S.
Total predoctoral enrollment: 400
Estimated entering class size: 95
Campus setting: Urban
Campus housing available: Yes

PREPARATION

Formal minimum preparation in semester/quarter hours: Semester: 90 Quarter: 120
Baccalaureate degree preferred: Yes
Number of first-year, first-time enrollees whose highest degree is:
- Baccalaureate: 84
- Master's: 7
- Ph.D. or other doctorate: 0

Of first-year, first-time enrollees without baccalaureates, the number with:
- Equivalent of 60 undergraduate credit hours or less: 0
- Equivalent of 61-90 undergraduate credit hours: 0
- Equivalent of 91 or more undergraduate credit hours: 4

PREREQUISITE COURSE	REQUIRED	RECOMMENDED	LAB REQUIRED	CREDITS (SEMESTER/QUARTER)
BCP (biology-chemistry-physics) sciences				
Biology	✓		✓	8/12
Chemistry, general/inorganic	✓		✓	8/12
Chemistry, organic	✓		✓	8/12
Physics	✓		✓	8/12
Additional biological sciences				
Anatomy		✓		
Biochemistry	✓			3/5
Cell biology		✓		3/5
Histology		✓		3/5
Immunology		✓		3/5

(Prerequisite Courses continued)

CONTACT INFORMATION

www.dentistry.vcu.edu
520 North 12th Street
P.O. Box 980566
Richmond, VA 23298-0566
Phone: 804-827-2077

OFFICE OF ADMISSIONS

Dr. Michael Healy
Associate Dean for Admissions
520 North 12th Street
P.O. Box 980566
Richmond, VA 23298
Phone: 804-828-9196

OFFICE OF FINANCIAL AID

Karen D. Gilliam
Director of Financial Aid
P.O. Box 980566
Richmond, VA 23298-0566
Phone: 804-828-9953

STUDENT SERVICES & MINORITY AFFAIRS

Dr. Carolyn Booker
Associate Dean for Student Services
520 North 12th Street
P.O. Box 980566
Richmond, VA 23298-0566
Phone: 804-828-9953

OFFICE OF ACADEMIC AFFAIRS

Dr. Ellen Byrne
Associate Dean for Academic Affairs
520 North 12th Street
P.O. Box 980566
Richmond, VA 23298-0566
Phone: 804-828-3784
Email: bebyrne@vcu.edu

HOUSING

P.O. Box 980243
Richmond, VA 23298-0243
Phone: 804-828-1800

INTERNATIONAL STUDENTS

Dr. Blair Brown
Director-Global Education
Millhiser House
916 West Franklin Street
Richmond, VA 23284
Phone: 804-828-6016

PREPARATION (CONTINUED)

PREREQUISITE COURSE	REQUIRED	RECOMMENDED	LAB REQUIRED	CREDITS (SEMESTER/QUARTER)
Microbiology		✓		3/5
Molecular biology/genetics		✓		3/5
Physiology		✓		
Zoology		✓		

Community college coursework accepted for prerequisites: Yes
Community college coursework accepted for electives: Yes
Limits on community college credit hours: Yes
Maximum number of community college credit hours: 60
Advanced placement (AP) credit accepted for prerequisites: Yes
Advanced placement (AP) credit accepted for electives: Yes
Comments regarding AP credit: Must be accepted by undergraduate institution
Job shadowing: Recommended
Number of hours of job shadowing required or recommended: 150
Other factors considered in admission: Whole file review

DAT

Mandatory: Yes
Latest DAT for consideration of application: 12/31/2013
Oldest DAT considered: 12/31/2010
When more than one DAT score is reported: Highest DAT exam is considered
Canadian DAT accepted: Yes
Application considered before DAT scores are submitted: No

DAT: 2012 ENTERING CLASS

ENROLLEE DAT SCORES	RANGE	MEAN
Academic Average	26.0-17.0	20.0
Perceptual Ability	27.0-16.0	20.0
Total Science	27.0-18.0	20.0

GPA: 2012 ENTERING CLASS

ENROLLEE GPA SCORES	RANGE	MEAN
Science GPA	2.33-4.05	3.50
Total GPA	2.47-4.04	3.57

APPLICATION AND SELECTION

TIMETABLE

Earliest filing date: 06/01/2013
Latest filing date: 11/01/2013
Earliest date for acceptance offers: 12/01/2013
Maximum time in days for applicant's response to acceptance offer:
30 days if accepted on or after December 1
15 days if accepted on or after February 1
Requests for deferred entrance considered: In exceptional circumstances only
Fee for application: Yes, submitted at same time as Associated American Dental Schools Application Service (AADSAS) application
Amount of fee for application:
In state: $80 Out of state: $80 International: $80
Fee waiver available: No

	FIRST DEPOSIT	SECOND DEPOSIT	THIRD DEPOSIT
Required to hold place	Yes	Yes	No
Resident amount	$500	$300	
Nonresident amount	$500	$300	
Deposit due	Indicated in acceptance offer	04/01/2014	
Applied to tuition	Yes	Yes	
Refundable	No	No	

APPLICATION PROCESS

Participates in AADSAS: Yes
Accepts direct applicants: No
Secondary or supplemental application required: Yes, for candidates invited for interview
Secondary or supplemental application website: Please visit www.dentistry.vcu.edu
Interview is mandatory: Yes
Interview is by invitation: Yes

RESIDENCY

Admissions process distinguishes between in-state/in-province and out-of-state/out-of-province applicants: Yes
Preference given to residents of: Virginia
Reciprocity Admissions Agreement available for legal residents of: None
Applications are accepted from non-U.S. citizens/non-U.S. permanent residents: Yes

APPLICATION AND ENROLLMENT	NUMBER OF APPLICANTS	ESTIMATED NUMBER INTERVIEWED	ESTIMATED NUMBER ENROLLED
In-state or province applicants	299	122	60
Out-of-state or province applicants	2,235	153	35

Generally and over time, percentage of your first-year enrollment is in-state: 65%
Origin of out-of-state enrollees (U.S.): Arizona-1, California-2, Florida-2, Georgia-1, Idaho-1, Illinois-1, Maine-1, Maryland-2, New Jersey-1, New York-2, North Carolina-1, Ohio-1, Pennsylvania-4, Tennessee-1, Texas-1, Utah-6, Vermont-1
Origin of international enrollees: Kuwait-3

DEMOGRAPHIC DESCRIPTIONS OF APPLICANTS: 2012 ENTERING CLASS

	APPLICANTS		ENROLLEES	
	M	W	M	W
Hispanic/Latino of any race	61	63	3	1
American Indian or Alaska Native	2	2	0	0
Asian	445	441	9	15
Black or African American	51	86	0	7
Native Hawaiian or Other Pacific Islander	3	4	0	0
White	838	539	28	28
Two or more races				
Race and ethnicity unknown	14	12		
International	36	28	3	0

	MINIMUM	MAXIMUM	MEAN
2012 entering class enrollees by age	19	40	25

Number of first-time enrollees over age 30: 10

CURRICULUM

The curriculum incorporates the basic sciences, preclinical sciences, and clinical skills experiences to develop competent practitioners who are lifelong learners. Students begin their preclinical-skills development early, utilizing virtual-reality type simulation laboratories. A continuing skills development program progresses throughout the first and second years of their education. Patient treatment begins prior to the end of the second year.

Our patient-centered clinical emphasis, including rural community-based clinics, promotes a strong clinical experience and provides a culturally competent environment to our students. During the third year, students reinforce clinical skill development in each of the dental specialties and general practice clinics. Clinical rotations are included to provide students a broad experience in patient management and treatment.

The multidisciplinary practice group model of our clinical component provides a diverse patient population for a variety of dental treatments. Our integrated preclinical and clinical curriculum educates dental professionals in critical thinking, professionalism, and practice management. The hallmark of our program is clinical dentistry, while our strength is our student body.

Student research opportunities: Yes

SPECIAL PROGRAMS AND SERVICES

PREDENTAL

Dental Career Exploration Program
Postbaccalaureate programs
Summer enrichment programs: VCU Summer Academic Enrichment Program (SAEP)
VCU Scholars Academic Year High School Program

DURING DENTAL SCHOOL

Academic counseling and tutoring
Community service opportunities: Required rotations
Internships, externships, or extramural programs
Mentoring
Personal counseling
Professional- and career-development programming
Training for those interested in academic careers
Transfer applicants considered if space is available: Sophomore year

ACTIVE STUDENT ORGANIZATIONS

American Association of Dental Research Student Research Group
American Dental Education Association (ADEA)
American Student Dental Association
Student National Dental Association
Uniformed Services Dental Student Association

INTERNATIONAL DENTISTS

Graduates of international dental schools considered for traditional predoctoral program: Yes
Advanced standing program offered for graduates of international dental schools: Yes
Advanced standing program description: International Dentist Program (IDP) provides a limited number of foreign-trained dentists an opportunity to continue their U.S. degree requirements in a 29-month D.D.S. program. Upon successful completion of this program, the IDP student will be awarded a dental degree.

COMBINED AND ALTERNATE DEGREES

Ph.D.	M.S.	M.P.H.	M.D.	B.A./B.S.	Other
✓	✓	✓	—	—	✓

Other Degree: D.M.D./Ph.D.

COSTS: 2012-13 SCHOOL YEAR

	FIRST YEAR	SECOND YEAR	THIRD YEAR	FOURTH YEAR
Tuition, resident	$25,982	$25,982	$25,982	$25,982
Tuition, nonresident	$50,205	$50,205	$50,205	$50,205
Tuition, other	NA	NA	NA	NA
Fees	$11,102	$10,677	$10,493	$10,493
Instruments, books, and supplies	$5,542	$1,890	$1,583	$4,081
Estimated living expenses	$16,744	$16,744	$16,744	$15,222
Total, resident	$59,370	$55,293	$54,802	$55,778
Total, nonresident	$83,593	$79,516	$79,025	$80,001
Total, other	NA	NA	NA	NA

FINANCIAL AID

Professional students are eligible to receive financial aid primarily in the form of student loans. Students interested in applying for financial aid should complete the Free Application for Federal Student Aid (FAFSA) online at www.fafsa.ed.gov. Failure to resolve any problems with the processing of the application, or delays in resolving the problems, may preclude the student from being considered for these loans. The maximum loan awards are $8,500 subsidized and $36,444 unsubsidized annually. Students must complete an Authorization Form, Master Promissory Note (MPN), and complete entrance counseling prior to funds disbursing.

There were 39 recipients of scholarships and grants in the 2011 entering class. Awards were between $1,000 and $12,000. Residents received an average of $3,600 and nonresidents received an average of $3,200. Eighty-eight students received student loans between $8,500 and $42,944. The average student loan was $51,444.

The average 2012 graduate indebtedness was $152,652.

UW School of Dentistry University of Washington

UNIVERSITY OF WASHINGTON
SCHOOL OF DENTISTRY

Dr. Joel H. Berg, Dean

GENERAL INFORMATION

The University of Washington School of Dentistry offers an excellent education leading to a professional health care career in a challenging and growing discipline. The School of Dentistry is located on the University of Washington's main campus, which occupies approximately 700 acres on the shores of Portage Bay and Lake Washington in north-central Seattle. Established in 1945, the School of Dentistry is one of six professional schools that are components of the state-supported Warren G. Magnuson Health Sciences Center, an internationally recognized teaching, research, and patient-care facility. The other components include the schools of Medicine, Nursing, Pharmacy, Social Work, and Public Health and Community Medicine; six special research centers and institutes; the University of Washington Medical Center; Harborview Medical Center; the Fred Hutchinson Cancer Research Center; and Children's Hospital and Regional Medical Center.

MISSION STATEMENT:

The school is an oral health care center of excellence serving the people of the state of Washington and the Pacific Northwest. Our primary mission, through educational, research, and service programs, is to prepare students to be competent oral health care professionals. The school's research programs contribute to the fundamental understanding of biologic processes and to the behavioral, biomedical, and clinical aspects of oral health. The service mission is to improve the health and well-being of the people of the community and the region through outreach programs that are especially attentive to minority and underserved populations. The school values diversity in its students, staff, faculty, and patient populations. It seeks to foster an environment of mutual respect where objectivity, imaginative inquiry, and the free exchange of ideas can flourish to facilitate personal development, professionalism, and a strong sense of self-worth.

Type of institution: Public
Year opened: 1945
Term type: Quarter
Time to degree in months: 40
Start month: August

Doctoral dental degree offered: D.D.S.
Total predoctoral enrollment: 252
Estimated entering class size: 63
Campus setting: Urban
Campus housing available: Yes

PREPARATION

Formal minimum preparation in semester/quarter hours: Semester: 120 Quarter: 180
Baccalaureate degree preferred: Yes
Number of first-year, first-time enrollees whose highest degree is:
- Baccalaureate: 62
- Master's: 1
- Ph.D. or other doctorate: 1

Of first-year, first-time enrollees without baccalaureates, the number with:
- Equivalent of 60 undergraduate credit hours or less: 0
- Equivalent of 61-90 undergraduate credit hours: 0
- Equivalent of 91 or more undergraduate credit hours: 1

PREREQUISITE COURSE	REQUIRED	RECOMMENDED	LAB REQUIRED	CREDITS (SEMESTER/QUARTER)
BCP (biology-chemistry-physics) sciences				
Biology	✓		✓	12/18
Chemistry, general/inorganic	✓		✓	8/12
Chemistry, organic	✓		✓	8/12
Physics	✓			12/18
Additional biological sciences				
Anatomy		✓		
Biochemistry	✓			8/12

(Prerequisite Courses continued)

CONTACT INFORMATION

www.dental.washington.edu
D322 Health Sciences Building
Box 356365
Seattle, WA 98195
Phone: 206-543-5982
Fax: 206-616-2612

STUDENT LIFE AND ADMISSIONS

Kathleen Craig
Admissions Officer, Student Life and Admissions
D323 Health Sciences Building
Box 356365
Seattle, WA 98195-6365
Phone: 206-685-9484
www.dental.washington.edu

Carol Brown
Manager, Student Life and Admissions
D323 Health Sciences Building
Box 356365
Seattle, WA 98195-6365
Phone: 206-685-2372
www.dental.washington.edu

Dr. Susan Coldwell
Associate Dean for Student Life and Admissions
D323 Health Sciences Building
Box 356365
Seattle, WA 98195-6365
Phone: 206-685-9484
www.dental.washington.edu

EDUCATIONAL PARTNERSHIPS AND DIVERSITY

Dr. Beatrice Gandara
Director, Educational Partnerships and Diversity
D323 Health Sciences Building
Box 356365
Seattle, WA 98195-6365
Phone: 206-616-6010
www.dental.washington.edu

INTERNATIONAL DDS PROGRAM

Memory Brock, Program Manager
D323 Health Sciences Building
Box 356365
Seattle WA 98195-6365
Phone: 206-685-7309
www.dental.washington.edu

HOUSING

http://hfs.washington.edu

PREPARATION (CONTINUED)

PREREQUISITE COURSE	REQUIRED	RECOMMENDED	LAB REQUIRED	CREDITS (SEMESTER/QUARTER)
Cell biology				
Histology		✓		
Immunology				
Microbiology	✓			8/12
Molecular biology/genetics				
Physiology				
Zoology				

Community college coursework accepted for prerequisites: Yes
Community college coursework accepted for electives: Yes
Limits on community college credit hours: No
Maximum number of community college credit hours: 90
Advanced placement (AP) credit accepted for prerequisites: Yes
Advanced placement (AP) credit accepted for electives: Yes
Job shadowing: Required
Number of hours of job shadowing required or recommended: Minimum 100 hours

DAT

Mandatory: Yes
DAT: Must complete by October 31 one year prior
Latest DAT for consideration of application: 10/31/2013
Oldest DAT considered: 06/01/2009
When more than one DAT score is reported: Highest score is considered.
Canadian DAT accepted: Yes
Application considered before DAT scores are submitted: No

DAT: 2012 ENTERING CLASS

ENROLLEE DAT SCORES	RANGE	MEAN
Academic Average	26.0-17.0	20.4
Perceptual Ability	30.0-17.0	21.3
Total Science	26.0-18.0	20.2

GPA: 2012 ENTERING CLASS

ENROLLEE GPA SCORES	RANGE	MEAN
Science GPA	2.97-4.00	3.51
Total GPA	2.98-4.00	3.58

APPLICATION AND SELECTION

TIMETABLE

Earliest filing date: 06/01/2013
Latest filing date: 11/01/2013
Earliest date for acceptance offers: 12/01/2013
Maximum time in days for applicant's response to acceptance offer:
30 days if accepted on or after December 1
15 days if accepted on or after January 1
Requests for deferred entrance considered: No
Fee for application: Yes, submitted only when requested.
Amount of fee for application:
In state: $35 Out of state: $35 International: NA
Fee waiver available: Yes

	FIRST DEPOSIT	SECOND DEPOSIT	THIRD DEPOSIT
Required to hold place	Yes	No	No
Resident amount	$500		
Nonresident amount	$500		
Deposit due	As indicated in admission offer		
Applied to tuition	Yes		
Refundable	No		

APPLICATION PROCESS

Participates in Associated American Dental Schools Application Service (AADSAS): Yes
Accepts direct applicants: No
Secondary or supplemental application required: Yes. Applicants are screened to receive a supplemental application.
Secondary or supplemental application website: NA
Interview is mandatory: Yes
Interview is by invitation: Yes

RESIDENCY

Admissions process distinguishes between in-state/in-province and out-of-state/out-of-province applicants: Yes
Preference given to residents of: Washington, followed by Western Interstate Commission for Higher Education (WICHE) state residents
Reciprocity Admissions Agreement available for legal residents of: None
Applications are accepted from non-U.S. citizens/non-U.S. permanent residents: No

APPLICATION AND ENROLLMENT	NUMBER OF APPLICANTS	ESTIMATED NUMBER INTERVIEWED	ESTIMATED NUMBER ENROLLED
In-state or province applicants	218	107	54
Out-of-state or province applicants	866	47	8

Generally and over time, percentage of your first-year enrollment is in-state: 90%
Origin of out-of-state enrollees (U.S.): Arizona-2, Alaska-1, Hawaii-1, Idaho-1, Montana-3,
Origin of international enrollees: NA

DEMOGRAPHIC DESCRIPTIONS OF APPLICANTS: 2012 ENTERING CLASS

	APPLICANTS		ENROLLEES	
	M	W	M	W
Hispanic/Latino of any race	40	37	3	0
American Indian or Alaska Native	1	1	0	0
Asian	173	174	10	7
Black or African American	5	14	0	0
Native Hawaiian or Other Pacific Islander	0	1	0	0
White	322	203	23	13
Two or more races	25	19	2	1
Race and ethnicity unknown	21	19	2	0
International	12	8	0	0

Note: 10 applicants did not report gender.

	MINIMUM	MAXIMUM	MEAN
2012 entering class enrollees by age	21	38	25

Number of first-time enrollees over age 30: 7

CURRICULUM

The School of Dentistry's four-year D.D.S. curriculum provides students with opportunities to learn the fundamental principles significant to the entire body of oral health. Students (approximately 63 per class) learn the basic health sciences, attain proficiency in clinical skills, develop an understanding of professional and ethical principles, and develop reasoning and critical decision-making skills that will enable implementation of the dental knowledge base. Elective courses are offered by all departments, including opportunities in independent study, research, seminars on various topics, and special clinical topics.

Year 1. Divided among lecture, laboratory, and preclinical activities in the basic sciences, dental anatomy, occlusion, and dental materials. There are also early clinical experiences in preventive dentistry and periodontics.

Year 2. Development of additional preclinical skills and learning how basic science principles are applied to the clinical setting.

Student research opportunities: Yes

SPECIAL PROGRAMS AND SERVICES

PREDENTAL

Association of American Medical Colleges/ADEA Summer Medical and Dental Education Program (AAMC/ADEA SMDEP)
Other summer enrichment programs

DURING DENTAL SCHOOL

Academic counseling and tutoring
Community service opportunities
Mentoring
Personal counseling

ACTIVE STUDENT ORGANIZATIONS

American Association of Dental Research Student Research Group
American Association of Women Dentists
American Dental Education Association (ADEA)
American Student Dental Association
Hispanic Dental Association
Student National Dental Association

INTERNATIONAL DENTISTS

Graduates of international dental schools considered for traditional predoctoral program: No

Advanced standing program offered for graduates of international dental schools: Yes (International Doctor of Dental Surgery [IDDS] program)

COMBINED AND ALTERNATE DEGREES

Ph.D.	M.S.	M.P.H.	M.D.	B.A./B.S.	Other
✓	—	✓	—	—	—

COSTS: 2012-13 SCHOOL YEAR

	FIRST YEAR	SECOND YEAR	THIRD YEAR	FOURTH YEAR
Tuition, resident	$32,948	$30,538	$39,313	$39,313
Tuition, nonresident	$53,018	$53,018	$69,743	$69,743
Tuition, other	NA	NA	NA	NA
Fees	$270	$135	$0	$0
Instruments, books, and supplies	$10,230	$10,479	$5,436	$3,280
Estimated living expenses	$17,427	$17,427	$23,236	$23,236
Total, resident	$60,875	$58,579	$67,985	$65,829
Total, nonresident	$80,945	$81,059	$98,415	$96,259
Total, other	NA	NA	NA	NA

FINANCIAL AID

Financial aid for students attending the University of Washington School of Dentistry is available through a variety of sources including scholarships from privately donated funds that do not have to be repaid; grants from federal and state funds that do not have to be repaid; and loans that generally must be repaid starting six months after a student leaves the program. See the University's Office of Student Financial Aid (OSFA) website at www.washington.edu/students/osfa for more detailed information.

To qualify for financial aid, you must be a U.S. citizen or permanent resident, be admitted to the university in a degree-granting program, provide financial information by submitting a Free Application for Federal Student Aid (FAFSA), demonstrate financial need, not be in default on a previous student loan or owe a repayment on a grant, and be making satisfactory progress toward a degree. To ensure you will continue to receive financial aid each quarter, you must be in good standing and be enrolled full time (at least 12 credits).

All students who anticipate a need for financial aid must complete the FAFSA each year. To ensure timely receipt of your application, we recommend that you mail the FAFSA or send it electronically no later than February 15, and preferably in early January. To be considered for aid at the University of Washington, you must submit our financial aid code of 003798 in Section H. If you miss the FAFSA filing deadline, your options for financial aid will be reduced, so it is extremely important that you file on time.

WEST VIRGINIA UNIVERSITY
SCHOOL OF DENTISTRY

Dr. David A. Felton, Dean

CONTACT INFORMATION

http://dentistry.hsc.wvu.edu
P.O. Box 9400
Morgantown, WV 26506-9400
Phone: 304-293-2521
Fax: 304-293-5829

OFFICE OF ADMISSIONS

Dr. Shelia S. Price
Associate Dean for Admissions, Recruitment, and Access
P.O. Box 9407
Morgantown, WV 26506-9407
Phone: 304-293-6646
Fax: 304-293-8561
Email: dentaladmit@hsc.wvu.edu
http://dentistry.hsc.wvu.edu

FINANCIAL AID

Candi Frazier
Associate Director
P.O. Box 9810
Morgantown, WV 26506-9810
Phone: 304-293-3706
www.hsc.wvu.edu/fin

STUDENT AND ALUMNI AFFAIRS

Dr. Robert L. Wanker
Assistant Dean
P.O. 9404
Morgantown, WV 26506-9404
Phone: 304-293-5589
http://dentistry.hsc.wvu.edu

HOUSING

Corey Farris
Director
P.O. Box 6430
Morgantown, WV 26506-6430
Phone: 304-293-4491
http://housing.wvu.edu

OFFICE OF INTERNATIONAL STUDENTS & SCHOLARS

Michael Wilhelm
Director
P.O. Box 6411
Morgantown, WV 26506-6411
Phone: 304-293-3519
http://oiss.wvu.edu

GENERAL INFORMATION

The West Virginia University (WVU) School of Dentistry opened in September 1957 and has been the oral health education center for West Virginia for more than five decades. The school is located in Morgantown, West Virginia, a community with a population of approximately 30,000. Morgantown has been ranked the number one small city in the nation and is one of the fastest growing areas in the state. The school enrolls approximately 300 students who appreciate the benefits of attending dental school in a small town and being members of a relatively small class. The school offers programs of education leading to a Doctor of Dental Surgery (D.D.S.) degree; Master of Science degrees in dental hygiene, endodontics, orthodontics, or prosthodontics; a Bachelor of Science degree in dental hygiene; a degree-completion program for dental hygiene associate degree holders; a one-year general practice residency; a one-year oral and maxillofacial surgery internship; and a four-year certificate program in oral and maxillofacial surgery. Dual-degree programs are offered as a curricular option enabling the dental student to also earn a master's degree in public health or business administration. Due to its location within the university's Health Sciences Center, the school is developing interprofessional educational opportunities for students with the schools of Medicine, Nursing, Pharmacy, and Public Health. Training is provided in a humanistic learning environment with state-of-the art technology, including electronic health records, digital radiography, digital implant planning and dental simulation technology. Dynamic educational, service, and research experiences help students become clinically competent and culturally aware oral health professionals.

MISSION STATEMENT:

It is the mission of the West Virginia University School of Dentistry to promote a diverse and dynamic learning environment that addresses the present and future oral health needs of the citizens of West Virginia and beyond by providing an oral health center committed to excellence and innovation in education, research, patient care, service and technology.

Type of institution: Public
Year opened: 1957
Term type: Semester
Time to degree in months: 45
Start month: August

Doctoral dental degree offered: D.D.S.
Total predoctoral enrollment: 203
Estimated entering class size: 60
Campus setting: Rural
Campus housing available: Yes

PREPARATION

Formal minimum preparation in semester/quarter hours: Semester: 90
Baccalaureate degree preferred: Yes
Number of first-year, first-time enrollees whose highest degree is:
- Baccalaureate: 47
- Master's: 2
- Ph.D. or other doctorate: 0

Of first-year, first-time enrollees without baccalaureates, the number with:
- Equivalent of 60 undergraduate credit hours or less: 0
- Equivalent of 61-90 undergraduate credit hours: 0
- Equivalent of 91 or more undergraduate credit hours: 11

PREREQUISITE COURSE	REQUIRED	RECOMMENDED	LAB REQUIRED	CREDITS (SEMESTER/QUARTER)
BCP (biology-chemistry-physics) sciences				
Biology	✓		✓	8/12
Chemistry, general/inorganic	✓		✓	8/12
Chemistry, organic	✓		✓	8/12
Physics	✓		✓	8/12
Additional biological sciences				
Anatomy	✓			3/5

(Prerequisite Courses continued)

PREPARATION (CONTINUED)

PREREQUISITE COURSE	REQUIRED	RECOMMENDED	LAB REQUIRED	CREDITS (SEMESTER/QUARTER)
Biochemistry	✓			3/5
Cell biology		✓		4/6
Histology		✓		4/6
Immunology		✓		4/6
Microbiology		✓		4/6
Molecular biology/genetics		✓		4/6
Physiology		✓		4/6
Zoology		✓		4/6
Other				
English composition	✓			6/10
Psychology		✓		3/5

Community college coursework accepted for prerequisites: Yes
Community college coursework accepted for electives: Yes
Limits on community college credit hours: Yes
Maximum number of community college credit hours: 64
Advanced placement (AP) credit accepted for prerequisites: No
Advanced placement (AP) credit accepted for electives: No
Comments regarding AP credit: AP credits are only accepted for English requirement.
Job shadowing: Required
Number of hours of job shadowing required or recommended: 50 minimum; variety of experiences recommended
Other factors considered in admission: The committee focuses on five parameters: academic achievement; Dental Admission Test scores; dental shadowing; life, career, and volunteer experiences; and personal interview.

DAT

Mandatory: Yes
Latest DAT for consideration of application: 11/01/2013
Oldest DAT considered: 11/01/2008
When more than one DAT score is reported: Highest overall score is considered.
Canadian DAT accepted: Yes
Application considered before DAT scores are submitted: Yes

DAT: 2012 ENTERING CLASS

ENROLLEE DAT SCORES	RANGE	MEAN
Academic Average	16.0-23.0	18.0
Perceptual Ability	14.0-24.0	19.0
Total Science	15.0-24.0	18.0

GPA: 2012 ENTERING CLASS

ENROLLEE GPA SCORES	RANGE	MEAN
Science GPA	2.44-4.00	3.47
Total GPA	2.43-4.00	3.62

APPLICATION AND SELECTION

TIMETABLE

Earliest filing date: 06/01/2013
Latest filing date: 11/01/2013
Earliest date for acceptance offers: 12/01/2013
Maximum time in days for applicant's response to acceptance offer:
30 days if accepted on or after December 1
15 days if accepted on or after February 1
Requests for deferred entrance considered: No
Fee for application: Yes, submitted only when requested.
Amount of fee for application:
In state: $50 Out of state: $50 International: $50
Fee waiver available: No

	FIRST DEPOSIT	SECOND DEPOSIT	THIRD DEPOSIT
Required to hold place	Yes	No	No
Resident amount	$400		
Nonresident amount	$800		
Deposit due	Indicated in admission offer		
Applied to tuition	Yes		
Refundable	Yes		
Refundable by	May 1		

APPLICATION PROCESS

Participates in Associated American Dental Schools Application Service (AADSAS): Yes
Accepts direct applicants: No
Secondary or supplemental application required: Yes, submitted only when requested of applicants
Secondary or supplemental application website: NA
Interview is mandatory: Yes
Interview is by invitation: Yes

RESIDENCY

Admissions process distinguishes between in-state/in-province and out-of-state/out-of-province applicants: Yes
Preference given to residents of: West Virginia

Reciprocity Admissions Agreement available for legal residents of: None
Applications are accepted from non-U.S. citizens/non-U.S. permanent residents: Yes

APPLICATION AND ENROLLMENT	NUMBER OF APPLICANTS	ESTIMATED NUMBER INTERVIEWED	ESTIMATED NUMBER ENROLLED
In-state or province applicants	78	78	41
Out-of-state or province applicants	1,138	62	19

Generally and over time, percentage of your first-year enrollment is in-state: 60%-70%
Origin of out-of-state enrollees (U.S.): Arkansas-1, Florida-1, Illinois-1, Maryland-1, New Mexico-1, North Carolina-2, Ohio-2, Pennsylvania-2, Tennessee-1, Utah-1, Virginia-4
Origin of international enrollees: Kuwait-2

DEMOGRAPHIC DESCRIPTIONS OF APPLICANTS: 2012 ENTERING CLASS

	APPLICANTS		ENROLLEES	
	M	W	M	W
Hispanic/Latino of any race	36	24	0	0
American Indian or Alaska Native	0	0	0	0
Asian	141	164	4	5
Black or African American	11	16	0	0
Native Hawaiian or Other Pacific Islander	0	0	0	0
White	411	284	26	21
Two or more races	14	15	0	1
Race and ethnicity unknown	24	10	1	0
International	29	21	2	0

Note: Sixteen (16) applicants did not report gender; of those 4 also did not report race..

	MINIMUM	MAXIMUM	MEAN
2012 entering class enrollees by age	21	34	23

Number of first-time enrollees over age 30: 4

CURRICULUM

The School of Dentistry recognizes its obligation to produce professionals capable of meeting the oral health needs of the public and providing leadership for the dental profession. The school offers a four-year program leading to the degree of Doctor of Dental Surgery (D.D.S.) and provides students with a learning environment in which to develop the technical competence, intellectual capacity, and professional responsibility necessary to meet the oral health needs of a globally diverse society in a state of constant transformation. The predoctoral curriculum consists of eight semesters and three summer sessions. Students are enrolled in courses designed primarily to prepare them for the general practice of dentistry. Student progress is monitored regularly by the Academic and Professional Standards Committee and a team leader program, which exists to ensure students have varied and appropriate learning experiences to achieve competency and to provide comprehensive health care to a family of patients.

Student research opportunities: Yes

SPECIAL PROGRAMS AND SERVICES

PREDENTAL

Special affiliations with colleges and universities: Shepherd University Dental Early Admissions Program
Summer enrichment programs

DURING DENTAL SCHOOL

Academic counseling and tutoring
Community service opportunities
Mentoring
Personal counseling
Professional- and career-development programming
Training for those interested in academic careers
Transfer applicants considered if space is available

ACTIVE STUDENT ORGANIZATIONS

American Association of Dental Research Student Research Group
American Student Dental Association
Delta Sigma Delta
Hispanic Dental Association

INTERNATIONAL DENTISTS

Graduates of international dental schools considered for traditional predoctoral program: Yes
Advanced standing program offered for graduates of international dental schools: No
Advanced standing program description: NA

COMBINED AND ALTERNATE DEGREES

Ph.D.	M.S.	M.P.H.	M.D.	B.A./B.S.	Other
—	—	✓	—	—	✓

Other degree: A dual degree in business administration is also available.

COSTS: 2012-13 SCHOOL YEAR

	FIRST YEAR	SECOND YEAR	THIRD YEAR	FOURTH YEAR
Tuition, resident	$20,503	$20,503	$20,503	$15,624
Tuition, nonresident	$51,337	$51,337	$51,337	$41,378
Tuition, other				
Fees	$2,667	$2,667	$2,667	$1,778
Instruments, books, and supplies	$16,229	$8,563	$6,821	$4,055
Estimated living expenses	$15,334	$14,809	$14,809	$10,188
Total, resident	$54,733	$46,542	$44,800	$31,645
Total, nonresident	$85,567	$77,376	$75,634	$57,399
Total, other				

FINANCIAL AID

To apply for financial aid at the West Virginia University (WVU) School of Dentistry, complete the Free Application for Federal Student Aid (FAFSA) online with the federal processor at www.fafsa.gov. WVU's school code is 003827. Although not required, it is recommended that parent information be included on the FAFSA to be considered for all available aid programs. Apply by March 1 to be considered for maximum financial aid. When WVU receives the results from the federal processor, financial aid eligibility is determined by the Financial Aid Office, and award notifications are mailed to students. Visit the WVU Financial Aid website at www.hsc.wvu.edu/fin for information on the application process, eligibility requirements, types of aid, etc.

MARQUETTE UNIVERSITY
SCHOOL OF DENTISTRY

Dr. William K. Lobb, Dean

GENERAL INFORMATION

The Marquette University School of Dentistry is an independent, coeducational institution of professional training founded in 1907 when the Milwaukee Medical College affiliated with Marquette College to become Marquette University. By August 2011, the School of Dentistry had graduated almost 9,000 dentists. The school is located near the business and cultural center of Milwaukee, Wisconsin, a city with a population of approximately 600,000. The campus includes 54 buildings and 90 acres, forming an attractive, self-contained campus in the heart of a major urban center.

MISSION STATEMENT:

The School of Dentistry is committed to excellence in education, scholarship, and the provision of high-quality oral health care. Consistent with Marquette University traditions and values, the school recruits and educates a diverse student body, fosters personal and professional excellence, and promotes leadership expressed in service to others.

Type of institution: Private and state-related
Year opened: 1894
Term type: Semester
Time to degree in months: 45
Start month: August

Doctoral dental degree offered: D.D.S.
Total predoctoral enrollment: 320
Estimated entering class size: 100
Campus setting: Urban
Campus housing available: No

PREPARATION

Formal minimum preparation in semester/quarter hours: Semester: 90 Quarter: 120
Baccalaureate degree preferred: Yes
Number of first-year, first-time enrollees whose highest degree:
- Baccalaureate: 59
- Master's: 4
- Ph.D. or other doctorate: 0

Of first-year, first-time enrollees without baccalaureates, the number with:
- Equivalent of 60 undergraduate credit hours or less: 0
- Equivalent of 61-90 undergraduate credit hours: 0
- Equivalent of 91 or more undergraduate credit hours: 17

PREREQUISITE COURSE	REQUIRED	RECOMMENDED	LAB REQUIRED	CREDITS (SEMESTER/QUARTER)
BCP (biology-chemistry-physics) sciences				
Biology	✓		✓	8/12
Chemistry, general/inorganic	✓		✓	8/12
Chemistry, organic	✓		✓	8/12
Physics	✓		✓	8/12
Additional biological sciences				
Anatomy		✓		
Biochemistry	✓			3/5
Cell biology		✓		
Histology		✓		
Immunology		✓		
Microbiology		✓		
Molecular biology/genetics		✓		
Physiology		✓		
Zoology		✓		

(Prerequisite Courses continued)

CONTACT INFORMATION

www.marquette.edu/dentistry
P.O. Box 1881
Milwaukee, WI 53201
Phone: 414-288-7485
Fax: 414-288-3586

OFFICE OF ADMISSIONS

Brian T. Trecek
Director of Admissions
P.O. Box 1881
Milwaukee, WI 53201
Phone: 800-445-5385
www.marquette.edu/dentistry

OFFICE OF FINANCIAL AID

Linda Gleason
Director of Student Services
P.O. Box 1881
Milwaukee, WI 53201
Phone: 414-288-5408
www.marquette.edu/dentistry

STUDENT SERVICES

Linda Gleason
Director of Student Services
P.O. Box 1881
Milwaukee, WI 53201
Phone: 414-288-5408
www.marquette.edu/dentistry

OFFICE OF DIVERSITY

Yvonne Roland
Director of Diversity
P.O. Box 1881
Milwaukee, WI 53201
Phone: 414-288-1533
www.marquette.edu/dentistry

UNIVERSITY APARTMENTS AND OFF-CAMPUS STUDENT SERVICES

1500 West Wells Street
Milwaukee, WI 53233
Phone: 414-288-7281
www.marquette.edu

OFFICE OF INTERNATIONAL EDUCATION

P.O. Box 1881
Milwaukee, WI 53201
Phone: 414-288-7289

PREPARATION (CONTINUED)

PREREQUISITE COURSE	REQUIRED	RECOMMENDED	LAB REQUIRED	CREDITS (SEMESTER/QUARTER)
Other				
English	✓			6/9

Community college coursework accepted for prerequisites: No
Community college coursework accepted for electives: Yes
Limits on community college credit hours: Yes
Maximum number of community college credit hours: 49
Advanced placement (AP) credit accepted for prerequisites: No
Advanced placement (AP) credit accepted for electives: Yes
Comments regarding AP credit: The amount of AP credit accepted is subject to change at the discretion of the Admissions Committee.
Job shadowing: Recommended
Other factors considered in admission: Trend of performance, rigor of university coursework, and quality of undergraduate institution attended

DAT

Mandatory: Yes
Latest DAT for consideration of application: 01/01/2014
Oldest DAT considered: 01/01/2011
When more than one DAT score is reported: Most recent score only is considered
Canadian DAT accepted: Yes
Application considered before DAT scores are submitted: No

DAT: 2012 ENTERING CLASS

ENROLLEE DAT SCORES	RANGE	MEAN
Academic Average	15.0-24.0	19.5
Perceptual Ability	14.0-24.0	19.6
Total Science	15.0-25.0	19.1

GPA: 2012 ENTERING CLASS

ENROLLEE GPA SCORES	RANGE	MEAN
Science GPA	2.52 – 4.00	3.58
Total GPA	2.68 – 4.00	3.63

APPLICATION AND SELECTION

TIMETABLE

Earliest filing date: 06/01/2013
Latest filing date: 01/01/2014
Earliest date for acceptance offers: 12/01/2013
Maximum time in days for applicant's response to acceptance offer:
30 days if accepted on or after December 1
15 days if accepted on or after February 1
Requests for deferred entrance considered: In exceptional circumstances only
Fee for application: Yes, submitted at same time as Associated American Dental Schools Application Service (AADSAS) application
Amount of fee for application:
In state: $45 Out of state: $45 International: $45
Fee waiver available: Yes

	FIRST DEPOSIT	SECOND DEPOSIT	THIRD DEPOSIT
Required to hold place	Yes	No	No
Resident amount	$1,000		
Nonresident amount	$1,000		
Deposit due	As indicated in admission offer		
Applied to tuition	Yes		
Refundable	No		

APPLICATION PROCESS

Participates in AADSAS: Yes
Accepts direct applicants: No
Secondary or supplemental application required: No
Interview is mandatory: Yes
Interview is by invitation: Yes

RESIDENCY

Admissions process distinguishes between in-state/in-province and out-of-state/out-of-province applicants: Yes
Preference given to residents of: None
Reciprocity Admissions Agreement available for legal residents of: None
Applications are accepted from non-U.S. citizens/non-U.S. permanent residents: Yes

APPLICATION AND ENROLLMENT	NUMBER OF APPLICANTS	ESTIMATED NUMBER INTERVIEWED	ESTIMATED NUMBER ENROLLED
In-state or province applicants	189	96	40
Out-of-state or province applicants	2,393	192	40

Generally and over time, percentage of your first-year enrollment is in-state: 50%
Origin of out-of-state enrollees (U.S.): Alaska-1, California-3, Colorado-1, Connecticut-1, Florida-2, Illinois-10, Indiana-3, Iowa-2, Michigan-1, Minnesota-4, Missouri-2, Nebraska-1, Nevada-1, Ohio-3, Oregon-1, Utah-1, Washington-1
Origin of international enrollees: Bahamas-1, South Korea-1

DEMOGRAPHIC DESCRIPTIONS OF APPLICANTS: 2012 ENTERING CLASS

	APPLICANTS		ENROLLEES	
	M	W	M	W
Hispanic/Latino of any race	21	32	1	2
American Indian or Alaska Native	2	3	0	1
Asian	272	268	3	4
Black or African American	24	40	3	1
Native Hawaiian or Other Pacific Islander	0	1	0	0
White	905	611	36	25
Two or more races	95	78	2	2
Race and ethnicity unknown	33	28	1	2
International	76	69	0	0

Notes: Some applicants did not report gender.

	MINIMUM	MAXIMUM	MEAN
2012 entering class enrollees by age	20	41	23

Number of first-time enrollees over age 30: 1

CURRICULUM

Marquette University School of Dentistry's competency-based dental curriculum develops the skills and knowledge students need to successfully enter their profession. It impresses on students an understanding of the responsibility of delivering oral health care in an ethical manner. The curriculum embraces a patient-centered, comprehensive care model. This model emphasizes active student learning, a mentoring/modeling role for faculty, and a clinical environment that closely matches the practice of dentistry in the community. To support this educational model, faculty will continuously develop their skills as scholars and educators, leading to recognition as innovators in educational design and instruction.

Student research opportunities: Yes

SPECIAL PROGRAMS AND SERVICES

PREDENTAL

DAT workshops
Other summer enrichment programs
Special affiliations with colleges and universities: Marquette University

DURING DENTAL SCHOOL

Academic counseling and tutoring
Community service opportunities
Internships, externships, or extramural programs
Mentoring
Opportunity to study for credit at institution abroad
Personal counseling
Professional- and career-development programming
Transfer applicants considered if space is available

ACTIVE STUDENT ORGANIZATIONS

American Association of Dental Research Student Research Group
American Student Dental Association
Hispanic Dental Association
Student National Dental Association

INTERNATIONAL DENTISTS

Graduates of international dental schools considered for traditional predoctoral program: No
Advanced standing program offered for graduates of international dental schools: Yes
Advanced standing program description: Program based on a space-available basis awarding a dental degree

COMBINED AND ALTERNATE DEGREES

Ph.D.	M.S.	M.P.H.	M.D.	B.A./B.S.	Other
✓	✓	—	—	✓	—

COSTS: 2012-13 SCHOOL YEAR

	FIRST YEAR	SECOND YEAR	THIRD YEAR	FOURTH YEAR
Tuition, resident	$40,990	$40,990	$40,990	$40,990
Tuition, nonresident	$49,650	$49,650	$49,650	$49,650
Tuition, other	NA	NA	NA	NA
Fees	NA	NA	NA	NA
Instruments, books, and supplies	$11,180	$6,335	$3,565	$885
Estimated living expenses	$24,495	$24,495	$24,495	$15,854
Total, resident	$76,665	$71,820	$69,050	$57,729
Total, nonresident	$85,325	$80,480	$77,710	$66,389
Total, other	NA	NA	NA	NA

FINANCIAL AID: 2012 ENTERING CLASS ESTIMATES

	SCHOLARSHIP/ GRANT RECIPIENTS	SMALLEST AWARD	LARGEST AWARD	MEAN AWARD
Residents	11	$6,000	$10,000	$8,181
Nonresidents	11	$10,000	$24,225	$11,293

	STUDENT LOAN RECIPIENTS	SMALLEST AWARD	LARGEST AWARD	MEAN AWARD
Residents	36	$8,500	$77,012	$57,355
Nonresidents	36	$8,500	$113,672	$71,359

Average 2012 graduate indebtedness: $201,783

Financial aid is available in the form of gift assistance, loans, educational opportunities, or a combination of these. To receive financial aid from federal and state programs, students must meet the following requirements:

1. Be a U.S. citizen or an eligible noncitizen. (Students with F1, F2, J1, or J2 visas are not eligible.)
2. Be registered with Selective Service (if male between the ages of 18 and 25 and not a current member of the active armed forces)
3. Be enrolled at least half time
4. Be working toward a degree or certificate
5. Be making satisfactory academic progress
6. Not be in default on any loan or owe a refund on any grant made under Title IV of the Higher Education Act of 1965, as amended, at any institution

Students can apply for financial aid through the Office of Student Financial Aid if they are presently enrolled or are applying for admission to Marquette. No offer of financial assistance will be made until a student has been formally admitted to the university. Further information can be obtained via the contact information available in this document.

UNIVERSITY OF ALBERTA
FACULTY OF MEDICINE & DENTISTRY
School of Dentistry

UNIVERSITY OF ALBERTA
DEPARTMENT OF DENTISTRY

Dr. Paul W. Major, Chair

GENERAL INFORMATION

The University of Alberta, Canada's second-largest university, is a publicly supported, nondenominational, coeducational institution. Founded in 1908, the university has developed an international reputation in many fields and excels in medical research and other areas. Faculty members are actively involved in basic, clinical, and educational research, as well as in maintaining their personal patient skills. Their research projects often involve students as permitted by their schedules. The Department of Dentistry provides many facilities such as a complete dental laboratory, instrument sterilization on the premises, and computer systems. The University of Alberta Hospital is in close proximity, which affords easy access to varied clinical instruction, and a rotation at the Youville Hospital provides experience with geriatric patients. A rotation to northern Alberta offers senior students extensive experience in operating a practice in an underprivileged area.

MISSION STATEMENT:

The Faculty of Medicine and Dentistry is dedicated to the improvement of health through excellence and leadership in health care, medical education, and medical research. Our mission is to prepare physicians, dentists, and other health care providers to provide the highest quality of health services to the people of Alberta and beyond, and to advance knowledge and skills through fundamental, clinical, and applied research.

Type of institution: Public
Year opened: 1917
Term type: Semester
Time to degree in months: 48
Start month: August

Doctoral dental degree offered: D.D.S.
Total predoctoral enrollment: 138
Estimated entering class size: 32
Campus setting: Urban
Campus housing available: Yes

CONTACT INFORMATION

www.dent.ualberta.ca
Phone: 780-492-3312
Fax: 780-492-7536

ADMISSIONS
5th floor, Edmonton Clinic Health Academy
11405 - 87 Ave NW
Edmonton, AB T6G 1C9
Phone: 780-492-1319
www.dentistry.ualberta.ca

SCHOLARSHIPS AND AWARDS
120 Admin Building
Edmonton, AB T6G 2M7
Phone: 780-492-3221
www.dent.ualberta.ca

STUDENT AFFAIRS
Dr. Steve Patterson
Phone: 780-492-7383

INDIGENOUS HEALTH INITIATIVES PROGRAM
Shelly Gladue
Administrator
2-115 Edmonton Clinic Health Academy
Edmonton, AB T6G 1C9
Phone: 780-492-9526
www.dentistry.ualberta.ca

RESIDENCE AND OTHER HOUSING
44 Lister Hall
Edmonton, AB T6G 2N8
Phone: 780-492-4281
www.dent.ualberta.ca

INTERNATIONAL ADMISSIONS
Phone: 780-492-1100
www.dent.ualberta.ca

PREPARATION

Formal minimum preparation in semester/quarter hours: Semester: 60 Quarter: 90
Baccalaureate degree preferred: No
Number of first-year, first-time enrollees whose highest degree is:
- Baccalaureate: 18
- Master's: 1
- Ph.D. or other doctorate: 0

Of first-year, first-time enrollees without baccalaureates, the number with:
- Equivalent of 60 undergraduate credit hours or less: 8
- Equivalent of 61-90 undergraduate credit hours: 3
- Equivalent of 91 or more undergraduate credit hours: 2

PREREQUISITE COURSE	REQUIRED	RECOMMENDED	LAB REQUIRED	CREDITS (SEMESTER/QUARTER)
BCP (biology-chemistry-physics) sciences				
Biology	✓		✓	2
Chemistry, general/inorganic	✓		✓	2
Chemistry, organic	✓		✓	2
Physics	✓		✓	2
Additional biological sciences				
Anatomy				
Biochemistry	✓			1
Cell biology				
Histology				
Immunology				
Microbiology		✓		

(Prerequisite Courses continued)

PREPARATION (CONTINUED)

PREREQUISITE COURSE	REQUIRED	RECOMMENDED	LAB REQUIRED	CREDITS (SEMESTER/QUARTER)
Molecular biology/genetics				
Physiology				
Zoology				
Other				
Statistics	✓			1
English	✓			2

Community college coursework accepted for prerequisites: Yes
Community college coursework accepted for electives: Yes
Limits on community college credit hours: No
Maximum number of community college credit hours: None
Advanced placement (AP) credit accepted for prerequisites: Yes
Advanced placement (AP) credit accepted for electives: Yes
Job shadowing: Recommended

DAT

Mandatory: Yes
Latest DAT for consideration of application: 11/30/2013
Oldest DAT considered: 11/01/2009
When more than one DAT score is reported: Highest score is considered
U.S. DAT accepted: No
Application considered before DAT scores are submitted: Yes

DAT: 2012 ENTERING CLASS

ENROLLEE U.S. DAT SCORES	RANGE	MEAN
Academic Average	NA	
Perceptual Ability	16-29	21.3
Total Science	NA	

ENROLLEE CANADIAN DAT SCORES	RANGE	MEAN
Reading and Comprehension	16-30	21.3
Manual Dexterity	16-30	23.4
Perceptual Ability	16-29	21.3

GPA: 2012 ENTERING CLASS

ENROLLEE GPA SCORES	RANGE	MEAN
Science GPA	NA	
Total GPA	3.66-4.0	3.86

APPLICATION AND SELECTION

TIMETABLE

Earliest filing date: 07/04/2013
Latest filing date: 11/01/2013
Earliest date for acceptance offers: 05/15/2014
Maximum time in days for applicant's response to acceptance offer: 14 days after receipt of the offer
Requests for deferred entrance considered: No
Fee for application: Yes, submitted only when requested
Amount of fee for application:
In province: $115 Out of province: $115 International: $115
Fee waiver available: No

	FIRST DEPOSIT	SECOND DEPOSIT	THIRD DEPOSIT
Required to hold place	Yes	No	No
Resident amount	$1,000		
Nonresident amount	$1,000		
Deposit due	As indicated in admission offer		
Applied to tuition	Yes		
Refundable	No		

APPLICATION PROCESS

Participates in Associated American Dental Schools Application Service (AADSAS): No
Accepts direct applicants: Yes
Secondary or supplemental application required: No
Interview is mandatory: Yes
Interview is by invitation: Yes

RESIDENCY

Admissions process distinguishes between in-state/in-province and out-of-state/out-of-province applicants: Yes
Preference given to residents of: Alberta
Reciprocity Admissions Agreement available for legal residents of: None
Applications are accepted from non-Canadian citizens/non-Canadian permanent residents: Yes

APPLICATION AND ENROLLMENT	NUMBER OF APPLICANTS	ESTIMATED NUMBER INTERVIEWED	ESTIMATED NUMBER ENROLLED
In-state or province applicants	239	80	32
Out-of-state or province applicants	160	20	0

Generally and over time, percentage of your first-year enrollment is in-state or in-province: 90%
Origin of out-of-state or out-of-province enrollees: NR
Origin of international enrollees: NR

DEMOGRAPHIC DESCRIPTIONS OF APPLICANTS: 2012 ENTERING CLASS

	APPLICANTS		ENROLLEES	
	M	W	M	W
Hispanic/Latino of any race				
American Indian or Alaska Native				
Asian				
Black or African American				
Native Hawaiian or Other Pacific Islander				
White				
Two or more races				
Race and ethnicity unknown	185	214	20	12
International				

	MINIMUM	MAXIMUM	MEAN
2012 entering class enrollees by age	20	32	23

Number of first-time enrollees over age 30: 1

CURRICULUM

The Faculty of Medicine and Dentistry offers a four-year D.D.S., a two-year Advanced Placement Program for dentistry graduates of nonaccredited dental programs, a preprofessional year plus two-year Dental Hygiene Diploma, a Dental Hygiene Diploma plus one-year Bachelor of Science (Dental Hygiene Specialization) degree, and a Master of Science in Orthodontics (two-year program). The first and second years of the dental program are combined with the M.D. program. The curriculum is taught in blocks and covers such areas as infection; immunity and inflammation; endocrine system; cardiovascular, pulmonary, and renal systems; gastroenterology and nutrition; musculoskeletal system; neurosciences; and oncology. In addition to bedside and operating instruction in medicine and surgery, junior and senior students are assigned to the dental clinic and the Department of Dentistry, University of Alberta Hospital.

Student research opportunities: Yes

SPECIAL PROGRAMS AND SERVICES

PREDENTAL

DAT workshops
Postbaccalaureate programs

DURING DENTAL SCHOOL

Academic counseling and tutoring
Community service opportunities
Internships, externships, or extramural programs
Mentoring
Personal counseling
Professional- and career-development programming
Training for those interested in academic careers

ACTIVE STUDENT ORGANIZATIONS

American Dental Education Association (ADEA)

INTERNATIONAL DENTISTS

Graduates of international dental schools considered for traditional predoctoral program: Yes
Advanced standing program offered for graduates of international dental schools: Yes

COMBINED AND ALTERNATE DEGREES

Ph.D.	M.S.	M.P.H.	M.D.	B.A./B.S.	Other
—	—	—	—	—	—

COSTS: 2012-13 SCHOOL YEAR

	FIRST YEAR	SECOND YEAR	THIRD YEAR	FOURTH YEAR
Tuition, resident	$21,312	$21,312	$21,312	$18,548
Tuition, nonresident	$41,000	$41,000	$41,000	$36,000
Tuition, other				
Fees				
Instruments, books, and supplies	$7,230	$9,661	$2,785	$3,000
Estimated living expenses	$11,500	$11,500	$11,500	$11,500
Total, resident	$40,042	$42,473	$35,597	$33,048
Total, nonresident	$59,730	$62,161	$55,285	$50,500
Total, other				

Comments: Costs are in Canadian dollars.

FINANCIAL AID

For information on financial aid, contact the school directly at 780-492-3221.

Faculty of Dentistry
The University of British Columbia
www.dentistry.ubc.ca

UNIVERSITY OF BRITISH COLUMBIA
FACULTY OF DENTISTRY

Dr. Charles F. Shuler, Dean

GENERAL INFORMATION

The University of British Columbia Faculty of Dentistry was officially established in 1962 and enrolled its first students in 1964. It is an integral part of the Health Sciences Centre, which includes the Faculties of Medicine and Pharmaceutical Sciences and the Schools of Nursing, Rehabilitation, Medicine, Clinical Psychology, Family and Nutritional Sciences, and Social Work. The university is located on a 1,000-acre site on the Point Grey Peninsula at the western end of the city of Vancouver. It has an enrollment of 35,000 undergraduate students and 8,000 graduate students plus several thousand part-time, evening, and continuing education students. The Faculty of Dentistry at present offers an undergraduate program leading to the D.M.D. degree. Graduate programs in dental science at the master's and doctorate levels can be arranged as well as clinical specialty programs in Endodontics, Orthodontics, Pediatric Dentistry, Periodontics, and Prosthodontics, and a Bachelor of Dental Science in dental hygiene is offered.

MISSION STATEMENT:

To advance oral health through outstanding education, research, and community service.

Type of institution: Public
Year opened: 1964
Term type: Semester
Time to degree in months: 40
Start month: August

Doctoral dental degree offered: D.M.D.
Total predoctoral enrollment: 216
Estimated entering class size: 48
Campus setting: Urban
Campus housing available: Yes

PREPARATION

Formal minimum preparation in semester/quarter hours: Semester: 90
Baccalaureate degree preferred: No
Number of first-year, first-time enrollees whose highest degree is:
Baccalaureate: 46
Master's: 2
Ph.D. or other doctorate: 0
Of first-year, first-time enrollees without baccalaureates, the number with:
Equivalent of 60 undergraduate credit hours or less: 0
Equivalent of 61-90 undergraduate credit hours: 0
Equivalent of 91 or more undergraduate credit hours: 0

PREREQUISITE COURSE	REQUIRED	RECOMMENDED	LAB REQUIRED	CREDITS (SEMESTER/QUARTER)
BCP (biology-chemistry-physics) sciences				
Biology	✓		✓	6/10
Chemistry, general/inorganic	✓		✓	6/10
Chemistry, organic	✓		✓	6/10
Physics				
Additional biological sciences				
Anatomy				
Biochemistry	✓			6/10
Cell biology				
Histology				
Immunology				
Microbiology				
Molecular biology/genetics				
Physiology		✓		
Zoology				

CONTACT INFORMATION
www.dentistry.ubc.ca
Phone: 604-822-8063

ADMISSIONS
Vicki Koulouris
Manager, Admissions
278-2199 Wesbrook Mall
Vancouver, BC V6T 1Z3
www.dentistry.ubc.ca

AWARDS AND FINANCIAL AID OFFICE
1036-1874 East Mall Brock Hall
Vancouver, BC V6T 1Z1
Phone: 604-822-5111
www.students.ubc.ca/finance

STUDENT AFFAIRS
Alex Hemming
Manager, Student Services
278-2199 Wesbrook Mall
Vancouver, BC V6T 1Z3
www.dentistry.ubc.ca

STUDENT HOUSING OFFICE
1874 East Mall Brock Hall
Vancouver, BC V6T 1Z1
Phone: 604-822-2811
www.housing.ubc.ca

INTERNATIONAL STUDENTS
www.dentistry.ubc.ca

PREPARATION (CONTINUED)

Community college coursework accepted for prerequisites: Yes
Community college coursework accepted for electives: Yes
Limits on community college credit hours: No
Maximum number of community college credit hours: 0
Advanced placement (AP) credit accepted for prerequisites: Yes
Advanced placement (AP) credit accepted for electives: Yes
Comments regarding AP credit: An AP transcript must be submitted
Job shadowing: Recommended
Other factors considered in admission: Interview and Problem-Based Learning (PBL) session

DAT

Mandatory: Yes
Latest DAT for consideration of application: 11/03/2013
Oldest DAT considered: 02/01/2009
When more than one DAT score is reported: Highest overall score is considered
U.S. DAT accepted: Yes
Application considered before DAT scores are submitted: Yes

DAT: 2012 ENTERING CLASS

ENROLLEE U.S. DAT SCORES	RANGE	MEAN
Academic Average		21.4
Perceptual Ability		22.1
Total Science		

ENROLLEE CANADIAN DAT SCORES	RANGE	MEAN
Academic Average	NR	
Manual Dexterity	NR	
Perceptual Ability	NR	NR
Total Science	NR	NR

GPA: 2012 ENTERING CLASS

ENROLLEE GPA SCORES	RANGE	MEAN
Science GPA		
Total GPA		80.55%

APPLICATION AND SELECTION

TIMETABLE

Earliest filing date: 09/14/2013
Latest filing date: 11/02/2013
Earliest date for acceptance offers: 02/28/2014
Maximum time in days for applicant's response to acceptance offer: 15
Requests for deferred entrance considered: In exceptional circumstances only
Fee for application: Yes.
Amount of fee for application:
In state/province: $200 Out of state/province: NR
International/province: NR
Fee waiver available: No

	FIRST DEPOSIT	SECOND DEPOSIT	THIRD DEPOSIT
Required to hold place	Yes	No	No
Resident amount	$11,000		
Nonresident amount			
Deposit due	As indicated in admission offer		
Applied to tuition	No		
Refundable	No		

APPLICATION PROCESS

Participates in Associated American Dental Schools Application Service (AADSAS): No
Accepts direct applicants: Yes
Secondary or supplemental application required: Yes
Secondary or supplemental application website: www.dentistry.ubc.ca
Interview is mandatory: Yes
Interview is by invitation: Yes
PBL session is mandatory: Yes
PBL session is by invitation: Yes
Open House is mandatory: Yes
Open House is by invitation: Yes

RESIDENCY

Admissions process distinguishes between in-state/in-province and out-of-state/out-of-province applicants: Yes
Preference given to residents of: British Columbia
Reciprocity Admissions Agreement available for legal residents of: None
Applications are accepted from non-Canadian citizens/non-Canadian permanent residents: No

APPLICATION AND ENROLLMENT	NUMBER OF APPLICANTS	ESTIMATED NUMBER INTERVIEWED	ESTIMATED NUMBER ENROLLED
In-state or province applicants	232	101	43
Out-of-state or province applicants	129	20	5

Generally and over time, percentage of your first-year enrollment is in-state: NR
Origin of out-of-state or -province enrollees: NR
Origin of international enrollees: NR

DEMOGRAPHIC DESCRIPTIONS OF APPLICANTS: 2012 ENTERING CLASS

	APPLICANTS		ENROLLEES	
	M	W	M	W
Hispanic/Latino of any race	NR			
American Indian or Alaska Native				
Asian				
Black or African American				
Native Hawaiian or Other Pacific Islander				
White				
Two or more races				
Race and ethnicity unknown				
International				

	MINIMUM	MAXIMUM	MEAN
2012 entering class enrollees by age	NR	NR	NR

Number of first-time enrollees over age 30: NR

CURRICULUM

The objective of the academic program is to prepare dentists who are able to practice their profession with a high degree of technical skill and competence, based on a sound understanding of the fundamental principles of basic biological sciences that underlie the practice of dentistry, and who have acquired a deep insight into their social, professional, and ethical responsibilities to the community at large. Students are given clinic exposure early in the program, and actual clinical instruction begins during the second half of the second year. The first two years are taken with students in the Faculty of Medicine and include a course—exclusively for dental students—that correlates biomedical sciences to clinical practice. Clinical and patient-management skills are developed through participation in integrated group practices of third- and fourth-year students managed by a faculty member.

Student research opportunities: Yes

SPECIAL PROGRAMS AND SERVICES

DURING DENTAL SCHOOL

Academic counseling and tutoring
Community service opportunities
Mentoring
Personal counseling
Professional- and career-development programming
Training for those interested in academic careers

INTERNATIONAL DENTISTS

Graduates of international dental schools considered for traditional predoctoral program: NR

Advanced standing program offered for graduates of international dental schools: Yes

Advanced standing program description: Program awarding a dental degree: Successful candidates are admitted via the International Dental Degree Completion Program (IDDCP) and receive the D.M.D. degree upon successful completion.

COMBINED AND ALTERNATE DEGREES

Ph.D.	M.S.	M.P.H.	M.D.	B.A./B.S.	Other
—	—	—	—	—	—

COSTS: 2012-13 SCHOOL YEAR

	FIRST YEAR	SECOND YEAR	THIRD YEAR	FOURTH YEAR
Tuition, resident	$16,082	$16,082	$16,082	$16,082
Tuition, nonresident	$16,082	$16,082	$16,082	$16,082
Tuition, other				
Fees	$30,882	$30,611	$30,574	$32,336
Instruments, books, and supplies	$6,546	$5,961	$3,461	$2,961
Estimated living expenses	$20,000	$20,000	$20,000	$20,000
Total, resident	$73,510	$72,654	$70,117	$71,379
Total, nonresident	$73,510	$72,654	$70,117	$71,379
Total, other				

Comments: Costs are in Canadian dollars.

UNIVERSITY OF MANITOBA
FACULTY OF DENTISTRY

Dr. Anthony M. Iacopino, Dean

CONTACT INFORMATION

www.umanitoba.ca/dentistry
D113-780 Bannatyne Avenue
Winnipeg, MB R3E 0W2
Phone: 204-789-3631

ADMISSIONS OFFICE
424 University Centre
Winnipeg, MB R3T 2N2
Phone: 204-474-8825
www.umanitoba.ca/dentistry

FINANCIAL AID AND AWARDS
422 University Centre
Winnipeg, MB R3T 2N2
Phone: 204-474-8197
http://umanitoba.ca/student/fin_awards

STUDENT AFFAIRS
Susan Petras
Student Affairs Coordinator
D113 - 780 Bannatyne Avenue
Winnipeg, MB R3E 0W2
Phone: 204-789-3484
www.umanitoba.ca/dentistry

HOUSING AND STUDENT LIFE
106 Arthur V. Mauro Residence
Winnipeg, MB R3T 2N2
Phone: 204-474-7662
http://umanitoba.ca/student/housing

INTERNATIONAL DENTIST DEGREE PROGRAM
Jean Lyon
IDDP Coordinator
D113 - 780 Bannatyne Avenue
Winnipeg, MB R3E 0W2
Phone: 204-977-5611
www.umanitoba.ca/faculties/dentistry/iddp

GENERAL INFORMATION

The Faculty of Dentistry is dedicated to educating dental, dental hygiene, and graduate students in a progressive learning environment; conducting research in oral health; and serving the community and the oral health professions as a source of knowledge and expertise. The faculty serves as a bridge between the fundamental scientific foundation of the profession and its translation into health care for the public. Because dentists enhance and promote the total health of patients through oral health management, our curriculum is designed to ensure that our students graduate as competent dentists prepared to meet the oral health care needs of their patients. It provides the knowledge of basic biomedical, behavioral and clinical sciences, and biomaterials; the cognitive and behavioral skills; and professional and ethical values necessary for practice as a dental professional.

MISSION STATEMENT:

The Faculty of Dentistry is dedicated to educating students to become caring oral health professionals in a progressive learning environment, conducting oral health and related research, and serving the oral health professions and society as a source of knowledge and expertise..

Type of institution: Public
Year opened: 1958
Term type: Semester
Time to degree in months: 48
Start month: August

Doctoral dental degree offered: D.M.D.
Total predoctoral enrollment: 128
Estimated entering class size: 29
Campus setting: Urban
Campus housing available: No

PREPARATION

Formal minimum preparation in semester/quarter hours: Semester: 60 Quarter: 90
Baccalaureate degree preferred: No
Number of first-year, first-time enrollees whose highest degree is:
- Baccalaureate: 11
- Master's: 0
- Ph.D. or other doctorate: 0

Of first-year, first-time enrollees without baccalaureates, the number with:
- Equivalent of 60 undergraduate credit hours or less: 3
- Equivalent of 61-90 undergraduate credit hours: 15
- Equivalent of 91 or more undergraduate credit hours: 0

PREREQUISITE COURSE	REQUIRED	RECOMMENDED	LAB REQUIRED	CREDITS (SEMESTER/QUARTER)
BCP (biology-chemistry-physics) sciences				
Biology	✓		✓	6/10
Chemistry, general/inorganic	✓		✓	6/10
Chemistry, organic	✓		✓	6/10
Physics	✓		✓	6/10
Additional biological sciences				
Anatomy				
Biochemistry	✓			6/10
Cell biology				
Histology				
Immunology				
Microbiology				
Molecular biology/genetics				
Physiology				
Zoology				

PREPARATION (CONTINUED)

Community college coursework accepted for prerequisites: No
Community college coursework accepted for electives: No
Limits on community college credit hours: NA
Maximum number of community college credit hours: NA
Advanced placement (AP) credit accepted for prerequisites: Yes
Advanced placement (AP) credit accepted for electives: Yes
Comments regarding AP credit: Upon written submission at time of application, Advanced Placement/International Baccalaureate (AP/IB) courses can be used to fulfill core course requirements. However, AP/IB courses shall not be used to fulfill the minimum new credit hour requirement. (see III A.2 of Applicant Information Bulletin).
Job shadowing: Recommended

DAT

Mandatory: Yes
Latest DAT for consideration of application: November 2013
Oldest DAT considered: February 2011
When more than one DAT score is reported: Highest score is considered
U.S. DAT accepted: No
Application considered before DAT scores are submitted: No

DAT: 2012 ENTERING CLASS

ENROLLEE U.S. DAT SCORES	RANGE	MEAN
Academic Average	NR	NR
Perceptual Ability	NR	NR
Total Science	NR	NR

ENROLLEE CANADIAN. DAT SCORES	RANGE	MEAN
Academic Average	16.0-24.0	19.5
Manual Dexterity	NR	NR
Perceptual Ability	18.0-30.0	22.1
Total Science	16.0-24.0	19.5

GPA: 2012 ENTERING CLASS

ENROLLEE GPA SCORES	RANGE	MEAN
Science GPA	3.40-4.35	3.86
Total GPA	3.44-4.36	4.02

APPLICATION AND SELECTION

TIMETABLE

Earliest filing date: 11/15/2013
Latest filing date: 01/18/2014
Earliest date for acceptance offers: 06/30/2014
Maximum time in days for applicant's response to acceptance offer: 10
Requests for deferred entrance considered: In exceptional circumstances only
Fee for application: Yes, submitted with application (no Associated American Dental Schools Application Service (AADSAS).
Amount of fee for application:
In state/province: $125 Out of state/province: $125
International: NA
Fee waiver available: No

	FIRST DEPOSIT	SECOND DEPOSIT	THIRD DEPOSIT
Required to hold place	Yes	No	No
Resident amount	$1,000		
Nonresident amount	$1,000		
Deposit due	As indicated in admission offer		
Applied to tuition	Yes		
Refundable	No		

APPLICATION PROCESS

Participates in AADSAS: No
Accepts direct applicants: Yes
Secondary or supplemental application required: Yes
Secondary or supplemental application website: www.umanitoba.ca/dentistry
Interview is mandatory: Yes
Interview is by invitation: Yes

RESIDENCY

Admissions process distinguishes between in-state/in-province and out-of-state/out-of-province applicants: Yes
Preference given to residents of: Manitoba
Reciprocity Admissions Agreement available for legal residents of: Manitoba
Applications are accepted from non-Canadian citizens/non-Canadian permanent residents: No

APPLICATION AND ENROLLMENT	NUMBER OF APPLICANTS	ESTIMATED NUMBER INTERVIEWED	ESTIMATED NUMBER ENROLLED
In-state or province applicants	99	61	27
Out-of-state or province applicants	186	12	3

Generally and over time, percentage of your first-year enrollment is in-state: 90%
Origin of out-of-state or -province enrollees: NR
Origin of international enrollees: NR

DEMOGRAPHIC DESCRIPTIONS OF APPLICANTS: 2012 ENTERING CLASS

	APPLICANTS		ENROLLEES	
	M	W	M	W
	146	139	23	7
Hispanic/Latino of any race				
American Indian or Alaska Native				
Asian				
Black or African American				
Native Hawaiian or Other Pacific Islander				
White				
Two or more races				
Race and ethnicity unknown				
International				

Note: Due to individual institution reporting procedures, the total number of applications and enrollees by race and gender may not match the total by residency.

	MINIMUM	MAXIMUM	MEAN
2012 entering class enrollees by age	NR	NR	NR

Number of first-time enrollees over age 30: NR

CURRICULUM

The Doctor of Dental Medicine (D.M.D.) program is a fully accredited four-year program. Following a minimum of two years of prerequisite studies, students complete four years of intense study including extensive clinical experience. Upon successful completion of the National Dental Examining Board of Canada examination, graduates can apply for license to practice in all provinces of Canada; however, other jurisdictions, both in Canada and the United States, have additional licensing requirements. The D.M.D. degree provides the foundation for a variety of career pathways, including further training in dental specialties and research. Over the course of the curriculum, emphasis shifts from teaching to learning, from guided to independent performance, from gaining knowledge in the foundation sciences and skills in the labs to treating patients in a simulated-practice setting working with dental hygiene student partners.

Student research opportunities: Yes

SPECIAL PROGRAMS AND SERVICES

DURING DENTAL SCHOOL

Academic counseling and tutoring
Community service opportunities
Internships, externships, or extramural programs
Mentoring
Personal counseling
Professional- and career-development programming

ACTIVE STUDENT ORGANIZATIONS

American Dental Education Association (ADEA)

INTERNATIONAL DENTISTS

Graduates of international dental schools considered for traditional predoctoral program: No

Advanced standing program offered for graduates of international dental schools: Yes

Advanced standing program description: Program awarding a dental degree

COMBINED AND ALTERNATE DEGREES

Ph.D.	M.S.	M.P.H.	M.D.	B.A./B.S.	Other
—	—	—	—	✓	—

COSTS: 2012-13 SCHOOL YEAR

CANADIAN DOLLARS	FIRST YEAR	SECOND YEAR	THIRD YEAR	FOURTH YEAR
Tuition, resident	$18,927	$18,486	$18,486	$18,486
Tuition, nonresident	$18,927	$18,486	$18,486	$18,486
Tuition, other	NA	NA	NA	NA
Fees	$774	$774	$774	$774
Instruments, books, and supplies	$17,912	$15,833	$7,267	$4,654
Estimated living expenses	NA	NA	NA	NA
Total, resident	$37,613	$35,093	$26,527	$23,914
Total, nonresident	$37,613	$35,093	$26,527	$23,914
Total, other	NA	NA	NA	NA

U.S. DOLLARS	FIRST YEAR	SECOND YEAR	THIRD YEAR	FOURTH YEAR
Tuition, resident	$19,177	$18,730	$18,730	$18,730
Tuition, nonresident	$19,177	$18,730	$18,730	$18,730
Tuition, other	NA	NA	NA	NA
Fees	$784	$784	$784	$784
Instruments, books, and supplies	$18,148	$16,042	$7,362	$4,715
Estimated living expenses	NA	NA	NA	NA
Total, resident	$38,109	$35,556	$26,876	$24,229
Total, nonresident	$38,109	$35,556	$26,876	$24,229
Total, other	NA	NA	NA	NA

DALHOUSIE UNIVERSITY
FACULTY OF DENTISTRY

Dr. Thomas L. Boran, Dean

CONTACT INFORMATION

www.dentistry.dal.ca
Phone: 902-494-2274
Fax: 902-949-2527

ADMISSIONS

Dr. Ronald A. Bannerman
5981 University Avenue
Halifax, NS B3H 1W2
Phone: 902-494-2274
www.dentistry.dal.ca

FINANCIAL AID

Dr. John Lovas
Assistant Dean
5981 University Avenue
Halifax, NS B3H 1W2
Phone: 902-494-2824
www.dentistry.dal.ca

STUDENT AFFAIRS

Dr. John Lovas
Assistant Dean
5981 University Avenue
Halifax, NS B3H 1W2
Phone: 902-494-2824
www.dentistry.dal.ca

MINORITY AFFAIRS/DIVERSITY

Dr. John Lovas
Assistant Dean
5981 University Avenue
Halifax, NS B3H 1W2
Phone: 902-494-2824
www.dentistry.dal.ca

INTERNATIONAL STUDENTS

Dr. Ronald Bannerman
5981 University Avenue
Halifax, NS B3H 1W2
Phone: 902-494-2824
www.dentistry.dal.ca

GENERAL INFORMATION

Dalhousie University is a comprehensive teaching and research institution located on the East Coast of Canada in Halifax, Nova Scotia. The university was founded in 1818 and is Atlantic Canada's leading research university, recognized for strengths in health and ocean studies. The university is affiliated with teaching hospitals throughout the Maritime Provinces, and its long tradition of excellence provides a solid foundation for a professional career. The Maritime Dental College was founded in 1908 and became the Faculty of Dentistry of Dalhousie University in 1912; it offers the only Doctor of Dental Surgery degree program in the Atlantic Provinces of Canada. The four-year program is offered in the modern dentistry buildings, which serve as the main clinical, didactic teaching, and research facilities. Students also complete classes and utilize the dental library in the adjacent Faculty of Medicine building. The program features clinical experiences beginning in the first year of the program with instruction in digital radiography and electronic patient records. Tuition and mandatory fees include a laptop computer, electronic textbook library and drug databases, related software and technical support, all clinical instruments, sterilization, and clinic attire.

MISSION STATEMENT:

The mission of the Faculty of Dentistry is to promote health in a caring and compassionate way through oral and maxillofacial health-based education, research, and service. The faculty will sustain a national and international learning community where we seek knowledge and skills (research), learn, and teach (education). We shall apply our knowledge and skills in an ethical, caring, and compassionate manner to promote and maintain oral and maxillofacial health in Atlantic Canada and to treat appropriately evolving oral health needs. As role models, we, the faculty, must possess the high degree of ethics, idealism, intellectual integrity, and enthusiasm for the scientific and professional activities required to pursue the mission of the faculty. Students in the faculty will be ethical, compassionate, caring, knowledgeable, and skilled practitioners through successful completion of the curriculum in which they have registered. Graduates will maintain these attributes as valued alumni.

Type of institution: Public
Year opened: 1908
Term type: Semester
Time to degree in months: 36
Start month: September

Doctoral dental degree offered: D.D.S.
Total predoctoral enrollment: 152
Estimated entering class size: 38
Campus setting: Urban
Campus housing available: Yes

PREPARATION

Formal minimum preparation in semester/quarter hours: Semester: 10 Quarter: 0
Baccalaureate degree preferred: Yes
Number of first-year, first-time enrollees whose highest degree is:
- Baccalaureate: 28
- Master's: 0
- Ph.D. or other doctorate: 0

Of first-year, first-time enrollees without baccalaureates, the number with:
- Equivalent of 60 undergraduate credit hours or less: 0
- Equivalent of 61-90 undergraduate credit hours: 2
- Equivalent of 91 or more undergraduate credit hours: 8

PREREQUISITE COURSE	REQUIRED	RECOMMENDED	LAB REQUIRED	CREDITS (SEMESTER/QUARTER)
BCP (biology-chemistry-physics) sciences				
Biology	✓		✓	8/12
Chemistry, general/inorganic	✓		✓	8/12
Chemistry, organic	✓		✓	8/12
Physics	✓		✓	8/12

(Prerequisite Courses continued)

PREPARATION (CONTINUED)

PREREQUISITE COURSE	REQUIRED	RECOMMENDED	LAB REQUIRED	CREDITS (SEMESTER/QUARTER)
Additional biological sciences				
Anatomy				
Biochemistry	✓	✓		4/6
Cell biology				
Histology				
Immunology				
Microbiology	✓	✓		4/6
Molecular biology/genetics				
Physiology	✓	✓		4/6
Zoology				

Community college coursework accepted for prerequisites: No
Community college coursework accepted for electives: No
Limits on community college credit hours: Yes
Advanced placement (AP) credit accepted for prerequisites: Yes
Advanced placement (AP) credit accepted for electives: Yes
Job shadowing: Recommended
Number of hours of job shadowing required or recommended: 3

DAT

Mandatory: Yes
Latest DAT for consideration of application: 02/28/2014
Oldest DAT considered: 01/01/2012
When more than one DAT score is reported: Highest score is considered
U.S. DAT accepted: Yes
Application considered before DAT scores are submitted: Yes

DAT: 2012 ENTERING CLASS

ENROLLEE U.S. DAT SCORES	RANGE	MEAN
Academic Average	NR	19
Perceptual Ability	NR	21
Total Science	NR	19

ENROLLEE CANADIAN DAT SCORES	RANGE	MEAN
Academic Average		
Manual Dexterity		
Perceptual Ability		
Total Science		

GPA: 2012 ENTERING CLASS

ENROLLEE GPA SCORES	RANGE	MEAN
Science GPA	NR	3.9
Total GPA	NR	4.0

APPLICATION AND SELECTION

TIMETABLE

Earliest filing date: 07/01/2013
Latest filing date: 09/01/2013
Earliest date for acceptance offers: 12/01/2013
Maximum time in days for applicant's response to acceptance offer: 30 days if accepted on or after December 1
Requests for deferred entrance considered: In exceptional circumstances only
Fee for application: Yes, submitted only when requested
Amount of fee for application:
In state/province: $70 Out of state/province: $70
International: $70
Fee waiver available: No

	FIRST DEPOSIT	SECOND DEPOSIT	THIRD DEPOSIT
Required to hold place	Yes	No	No
Resident amount	$200		
Nonresident amount	$2,500		
Deposit due	As indicated in admission offer		
Applied to tuition	Yes		
Refundable	No		

APPLICATION PROCESS

Participates in Associated American Dental Schools Application Service (AADSAS): Yes
Accepts direct applicants: Yes
Secondary or supplemental application required: No
Interview is mandatory: Yes
Interview is by invitation: Yes

RESIDENCY

Admissions process distinguishes between in-state/in-province and out-of-state/out-of-province applicants: Yes
Preference given to residents of: Atlantic Provinces of Canada
Reciprocity Admissions Agreement available for legal residents of: None
Applications are accepted from non-Canadian citizens/non-Canadian permanent residents: Yes

APPLICATION AND ENROLLMENT	NUMBER OF APPLICANTS	ESTIMATED NUMBER INTERVIEWED	ESTIMATED NUMBER ENROLLED
In-state or province applicants	210	90	29
Out-of-state or province applicants	200	30	9

Generally and over time, percentage of your first-year enrollment is in-state or in-province: 75%

Origin of out-of-state or out-of-province enrollees: Alberta-1

Origin of international enrollees: Kuwait -2, United States-6

DEMOGRAPHIC DESCRIPTIONS OF APPLICANTS: 2012 ENTERING CLASS

	APPLICANTS		ENROLLEES	
	M	W	M	W
Hispanic/Latino of any race	NR			
American Indian or Alaska Native				
Asian				
Black or African American				
Native Hawaiian or Other Pacific Islander				
White				
Two or more races				
Race and ethnicity unknown				
International				

	MINIMUM	MAXIMUM	MEAN
2012 entering class enrollees by age	21	31	24

Number of first-time enrollees over age 30: 4

CURRICULUM

The curriculum emphasizes the integration of the biological, behavioral, and dental sciences with the introduction to patient treatment in the first year of the program. There is a major emphasis on the biological and behavioral sciences as applied to clinical dentistry with basic foundation sciences continuing in the third and fourth years at advanced level. Clinical patient treatment receives greater emphasis in the second year, with continued emphasis on integration of the biological and behavioral sciences. Students practice a total patient care philosophy in the third- and fourth-year clinic, within clinical-oriented disciplines. Students are provided with laptop computers in the first year of the program, and all textbooks are included in searchable electronic formats.

Student research opportunities: Yes

SPECIAL PROGRAMS AND SERVICES

DURING DENTAL SCHOOL

Academic counseling and tutoring: Contact Assistant Dean for Student Affairs to coordinate academic counseling and tutoring.

Internships, externships, or extramural programs: Senior electives, externships for senior students

Mentoring

Personal counseling: Available through Counseling Services, coordinated by Assistant Dean for Student Affairs

Training for those interested in academic careers

ACTIVE STUDENT ORGANIZATIONS

Dalhousie Dental Student Society, Dalhousie Student Union

INTERNATIONAL DENTISTS

Graduates of international dental schools considered for traditional predoctoral program: Yes

Advanced standing program offered for graduates of international dental schools: No

COMBINED AND ALTERNATE DEGREES

Ph.D.	M.S.	M.P.H.	M.D.	B.A./B.S.	Other
—	✓	—	✓	—	—

M.S. in Periodontics; M.D./M.Sc. in Oral and Maxillofacial Surgery

COSTS: 2012-13 SCHOOL YEAR

	FIRST YEAR	SECOND YEAR	THIRD YEAR	FOURTH YEAR
Tuition, resident	$17,013	$17,013	$17,013	$17,013
Tuition, nonresident	$40,000	$40,000	$40,000	$40,000
Tuition, other				
Fees	$988	$988	$988	$988
Instruments, books, and supplies	$16,114	$13,219	$11,122	$10,888
Estimated living expenses	$9,000	$9,000	$9,000	$9,000
Total, resident	$43,115	$40,220	$38,123	$37,889
Total, nonresident	$66,102	$63,207	$61,110	$60,876
Total, other				

Comments: All monetary values in this profile are in Canadian Dollars.

FINANCIAL AID

Students are eligible for government and provincial/state loans, as well as a professional line of credit from major banks. The student loans officer at Dalhousie University provides individual counseling and information to students who require assistance.

UNIVERSITY OF TORONTO
FACULTY OF DENTISTRY

Dr. Daniel Haas, Dean

GENERAL INFORMATION

The University of Toronto Faculty of Dentistry is Canada's leading research centre for dentistry and offers state-of-the-art laboratory; technical, and clinical facilities, including a computerized clinic management system, and an extensive dental library, equipped with a full-service information commons that enables the faculty to provide the best possible climate for teaching and research. In addition to a rich undergraduate tradition, the faculty offers comprehensive graduate educational opportunities and broadly based dental research opportunities. It is the only faculty in Canada to provide advanced clinical training in 10 dental specialty disciplines: dental anesthesia, dental public health, endodontics, oral pathology and oral pathology and medicine, oral radiology, orthodontics, oral and maxillofacial surgery and anesthesia, pediatric dentistry, periodontology, and prosthodontics.

MISSION STATEMENT:

The University of Toronto Faculty of Dentistry is the oldest dental school in Canada. Founded by the Royal College of Dental Surgeons of Ontario, the school began its affiliation with the University of Toronto (U of T) in 1888, when the degree of Doctor of Dental Surgery (D.D.S.) was established. Today, the faculty graduates more than 90 dentists annually.

Type of institution: Public
Year opened: 1875
Term type: Semester
Time to degree in months: 48
Start month: September

Doctoral dental degree offered: D.D.S.
Total predoctoral enrollment: 332
Estimated entering class size: 66
Campus setting: Urban
Campus housing available: Yes

CONTACT INFORMATION

www.utoronto.ca/dentistry
124 Edward Street
Toronto, ON M5G 1G6
Phone: 416-979-4901

ADMISSIONS

124 Edward Street
Toronto, ON M5G 1G6
Phone: 416-979-4901
Email: admissions@dentistry.utoronto.ca
www.utoronto.ca/dentistry

FINANCIAL AID

172 St. George Street
Toronto, ON M5R 0A3
Phone: 416-978-2190
http://www.adm.utoronto.ca/adm-awards/html/awards/mainawdpage.htm

STUDENT AFFAIRS

Margaret Edghill
Faculty Registrar
124 Edward Street
Toronto, ON M5G 1G6
Phone: 416-979-4901
www.utoronto.ca/dentistry

HOUSING

214 College Street
Toronto, ON M5G 1G6
Phone: 416-978-8045
Email: housing.services@utoronto.ca
www.housing.utoronto.ca

PREPARATION

Formal minimum preparation in semester/quarter hours: Semester: 6 Quarter: 10
Baccalaureate degree preferred: No
Number of first-year, first-time enrollees whose highest degree is:
- Baccalaureate: 29
- Master's: 28
- Ph.D. or other doctorate: 0

Of first-year, first-time enrollees without baccalaureates, the number with:
- Equivalent of 60 undergraduate credit hours or less: 0
- Equivalent of 61-90 undergraduate credit hours: 0
- Equivalent of 91 or more undergraduate credit hours: 9

PREREQUISITE COURSE	REQUIRED	RECOMMENDED	LAB REQUIRED	CREDITS (SEMESTER/QUARTER)
BCP (biology-chemistry-physics) sciences				
Biology	✓			3/5
Chemistry, general/inorganic				3/5
Chemistry, organic				3/5
Physics		✓	✓	3/5
Additional biological sciences				
Anatomy				
Biochemistry	✓			
Cell biology	✓			
Histology				
Immunology				
Microbiology				
Molecular biology/genetics				

(Prerequisite Courses continued)

PREPARATION (CONTINUED)

PREREQUISITE COURSE	REQUIRED	RECOMMENDED	LAB REQUIRED	CREDITS (SEMESTER/QUARTER)
Physiology	✓			
Zoology				

Community college coursework accepted for prerequisites: No
Community college coursework accepted for electives: No
Limits on community college credit hours: Yes
Maximum number of community college credit hours: NA
Advanced placement (AP) credit accepted for prerequisites: No
Advanced placement (AP) credit accepted for electives: No
Job shadowing: NA

DAT

Mandatory: Yes
Latest DAT for consideration of application: 11/30/2013
Oldest DAT considered: 01/01/2012
When more than one DAT score is reported: Highest total score is considered
U.S. DAT accepted: Yes, only from students living in or pursuing full-time studies at a U.S. educational institution
Application considered before DAT scores are submitted: No

DAT: 2012 ENTERING CLASS

ENROLLEE U.S. DAT SCORES	RANGE	MEAN
Academic Average	NR	NR
Perceptual Ability	NR	NR
Total Science	NR	NR

ENROLLEE CANADIAN DAT SCORES	RANGE	MEAN
Academic Average	17.0–26	21.0
Manual Dexterity	NR	NR
Perceptual Ability	18.0–28.0	22.0
Total Science	NR	NR

GPA: 2012 ENTERING CLASS

ENROLLEE GPA SCORES	RANGE	MEAN
Science GPA	NR	NR
Total GPA	3.84–4.00	3.85

APPLICATION AND SELECTION

TIMETABLE

Earliest filing date: 08/01/2013
Latest filing date: 12/01/2013
Earliest date for acceptance offers: 05/01/2014
Maximum time in days for applicant's response to acceptance offer: 14 days
Requests for deferred entrance considered: In exceptional circumstances only
Fee for application: Yes
Amount of fee for application:
In state/province: $250 Out of state/province: $250
International: $250
Fee waiver available: No

	FIRST DEPOSIT	SECOND DEPOSIT	THIRD DEPOSIT
Required to hold place	Yes	Yes	No
Resident amount	$2,000	$2,000	
Nonresident amount	$2,000	$2,000	
Deposit due	As indicated in admission offer	As indicated in admission offer	
Applied to tuition	Yes	Yes	
Refundable	No	No	

APPLICATION PROCESS

Participates in Associated American Dental Schools Application Service (AADSAS): No
Accepts direct applicants: Yes
Secondary or supplemental application required: No
Interview is mandatory: Yes
Interview is by invitation: Yes

RESIDENCY

Admissions process distinguishes between in-state/in-province and out-of-state/out-of-province applicants: Yes
Preference given to residents of: Ontario
Reciprocity Admissions Agreement available for legal residents of: None
Applications are accepted from non-Canadian citizens/non-Canadian permanent residents: Yes

APPLICATION AND ENROLLMENT	NUMBER OF APPLICANTS	ESTIMATED NUMBER INTERVIEWED	ESTIMATED NUMBER ENROLLED
In-state or province applicants	399	133	60
Out-of-state or province applicants	96	23	6

Generally and over time, percentage of your first-year enrollment is in-province: 0
Origin of international enrollees: NR

DEMOGRAPHIC DESCRIPTIONS OF APPLICANTS: 2012 ENTERING CLASS

	APPLICANTS		ENROLLEES	
	M	W	M	W
Hispanic/Latino of any race				
American Indian or Alaska Native				
Asian				
Black or African American				
Native Hawaiian or Other Pacific Islander		NR		
White				
Two or more races				
Race and ethnicity unknown				
International				

	MINIMUM	MAXIMUM	MEAN
2012 entering class enrollees by age	NR	NR	NR

Number of first-time enrollees over age 30: NR

CURRICULUM

Dental education is designed to unify the basic and clinical sciences, as it is believed that scientific and professional development cannot be sharply differentiated but should proceed concurrently throughout the dental program.

Year 1: Basic sciences with introduction to dentally relevant material

Year 2: Completion of basic sciences and greater emphasis on the study of dental disease and its prevention and treatment

Year 3: Intensive clinical study of each of the dental disciplines with emphasis on the assessment and management of patients

Year 4: Further clinical experience and familiarity with more advanced treatment services; emphasis upon integration of the various disciplines and overall management of patient treatment in preparation for general practice; participation in elective programs, clinical conferences, and hospital-based experiences

Student research opportunities: Yes

SPECIAL PROGRAMS AND SERVICES

DURING DENTAL SCHOOL

Internships, externships, or extramural programs
Mentoring
Personal counseling
Transfer applicants considered if space is available

INTERNATIONAL DENTISTS

Graduates of international dental schools considered for traditional predoctoral program: Yes

Advanced standing program offered for graduates of international dental schools: Yes

Advanced standing program description: Two-and-a-half-year program awarding a dental degree.

COMBINED AND ALTERNATE DEGREES

Ph.D.	M.S.	M.P.H.	M.D.	B.A./B.S.	Other
✓	—	—	—	—	✓

Other: M.Sc.

COSTS: 2012-13 SCHOOL YEAR

	FIRST YEAR	SECOND YEAR	THIRD YEAR	FOURTH YEAR
Tuition, resident	$30,763	$29,624	$28,527	$27,470
Tuition, nonresident	$58,710	$58,710	$58,710	$58,710
Tuition, other	NA	NA	NA	NA
Fees	$1,135	$1,135	$1,135	$1,135
Instruments, books, and supplies	$6,596	$6,670	$4,090	$2,860
Estimated living expenses	NA	NA	NA	NA
Total, resident	$38,494	$37,429	$33,752	$31,465
Total, nonresident	$66,441	$66,515	$63,935	$62,705
Total, other	NA	NA	NA	NA

Comments: All costs provided are shown in Canadian dollars.

FINANCIAL AID

The University of Toronto is committed to providing financial support to students. For students who are assessed by the Ontario Student Assistance Program (OSAP) or by another Canadian provincial government financial aid program as requiring maximum assistance, and whose assessed need is not fully covered by government aid, the University will ensure that the full need is met. For every new and returning student, the university examines the OSAP (or other Canadian provincial government financial aid program) assessment in the fall term and identifies all students who qualify for grants through the University of Toronto Advance Planning for Students (UTAPS) program. The university writes to students directly to notify them of their eligibility. For students in second-entry programs, including dentistry, the additional assistance may be a mix of grant and loan.

Since the tuition fees for the D.D.S. program have been deregulated by the Ontario Ministry of Education and Training, the university has arranged for different ways to assist students with financial need. Canadian citizens and permanent residents who are eligible for assistance from the federal or provincial governments may receive up to $2,000 in grants from the university to help meet financial need recognized but not fully covered by the government assistance program. Students whose financial need is unusually high may be offered additional grant assistance. In addition, the Bank of Nova Scotia has made a line of credit available to qualified students under the Scotia Professional Student Plan. The University will provide a grant to cover interest on loans borrowed under this plan up to the level of the assessed unmet need. For further information, please contact the Student Services Office of the Faculty of Dentistry or visit the university's Student Financial Support website.

International students are not eligible for University of Toronto or government assistance. The Faculty of Dentistry and the University of Toronto expect incoming students to be responsible for securing their own sources of funding. Therefore, we do not normally offer financial assistance to international students. Potential visa students are advised that they will be required to provide evidence that they have sufficient funds to study and live in Toronto for the length of their program. Applicants should consider coming to Toronto only if they are able to obtain the necessary funds prior to their arrival in Canada.

There are sources of financial aid, not specifically directed to students in dentistry that are not listed here. Information about these funds may be obtained from the Student Services Office.

WESTERN UNIVERSITY
SCHULICH SCHOOL OF MEDICINE & DENTISTRY

Dr. Harinder S. Sandhu, Director

GENERAL INFORMATION

Schulich Dentistry, which was officially established at the University of Western Ontario on January 1, 1965, enrolled its first students the following year. In 1997 Schulich Dentistry merged with the Faculty of Medicine, and in 2005 the new faculty was renamed the Schulich School of Medicine & Dentistry because of a generous contribution to the two programs. Western is a publicly supported institution, chartered by the legislature of Ontario in 1878 as the Western University of London, changing its name to the current one in 1923. Western is one of Canada's oldest, largest, and most beautiful universities, situated on an all-contained campus of 162 hectares of picturesque, park-like land in the north end of London, a city of 352,000. More than 26,000 students are enrolled in more than 300 programs offered by 17 faculties and professional schools.

MISSION STATEMENT:

We will develop in dental professionals the knowledge and skills to provide exemplary care to the diverse communities that we serve. We will influence the future of undergraduate and postgraduate dental education through scholarly inquiry, innovation, and research.

Type of institution: Public
Year opened: 1965
Term type: Semester
Time to degree in months: 48
Start month: September

Doctoral dental degree offered: D.D.S.
Total predoctoral enrollment: 266
Estimated entering class size: 56
Campus setting: Urban
Campus housing available: Yes

PREPARATION

Formal minimum preparation in semester/quarter hours: Semester: 8
Baccalaureate degree required by all incoming students as of September 2012: Yes
Number of first-year, first-time enrollees whose highest degree is:
- Baccalaureate: 41
- Master's: 7
- Ph.D. or other doctorate: 0

Of first-year, first-time enrollees without baccalaureates, the number with:
- Equivalent of 60 undergraduate credit hours or less: 1
- Equivalent of 61-90 undergraduate credit hours: 6
- Equivalent of 91 or more undergraduate credit hours: 1

PREREQUISITE COURSE	REQUIRED	RECOMMENDED	LAB REQUIRED	CREDITS (SEMESTER/QUARTER)
BCP (biology-chemistry-physics) sciences				
Biology		✓		
Chemistry, general/inorganic		✓		
Chemistry, organic	✓		✓	Minimum 3/5
Physics		✓		
Additional biological sciences				
Anatomy				
Biochemistry	✓			Minimum 3/5
Cell biology				
Histology				
Immunology				
Microbiology				
Molecular biology/genetics				
Physiology	✓			6/10
Zoology				

CONTACT INFORMATION

www.schulich.uwo.ca/dentistry
Dentistry Program
Schulich School of Medicine & Dentistry
London, ON N6A 5C1
Phone: 519-661-3330
Fax: 519-661-3875
Email: schulich.dentistry@schulich.uwo.ca

ADMISSIONS

Trish Ashbury
Admissions Coordinator
Schulich School of Medicine & Dentistry
Western University
London, ON N6G 1H1
Phone: 519-661-3744
Fax: 519-519-850-2360
Email: admissions.dentistry@schulich.uwo.ca
www.schulich.uwo.ca/dentistry

FINANCIAL AID

Western University
Western Student Services Building
Room 1100
London, ON N6A 5B8
Phone: 519-661-2100
Email: finaid@uwo.ca
www.registrar.uwo.ca/FinancialServices/index.cfm#need

LEARNER EQUITY AND WELLNESS

Schulich School of Medicine & Dentistry
Western University
London, ON N6A 5C1
Phone: 519-661-2111 Ext. 86250
www.schulich.uwo.ca

EQUITY SERVICES

Western University
Arthur & Sonia Labatt Health Sciences Building
Rooms 330 – 335
London, ON N6A 5B9
Phone: 519-661-3334

HOUSING

Western University
Elgin Hall, Room 102
1421 Western Road
London, ON N6G 4W4
Phone: 519-661-3549
www.schulich.uwo.ca/dentistry

INTERNATIONALLY TRAINED DENTISTS PROGRAM

Dentistry Program
Schulich School of Medicine & Dentistry
Western University
London, ON N6A 5C1
Phone: 519-661-3582
www.schulich.uwo.ca/dentistry

PREPARATION (CONTINUED)

Community college coursework accepted for prerequisites: No
Community college coursework accepted for electives: No
Limits on community college credit hours: NA
Maximum number of community college credit hours: 0
Advanced placement (AP) credit accepted for prerequisites: Yes
Advanced placement (AP) credit accepted for electives: No
Comments regarding AP credit: AP credits are not assessed a grade, but if the material covered in the course is equivalent to an approved prerequisite course, the requirement is considered fulfilled. We do not have requirements for electives.
Job shadowing: Recommended
Number of hours of job shadowing required or recommended: 0

DAT

Mandatory: Yes
Latest DAT for consideration of application: 11/02/2013 (Canadian DAT)
Oldest DAT considered: 01/01/2012
When more than one DAT score is reported: Most recent score only is considered.
U.S. DAT accepted: Yes, only for internationals and Canadians living outside of Canada.
Application considered before DAT scores are submitted: No

DAT: 2012 ENTERING CLASS

ENROLLEE U.S. DAT SCORES	RANGE	MEAN
Academic Average	NA	NA
Perceptual Ability	NA	NA
Total Science	NA	NA

ENROLLEE CANADIAN DAT SCORES	RANGE	MEAN
Academic Average	14 - 25	21
Manual Dexterity	NA	NA
Perceptual Ability	NA	NA
Total Science	NA	NA

GPA: 2012 ENTERING CLASS

ENROLLEE GPA SCORES	RANGE	MEAN
Science GPA	NA	NA
Total GPA	3.7 – 4.0 (using OMSAS scale)	3.9

APPLICATION AND SELECTION

TIMETABLE

Earliest filing date: 10/01/2013
Latest filing date: 12/01/2013
Earliest date for acceptance offers: 05/01/2014
Maximum time in days for applicant's response to acceptance offer: 10 business days after offer made
Requests for deferred entrance considered: In exceptional circumstances only
Fee for application: Yes, submitted only when requested
Amount of fee for application:
In state/province: $250 Out of state/province: $250
International: $250
Fee waiver available: No

	FIRST DEPOSIT	SECOND DEPOSIT	THIRD DEPOSIT
Required to hold place	Yes	No	No
Resident amount	$1,000		
Nonresident amount	$1,000		
Deposit due	As indicated in admission offer		
Applied to tuition	Yes		
Refundable	No		

APPLICATION PROCESS

Participates in Associated American Dental Schools Application Service (AADSAS): No
Accepts direct applicants: Yes
Secondary or supplemental application required: No
Interview is mandatory: Yes
Interview is by invitation: Yes

RESIDENCY

Admissions process distinguishes between in-state/in-province and out-of-state/out-of-province applicants: No
Applications are accepted from non-Canadian citizens/non-Canadian permanent residents: Yes

APPLICATION AND ENROLLMENT	NUMBER OF APPLICANTS	ESTIMATED NUMBER INTERVIEWED	ESTIMATED NUMBER ENROLLED
In-state or province applicants	392	47	50
Out-of-state or province applicants	115	208	6

Generally and over time, percentage of your first-year enrollment is in-state: 89%
Origin of out-of-state or -province enrollees: Alberta-2, British Columbia-1, Prince Edward Island-1
Origin of international enrollees: California-1, New York-1

DEMOGRAPHIC DESCRIPTIONS OF APPLICANTS: 2012 ENTERING CLASS

	APPLICANTS		ENROLLEES	
	M	W	M	W
Hispanic/Latino of any race				
American Indian or Alaska Native				
Asian				
Black or African American				
Native Hawaiian or Other Pacific Islander				
White				
Two or more races				
Race and ethnicity unknown				
International	5	4	2	2

Notes: With the exception of international, this information is unknown. We do not keep statistics on race/ethnicity.

	MINIMUM	MAXIMUM	MEAN
2012 entering class enrollees by age	21	39	23

Number of first-time enrollees over age 30: 5

CURRICULUM

The four-year D.D.S. program is designed to graduate dentists who possess the knowledge and skill to conduct a superior general practice and also sufficient knowledge of basic and applied science to permit and stimulate professional and intellectual growth. Rapid advances in science, medicine, and technology; an accelerated pace in the delivery of information; and the importance of knowledge in meeting today's health care needs continue to change Western approaches dental education.

Year 1: Basic medical/dental sciences with introduction to clinical situations

Year 2: Basic medical/dental sciences plus courses that are clinically focused in preparation for third year in the dental clinic and in hospital electives

Years 3 and 4: Basic dental sciences together with lectures and rotations in clinical disciplines; delivery of comprehensive dental care to patients in a clinical setting

Student research opportunities: Yes

SPECIAL PROGRAMS AND SERVICES

PREDENTAL

Postbaccalaureate programs

DURING DENTAL SCHOOL

Academic counseling and tutoring
Community service opportunities
Internships, externships, or extramural programs
Mentoring
Personal counseling
Professional- and career-development programming
Training for those interested in academic careers
Transfer applicants, into second year, considered if space is available

ACTIVE STUDENT ORGANIZATIONS

Canadian Dental Association
Ontario Dental Association
University of Western Ontario Dental Students Society

INTERNATIONAL DENTISTS

Graduates of international dental schools considered for traditional predoctoral program: Yes
Advanced standing program offered for graduates of international dental schools: Yes
Advanced standing program description: Program awarding a dental degree

COMBINED AND ALTERNATE DEGREES

Ph.D.	M.S.	M.P.H.	M.D.	B.A./B.S.	Other
—	✓	—	✓	—	✓

Other Degree: Oral and Maxillofacial Surgery degree program which, when completed, allows the candidate to have both an M.Sc. and an M.D. degree.

COSTS: 2012-13 SCHOOL YEAR

	FIRST YEAR	SECOND YEAR	THIRD YEAR	FOURTH YEAR
Tuition, resident (Canadian)	$29,305	$28,220	$27,175	$26,168
Tuition, nonresident (International)	$51,730	$49,814	$47,969	$47,969
Tuition, other	NA	NA	NA	NA
Fees	$1,300	$1,300	$1,300	$1,300
Instruments, books, and supplies	$11,525	$22,325	$4,200	$2,300
Estimated living expenses	$11,250	$11,250	$11,250	$11,250
Total, resident	$53,380	$63,095	$43,925	$41,018
Total, nonresident	$75,805	$84,689	$64,719	$62,819
Total, other	NA	NA	NA	NA

Comments: All figures in the table are reported in Canadian dollars.

FINANCIAL AID

For this information, please see the University of Western Ontario's Office of the Registrar's website: www.registrar.uwo.ca.

McGILL UNIVERSITY
FACULTY OF DENTISTRY

Dr. Paul J. Allison, Dean

CONTACT INFORMATION

www.mcgill.ca/dentistry
3640 University Street
Montreal, QC H3A 0C7
Phone: 514-398-7203
Fax: 514-398-8900

ADMISSIONS

3550 University Street
Room 203
Montreal, QC H3A 2A7
Phone: 514-398-7203 ext. 00063
www.mcgill.ca/dentistry/prospective

FINANCIAL AID

3600 McTavish Street
Suite 3200
Montreal, QC H3A 0G3
Phone: 514-398-6015
www.mcgill.ca/studentaid

STUDENT AFFAIRS

Admissions and Student Affairs Office
Phone: 514-398-7203

HOUSING

3473 University Street
Montreal, QC H3A 2H8
Phone: 514-398-6368
www.mcgill.ca/students/housing

GENERAL INFORMATION

The McGill Dental School was established in June 1904 as a department in the Faculty of Medicine and continued as such until 1920, when it became known as the Faculty of Dentistry. The Faculty of Dentistry has always been closely associated with the Montreal General Hospital, where the clinical teaching in the faculty is mainly carried out, along with rotations to other teaching hospitals. The preclinical teaching laboratory is housed in the Strathcona Anatomy and Dentistry Building on campus. With the introduction of the "New Curriculum" in 1996, basic science subjects are taught in conjunction with the Faculty of Medicine during the first 18 months of the program. To reflect the increase in curricular content of basic science and medical courses in recent years, the faculty requested that the degree program be renamed. The change, to Doctor of Dental Medicine (D.M.D.), received university approval in spring 2000.

MISSION STATEMENT:

Our Vision: The Faculty of Dentistry, McGill University, envisions a healthy and equitable society. The Faculty of Dentistry is committed to the promotion of oral health and quality of life in the whole population, with emphasis on the needs of underserved communities and individuals. Our main goals are to enable oral health professionals to attain the highest levels of competence and commitment to patients and to the community; to foster outstanding research; and to educate and nurture students in order to increase knowledge and improve the well-being of the population; to serve the population through the delivery of oral health care in hospital facilities and through outreach programs in underprivileged communities; and to maintain a leadership role in oral health education, in scientific research, and in the shaping of public health policy, with an emphasis on reducing health inequalities. Our core values are commitment to excellence and innovation.

Type of institution: Public
Year opened: 1821
Term type: Semester
Time to degree in months: 48
Start month: August

Doctoral dental degree offered: D.M.D.
Total predoctoral enrollment: 134
Estimated entering class size: 35
Campus setting: Urban
Campus housing available: Yes

PREPARATION

Formal minimum preparation in semester/quarter hours: Semester: 8 Quarter: 8
Baccalaureate degree preferred: No
Number of first-year, first-time enrollees whose highest degree is:
- Baccalaureate: 16
- Master's: 9
- Ph.D. or other doctorate: 1

Of first-year, first-time enrollees without baccalaureates, the number with:
- Equivalent of 60 undergraduate credit hours or less: 0
- Equivalent of 61-90 undergraduate credit hours: 10
- Equivalent of 91 or more undergraduate credit hours: 0

PREREQUISITE COURSE	REQUIRED	RECOMMENDED	LAB REQUIRED	CREDITS (SEMESTER/QUARTER)
BCP (biology-chemistry-physics) sciences				
Biology	✓		✓	
Chemistry, general/inorganic	✓		✓	
Chemistry, organic	✓		✓	
Physics	✓		✓	
Additional biological sciences				
Anatomy		✓		
Biochemistry		✓		

(Prerequisite Courses continued)

PREPARATION (CONTINUED)

PREREQUISITE COURSE	REQUIRED	RECOMMENDED	LAB REQUIRED	CREDITS (SEMESTER/QUARTER)
Cell biology		✓		
Histology		✓		
Immunology		✓		
Microbiology		✓		
Molecular biology/genetics		✓		
Physiology		✓		
Zoology		✓		

Community college coursework accepted for prerequisites: No
Community college coursework accepted for electives: Yes
Limits on community college credit hours: Yes
Maximum number of community college credit hours:
Advanced placement (AP) credit accepted for prerequisites: No
Advanced placement (AP) credit accepted for electives: No
Comments regarding AP credit: No
Job shadowing: Recommended
Number of hours of job shadowing required or recommended: None specified

DAT

Mandatory: No longer required
Latest DAT for consideration of application: NR
Oldest DAT considered: NR
When more than one DAT score is reported: NR
U.S. DAT accepted: NR
Application considered before DAT scores are submitted: NR

DAT: 2012 ENTERING CLASS

ENROLLEE U.S. DAT SCORES	RANGE	MEAN
Academic Average	NR	NR
Perceptual Ability	NR	NR
Total Science	NR	NR

ENROLLEE CANADIAN DAT SCORES	RANGE	MEAN
Academic Average	NR	NR
Manual Dexterity	NR	NR
Perceptual Ability	NR	NR
Total Science	NR	NR

GPA: 2012 ENTERING CLASS

ENROLLEE GPA SCORES	RANGE	MEAN
Science GPA	NR	NR
Total GPA	3.41 – 3.98	3.71

APPLICATION AND SELECTION

TIMETABLE

Earliest filing date: 09/01/2013
Latest filing date: 01/15/2014
Earliest date for acceptance offers: 04/01/2014
Maximum time in days for applicant's response to acceptance offer: 14 days
Requests for deferred entrance considered: In exceptional circumstances only
Fee for application: Yes, submitted at same time as Associated American Dental Schools Application Service (AADSAS) application.
Amount of fee for application:
In state/province: $100 Out of state/province: $100
International: $100
Fee waiver available: No

	FIRST DEPOSIT	SECOND DEPOSIT	THIRD DEPOSIT
Required to hold place	Yes	No	No
Resident amount	$500		
Nonresident amount	$500		
Deposit due	As indicated in admission offer		
Applied to tuition	Yes		
Refundable	50% refundable up to 6/15		

APPLICATION PROCESS

Participates in Associated American Dental Schools Application Service (AADSAS): No
Accepts direct applicants: No
Secondary or supplemental application required: No
Interview is mandatory: Yes
Interview is by invitation: Yes

RESIDENCY

Admissions process distinguishes between in-state/in-province and out-of-state/out-of-province applicants: Yes
Preference given to residents of: Quebec
Reciprocity Admissions Agreement available for legal residents of: None
Applications are accepted from non-Canadian citizens/non-Canadian permanent residents: Yes

APPLICATION AND ENROLLMENT	NUMBER OF APPLICANTS	ESTIMATED NUMBER INTERVIEWED	ESTIMATED NUMBER ENROLLED
In-state or province applicants	110	36	19
Out-of-state or province applicants	251	30	7

Generally and over time, percentage of your first-year enrollment is in-province: 70%

Origin of out-of-province enrollees: NR

Origin of international enrollees: NR

DEMOGRAPHIC DESCRIPTIONS OF APPLICANTS: 2012 ENTERING CLASS

	APPLICANTS		ENROLLEES	
	M	W	M	W
Hispanic/Latino of any race	NR	NR	NR	NR
American Indian or Alaska Native	NR	NR	NR	NR
Asian	NR	NR	NR	NR
Black or African American	NR	NR	NR	NR
Native Hawaiian or Other Pacific Islander	NR	NR	NR	NR
White	NR	NR	NR	NR
Two or more races	NR	NR	NR	NR
Race and ethnicity unknown	NR	NR	NR	NR
International	NR	NR	NR	NR

	MINIMUM	MAXIMUM	MEAN
2012 entering class enrollees by age	NR	NR	NR

Number of first-time enrollees over age 30: NR

CURRICULUM

The Faculty of Dentistry is dedicated to the concept that graduates from a dental school should have reasonable competence to begin practice as general practitioners, regardless of what their future aspirations may be. The should develop the understanding and competence both to cope with the dental diseases they will encounter and to apply the preventive and treatment measures of the present and those predicted for the future. Basic sciences in the dental curriculum are taught in the Faculty of Medicine. Introduction to clinical experience begins in the first year, and the integration of basic sciences into clinical dentistry, in the second year. Students are evaluated on the basis of daily progress and end-of-term examinations..

Student research opportunities: Yes

SPECIAL PROGRAMS AND SERVICES

PREDENTAL

Postbaccalaureate programs

DURING DENTAL SCHOOL

Academic counseling and tutoring
Community service opportunities
Internships, externships, or extramural programs
Mentoring
Personal counseling
Professional- and career-development programming
Transfer applicants considered if space is available

ACTIVE STUDENT ORGANIZATIONS

American Dental Education Association (ADEA)

INTERNATIONAL DENTISTS

Graduates of international dental schools considered for traditional predoctoral program: Yes

Advanced standing program offered for graduates of international dental schools: Yes

Advanced standing program description: Program awarding a dental degree

COMBINED AND ALTERNATE DEGREES

Ph.D.	M.S.	M.P.H.	M.D.	B.A./B.S.	Other
✓	✓	—	—	—	—

COSTS: 2012-13 SCHOOL YEAR

	FIRST YEAR	SECOND YEAR	THIRD YEAR	FOURTH YEAR
Tuition, resident	$5,651	$5,005	$4,198	$2,286
Tuition, nonresident	$14,363	$12,721	$10,669	$7,181
Tuition, other	$38,732	$34,305	$28,772	$19,366
Fees	$1,751	$1,751	$1,751	$1,751
Instruments, books, and supplies	$788	$21,952	$5,931	$3,568
Estimated living expenses	NR	NR	NR	NR
Total, resident	$8,190	$28,708	$11,860	$7,870
Total, nonresident	$16,902	$36,424	$18,332	$12,226
Total, other	$41,964	$58,702	$37,128	$25,104

Comments: Costs are in Canadian dollars.

Note: Some total costs include fees not indicated on this table.

FINANCIAL AID

McGill University offers financial aid in the form of loans (money that needs to eventually be repaid) and bursaries (money that does not need to be repaid) to eligible students who demonstrate financial need. Our assistance is meant to supplement other sources of core funding, such as government aid, parental support, part-time work, and, in some cases, a student line of credit from the bank. For more information, go to www.mcgill.ca/studentaid/awards/prospective.

UNIVERSITÉ DE MONTRÉAL
FACULTÉ DE MÉDECINE DENTAIRE

Dr. Gilles Lavigne, Dean

GENERAL INFORMATION

The Faculté de Médecine Dentaire of the Université de Montréal was founded in 1904. It is publicly funded by the Province of Québec. The faculty is located in the main building of the university and occupies the first, second, and fifth floors of the east wing. The teaching facilities allow up to 90 students to be admitted. Graduate programs are available in orthodontics, pediatric dentistry, and dental sciences (master's degrees). We also have a one-year multidisciplinary residency program. There are joint postgraduate programs in biomedical sciences (M.Sc. and Ph.D.) with the Faculté de Médecine. The Faculté de Médecine Dentaire is one of the two francophone dental schools in North America.

MISSION STATEMENT:

To contribute to the development of knowledge and best practices in dentistry as well as oral health promotion of the population in Quebec and elsewhere, according to the highest national and international standards.

Type of institution: Public
Year opened: 1904
Term type: Trimester (yearly promotion)
Time to degree in months: 58
Start month: August

Doctoral dental degree offered: D.M.D.
Total predoctoral enrollment: 90
Estimated entering class size: 90
Campus setting: Urban
Campus housing available: Yes

PREPARATION

Formal minimum preparation: Candidates must have completed CEGEP (college degree) or equivalent.
Baccalaureate degree preferred: No
Number of first-year, first-time enrollees whose highest degree is:
- Baccalaureate: 38
- Master's: 0
- Ph.D. or other doctorate: 0

Of first-year, first-time enrollees without baccalaureates, the number with:
- Equivalent of 60 undergraduate credit hours or less: 52
- Equivalent of 61-90 undergraduate credit hours: 0
- Equivalent of 91 or more undergraduate credit hours: 0

PREREQUISITE COURSE	REQUIRED	RECOMMENDED	LAB REQUIRED	CREDITS (SEMESTER/QUARTER)
BCP (biology-chemistry-physics) sciences				
Biology	301 and 401		✓	6
Chemistry, general/inorganic	101		✓	3
Chemistry, organic	201 and 202		✓	6
Physics	101, 201, and 301		✓	9
Additional biological sciences				
Anatomy				
Biochemistry				
Cell biology				
Histology				
Immunology				
Microbiology				
Molecular biology/genetics				
Physiology				
Zoology				

(Prerequisite Courses continued)

CONTACT INFORMATION

www.medent.umontreal.ca
C.P. 6128, succursale Centre-ville
Montréal, QC H3C 3J7
Phone: 514-343-6111, ext. 3437
Fax: 514-343-2233

ADMISSIONS

Marie Nadeau
C.P. 6128, succursale Centre-ville
Montréal, QC H3C 3J7
Phone: 514-343-7076
Email: marie.nadeau@umontreal.ca
www.futursetudiants.umontreal.ca/admission/demande

FINANCIAL AID

Sylviane Latour
Aide financière
2332 Edouard-Montpetit
Montréal, QC H3C 3J7
Phone: 514-343-3399
Email: sylviane.latour@umontreal.ca
www.baf.umontreal.ca

STUDENT AFFAIRS

Dr. Annie St-Georges
Associate Dean for Undergraduate Studies and Students Affairs
C.P. 6128, succursale Centre-ville
Montréal, QC H3C 3J7
Phone: 514-343-5761
www.medent.umontreal.ca

HOUSING

Lyne Mckay
2350 Edouard-Montpetit
Montréal, QC H3C 3J7
Phone: 514-343-7697

PREPARATION (CONTINUED)

PREREQUISITE COURSE	REQUIRED	RECOMMENDED	LAB REQUIRED	CREDITS (SEMESTER/QUARTER)
Other				
Mathematics	103 and 203			

Community college coursework accepted for prerequisites: Yes
Community college coursework accepted for electives: No
Limits on community college credit hours: No
Maximum number of community college credit hours: No
Advanced placement (AP) credit accepted for prerequisites: No
Advanced placement (AP) credit accepted for electives: No
Comments regarding AP credit: No
Job shadowing: No
Number of hours of job shadowing required or recommended: None
Other factors considered in admission: Motivation letter and Dental Aptitude Test

DAT

Mandatory: Quebec
Latest DAT for consideration of application: 01/02/2013
Oldest DAT considered: 01/02/2006 When more than one DAT score is reported: Highest score is considered.
U.S. DAT accepted: No
Application considered before DAT scores are submitted: No

DAT: 2012 ENTERING CLASS

ENROLLEE U.S. DAT SCORES	RANGE	MEAN
Academic Average	NR	NR
Perceptual Ability	NR	NR
Total Science	NR	NR

ENROLLEE CANADIAN DAT SCORES	RANGE	MEAN
Academic Average		
Manual Dexterity		
Perceptual Ability		
Total Science		

GPA: 2012 ENTERING CLASS

ENROLLEE GPA SCORES	RANGE	MEAN
Science GPA	NR	NR
Total GPA	NR	NR

APPLICATION AND SELECTION

TIMETABLE

Earliest filing date: 12/01/2013
Latest filing date: 03/01/2014
Earliest date for acceptance offers: 05/01/2014
Maximum time in days for applicant's response to acceptance offer: 30
Requests for deferred entrance considered: No
Fee for application: Yes, submitted only when requested
Amount of fee for application:
In state/province: $85 Out of state/province: $85 International: NA
Fee waiver available: NR

	FIRST DEPOSIT	SECOND DEPOSIT	THIRD DEPOSIT
Required to hold place	Yes	No	No
Resident amount	$200		
Nonresident amount			
Deposit due	As indicated in admission offer		
Applied to tuition	NR		
Refundable	NR	No	
Refundable by	NR		

Note: Costs are in Canadian dollars

APPLICATION PROCESS

Participates in Associated American Dental Schools Application Service (AADSAS): No
Accepts direct applicants: Yes
Secondary or supplemental application required: No
Interview is mandatory: No
Interview is by invitation: Yes

RESIDENCY

Admissions process distinguishes between in-state/in-province and out-of-state/out-of-province applicants: Yes
Preference given to residents of: Quebec
Reciprocity Admissions Agreement available for legal residents of: None
Applications are accepted from non-Canadian citizens/non-Canadian permanent residents: Yes for graduate studies only

APPLICATION AND ENROLLMENT	NUMBER OF APPLICANTS	ESTIMATED NUMBER INTERVIEWED	ESTIMATED NUMBER ENROLLED
In-state or province applicants	637	NR	86
Out-of-state or province applicants	106	NR	4

Generally and over time, percentage of your first-year enrollment is in-state: 95 %
Origin of out-of-state enrollees (U.S.):
Origin of international enrollees:

DEMOGRAPHIC DESCRIPTIONS OF APPLICANTS: 2012 ENTERING CLASS

	APPLICANTS		ENROLLEES	
	M	W	M	W
Total	310	433	39	51
Hispanic/Latino of any race				
American Indian or Alaska Native				
Asian				
Black or African American				
Native Hawaiian or Other Pacific Islander				
White				
Two or more races				
Race and ethnicity unknown				
International				

Notes: Not available

	MINIMUM	MAXIMUM	MEAN
2012 entering class enrollees by age			

Number of first-time enrollees over age 30: NA

CURRICULUM

Training in the basic sciences and preclinical disciplines is emphasized in the first two years of the program. Clinical training starts during the second semester of the second year. Senior students spend three weeks in hospitals off campus to become acquainted with oral surgery and for training in pediatric dentistry. The clinical program of the senior year also offers optional clinical courses. In addition to traditional clinical training such as implantology, periodontics/endodontics, and constructive dentistry, off-campus activities in student exchange programs, clinical activities in international cooperation humanitarian projects, and off-campus clinics are available. Student performance is evaluated qualitatively and quantitatively throughout the entire clinical program.

Student research opportunities: Yes

SPECIAL PROGRAMS AND SERVICES

PREDENTAL

Other summer enrichment programs

DURING DENTAL SCHOOL

Academic counseling and tutoring
Community service opportunities
Personal counseling
Training for those interested in academic careers

ACTIVE STUDENT ORGANIZATIONS

Association des étudiants en médecine dentaire de l'Université de Montréal (AEMDUM)
Canadian Student Dental Association

INTERNATIONAL DENTISTS

Graduates of international dental schools considered for traditional predoctoral program: Yes
Advanced standing program offered for graduates of international dental schools: No

COMBINED AND ALTERNATE DEGREES

Ph.D.	M.S.	M.P.H.	M.D.	B.A./B.S.	Other
—	—	—	—	—	✓

Other Degree: M.Sc. in dentistry, M.Sc. in dental sciences, and a one-year multidisciplinary residency program.

COSTS: 2012-13 SCHOOL YEAR

	FIRST YEAR	SECOND YEAR	THIRD YEAR	FOURTH YEAR
Tuition, resident	$3,229	$3,267	$4,844	$3,310
Tuition, nonresident *	$8,207	$8,310	$12,311	$8,412
Tuition, other				
Fees	$826	$876	$974	$826
Instruments, books, and supplies	$16,000	$10,000	$5,000	$1,200
Estimated living expenses	$14,700	$13,200	$13,200	$13,200
Total, resident	$34,755	$27,343	$24,018	$18,536
Total, nonresident	$39,733	$32,386	$31,485	$23,638

*Nonresident: Students from Canada but outside of the province of Québec.

Comments: Costs are in Canadian dollars

FINANCIAL AID

Approximately 20 scholarships are awarded to students every year. For details, please see www.medent.umontreal.ca/fr/dons-partenariats/prix-bourses.htm and www.bourses.umontreal.ca/boursesPrix/index.htm.

UNIVERSITÉ LAVAL
FACULTÉ DE MÉDECINE DENTAIRE

Dr. André Fournier, Dean

CONTACT INFORMATION

www.fmd.ulaval.ca
fmd@fmd.ulaval.ca
Pavillon de Médecine dentaire
2420, rue de la Terrasse, Suite 1615
Québec, QC, Canada G1V 0A6
Phone: 418-656-7532
Fax: 418-656-2720

ADMISSIONS

Dr. Denis Robert
Chairman, Admission Committee
Pavillon de Médecine dentaire
2420, rue de la Terrasse
Québec, QC, Canada G1V 0A6
Phone: 418-656-2095
denis.robert@fmd.ulaval.ca
www.reg.ulaval.ca

FINANCIAL AID

Pavillon Alphonse-Desjardins
2325, rue de l'Université, Suite 2546
Québec, QC, Canada G1V 0A6
Phone: 418-656-3332
www.bbaf.ulaval.ca

STUDENT AFFAIRS

Dr. Cathia Bergeron
Vice Dean, Academic Affairs
Pavillon de Médecine dentaire
2420, rue de la Terrasse
Québec, QC, Canada G1V 0A6
Phone: 418-656-2131, ext. 2741
cathia.bergeron@fmd.ulaval.ca

MINORITY AFFAIRS/DIVERSITY

Pavillon Alphonse-Desjardins
Suite 2344
Québec, QC, Canada G1K 7P4
Phone: 418-656-2765
www.bve.ulaval.ca

HOUSING

Pavillon Alphonse-Marie Parent
2255, rue de l'Université, Suite 1604
Québec, QC, Canada G1V 0A7
Phone: 418-656-2921
www.residences.ulaval.ca

INTERNATIONAL STUDENTS

Maison Eugène-Roberge
2325, rue des Arts
Québec, QC, Canada G1V 0A6
Phone: 418-656-3994
www.bi.ulaval.ca

GENERAL INFORMATION

The Faculty of Dental Medicine was founded in 1969 and accepted its first students in 1971. All teaching is done in the French language. The faculty occupies permanent quarters suitable for the training of 48 students for each of the four years of the program. A maximum of 54 students per year can be accommodated with the present facilities. The faculty also offers postgraduate programs: Master in Dental Sciences, Master in Sciences in Oral and Maxillofacial Surgery, Master in Sciences in Periodontics, Master in Sciences in Geriatric Dentistry, and a one-year residency program in general dentistry.

MISSION STATEMENT:

The faculty is devoted to research, continuing education, and dental training in the spirit of enhancing the health care of the population.

Type of institution: State-related
Year opened: 1971
Term type: Trimester
Time to degree in months: 48
Start month: September

Doctoral dental degree offered: D.M.D.
Total predoctoral enrollment: 0
Estimated entering class size: 48
Campus setting: Urban
Campus housing available: Yes

PREPARATION

Formal minimum preparation in semester/quarter hours: Semester: 4
Baccalaureate degree preferred: No
Number of first-year, first-time enrollees whose highest degree is:
- Baccalaureate: 1
- Master's: 1
- Ph.D. or other doctorate: 0

Of first-year, first-time enrollees without baccalaureates, the number with:
- Equivalent of 60 undergraduate credit hours or less: 20
- Equivalent of 61-90 undergraduate credit hours: 25
- Equivalent of 91 or more undergraduate credit hours: 1

PREREQUISITE COURSE	REQUIRED	RECOMMENDED	LAB REQUIRED	CREDITS (SEMESTER/QUARTER)
BCP (biology-chemistry-physics) sciences				
Biology	✓		✓	6
Chemistry, general/inorganic	✓		✓	6
Chemistry, organic	✓			3
Physics	✓		✓	9
Additional biological sciences				
Anatomy				
Biochemistry				
Cell biology				
Histology				
Immunology				
Microbiology				
Molecular biology/genetics				
Physiology		✓		
Zoology				

PREPARATION (CONTINUED)

Community college coursework accepted for prerequisites: Yes
Community college coursework accepted for electives: Yes, dental hygiene
Limits on community college credit hours: Yes
Maximum number of community college credit hours: 1
Advanced placement (AP) credit accepted for prerequisites: No
Advanced placement (AP) credit accepted for electives: No
Comments regarding AP credit: not available in Québec
Job shadowing: not required
Number of hours of job shadowing required or recommended: Not required

DAT

Mandatory: Yes
Latest DAT for consideration of application: February 2013
Oldest DAT considered: 02/01/2007
When more than one DAT score is reported: Latest score is considered
U.S. DAT accepted: No
Application considered before DAT scores are submitted: No

DAT: 2012 ENTERING CLASS

ENROLLEE U.S. DAT SCORES	RANGE	MEAN
Academic Average	NR	NR
Perceptual Ability	NR	NR
Total Science	NR	NR

ENROLLEE CANADIAN DAT SCORES	RANGE	MEAN
Academic Average	NR	NR
Manual Dexterity	NR	15.0/30
Perceptual Ability	NR	19.0/30
Total Science	NR	NR

GPA: 2012 ENTERING CLASS

ENROLLEE GPA SCORES	RANGE	MEAN
Science GPA	NR	NR
Total GPA	NR	32.23/40

APPLICATION AND SELECTION

TIMETABLE

Earliest filing date: 03/01/2013
Latest filing date: 03/01/2014
Earliest date for acceptance offers: NR
Maximum time in days for applicant's response to acceptance offer: NR
Requests for deferred entrance considered: No
Fee for application: Yes, submitted only when requested.
Amount of fee for application:
In state/province: $64 Out of state/province: NR
International: NR
Fee waiver available: No

	FIRST DEPOSIT	SECOND DEPOSIT	THIRD DEPOSIT
Required to hold place	No	No	No

APPLICATION PROCESS

Participates in Associated American Dental Schools Application Service (AADSAS): No
Accepts direct applicants: Yes
Secondary or supplemental application required: No
Interview is mandatory: Yes
Interview is by invitation: Yes

RESIDENCY

Admissions process distinguishes between in-state/in-province and out-of-state/out-of-province applicants: Yes
Preference given to residents of: New Brunswick, Ontario, Quebec
Reciprocity Admissions Agreement available for legal residents of: NR
Applications are accepted from non-Canadian citizens/non-Canadian permanent residents: No

APPLICATION AND ENROLLMENT	NUMBER OF APPLICANTS	ESTIMATED NUMBER INTERVIEWED	ESTIMATED NUMBER ENROLLED
In-state or province applicants	532	154	48
Out-of-state or province applicants	43	NR	0

Generally and over time, percentage of your first-year enrollment is in-province: 96.9%
Out-of-province enrollees: 0
Origin of international enrollees: NA

DEMOGRAPHIC DESCRIPTIONS OF APPLICANTS: 2012 ENTERING CLASS

	MINIMUM	MAXIMUM	MEAN
Previous year enrollees by age	19	30	21

Number of first-time enrollees over age 30: 0

CURRICULUM

The program is designed to give its graduates a thorough grounding in the basic sciences and broad clinical experience. Basic health sciences are taught in an integrated health science complex. Preclinical and clinical subjects are under the direct control of dental school personnel. The first two years of the program are devoted to the basic and preclinical sciences. The last two years are devoted almost entirely to clinical work.

Student research opportunities: Yes

SPECIAL PROGRAMS AND SERVICES

ACTIVE STUDENT ORGANIZATIONS

American Association of Dental Research Student Research Group
American Dental Education Association (ADEA)

INTERNATIONAL DENTISTS

Graduates of international dental schools considered for traditional predoctoral program: No
Advanced standing program offered for graduates of international dental schools: No
Advanced standing program description: Program awarding a certificate, program awarding a dental degree, and continuing education courses

COMBINED AND ALTERNATE DEGREES

Ph.D.	M.S.	M.P.H.	M.D.	B.A./B.S.	Other
—	✓	—	—	—	—

COSTS: 2012-13 SCHOOL YEAR

	FIRST YEAR	SECOND YEAR	THIRD YEAR	FOURTH YEAR
Tuition, resident	$3,657	$3,657	$4,091	$3,729
Tuition, nonresident	NR	NR	NR	NR
Tuition, other				
Fees (included in tuition)	NR	NR	NR	NR
Instruments, books, and supplies	$8,033	$7,265	$3,782	$189
Estimated living expenses				
Total, resident	$11,690	$10,922	$7,873	$3,918
Total, nonresident	NR	NR	NR	NR
Total, other				

Comments: Costs are in Canadian dollars.

FINANCIAL AID

To receive more information about financial programs, students may contact the Office of Scholarships and Financial Aid in Université Laval's Department of Student Services (www.bbaf.ulaval.ca).

UNIVERSITY OF SASKATCHEWAN
COLLEGE OF DENTISTRY

Dr. Gerry Uswak, Dean

CONTACT INFORMATION

www.usask.ca/dentistry
Room 331, Dental Clinic
105 Wiggins Road
Saskatoon, SK S7N 5E4
Phone: 306-966-5121
Fax: 306-966-5132

OFFICE OF STUDENT SERVICES

Maureen Webster
Director of Academic and Student Affairs
Room 310, Dental Clinic
105 Wiggins Road
Saskatoon, SK S7N5E4
Phone: 306-966-2760
www.usask.ca/dentistry

HOUSING

Phone: 306-966-6775
http://explore.usask.ca/housing

GENERAL INFORMATION

The College of Dentistry is a dynamic college with a reputation for excellence in both teaching and research. By providing students with a well-balanced dental education, it is our goal to produce graduates who will be adaptable to rapid change and competitive with their peers around the world. At the University of Saskatchewan, our enrollment is more than 19,000 students. In the College of Dentistry, there are currently 112 students enrolled. We value the diversity of our university community, the people, their points of view, and the contributions they make to our scholarly endeavors. Our preclinical teaching area includes a state-of-the-art clinical simulation facility where students learn basic procedures in a clinical setting with current techniques in infection control, fiber optic technology, and intraoral television.

MISSION STATEMENT:

To educate dentists to provide high-quality oral health care to the people of Saskatchewan and to advance clinical and scientific knowledge through research

Type of institution: Public
Year opened: 1965
Term type: Semester
Time to degree in months: 35
Start month: August

Doctoral dental degree offered: D.M.D.
Total predoctoral enrollment: 112
Estimated entering class size: 28
Campus setting: Urban
Campus housing available: Yes

PREPARATION

Formal minimum preparation in semester/quarter hours: Semester: 60 Quarter: 90
Baccalaureate degree preferred: Not required
Number of first-year, first-time enrollees whose highest degree is:
- Baccalaureate: 6
- Master's: 0
- Ph.D. or other doctorate: 0

Of first-year, first-time enrollees without baccalaureates, the number with:
- Equivalent of 60 undergraduate credit hours or less: 6
- Equivalent of 61-90 undergraduate credit hours: 6
- Equivalent of 91 or more undergraduate credit hours: 10

PREREQUISITE COURSE	REQUIRED	RECOMMENDED	LAB REQUIRED	CREDITS (SEMESTER/QUARTER)
BCP (biology-chemistry-physics) sciences				
Biology	✓		✓	6
Chemistry, general/inorganic	✓		✓	3
Chemistry, organic	✓		✓	3
Physics	✓		✓	6
Additional biological sciences				
Anatomy				
Biochemistry	✓			6
Cell biology				
Histology				
Immunology				
Microbiology				
Molecular biology/genetics				
Physiology				

(Prerequisite Courses continued)

PREPARATION (CONTINUED)

PREREQUISITE COURSE	REQUIRED	RECOMMENDED	LAB REQUIRED	CREDITS (SEMESTER/QUARTER)
Zoology				
Other				
Social Science/Humanities	✓			6
Human Physiology		✓		6

Community college coursework accepted for prerequisites: Yes
Community college coursework accepted for electives: Yes
Limits on community college credit hours: Yes
Maximum number of community college credit hours: 30
Advanced placement (AP) credit accepted for prerequisites: Yes
Advanced placement (AP) credit accepted for electives: No
Job shadowing: We do not require or recommend job shadowing.

DAT

Mandatory: Yes
Latest DAT for consideration of application: 02/19/2013
Oldest DAT considered: February 2010
When more than one DAT score is reported: Highest score is considered
U.S. DAT accepted: Yes, but students must write the Canadian DAT by November of the year in which they are accepted.
Application considered before DAT scores are submitted: Yes

DAT: 2012 ENTERING CLASS

ENROLLEE U.S. DAT SCORES	RANGE	MEAN
Academic Average		
Perceptual Ability		
Total Science		

ENROLLEE CANADIAN DAT SCORES	RANGE	MEAN
Academic Average	16 - 22	18.7
Manual Dexterity		
Perceptual Ability	15 - 23	19.7
Total Science	NA	NA

GPA: 2012 ENTERING CLASS

ENROLLEE GPA SCORES	RANGE	MEAN
Science GPA		
Total GPA	82.6% - 94.35%	89.66%

APPLICATION AND SELECTION

TIMETABLE

Earliest filing date: 08/01/2013
Latest filing date: 01/15/2014
Earliest date for acceptance offers: 06/30/2014
Maximum time in days for applicant's response to acceptance offer: 5 working days
Requests for deferred entrance considered: Yes
Fee for application: Yes, submitted with online application
Amount of fee for application:
In state: $170 Out of state: $170 International: $170
Fee waiver available: No

	FIRST DEPOSIT	SECOND DEPOSIT	THIRD DEPOSIT
Required to hold place	Yes	n/a	n/a
Resident amount	$4,944 (15% of tuition)		
Nonresident amount	$4,944 (15% of tuition)		
Deposit due	As indicated in admission offer		
Applied to tuition	Yes		
Refundable	No		

APPLICATION PROCESS

Participates in Associated American Dental Schools Application Service (AADSAS): No
Accepts direct applicants: Yes
Secondary or supplemental application required: No
Interview is mandatory: Yes
Interview is by invitation: Yes

RESIDENCY

Admissions process distinguishes between in-state/in-province and out-of-state/out-of-province applicants: Yes
Preference given to residents of: Saskatchewan
Reciprocity Admissions Agreement available for legal residents of: None
Applications are accepted from non-Canadian citizens/non-Canadian permanent residents: Yes

APPLICATION AND ENROLLMENT	NUMBER OF APPLICANTS	ESTIMATED NUMBER INTERVIEWED	ESTIMATED NUMBER ENROLLED
In-state or province applicants	115	53	21
Out-of-state or province applicants	288	26	7

Generally and over time, percentage of your first-year enrollment is in-state: 79%
Origin of out-of-state or -province enrollees: Alberta-1, Ontario-4, Not Reported-2
Origin of international enrollees: NA

DEMOGRAPHIC DESCRIPTIONS OF APPLICANTS: 2012 ENTERING CLASS

	APPLICANTS		ENROLLEES	
	M	W	M	W
Hispanic/Latino of any race	NR			
American Indian or Alaska Native				
Asian				
Black or African American				
Native Hawaiian or Other Pacific Islander				
White				
Two or more races				
Race and ethnicity unknown				
International				

	MINIMUM	MAXIMUM	MEAN
2012 entering class enrollees by age	19	28	22

Number of first-time enrollees over age 30: 0

CURRICULUM

The program is four years in length (August to May). There are no course/program offerings during the summer session. The curriculum is structured on a diagonal pattern: The earlier years are heavily weighted with the basic sciences, but some dental sciences are taken in each year. The balance gradually shifts to the dental sciences, so that the program is devoted almost entirely to the dental sciences after the end of the second year. Positive efforts are made at all levels to closely integrate the basic and dental sciences and the theoretical and applied aspects of the dental curriculum..

Student research opportunities: Yes

SPECIAL PROGRAMS AND SERVICES

PREDENTAL

Postbaccalaureate programs: Advanced Dental Education Clinical 1-year (Hospital Dental)

DURING DENTAL SCHOOL

Community service opportunities: Outreach opportunities

ACTIVE STUDENT ORGANIZATIONS

Saskatchewan Dental Student Society

INTERNATIONAL DENTISTS

Graduates of international dental schools considered for traditional predoctoral program: Yes

Advanced standing program offered for graduates of international dental schools: No

COMBINED AND ALTERNATE DEGREES

Ph.D.	M.S.	M.P.H.	M.D.	B.A./B.S.	Other
—	—	—	—	—	—

COSTS: 2012-13 SCHOOL YEAR

	FIRST YEAR	SECOND YEAR	THIRD YEAR	FOURTH YEAR
Tuition, resident	$32,960	$32,960	$32,960	$32,960
Tuition, nonresident	$32,960	$32,960	$32,960	$32,960
Tuition, other				$2,000
Fees	$830	$830	$830	$830
Instruments, books, and supplies	$8,820	$7,197	$2,160	$1,420
Estimated living expenses	$7,200	$7,200	$7,200	$7,200
Total, resident	$49,810	$48,187	$43,150	$44,410
Total, nonresident	$49,810	$48,187	$43,150	$44,410
Total, other				

Comments: Costs are in Canadian Dollars

FINANCIAL AID

Financial aid is mainly from government student loans for Canadian residents. Applicants can search for other sources of financial aid on the university website at http://students.usask.ca/moneymatters/awards. Awards and scholarships for continuing students are available; however, students should search the website to determine whether or not they are eligible to apply.

ADEA AADSAS℠

ADEA Associated American Dental Schools Application Service

Information for Dental School Applicants for the 2014 Entering Class

ADEA AADSAS℠

The mission of the American Dental Education Association (ADEA) is to lead the dental education community and to address contemporary issues influencing education, research, and the delivery of oral health care for the public.

ADEA AADSAS℠ (Associated American Dental Schools Application Service) is a centralized application service for individuals applying to dental school. ADEA AADSAS simplifies the application process for both applicants and schools by allowing applicants to complete one application form.

Why Consider a Career in Dentistry?

- Dentistry was ranked #1 in the *U.S. News & World Report*'s 100 Best Jobs of 2013.
- The dental profession offers a wide range of clinical, research, and academic opportunities.
- Students have the option to enter practice immediately following graduation or to pursue residency training in general dentistry or one of nine recognized dental specialties.
- Dentists improve lives by bettering the oral and general health of individuals.
- Dentists are respected professionals and leaders within the health care community.
- Dentists are among the top wage earners in the U.S.

Resources for Applicants

ADEA Official Guide to Dental Schools

Access the most authoritative information available about admissions requirements for all U.S. and Canadian dental schools in this handy guide. It contains information for preparing for dental school, applying to dental school, and financing a dental education. The ADEA *Official Guide to Dental Schools* is available in print and electronic formats. Visit **www.adea.org/publications**.

NEW! *ADEA AADSAS Mobile Portal*

The ADEA AADSAS mobile portal is available for all applicants. The mobile portal enables applicants to view parts of their application such as DAT scores and receipt dates of transcripts and letters of evaluation on their smartphones. Access the mobile portal at **https://portal.aadsasweb.org/sessions/new**.

goDental®

GoDental® is a networking website for students interested in dentistry. The site provides an interactive experience for networking, creating community, and encouraging dialogue. Thousands of students continue to visit the website for advice on how best to pursue a dental career. For more information, visit **www.godental.org**.

ADEA | AMERICAN DENTAL EDUCATION ASSOCIATION | Division of Educational Pathways